C. 50

W9-BQM-344

Conserving American Resources

Ruben L. Parson

Professor of Geography
East Tennessee State College

Conserving

American

Resources

ENGLEWOOD CLIFFS, N.J.

PRENTICE-HALL, INC.   1956

15011

Preface

A LIGHTER, LIVELIER TREATMENT OF A USUALLY SERIOUS SUBJECT IS SOME-times justified, especially if it can thereby attract a wider audience without sacrificing its inherent truths and objectives. This seems to apply to conservation and its problems; more busy Americans can and should become interested in the story of our national resources and the ways they can be conserved. For a simple, readable statement of those fundamentals of conservation pertinent to America's major natural resources, all citizens, whether they be laymen, teachers, students, or novices, are respectfully invited to participate in the following discussion.

In our great American democracy the citizen governs; if he would govern well, he must be well informed on issues involving his entire nation, as well as those limited in effect to his own state, county, or community. With these goals in mind, he will find herein a broad survey of his resource heritage by categories, and some ideas for improving its usefulness through intelligent conservation. That he may be informed without boredom, and stimulated without misrepresentation, is the author's purpose and hope.

ACKNOWLEDGMENTS

MANY PERSONS ASSISTED ME WITH THE PREPARATION OF THIS VOLUME. I AM sincerely grateful to them, and I hope they may find in the book some small recompense. I have tried diligently with such faculties as I possess to justify their help and confidence. The pictorial treatment owes much to the line drawings of Mr. Lee B. Andrews, the cartography of Mrs. Kathryn Martin, and to the special plates in Chapter 15 which are the work of Mr. Kenneth R. Holmes.

But for the encouragement of my friends, John A. Clack and James W. Woolwine, Jr. the manuscript might never have been completed.

Specialists in various resource fields gave me editorial assistance and technical advice in their areas of interest. Mr. E. W. Bennison, Member, American Society of Civil Engineers, and Office Engineer, Edward E. Johnson, Inc., read the water chapters. Mr. Axel R. Hansen, Agricultural Director, *Minneapolis Star and Tribune,* appraised the discussion of soils and land management. Mr. Ben Juskie, Consulting Forester, reviewed the chapters on forestry. Dr. F. W. Albertson, Professor of Botany, Fort Hays Kansas State College, supplied several technical references, and suggested minor changes in the grasslands chapter. Mr. Richard W. Westwood, President, American Nature Association and Editor, *Nature Magazine,* made numerous corrections and editorial improvements in the wildlife treatment. Mr. Howard Zahniser, Executive Secretary, Wilderness Society and Editor, *The Living Wilderness,* corrected and edited the chapter on aesthetic resources—Chapter 14. Mr. Charles E. Jackson, General Manager, National Fisheries Institute made several corrections in Chapter 15. (The voluntary assistance of the four gentlemen just named—Albertson, Westwood, Zahniser, and Jackson—was especially gratifying, because I am acquainted with none of them except through correspondence pertaining to this book.) The Reverend Elmore P. Nelson added his endorsement of Chapter 14 to that of Mr. Zahniser. Mr. Charles K. Carroll, scholar and world traveler, made several suggestions that improved the concluding chapter. Two of my friends, Frederick H. Willcox and Eugene E. Brown, read the entire first draft from a layman's point of view and made many suggestions that were later incorporated. Much credit is due each of these helpful critics for enhancing the quality of the book. None of them must be blamed for any error or fault in the published work, especially as the text was changed in many places after they saw it.

I am indebted to the librarians at the Rayners Lane Branch Library, Harrow, England, and the librarians at the Charles C. Sherrod Library, East Tennessee State College for procuring necessary references. Special credit is due Mr. Hal Smith, Librarian, and Miss Mary Lyons, Assistant Librarian at the college. The generosity of President Burgin E. Dossett and his administrative staff in making our college facilities available was most encouraging and gratifying.

Many, many more individuals whose contributions to the development of this book were material could not be appropriately credited in it; nor would it be fair to single out a few to the exclusion of still others. Perhaps the book itself may in some measure do justice to their wholehearted assistance.

The writers, officials, publishers, industries, and agencies named in the appendix and references made my writing of this book possible. I am sincerely grateful to each of them. To the photographers, artists, publishers, and administrators who helped me illustrate the book I am also deeply indebted. Wherever permissible, they are identified on the illustrations or in appropriate credit lines, but many must remain anonymous.

The quotation on the frontispiece of Chapter 2 is from Emerson's *The Mountain and the Squirrel*, and is used with the permission of the publishers, Houghton Mifflin Company, Boston.

Several persons lent their skills to the mechanical preparation of the manuscript, and I am grateful to all of them. Most expressly do I wish to thank Daniel P. Carrier, Catharine P. Baker, Jean Scott Copeland and Tresa L. Underwood for stenographic and secretarial work.

Finally, thanks to my family, friends, and colleagues for tolerating me during my six-year servitude to the book at the expense of sociality. I regret exceedingly that I spent more time on the book than with my two growing sons. I hope that my neglect of Ronal and Charles will be compensated in some degree by their pride in my work.

RUBEN L. PARSON
Johnson City, Tennessee

*To all those who have toiled
on my grandfather's homestead,
and especially to Lillian,
this book is dedicated.*

Contents

Conserving American Resources

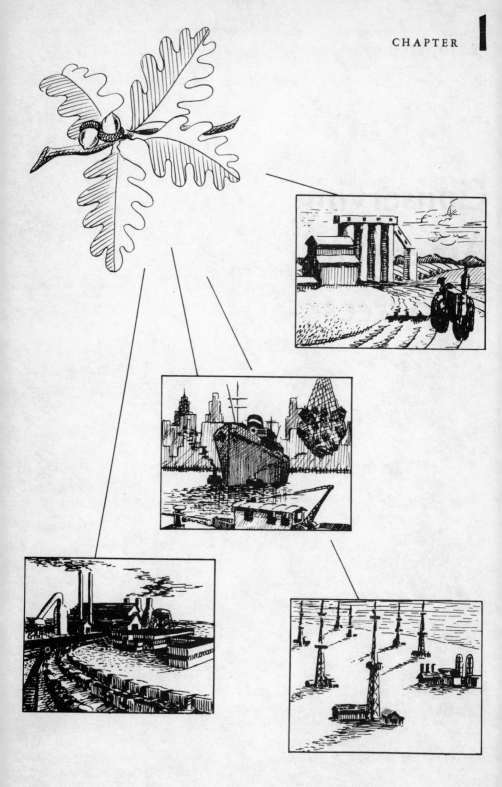

CHAPTER 1

The Idea
and the Book

our material culture derives from natural wealth

CONSERVATION IS AN OLD THEME THAT HAS BEEN PLAYED MANY times before, but usually in a somber and depressing key. The present discussion is an optimistic variation on this theme, attempting to transpose from B minor to F Major a subject so important to America and Americans that each of us should have a "whistling knowledge" of it. So we will not play a dirge to mourn lost possessions, nor concoct a recipe for allaying any imaginary pangs of hunger in a full stomach. We will find no threat of impending poverty and starvation, because America is far removed from both. The arrangement presented is neither technical nor exhaustive, and requires no special background or training on the part of the reader.

Be optimistic!

What follows is largely an attempt to acquaint thinking Americans with the broad categories of natural wealth upon which their well-being depends. The treatment of each category includes a brief statement of its usefulness, a quick glance at its past history, and several suggestions for getting greater benefit from it in the future. The entire discussion is a development of concepts rather than a recitation of facts; an exhortation to think

3

and participate rather than an exposition on statistics and techniques.

Be informed!
Every American owes it to himself to be informed on resources and their conservation. That is our premise. If this volume generates sufficient interest in conservation to prompt further inquiry and action it will have justified itself. If it arouses real curiosity about their stock-interest in the problem among our citizens, especially those quite detached from any kind of primary production, it will have served its main purpose. Only when enough Americans become conversant on the subject of conservation can the democratic process operate to ensure desirable application.

Be a
conservator!
Anyone who reads carefully should acquire enough ideas here to discuss the subject of conservation intelligently. He can then serve himself and his country by imparting that knowledge to others. In so doing, he can become an American "conservator," the hero of our story. *Conservationists* are those persons who prescribe, administer, or supervise the various conservation techniques and programs. They are the technical, professional, and practical experts who actually plan and organize the work. The *conservators* mentioned so frequently in this book are the laymen who practice conservation themselves and accept a personal responsibility for improving our use of resources as an obligation of citizenship. They are the informed citizens who awaken a favorable public opinion. They are the voters who support good policies and programs, and appropriate the funds necessary to implement them. In a manner of speaking, the conservator, representing the public, employs or sponsors the conservationist by authorizing and financing his work. The conservator "sweeps his own doorstep" as an example for others. He is the decisive factor in determining how well we shall manage our natural wealth. We need many more confirmed conservators, and this discussion is therefore addressed primarily to prospective converts.

Natural
resources
sustain our
culture
The natural resources with which we shall concern ourselves are the basic earth materials—water, soil, plants, animals, and minerals—that we employ or convert to sustain our material culture. They supply food, clothing, and shelter; fuel for heating, cooking, and lighting; power and raw materials for industry; vehicles and carriers for trade and travel; luxuries and conveniences; machines and medicines; weapons and munitions for national defense; protective coatings and containers; fish lines, shotguns, and baseball bats. They serve us every day of our lives in almost everything we do. They are essential to our existence, and our con-

tinued prosperity depends on the wisdom with which we use them. There is much room for improvement, as we shall see.

Resources differ as to how they are used—and as to what happens to them in the process of consumption. Water comes to the land again and again no matter how badly it is abused each time around. Plants and animals will reproduce and maintain their numbers unless they are very badly treated. Soils can be maintained, and even improved, under productive use. But minerals extracted from the earth serve us only once, although certain metals can be salvaged and re-used before they are spent. Thus, the conservator deals with two great groups of resources, one renewable or *perpetual,* and the other nonrenewable or *fugitive.*

Some resources are perpetual; others serve only once

Minerals, the "one-time" servants, have attained pre-eminence in this, the age of technology; but they will surely lose that position as one after another becomes exhausted. As minerals grow scarce, we will gradually lean more and more heavily upon the renewables. Our eventual dependence must be upon those resources which can be used without destroying them. Being consumed by use, minerals are conservable only by more thorough exploitation and more efficient employment. Since we as conservators will have to leave most of these problems up to the technicians, our discussion of mineral conservation will be brief despite the importance of minerals in our economy.

Our emphasis is on renewable resources, and the book is so organized that they come in logical order. This natural unity is discussed in Chapter 2, and succeeding chapters present the separate categories according to their logical places. Water comes first because it is essential to all the others, including normally developed soil. Secondly come the soils in which the plants grow. Then come the plants (forests and grasslands) that support the animals. And, finally, come the animals (wildlife) that climax the whole progression. Thus the arrangement of our investigation coincides with the natural scheme of things. Chapters 3 and 4 treat water and soils as the basic resources they are. Chapter 5 on land management serves as a frame of reference for discussing the conservation of all resources that attach primarily to the land surface (Chapters 6 through 14). In Chapter 15 we put out to sea; in Chapter 16 we spend most of our time underground. Chapter 17, which concludes the book, charges the citizen-conservator with a patriotic responsibility by means of which he may envisage for himself, for his children, and for his country, a bright and prosperous future.

Subjects presented in this book follow a natural sequence

Conservation of natural resources means the fullest possible use of them without abusing the ones exploited, without destroying any needlessly, and without neglecting any that can be used. It is not necessarily "conservative" in the ordinary sense of the word. It means thrift, but not denial; frugality, but not privation; efficiency, but not austerity. Nor does "exploitation" as used here necessarily mean piracy; exploitation and conservation are not opposites.

Conservation involves exploiting our natural gifts so that they serve us better and longer than they would otherwise. It does not mean hoarding or storing anything for possible use in the future if we can make constructive use of it in the present. It is not a daydreamer's vision for the distant future, but rather the means of immediate and progressive improvement. Conservation concerns us here and now, and its dividends come at once, or within the predictable future. Its application is well advanced; its proceeds already substantial.

We conserve a resource when we make the best use of it, not when we let it be idle. We conserve renewable resources when we use and re-use them without destroying them or overtaxing their regenerative powers. Soils are conserved when they are so tilled that they produce good crops and yet retain their fertility. Forests are conserved when they are so managed that they produce one generation of useful trees after another. Coal is conserved when we burn it in efficient furnaces; not when we leave it in the ground. We conserve the "fugitive" resources by making them do as much work as possible before they expire.

Maximum use and maximum benefit from resources are the objectives of conservation. Frozen assets are of little interest in conservation. Neglect can be quite as wasteful as abuse. In conservation, as in life, there are sins of omission as well as commission.

Preservation has a place in conservation, but only in exceptional phases of it. We conserve natural *treasures*, such as wilderness, geologic wonders and rare animal species, by restricting their use and protecting them against damage or injury. Aesthetic resources are like prized antiques and heirlooms: displayed with pride, but not used for profit. Their worth is lost, or impaired, unless they be retained in their original state. Thus, conservation excludes them from productive exploitation for material gain. The lofty purpose of conserving wilds and wonders, as discussed in Chapter 14, concerns intangible benefits derived from natural wealth. That is the only chapter in which we shall stress *preservation* as a necessary form of conservation.

Sentiment and theory have fostered the conservation movement, but the real test comes with practical application. Many conservation enthusiasts are like new converts to a religion, eager to spread the gospel; but in their enthusiasm they often overlook the practical aspects of a problem. They intone splendid pledges to posterity, committing us to deliver all nature, as a sacred trust, from generation to generation. Sometimes they seem to forget that one generation becomes the ancestor of another, that ancestral initiative and progress may be a richer legacy than undeveloped resources. Pity the woodsman who sees in a tree only board feet and the huntsman who sees in it only a home for squirrels, but pity also him who sees in it only poetry. We would not ridicule sentiment, but we would temper it with realism. We can have board feet and squirrels today and still have trees tomorrow.

Practice versus theory

Theoretically we might wish that all our streams were so clean and pure that we might safely drink out of them, but practically streams cannot be so while people occupy and use the lands they drain. In this and many other facets of conservation we must strike a compromise between a theoretical ideal and its practical feasibility. We could save all our soils by retiring them from use, but as long as we wish to eat we must conserve soil while employing it to produce food.

For the most part, conservation must pay its own way and show return on investment. The miner cannot conserve minerals, the farmer cannot conserve soils, the lumberman cannot conserve forests if he must do it at a loss, year after year. Conservation practices that require additional application of work or money must also bring additional compensation to the operator in a reasonable time. Those that bring no reward might almost as well be ignored because they can have little more than theoretical value. Conservation must be consistent with economics.

Exploitation of resources produces our wealth and builds our prosperity, and the profit motive keeps the exploiter going. The farmer, the logger, the miner, or the fisherman is pleased to conserve the resource he works, unless thereby he narrows his margin of profit. If he appears at times to be wasteful and slovenly, it may be because more meticulous practices would increase his production costs and reduce his income. One cannot pay wages for the salvage of waste unless that waste can be marketed profitably. Here, once again, conservation becomes involved with economics.

The conservator must distinguish between "material" waste and "economic" waste, particularly when he votes for a regulatory

Exploitation for profit versus salvage of waste

measure or chooses a policy. Compulsory salvage of material waste could easily place such a burden on an operator that he would change to another pursuit, and leave entirely unexploited the very resource that the mandate was intended to conserve. Better that some part of an exploitable resource be wasted than that all of it be abandoned. It may be better conservation to cut and sell one log length from a tree and leave the rest of it in the woods than to abandon the whole tree; better to pump oil from a pool than to leave it in the ground, even though its taking entails the loss of natural gas that cannot be piped to a market profitably. When the branches of the tree and the gas from the oil well can pay their way to a consumer and still are not utilized they become *economic* waste, the kind that a conservator need not condone. The methods and arrangements whereby material waste can be converted into economic goods constitute, in fact, a significant problem of conservation. Until we find all the solutions to that problem we must tolerate many forms of waste incidental to our exploitation and use of natural resources.

Conservation must accompany competitive enterprise

Government has a unique responsibility as coordinator and supervisor of conservation programs and policies, but the actual application of conservation practices devolves largely upon private enterprise. Since resources pertain to property, and most of our American property is privately owned, it follows that private citizens and private capital must do a major share of the work.

Especially effective conservators are some of the large corporations so conspicuous in the American scene. The well-organized company, efficiently operated to succeed in open competition, is often our greatest exponent of conservation. Corporate organization implies continuity beyond the life of any individual stockholder. The company can look far ahead and pursue a program that no individual could attempt. There is no time limit on dividends, and the longevity of the company depends upon the endurance of the resource it works.

Where does government come in? Government must be the moderator among competing users, the protector of public interests that conflict with selfish pursuits, and the sponsor of projects that exceed private means. Government is the "benevolent despot" of conservation, and no one else can play that important role. None but the national government could adequately preserve our aesthetic resources. Only government can prescribe and finance conservation of such scope as flood prevention, forest fire protection, and range restoration. Only government can establish and enforce regulations for cleansing our streams and puri-

FIGURE 1. *Ignorance and apathy are major obstacles to conservation.*

fying the air we breathe. Indeed, the function of government in conservation is attested by public conservation agencies at every administrative level—county, city, state, and national. Our progress to date has come largely through publicly constituted agencies. It is our duty as citizens to see that such agencies are properly organized, adequately financed, and headed in the right direction: politics is one of the tools of the conservator.

In conservation as in any worthwhile endeavor, accomplishment becomes commensurate with the planning that precedes the action. The great planning movement that emerged from economic depression in the 1930's gave tremendous impetus to conservation. In 1934 the National Resources Board published an inventory of our natural wealth and a comprehensive set of recommendations based upon the inventory. Those facts and findings of more than two decades ago are a milepost to both planners and conservators. Economic depression aggravated by haphazard exploitation recalled to mind the continuing urgency of conservation, and we determined to plan our future course more carefully than ever before.

Planning sets the course

Planning brought system and direction to conservation; and the two ideas often became intimately associated, as they should be. Certainly the planner should be a conservator, and the conservator who would be effective must also be a good planner. Conservation without planning would be like traveling without a map. In Chapter 5 we shall consider the importance of planning to the development and use of land resources.

Ignorance and apathy are the greatest obstacles to conservation (Figure 1). Much waste and abuse of resources stems from inadequate understanding of their nature and importance—from

Our people must be informed

FIGURE 2. *Wars are doubly wasteful, and conservation pays the price of victory.*

the innocent behavior of well-meaning fools. Many a present-day voter sees no connection between last year's forest fire and this year's flood. Too few New Yorkers appreciate fully how dust storms in Texas can raise the price of steaks in Manhattan, or how the draining of marshes can ruin their duck-shooting. This situation can become intolerable in a democracy, where voters are the policy makers.

Our people must be informed; until they are, education will remain a most important conservation activity. The individual American must be shown the advantages accruing to him, personally, before he can be expected to take a real interest in conservation. He must be made to see the light. Where laws and penalties often fail despite rigid enforcement, a genuine appreciation of their purposes might render them quite effective, if not altogether unnecessary. When understanding replaces compulsion, conservation may become a reality.

Our nation must be defended

Since national security is one major objective of conservation, it assumes great importance to the conservator. Conservation bolsters the material means necessary for waging war, and neglect of conservation is usually a price paid for victory. Renewable resources carefully developed during peace for long-range benefits have often become casualties of war. Planned schedules for the best exploitation of minerals have been abandoned when wars intervened. War disrupts conservation, yet conservation remains a first line of defense.

War is a paradox of terrible destruction (Figure 2) and accelerated progress. Its consequences are not entirely negative; on the contrary, war also brings its benefits. The extremes and strains of war compel us to conserve by means we might never adopt

10

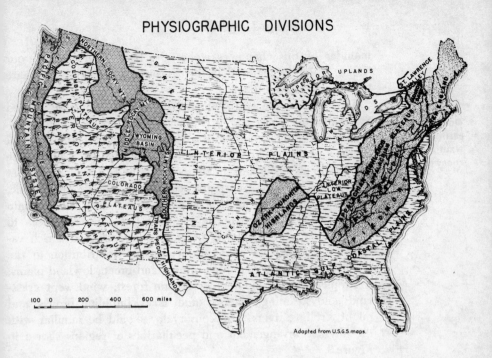

FIGURE 3. *Learn the floor plan of our estate for future reference. National planning and conservation must be correlated with regional geography.*

except under stress. During an emergency we outdo ourselves in the conservation of scarce materials, and at war's end certain substitutions and other innovations developed to win the war become established peacetime practices. Thus, war, the most wasteful destroyer of resources, helps conserve those it does not consume.

The mention of defense and national security turns our attention to the geographic compass of this book—the continental United States. Isolationism is neither intended nor implied in the limitation of our subject, but the focus is strictly on America and Americans. We acknowledge that no nation can prosper on our shrunken globe except as a participating member of the international family. We insist that the American member shall be strong at home, and being strong, shall remain helpful and influential abroad. We assert that American wealth, integrity, and vigor are so important in the world that American conservation concerns all freedom-loving peoples everywhere.

Conserve, America, with malice toward none!

It is not with malice toward our neighbors that we would live well and keep our own house in order; it is simply that we have a good home, and we wish to enjoy it as long as possible. The re-

11

mainder of this chapter sketches the basic floor plan of our "house," and intimates that the "furnishings" need better care than we have given them.

That part of the earth which is now the continental United States of America was well endowed by nature. Its middle-latitude location gives much of it a moderate climate, with seasonal rhythm conducive to vigorous human activity. Its massive size imparts to its occupants broad horizons and grand visions. Set betwixt the two great northern oceans, the Atlantic and Pacific, with a warm sea, the Gulf of Mexico, at the south, and a chain of Great Lakes at the north, the area is readily accessible to world commerce. Within its boundaries is contained a rich variety of landscapes, each with its unique contribution to the whole—high, rugged mountain ranges and broad, lowland plains; subtropical desert and temperate rain forest; windswept grasslands and steaming swamps; quiet lakes, bubbling brooks, and mighty, rolling rivers. The conservator should be familiar with the physical arrangement and peculiarities of regions shown in Figure 3.

As depicted by the maps opposite (Figures 4 and 5), most of the area is sufficiently watered to be highly productive of cultivated plants; geographic gradations of sunshine and length of growing season permit a wide choice of crops. Generously dispersed, rich and varied mineral deposits are available for conversion into tools and implements with which to occupy and develop the good land as a home for enlightened people.

To this wonderland of the New World came European seekers after freedom and fortune only a few centuries ago, and laid the foundation for our great nation of today. Based on incomparable natural wealth, and projected by democratic principles, there arose from that foundation the proud nation we now jealously guard, and others acknowledge, as the richest, most powerful country on earth.

In infancy the nation was immeasurably rich in natural resources appropriate to the traditions and skills of the colonials. Forests, fish, and game seemed utterly inexhaustible. Fish, furs, timbers, and naval stores—pitch, turpentine, and so on—were early American contributions to world trade. The market was strong; reserves, unlimited; and the commodities went out as fast as the short manpower and crude methods could deliver them. Only the best was desirable, and the best was taken without regard for any destruction incidental to its taking.

Trees, birds, and animals were regarded as natural obstacles to the white man's advancing dominion, so he destroyed them

Our part of the earth was by Nature well endowed

In infancy our nation was immeasurably rich

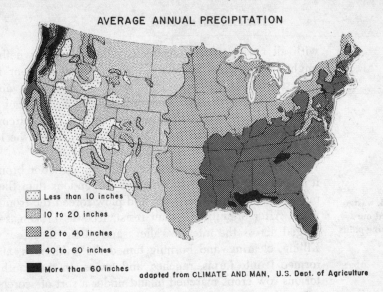

AVERAGE ANNUAL PRECIPITATION

[ ] Less than 10 inches
[ ] 10 to 20 inches
[ ] 20 to 40 inches
[ ] 40 to 60 inches
[ ] More than 60 inches

adapted from CLIMATE AND MAN, U.S. Dept. of Agriculture

FIGURES 4 and 5. *Climatic conditions of warmth and moisture contribute to a rich regional variety of resources and occupations, with a related variety of conservation problems. Average annual rainfall and length of growing season are general indicators of regional land capabilities.*

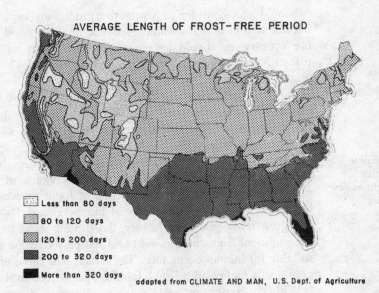

AVERAGE LENGTH OF FROST–FREE PERIOD

[ ] Less than 80 days
[ ] 80 to 120 days
[ ] 120 to 200 days
[ ] 200 to 320 days
[ ] More than 320 days

adapted from CLIMATE AND MAN, U.S. Dept. of Agriculture

with all means at his command. One wonders whether there might be a United States of America today had our founding fathers brought tractors, chain saws, Tommy guns, and steam trawlers. However, their destructive behavior was not wasteful except as later viewed in retrospect. At the time, circumstances made it expedient and productive. Unfortunately, the idea outlived its necessity.

Rank waste salved our growing-pains

Westward expansion of our young, vigorous nation brought with it a waste of natural wealth no less stupendous than the historic movement itself. Axe, musket, and plow forced the frontier westward. After organized Indian resistance was broken, settlement surged across the interior valleys and plains in a few decades. Killing, clearing, and burning tamed the wilderness, and transformed it into farms, ranches, and towns. In the South the notorious row crops marched inland under a sort of scorched earth policy, leaving mutilated lands in their wake. In New England the thin upland fields, once laboriously cleared of trees and stones, reverted to nature when the richer western lands sent grain and meat to the Yankee markets. Crumbled stone walls attest the apparent waste of resources and human energy which attended their building. When better farm lands in the Old West changed the use capability of poor fields in New England those fields reverted to pasture and forest. Economics dictated the adjustment, just as it dictates many of our resource activities at present.

Should one consider as waste the prodigious expenditure of natural wealth which accompanied the feverish development of our country, or should he count the destruction an inevitable price of precocious national strength? Are not recklessness and wastefulness normal releases for growing pains? Is the energetic, ambitious young man also cautious and conservative? Who will assert that our pioneers were truly wasteful, that they should have bridled their greed, spared the means to quick riches—and postponed our rise to national greatness?

Geographic maturity brought us new frontiers

Nations, like people, grow more deliberate and moderate with age. Maturity tempers the rash impetuousness of youth, and applies sober judgment to the correction of foolish mistakes. After little more than a hundred years of independence, its expansion and growth unequalled in history, the United States had secured the continent from coast to coast and settled the major areas most suitable for human occupance. The nation had come of age geographically and politically at a fabulous price in natural resources.

With geographic maturity came moderation of extravagance, and a critical examination of depreciated assets. There was no more new land to appropriate as the old wore out. Good trees for lumber were fewer and farther between. Streams flowed with less regularity; waters were less transparent. And men could no longer escape the environment they had defaced. The geographic frontier had attained coincidence with geographic boundary. Their spacial limits fixed, Americans turned to new frontiers, more challenging, more rewarding, and infinitely more expansive than any known to the pioneer—the modern frontiers of conservation. The exploration and development of these frontiers will continue to determine the strength and endurance of our nation.

The conservator becomes our contemporary pioneer whose far horizons are the limits of his own imagination. He is not the rugged individualist who blunders about among his fellows; he is the social being who works with his group or community for the common benefit of all its members. He is the kind of leader who advances his society by behaving intelligently himself and by cooperating actively to promote the best group interests.

Individualism yields to society

Conservation becomes part of our social philosophy and is, in turn, fostered by a stronger social consciousness. The two have often developed together, and their closer union will strengthen both in the future. Better use of resources elevates both the individual and the group, both the private citizen and the general public. It must therefore be a collective endeavor, each participant helping his nation while helping himself.

Conservation is not a punitive campaign to regiment the individual. Instead, it is his challenge and opportunity, his hope for a bright future. Every American can be a conservator, and without straining himself unduly. He can acquire the art easily, and practice it with distinction. He can begin by using sidewalks to conserve the grass. He can use caution with matches and cigarettes in the woods. He can refrain from throwing trash on the roadsides. He can join an organization that practices or sponsors conservation. He can patronize businessmen who are conservators. He can buy the products of manufacturers who practice conservation. He can turn off a water faucet left running, and switch off the light in an empty room. He can vote for men who will promote conservation through public office. He can read and discuss the writings of conservationists and conservators. He can teach others conservation by example, the best possible form of instruction. He can take greater pride in our achievements to date, and have even greater confidence in our prospect for the future. He is our hope. We must have faith in him. He is becoming more numerous and more optimistic. Perhaps he will be set on his path by the discussions that follow.

Everyone can help!

CHAPTER 2

"---ALL SORTS OF THINGS AND WEATHER MUST BE TAKEN IN TOGETHER." — *Emerson*.

Natural Environment
and Resources

*unity of natural environment and resources
demands a unified approach to conservation*

NATURAL RESOURCES ARE ESSENTIALLY PARTS OF THE ENVIRONMENT
to which man adapts himself, often neither wisely nor well, and
from which he derives his worldly goods. As his intellect grows
and his numbers multiply, his needs become ever greater, and he
must of necessity adjust his activities more carefully to accord
with natural conditions, and to utilize more efficiently the natural
resources available to him. He can achieve such adjustment and
utilization only when he comprehends his environment as a whole,
and recognizes the intricate relationships among its parts. As
conservator he must interpret the relationship and unity of place
attributes (qualities of an area, including natural resources), and
strive to manipulate them so that each will render optimum service without adverse influence upon another.

Several
components
contribute to
environment

As a framework for understanding the unity and interdependence of natural resources one might best employ the catalog of
factors ordinarily taken by earth scientists to compose the natural
environment. These basic factors include climate, rock materials
and structures, water and drainage, topography, soils, natural
vegetation, and native animal life. All are mutually interdependent, though some are qualities and others, resources. The character
of one influences the character of the others. A change in one

17

produces, more or less, the modification of all. Therefore the conservator should understand the concept of composite environment, lest he condone the development of one resource to the detriment of another or fail to enlist the natural interactions at his service. Without that concept his thinking will be piecemeal, and he might be likened to a carpenter who constructs roofs, walls, and floors, and never builds a house.

Climate: prime attribute of place

Among the attributes of place, climate holds high rank; but it cannot be regarded a natural resource in the ordinary sense, being essentially neither mutable nor destructible. To date man has wrought no real change in it, nor has he consumed any quantity of it. Yet he cannot escape its influence and he cannot prosper without heeding its dictates as to the accumulation or growth of other types of resources.

Amounts, ratios, and variations of heat and moisture *condition* the disintegration and decomposition of rocks, the formation and development of soils, the shape and arrangement of land forms, the quality, quantity, and availability of water, and the kinds and numbers of plants and animals.

Whereas a favorable combination of sunshine and rain is fundamental to good environment, deficiency of one or the other imposes distinct environmental limitations—cold and drought. Where cold or drought prevails, it reduces or excludes vegetation and causes a desert. It restricts the development of renewable resources and complicates the utilization of the nonrenewable ones, which may exist because of or despite climatic adversity. Consider the accumulation of water-soluble minerals in dessicated regions, e.g., the borax in Death Valley. If there were enough rain to grow grass the borax would be washed away.

Neither abundance nor poverty, generation nor exhaustion, conservation nor waste of natural resources can be interpreted intelligently without constant regard for the inevitable, persistent influences of climate.

Rocks yield the fundamental raw materials

From the rocks of the earth come our basic raw materials—the elements and their compounds. The rocks are both foundation and source for our surface existence. From the rocks we loosen and raise our minerals and expend them in surface development.

Under the impacts of sun, wind, and water and the activity of organisms, exposed rock disintegrates into grains and fragments, and decomposes into sand, silt, and clay—parent materials of soil. Soils as we know them could not develop except upon a mineral base, be it solid bedrock or loose gravel.

Rock structures may be regarded as the skeletons of landscape,

:he foundation of topography. When uplifted, their etching is ac-
:omplished by wind and water, agents that are generated by
gravity and that reduce high places while filling in low ones. We
term the removal of materials etched away "erosion"; the filling of
low areas is called "deposition." Removal, transportation, and
deposition are parts of the endless geologic process shaping the
earth. Deep in the earth rock structures confine nature's mineral
assets and by their disposition determine the ease with which
oil pools, ore bodies, and coal seams may be extracted. By their
permeability and solubility rocks contribute to the composition
and behavior of both surface and ground waters.

Where soil has developed naturally and remains undisturbed,
it reflects the whole composite of environmental properties. It
combines air and water with mineral and organic materials and **Soils unite the**
forms an entity which helps to sustain life. It has been called the **organic with**
zone of life, or biosphere, because all life on earth depends upon **the mineral**
it, directly or indirectly. Within it and contributing to it are a
host of organisms, plant and animal, living and dead. From it
spring the higher plants which feed the higher animals; and in
due course all these add their substance to it. In youth it resembles
its parent rock material; in maturity it conforms to its climatic and
topographic situation. Indeed, soils epitomize the entire gamut
of environmental factors and functions.

Water permeates every segment of surface environment and
influences the character of each. In liquid, solid, or gaseous state
it preforms unique and vital functions. Streams and glaciers are
prime movers among the agents that shape the earth's surface. **Water is**
Another agent, wind, bears water to the stream or glacier but **nature's blood**
paradoxically loses its own erosive power in proportion to the **stream**
water delivered. Freezing water helps rend rocks asunder and
prepare them for transport from high to low places.

Percolating water is essential in the normal development of
soil, and within certain limits soil fertility depends upon moisture content. Plants take their nourishment in solution and starve
to death in the absence of water. Water, charged with nutrients
dissolved from the soil it helped to form, delivers those foods to
the assimilating plant parts. Vegetable tissue thus produced
cannot sustain animal life and build animal tissue without the
aid of water. Water operates a wholesale "pick-up and delivery"
service upon which life depends—it is the blood-stream of nature.
The quick, often spectacular verdure of a desert after rain demonstrates the vital role of water.

Surface configuration of the land—topography—lends variety

FIGURE 6. *The single topographic element, exposure, can be a critical environmental factor.*

Topography designs the environmental composite

and design to the composite scheme. Forces deep in the earth construct the major framework of mountains, plains, and plateaus, while surface forces carve and shape the more intricate details. Most proficient among the surface sculptors is running water; as if in gratitude for the height that gives it strength, water works most diligently in the high, steep places, and as if in indignation casts its debris upon the low places that frustrate and weaken it.

Topography includes relief and drainage, slope, elevation, and exposure. It is at once both product of and contributor to environmental factors. Windward slopes receive more rain than leeward ones because they deflect the air upward, causing it to cool by expansion and condense its water vapor (see Figure 6). The intercepted moisture promotes plant growth and normal soil development. The vegetative cover, itself a product of rain and soil, protects the soil against erosion and enriches it with humus which increases its water-storing capacity. Water storage reduces soil injury by leaching. Let this suffice to indicate the profound peculiarities and exchanges of environmental factors instituted by a single topographic element—exposure to winds. A score of other situations might be similarly attributed, the more significant when one considers that exposure remains the least tangible aspect of topography. Each of its partners operates with equal, or even greater, potency in the variegation and arrangement of the environmental composite. Every one contributes to the development and distribution of natural resources; yet none holds resource status in its own right. Like climate, they are properties,

ot materials. But those properties, especially as they delimit
pacial units and contrive certain zonations of renewable re-
ources, must be recognized and respected by the conservator.

Plants and animals comprise our *living* natural resources; and,
being alive, they respond readily to conservation. They are
endowed with a degree of mobility enabling them to discriminate
in their choice of habitat. Unrestrained, they invade and occupy
those sites which best suit them, or sites so favorable to them
that they can compete for the space successfully. Nor do they
lack organization and system in their migration and occupance:
they live in elaborate, cooperative associations, and move in
ordered sequence, each form or species breaking trail for another
until the entire group becomes established. In the vanguard stand
the flora, providing food and shelter for the fauna.[f]

Plants and
animals select
their habitats

Natural vegetation reflects in its form, density, and variety
the gradations of quality in the environment. Being fixed in
place, every tree, bush, grass, and forb must be adapted to the
situation or die, yielding its place to another better adapted or
more capable of adaptation. Furthermore, by the slow process
of seed dispersal, growth, and reproduction, vegetation conforms
to environmental changes, advancing and retreating in response to
mutation of site factors. So accurately do certain plant species
evince particular climatic or soil conditions that they are recognized as "plant indicators." With such the conservator seeks acquaintance.

An intimate reciprocity operates between vegetation and soils.
Soil sustains the growth with its substance; the growth in turn
protects the soil and enriches it with humus that aids in water
storage. Without soil there can be only scant vegetation, but without vegetation there can be no true soil.

There exists also a notable exchange between vegetation and
climate. Climatic conditions, obviously, exert a direct influence
over vegetation distribution, and in varying degree vegetation
moderates light and temperature, reduces wind velocity, promotes water absorption and storage, and impedes run-off. Here, as
between and among all the environmental constituents, there is a
real and vital *mutuality*. That is the latch-string to nature's store-
house. The vegetation map (Figure 7) merits careful study because it portrays the culmination of several natural environmental
attributes.

Lest the discussion of environment appear to neglect the "birds
and bees" and admit a common error, be it asserted that plant-
animal relationships involve a nice reciprocity. As if in payment

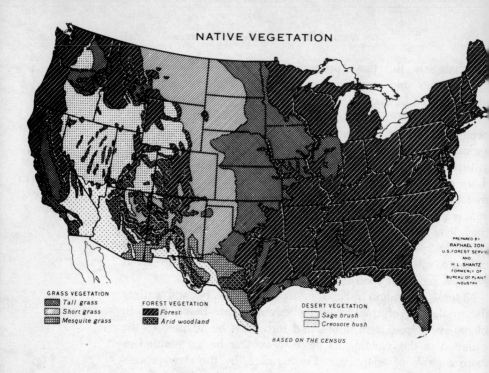

GRASS VEGETATION
- Tall grass
- Short grass
- Mesquite grass

FOREST VEGETATION
- Forest
- Arid woodland

DESERT VEGETATION
- Sage brush
- Creosote bush

PREPARED BY
RAPHAEL ZON
U.S. FOREST SERVICE
AND
H. L. SHANTZ
FORMERLY OF
BUREAU OF PLANT
INDUSTRY

BASED ON THE CENSUS

FIGURE 7. *Vegetation reflects the quality and arrangement of other environmental attributes.* (U.S.D.A. map.)

for their food, birds and rodents disperse the seeds, berries, and nuts they feed upon. As reward for her nectar the bee fertilizes the flower. All the exchanges are not beneficial; there is both cooperation and competition. And plants are not solely the benefactors. The arrangement is not entirely one-sided. Animals, large and small, contribute infinitely more to total environment than is generally understood.

To this wonderful composition man fell heir, with a strict charge—as the Bible says—to "multiply and fill the earth." Multiplication he has achieved admirably, numbering now about two and a half billions; but he has "filled" only a few places to date, many of them ill-suited to his kind. Many spaces suitable for human habitation remain only partially occupied, neglected portions of the grand legacy. Man has behaved like a playboy who inherits more than he can squander; and has neither the incentive nor the wisdom to appraise and employ his unearned wealth. Man has until now demonstrated neither the competence nor the vision commensurate with his endowment.

Despite his superior intellect and mobility, man has during

Conceited man presumes ownership of all!

his brief domination frequently devastated occupied areas by misappropriation and waste; and often, as if restrained by something akin to brute instinct, lingered and rotted in his own desolation. By so mean a process have nations and cultures vanished from the earth. From time to time man has ventured forth into unspoiled areas to replenish his exhausted stores at home; but only rarely has he attached himself to a new area without the compulsion of hunger, expulsion by force, or threat of destruction. Driven rather than drawn, fleeing rather than pursuing, he has shown little wisdom in his dispersal. Until he has better fitted his occupance pattern to his earth environment, until he has occupied and developed all the good places now empty, let him blame himself for his regional poverty. Let him correct his inequitable distribution before he mourns a lost estate. Meanwhile, the nobler objectives of conservation are two-fold: better distribution and wiser occupance.

Shifting his focus from the general to the specific the conservator becomes concerned with landscape, the spacial combination of natural features and works of man. The whole complex, and its arrangement, must be considered in resource conservation. From the landscape one takes the pulse of the community before proceeding to more careful diagnosis. Well-kept buildings, clean roadsides, living fences, green fields, and wooded slopes are as symptomatic for the community as are rosy cheeks for the barefoot boy.

Landscape portrays an intricate complex logically arranged

Simple, discerning interpretation of landscape is a prerequisite to planning and conservation. Roads and homesteads conform to land use. Land use conforms to drainage and relief. A sawmill means timber and logging; a quarry, solid country rock. And the entire, intricate complex hangs together. Figure 8 indicates several criteria by which a good, functional landscape may be judged.

Where nature operates without interference she maintains a nicely balanced organization. Organisms live together both cooperatively and competitively. Similar species eat together at a common table. Those with the best boarding-house reach grow fat and numerous until they have consumed their favorite menu; then another group with different tastes takes its turn at the table. The stronger crowd out the weaker until hunger finally curbs even the hardiest. (The cottontail rabbit will eat himself right out of house and home unless checked by his natural enemies.) Food supply controls the numbers of all animals, whether herbivorous, carnivorous, or omnivorous. Among the carnivores each falls

Undisturbed, nature maintains a nice balance

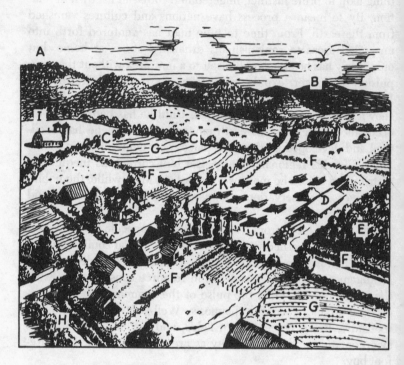

FIGURE 8. *A good cultural landscape fits harmoniously into its natural setting (see legend below).*

A. *Tree farming on steep slopes.*

B. *Protected watershed.*

C. *Wooded strips for wildlife cover and windbreak.*

D. *A sawmill utilizes the timber crop.*

E. *Well-kept woods serve for water-storage, wind-break, and wildlife habitat.*

F. *Living fences restrain domesticated animals and provide homes for wild ones.*

G. *Contoured slopes conserve soil and water for crops.*

H. *A clean, perennial stream reflects community health.*

I. *Good homes are the product of good adjustment to the environment.*

J. *Permanent meadow: slopes suitable for grazing, but subject to erosion if plowed.*

K. *Roads for convenient access, their sides clean and unscarred.*

prey to another until the fiercest predator, finding little to kill, becomes weak and improvident. Ultimately, he succumbs, his young starve, and the proud family lies as carrion—food for scavengers.

Plants, as well as animals, live in balanced communities. Tall plants shade the short ones, and those at the bottom develop the ability to utilize partial light. Under a dense forest canopy the green ones that live by photosynthesis give way to parasites and saprophytes that rely on ready-made food. Differing in their food requirements, many species live harmoniously together without disturbing the balance of soil elements. Loss of a single member species disrupts the entire cooperative society. A single intruder can precipitate group disaster. In a rich habitat plants stand close together; in a poor one they space themselves according to the availability of nutrients. In the natural scheme of things plants and animals maintain a certain balance between associated species, and a distribution precisely fixed by food supply.

It behooves the conservator to comprehend the natural cycles in which environmental factors move. The regular round of day and night assumes significance in terms of daily temperature ranges and duration of life-giving sunlight. The annual round of seasons takes on vital realism when transposed into vegetation cycle, temperature variation, and rainfall regimen, every one of which influences conservation practices. Profoundly important to the conservator are the long-range climatic cycles which bring alternate excess and deficiency of moisture, peculiarly characteristic of marginal moisture belts such as the steppe lands. Periodic and recurring changes are found in all the resources we are concerned with.

Nature moves in finite cycles

Lest one attempt to stop everything, let him ponder the magnificent revolution operative in the cycle of erosion. Rocks break into fragments; gravity causes them to fall or slide into a stream; the stream tumbles them and rounds them and reduces them to grains of sand. At its mouth, the river deposits the grains in layers under the sea, sorted by their density. Compressed and cemented together, the sorted grains become rock once more; and when in due course the rock emerges from the sea, the cycle begins anew. With this cycle the conservator does not presume to interfere; he seeks only to stem its acceleration by man, wherever this is harmful.

Processes of soil formation evince a certain cyclic character. While, in effect, they bring up into the soil from the bottom the parent mineral materials, they release from the surface a residue of those same materials which have passed upward through the soil section during its downward development. If the statement be involved, it suits the case! But its implications are simpler—the sterile residue needs removal, for its retention may be detrimental, unduly impeding renewal of the soil by burying it under debris.

If careless observation seems to show that water only runs down hill, even common sense tells us that what comes down must have gone up. Water is no exception, and its endless changes of state and position are described as the hydrologic cycle. Air over the ocean takes up water vapor; winds carry the moist air onto the land; and the processes of condensation and precipitation deposit it upon the surface. Thence, both by overland flow and sub-surface percolation, it moves back to its source, the sea. In its circuit it becomes alternately salty and fresh, clear and polluted, gas, solid, and liquid, servant and menace, solvent and precipitator—and through all these retains its basic characteristics and potentialities. Here is a wonder of nature that no one should view casually, least of all the conservator.

The organisms, plants and animals, respond to environment in ordered circuits and sequences, many of them so apparent and simple that man has detected their modes with little trouble. Many invite his attention; a few command his respect. An established, balanced plant association may not occupy the site indefinitely, for when its dominant growth form matures and dies another form previously subdued takes advantage of the situation and attains prominence. When that one expires another gains supremacy, then another and another until a long line of pretenders have held temporary sway. Finally, a new generation of the original royal family, like heirs apparent, re-establish their sovereignty—"vegetation climax." Such is the natural rotation in which the noble oaks yield to aspens, and wait their turn to rise again in proper company.

Animals attain social prominence according to available food supply and their ability to compete for it. Squirrels cannot be social climbers without oaks or other nut trees. They bow to the beaver when aspens succeed the oaks. There is a close parallel between plant and animal cycles.

Animal rotation serves as a safety valve for the natural balance of life already mentioned. For example, when conditions favor the increase of field mice, owls flourish until they decimate the mouse population. By that time unwisely numerous, the owls decrease while the mice regain momentum. Nature survives her economic cycles without opposing the law of supply and demand.

Be mindful that all life on earth follows the inevitable "dust to dust" cycle. Every organism in some way takes its substance from the earth and reverts to it. Nature would perpetuate her own fertility!

Ever since his career began man has flagrantly violated the laws of nature; the daughters of Eve are surely accessories before the fact. More intelligent than his fellow creatures, he has nonetheless often shown dubious superiority in the use of his environment. In fact, he appears to be the worst misfit of the lot, doing more damage than all the others together. He was gifted with enough intelligence to mutilate and destroy efficiently; but apparently not with enough to appraise the destruction and foresee its consequences. Man's technology too often exceeds his wisdom.

Man violates the laws of nature

Failing to comprehend the error of his doing, man has often curtailed the very resource he prized most highly, and injured the very one he sought to develop. He has drained swamps and marshes where his idea of surface utilization was not nearly so good as the natural condition of swamp or marsh, where drainage broke the vital moisture relations in large adjacent areas. By irrigating dry lands he has sometimes precipitated salts in toxic concentrations, rendering the desert more forbidding than it was before he meddled. In other places he has expended water for irrigation of crops adequately produced in areas nearby, creating by waste a problem of surplus.

He has killed trees to clear land utterly unsuited to anything more productive than forest. He has broken the sod and sown crops where native grasses were his best resource. He has exposed the soil to wind and wash where natural cover was its only defense against their ravage. He has opened festering sores on the land, and spurned nature's aids for their healing.

He has exterminated several animal species desirable to him and unwittingly propagated others in his disservice. He has killed one predator and thereby encouraged another more predacious. In many ways he has upset the balance in nature and obstructed natural processes that would regain it.

Gently yet firmly nature instructs her "problem child." When he errs she corrects with infinite patience; when he rejects her suggestion she disciplines severely. Where he clears a wooded slope he is warned by a hurried run-off; where, impudently, he strips a watershed, he is chastened by death and destruction in the valley.

Nature instructs both gently and severely

Like an indulgent mother, nature spoils man by generosity, but like a strict father she teaches him industry and frugality through denial. She molds character and inspires faith more with improvidence than with abundance. Consider how both civilization and religion have evolved and flourished in desert environments. In resource conservation one must beware lest human quality decline in the face of plenty. The greater man's material wealth, the less may be his inclination to guard it; easy living tends to beget indolence.

Had man better attended nature's instruction he might have attained a higher state of well-being without impairment of the source. Were he to mend his ways and learn her lessons she would even now help him repair the damage wrought, and ensure his future prosperity without further shrinkage of its base. The good conservator gets his training from tolerant, deliberate nature. Conservation becomes in fact an expression of obedience to her dictates.

A few conspicuous, even spectacular, adjustments to his natural environment have made man so confident and conceited that he **Man's arrogant** boasts of *controlling* nature. He has accomplished no such thing! **"controls" are** The same advancement in knowledge and technology which has **really feeble** magnified his destructive exploitation has merely advanced, also, **adaptations** his constructive adaptation. His so-called "controls" are simply the more tangible responses to environment. Many less apparent responses are actually much more considerable and enduring. Man *adapts* continually and progressively; but he *controls* neither nature nor her rewards.

At least since the Tower of Babel man has presumed upon nature's omnipotence. His command has never been more than misinterpretation. He develops an economic community in a valley shaped by nature. Nature provides the footing for the bridge with which he spans the river. Some distinguished product of the fertile valley environment dons a silk hat to cut a fancy tape, and proclaims that "a natural obstacle has been overcome." But there has been no removal! There has been no change in the valley or in the river that built it. There has come a new element of human adaptation—a bridge. And when nature finally asserts her dominance she topples the steel-and-concrete adaptation into the river. After the silk hat character has been long forgotten the river dumps the last fragment of his monumental structure into the sea. A comparable misconception attends man's "control" of surface waters with a dam. The effective life of the structure is extremely limited—a few decades or centuries, depending upon the natural arrangement of rainfall and slope. In any case, the adaptation is temporary. Its more profound resistance of natural forces stems from the incidental interruption of stream profile and consequent delay of valley development.

Man seeds a cloud and makes rain, cracks the atom and makes a terrible bomb. In both cases he merely employs natural functions previously unknown to him. In the first his vaunted "control" fails when the winds bring insufficient moisture; in the second, nature may save him from self-destruction—perhaps only by withholding the necessary supply of fissionable materials. Even atomic energy represents a human adaptation to environmental factors, not control over them. Man might well be less arrogant about controls and more humbly grateful for the privilege of adaptation.

Every mode of resource conservation represents a refinement of man's adjustment to his earth environment. When he leaves a steep, rocky slope forested, when he leaves dry grassland unbroken, when he plows along the contour and rotates his crops, when he keeps the waters clear, when he levels and plants the gigantic furrows of strip-mining, when he reserves a little space for wild creatures, and when he repairs a dripping faucet, man improves his adaptation to the natural environment.

It devolves upon resource conservation to make human culture more compatible with its natural setting. Conservation can serve its full purpose only when it employs the interactions of environmental factors. The conservator will multiply his services and progressively extend their yields when he fits each endeavor into nature's scheme of things. His frustrations to date have come from a failure to see how things hang together. Let him, henceforth, be sure he understands the *unity of environment* before he works the least change in any of the components. Let him study first the influences of environment, and then the techniques for conserving natural resources. Let him always consider prevailing economic and social forces in planning his work. The American conservator should know the *whole American landscape,* its regional attributes and traditions, before he meddles with any part of it, anywhere.

Conservator, look to environment!

VERSATILE
SERVANT

WARM
WELCOME

RUDE
EVICTION

VINDICTIVE ROBBER

Water on the Land

water, life-blood of the earth,
circulates through many forms and moods

Oceans and seas cover almost three quarters of the earth's surface, to an average depth of almost two and one half miles. A maximum depth of more than six miles has been sounded (1).* Mount Everest would disappear if it were dropped into the deepest part of the Pacific. On the land surfaces—in lakes, sloughs, streams, and glaciers—there is in total another tremondous quantity of water, most of it fresh. In the air, in the soil, in the rocks, and in subterranean channels there are varying amounts of water, aggregating an uncalculated total. Plants and animals are literally full of water. The living human body is largely water.

Much of the earth is water

With all this water, why be concerned about water shortage and conservation? Because there is a significant distinction between water and *useful* water. Time, place, and quality lend it resource value (2, p. 312). Clear, clean water on the land is an asset anywhere. It is more useful in summer than in winter, more valuable in metropolitan areas than in sparsely populated rural areas with water easily obtainable. Many places are handicapped by a dearth of good water.

Life stops in the absence of water. Plants and animals can survive hunger much longer than thirst, and water can revive them when food fails. Without water they starve amid plenty.

Without water life must stop

The distribution of plants and animals tends to accord with the availability of useable water. Where water is abundant life flourishes and multiplies; where it is limited life shrinks accordingly. Seasonal moisture promotes seasonal growth and reproduction.

---

* Numbers in parentheses refer to bibliographical sources at the end of each chapter.

Within the figure:

FURTHER COOLING RESULTS IN PRECIPITATION

ASCENDING AIR IS COOLED WATER VAPOR CONDENSES INTO VISIBLE CLOUD FORM

SUN

LAND GIVES SOME WATER BACK TO AIR BY EVAPORATION

ONSHORE WIND MOVES MOISTURE LADEN AIR ONTO THE LAND

SOME WATER SEEPS INTO GROUND

IN TIME AIR BECOMES CHARGED WITH WATER VAPOR

WATER FLOWS OFF SLOPES INTO STREAMS AND RIVERS

UNDERGROUND WATER RETURNS TO THE SEA

AIR OVER OCEAN TAKES UP WATER IN VAPOR FORM

RIVERS RETURN WATER TO THE OCEAN

PLANTS RETURN MOISTURE TO AIR BY TRANSPIRATION

THE ENDLESS ROUND OF WATER CALLED THE HYDROLOGIC CYCLE
From sea to air to land and back to air and sea.

FIGURE 9. *The Hydrologic Cycle.*

By either deficiency or excess water expels, excludes, and selects species, restricts and modifies growth form, and narrows the margin of health and survival. Only where favorable water conditions prevail will the habitat sustain a full, vigorous community (3, p. 121).

Water resembles an itinerant peddler in its transient character, and it outdoes the peddler at changing mood, appearance, behavior, and quality in the course of its regular circuit. From sea to air, to land, and back to sea again goes the endless round of water movement. It is perhaps the most significant cycle in all nature; the fundamental medium and facility for conserving our renewable resources. It is the ordered rotation of water, called the *hydrologic cycle*, which is traced pictorially in Figure 9.

Given time to do so, air over the ocean takes up water in vapor form until it is full—saturated. Given less time, it becomes more or less charged with water vapor. With on-shore wind the moisture-laden air moves onto the land, and there, its moisture capacity reduced by cooling, mainly by ascent and expansion, the water vapor condenses into visible cloud form. Accretion of vapor particles causes precipitation of cloud moisture as rain, snow, hail, or sleet—*meteoric water*—its form and arrival on the land

The hydrologic cycle never falters

surface related to temperature and other variable atmospheric properties. To the conservator the form, intensity and volume of precipitation have tremendous significance. Liquid water in large drops causes "splash" erosion when it strikes bare soil. Rain runs off as it falls, while snow contributes no run-off until it melts. Snow stores moisture for future use. Many valleys owe their verdure to mountain snows that melt in summer.

Water precipitated upon the land begins its journey back to the sea by devious and circuitous routes. Some runs off surface slopes into brooks and rivers, hurrying toward the ocean. Some soaks into the ground, moistening the soil as it percolates through, filling rock crevices and pores as it seeps deeper into the earth. Such water in transition between the surface and the zone of saturation underneath is called *vadose* water. Its true character is lost where seepage enters open channels and flows seaward in subterranean streams. It falls short of its mission when it fails to replenish the ground-water supply, being dissipated before it penetrates to the water table. Such failure means that water pumped from a well in the area comes from rain that fell elsewhere.

Much of the water that falls upon the land takes a short cut by evaporating directly back into the air (4), postponing its long journey to the sea. Some prolongs its sojourn on the land as capillary water in soil and as body fluid in plants and animals. Plants release their portion to the air by transpiration; animals expel their share by various means. Whatever the detour or delay, all water travels back to its origin, the sea; thence to rise again as vapor, to fall again as rain, and to return again, eventually.

The earth's waters are everywhere transient. To intercept and detain them where they are beneficial, to restrain them where they would be violent, to quicken them where they would stagnate, contributes to water conservation.

The distribution of precipitation—regional, seasonal, and quantitative—affects every kind of resource conservation, but more especially that of water. The *amount* of rain that falls in a certain place has obvious implications for conservation, but its *time* and *manner* of arrival may be quite as important as quantity. Nor may one disregard the geographic location, the topographic position, or any other attribute of the place itself when he examines its rainfall. Winter rain on dormant vegetation may do little good. Unless the soil be frozen or otherwise protected against erosion winter rain may be extremely destructive. A twenty-inch rainfall well distributed during the growing season can develop a good stand of wheat; but twenty inches of rain in as many days

Distribution of rainfall implies both time and place

might ruin the crop and injure the field. If the field were in the northern United States, the seasonal twenty-inch rainfall would better mature a crop than it could in the South where greater evaporation steals more moisture. If it fell on a steep slope, the twenty-day rain might erode the soil; if on a low flat, it might waterlog and inundate. Many more situations might be cited to illustrate the extreme variability of precipitation efficiency incidental to time and place factors.

Climatic diversity in the United States poses many different water problems attendant upon the vagaries of precipitation (5). Averages of rainfall have only limited value for conservation—mainly as a general frame of reference. Locally it may be most significant that certain mountain slopes get 100 inches or more annually and that sheltered valleys below get their total supply from those slopes. Wet slopes and dry valleys afford obvious opportunities for utilizing water, but deviation from normal expectancy creates problems. Even more challenging to the conservator are the erratic fluctuations of rainfall in areas moderately supplied. Drought in moist regions and flood in dry regions, heavy rain in the "dry season" and dryness during the "wet season"—every deviation from normal expectancy tests the conservator's mettle.

Hyetal (rainfall) maps incorporate data indispensable to water conservation, but they require cautious interpretation. Their application must be no more specific or detailed than their representation. They must be viewed in the light of several other environmental factors, such as slope, soil, vegetation, and evaporation. They constitute an essential frame of reference for any discussion of renewable resources.

Rapid run-off presents problems

Rain that falls on the ground and cannot soak in becomes surface run-off, water with a return ticket to the ocean by the fastest route. In their down hill hurry, rivulets merge into brooks and brooks join to form rivers. Every merger, or confluence, augments and accelerates the flow. Every pool, pond, and lake retards and equalizes it, by interrupting the gradient down which it speeds. Unhampered, little rills on high slopes can grow into torrents before they reach the valley. Heavy, sudden rain on bare, steep slopes produces the most excessive run-off, which, gathering force as it goes, displays its unbridled power in the damage done by rampant streams and flash floods. Throughout its journey from land to sea, from initial diffusion to ultimate aggregation, run-off harms and hinders man where it moves too rapidly, and serves him best where its movement is leisurely and regular. It is the phase of the hydrologic cycle with which we are most con-

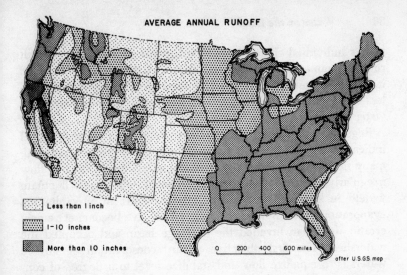

AVERAGE ANNUAL RUNOFF

Less than 1 inch

1-10 inches

More than 10 inches

0   200   400   600 miles

after U.S.G.S. map

FIGURE 10. *Run-off presents the most obvious problems and opportunities in water conservation. It reacts violently to neglect, and responds readily to good management. Compare this map with Figure 4 and note the regional disparity between rainfall and run-off. Why do they not coincide?*

cerned, because its behavior and manipulation influence all aspects of resource conservation. The map (Figure 10) shows the approximate amount of run-off in each part of the United States during a normal year.

Whereas it would be neither possible nor desirable to stop run-off, it behooves man to counter the acceleration his work has caused and avail himself more fully of the benefits proffered by run-off. Perhaps nowhere else in his environment are there problems more momentous and more neglected, yet more amenable to solution. Therein lies one of man's most conspicuous failures as well as a most urgent opportunity for conserving the regenerative natural resources. Therein lies a unique prospect of succeeding by beginning at the top (6).

Whether composed of direct run-off or ground water reissued through springs and seepage zones, surface waters are most readily available to man, and affect his occupance of land through a multiplicity of means. Surface waters fall into two general categories: *running* water in streams, and *standing* water in lakes, sloughs, swamps, and marshes. The latter may be subdivided into at least two major classes: that which is open, such as in a deep, clear lake, and that which is choked with vegetation more or less submerged, such as in a marsh or swamp. Each form

Surface waters have various forms and functions

has its individual characteristics and its peculiar functions. Each rewards man according to the intelligence with which he manages it. When he views each water state and form as a link in an endless chain, he has acquired the basic attitude for hydrology and water conservation.

Regular stream flow and moderate fluctuation of water level indicate a desirable, healthy state of surface waters, and obviate many needs for conservation. Unfortunately, many streams flow irregularly, even intermittently, and many lake levels fluctuate widely in consequence of natural variations in precipitation, evaporation, freezing, and thawing. Some have become extremely erratic after man invaded the drainage basin and occupied the watershed. The first objective toward conservation of surface waters is to equalize flow and stabilize level to a degree of constancy as good as or better than that obtaining before human intrusion.

Ground water constitutes the critical phase

At varying depths below the surface lies a zone of permanent saturation, where water-filled crevices and interstices comprise a natural storage reservoir for moisture. Water thus held against quick release to the sea and protected against evaporation is called *ground water,* which, because it is most reliable but least understood, constitutes a critical phase in water use and conservation. Its magnitude and accessibility vary greatly from place to place, but it is probably present everywhere, extending in places to depths of several thousand feet (7, p. 42). See the diagram on page 37 (Figure 11) and the map on page 38 (Figure 12).

Notwithstanding the tremendous quantities of ground water in the earth, it is *not unlimited;* neither is it everywhere available economically. The water-filled spaces and cavities in earth and soil can store a fixed volume, and no more. Since the stores derive almost entirely from rainfall, they must shrink whenever drain exceeds replenishment from surface sources. Far from being separate, independent entities, surface and ground waters are mutually complementary. In a manner of speaking, ground water provides "defense in depth" for our water resources and fights a "delaying action" against wholesale plundering of the total supply.

The water table fluctuates with supply

The top of the zone saturated with ground water has become known as the *water table,* a term that requires liberal interpretation. The water table is neither flat nor horizontal, as a table should be; and it has neither standard dimensions nor conventional design. The level at which water stands in a hole dug into the ground marks the water table, if that water be free—con-

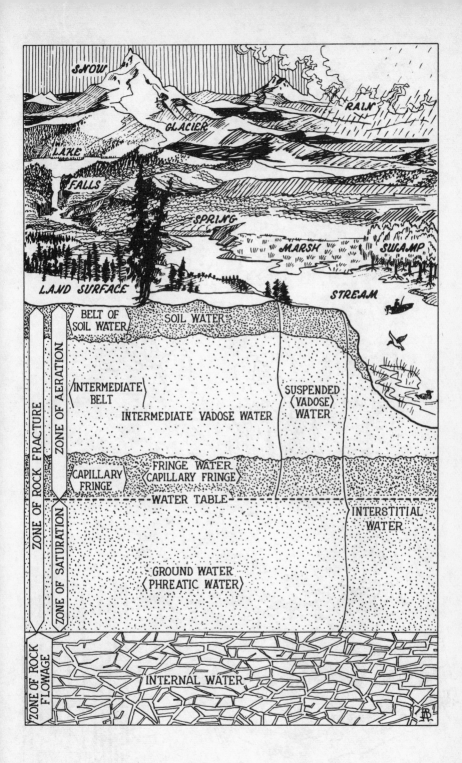

FIGURE 11. *The subterranean detour is slower than the overland route.*

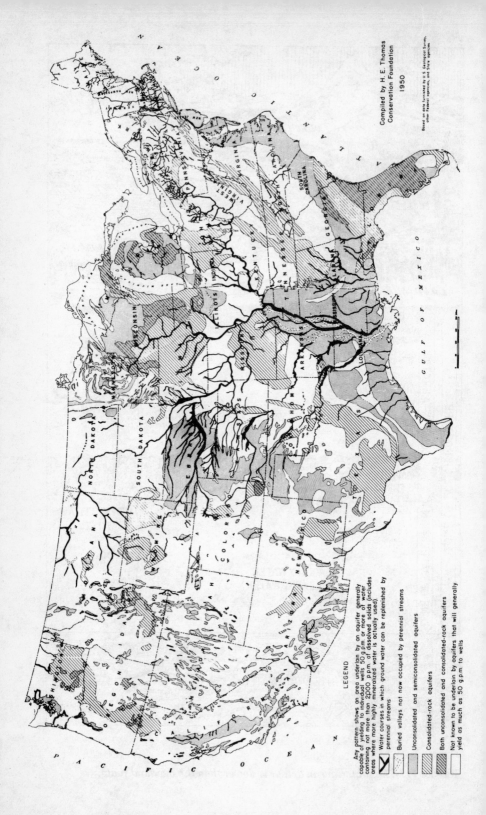

Compiled by H. E. Thomas
Conservation Foundation
1950

Based on data furnished by U.S. Geological Survey,
other Federal agencies, and State agencies.

LEGEND

Any pattern shows an area underlain by an aquifer generally capable of yielding to individual wells 50 g.p.m. or more of water containing not more than 2000 p.p.m. of dissolved solids (includes areas where more highly mineralized water is actually used).

Water courses in which ground water can be replenished by perennial streams

Buried valleys not now occupied by perennial streams

Unconsolidated and semiconsolidated aquifers

Consolidated-rock aquifers

Both unconsolidated and consolidated-rock aquifers

Not known to be underlain by aquifers that will generally yield as much as 50 g.p.m. to wells

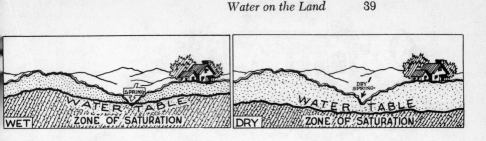

FIGURE 13. *The water table rises during a rainy period and falls during dry weather.*

tained among earth particles rather than confined between rock layers. That level conforms more or less to surface topography, being most nearly accordant during the wet season, and receding from the higher places toward a lower, less undulating surface during drought, since ground water moves both vertically and horizontally. Unless replenishment equals removal, the water table fluctuates. It rises during rainy weather, and sinks during dry. The fluctuation amounts to several feet where precipitation is erratic and abundant. See Figures 13 and 14.

Normal water table conditions exist only where moisture is adequate and the earth materials are pervious to water. Unless there is sufficient moisture and unless it can penetrate, there can be no water table in the ordinary sense. An impervious surface prohibits the absorption by which ground water accumulates. An impervious layer below the surface causes an abnormality called a "perched" water table (Figure 15). Where ground water moves in open subterranean channels, as under solution topography (karst), the top of the stream may simulate a water table.

Porous rock strata between dense, impervious layers above and below them carry confined ground water under appropriate conditions of exposure. With sufficient moisture where they crop out and moderate inclination downward from an extensive catchment area they become charged with water. Water from such strata—called *aquifers*—has several desirable characteristics.

Aquifers carry naturally filtered water

Confined water in an aquifer becomes naturally filtered as it passes through the rock formation and is therefore generally

FIGURE 12 (opposite). *Availability of water from underground storage has been a prominent factor in regional development, but in many places ground water has been used faster than nature can re-charge the reservoirs.* (Map by permission from H. E. Thomas, *The Conservation of Ground Water.* Copyright, 1951, McGraw-Hill Book Company, Inc.)

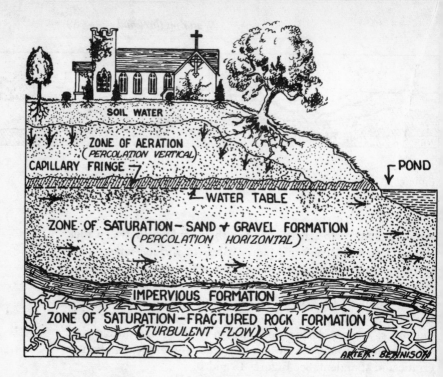

FIGURE 14. *The level of a surface water body is often a continuation of the water table.* (Diagram courtesy Edward E. Johnson, Inc.)

purer and clearer than free water under an ordinary water table. As it fills, an aquifer builds up hydrostatic pressure comparable with "head" in surface water, and resembles a stand-pipe installed in an attitude more nearly horizontal than vertical. Much the same as with the man-made contrivance, any puncture of the natural stand-pipe by drilling a well brings water up to a level approximating the water line. If the top of the well be lower than the head, water flows out upon the surface. Rock fissures or fractures similarly disposed give rise to all-weather springs. Whether it gushes forth from an opening, or merely rises above the water table, water under hydrostatic pressure in an aquifer becomes artesian water, the ultimate in ground water supply. Cooled deep in the earth, its temperature lends special values. Derived from a colossal reservoir, it has uniform quality and reliable quantity. Translated horizontally long distances from its intake, it can supply areas otherwise deficient in moisture. Artesian waters have given life and verdure to deserts, creating garden spots where all was barren waste before they were tapped.

Water has a multiple personality

The multiple personality of water magnifies the scope of its conservation, and complicates the procedures by which optimum

40

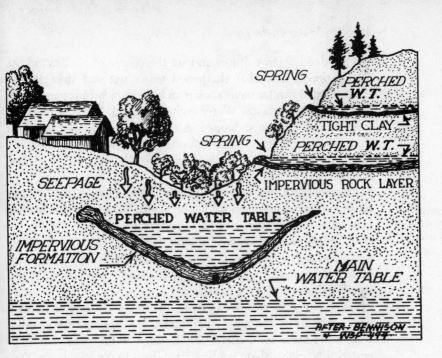

FIGURE 15. *A perched water table can be as deceptive as a false bottom in a box.*

conservation may be achieved. Many a "sweet Afton" flows gently only during brief poetic moods, shrinks to nothing at other times, and too often rises in fits of noisy anger. Floods that destroy crops and buildings may also deposit fertile silt in which succeeding crops can flourish and defray the costs of reconstruction; but the silt itself represents grand larceny of upland soils. Although water is essential to our existence, it is also a dangerous medium of infection. Most epidemics of intestinal diseases are spread by water. Shoal waters that stand at a constant level are generally most productive of fish and other desirable life forms, but they also breed the biggest swarms of mosquitos.

The contradictory, impetuous nature of water imposes upon its conservator the momentous responsibility of adjudicator between good and evil: Shall he try to prevent floods, or shall he encourage them to enrich the valleys over which they spread? He must discover the natural tolerance beyond which he dare not preside: How much waste can a stream carry without becoming more detrimental than beneficial? Where can he drain, and where irrigate, without regretting it later?

Water, more than stone or bronze or iron or any other substance,

41

has molded human cultures and set the course of civilization (8). Water procurement has sharpened man's wit and strengthened his society. By water navigation man has expanded his geographic and scientific horizons. Water courses have directed human migration and patterned human settlement, precipitated wars for their control, and served as boundary between the aspiring nations. In several great religions water symbolizes divine cleansing and purity.

Primitive folk live intimately with water

Primitive folk live intimately with water. Their typical village clusters about a common source of water, be it a stream, spring, lake, well, or reservoir; and that single source furnishes water for their simple requirements—drinking, bathing, cooking, cleansing, and watering of animals. Crocks, pots, and buckets are standard household utensils in huts otherwise devoid of furnishings. Water stands first among family provisions.

The life of a rice farmer in Bengal is so closely associated with water that he is virtually amphibious. He encloses his paddies with hand-made mud dikes, floods them with crude, hand-operated lifts, plants them wading knee-deep in muddy water, then daubs mud and sloshes more water to keep them inundated until the rice matures. And all his sodden drudgery comes to naught if his paddies lie the least bit high and the monsoon short-changes him. The rice turns yellow and the farmer faces hunger.

The Indian jheel, or tank, outdoes all that the immortal Kipling ascribed to it. In it the villagers bathe themselves and their bullocks, wash their clothes and worship their gods, cleanse their mouths and catch their fish, and fill their brass or earthen vessels after scouring them. Little wonder that the over-worked water, taxed by many pot-bearing women and rapid evaporation, shrinks to a green, stinking slime as the dry season wears on. Little wonder the Hindu worships those waters that serve his needs without stagnating—the holy, tawny rivers which at last carry away the ashes of his mortal remains. For centuries past his ancestors have lived and worked with water, died of diseases carried by it, and been consigned to it upon death.

Modern society imposes new demands

Space forbids our tracing hydraulic engineering from Babylonian or Roman aqueducts to its elaborate development and complex employment in an advanced society such as ours, but it must be asserted that new demands on water have accompanied the progress of civilization, and that these increasing water requirements compel improvement of water conservation. The Indian woman who dips "natural" water from a jheel knows little of water qualities other than wetness; but the 20th century

American rates the *quality* of water by several criteria: chemical hardness, sediment, bacteria count, aeration, taste, precipitate (9). The degree or proportion of a single one may determine the value of the water for a specific purpose. Hard water, with calcium and magnesium carbonates dissolved in it, refuses to associate with ordinary soap in a washtub and fouls up indoor plumbing. Steam engineers avoid it because it chokes the boiler tubes with scale. Water with a high bacteria count may be dangerous to drink. Water with sulphur in it, however harmless, disgusts both smell and taste. Water charged too highly with salts may not be used for irrigation because it poisons the very land it should make productive.

For the most important modern uses, water needs to be clear, pure, and soft. To correct deficiencies, natural or induced, modern technology applies specific treatments, some simple, like softening, filtering, or chlorinating, and others complex and costly beyond practical feasibility. Nor are quality and quantity enough to satisfy modern water demands; storage, pressure, transport, and distribution are also ordinary requisites. Good water conservation means optimum provision of water for all special purposes without undue expenditure for artificial treatment.

Whether a squalid, straw-thatched, Indian village or an American skyscraper metropolis, every community arises where there is water to drink—*potable* water; and none can grow beyond the available supply, although we must remember that in the modern community availability is a matter of cost, not of distance, depth, or anything else. If the supply diminishes, the community shrinks accordingly. If the supply fails, the community moves away or dies. The minimum water supply available at any given time fixes the ultimate size to which a permanent agglomeration of people can grow. Fortunately, the minimum asserts itself in higher costs, restrictions, or other inconveniences before its absolute limits are reached, and the population becomes static before it thirsts. Our daily use of water in the United States, taking each withdrawal at face value whether or not the same water is used more than once, exceeds a thousand gallons per capita (10, p. 13). The entire population of the country drinks perhaps less than a million gallons of water daily, a mere trickle compared with other uses. But that little trickle receives more attention than all the rest; and, in any circumstance of limited supply, it holds top priority (11). Note the comparative volume of water uses shown in Figure 16.

Running water, hot and cold, has become so nearly universal

Potable water supply limits population density

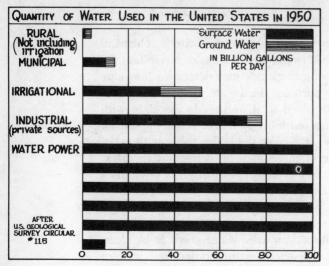

FIGURE 16. *Water power uses the most water but consumes the least.*

Domestic tranquility runs from a faucet

in American homes that the "modern conveniences" once proudly exhibited are now taken for granted. Sinks, showers, and lavatories have all but displaced dishpans, wash-dishes, water pitchers, and tubs. The ever-empty water pail and family dipper that once menaced both health and connubial bliss gave way to the domestic tranquility that should run from a faucet—unless it drips. Every added convenience and facility has increased the use—and waste—of domestic water. When grandpa drew the water by hand and fetched it in a bucket grandma used it sparingly, to save the man if not the well. The Monday wash and the Saturday-night bath were sizeable undertakings and expended several tubfulls; but the privy did not flush, and the lawn shifted for itself between rains. The average household of the water-pail era used less water in a week than the modern family uses in a day. However, the total water used for domestic purposes still remains less than that for any other major use category. Least in quantity, it holds first rank in both quality and importance. A good supply guards its users against infection, and their property against fire. It promotes health, hygiene, and sanitation—personal well-being.

Certain industries use vast volumes of water

Few people realize how much modern industry depends upon water, not only as a source of power or raw material, but infinitely more as a conditioning agent and processing medium (12). In canneries, breweries, distilleries, and other food plants water does four-way duty. It cleans ingredients and containers; it cools the coils or boils the brew, as the case may be; it becomes part of the product; and, finally, it washes away the wastes. (At best they are so distinctively scented that one wonders how a

WATER USED PER DOLLAR VALUE ADDED BY MANUFACTURE*

Industry	Gallons of Water
Steel	1,400
Wood pulp	1,352
Oil refining	973
Paper and board	527
Beer	51
Wool scouring	49
Whiskey	45
Soft drinks	15
Woolen and worsted fabrics	5.4
Tanning	4.7
Rayon	3.6

* From Powell and Bacon, "Magnitude of Industrial Demand for Process Water," *Journal, American Water Works Association*, XLII, No. 8, August 1950, p. 783.

fish cannery or a slaughter house would smell were they not constantly washed with water.) As steam, water remains the medium whereby fuels turn power shafts. In many factories water is used to prevent overheating of certain machine parts, while in others it is used to heat essential parts of the machinery. High-speed cutting tools need cooling; drying rolls in a paper machine need heating. The bulk of industrial water goes for power and cooling (13); fortunately, cooling may be done with low-quality water. A considerable volume of water in manufacturing serves as a medium for dissolving, mixing, precipitating, cleansing, or otherwise changing the materials being processed. Paper is literally made in water. Certain synthetics require tremendous quantities of process water. In these and other manufactures water serves also as transporter of materials through various stages of fabrication. About 30 gallons of water were employed to convert from wood the paper in this book. A ton of steel represents the use of 65,000 gallons of water in its manufacture. One ton of rayon yarn may represent the use of 100,000 gallons or more. It takes 500 gallons of water to make a ton of soap; 160 gallons to make a pound of aluminum (14, p. 84). The table above shows the importance of water in several different manufactures.

Obviously, industrial water supply is a prime factor in plant location, and in the geographic distribution of manufactures (15). Water is essential to the production, exploitation, and utilization

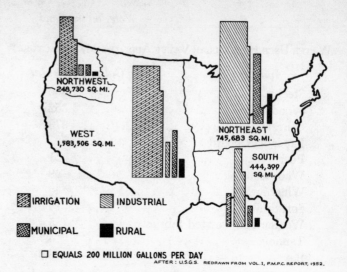

FIGURE 17. *Water supply and use, major regions of the United States. Leading water consumers: in the East, industry; in the West, irrigation.*

of many other resources, be they vegetable, animal, or mineral. See the map above (Figure 17).

Hydraulic mining has long been a large water user, and more recently the flotation process of separating or concentrating minerals from low grade ores has greatly increased the use of water in the mining industry. Many minerals laid down by water—potash, salt, placer gold—are now recovered by the same agent that deposited them. Many previously worthless are extracted profitably by flotation or leaching with water as described in Chapter 16.

Water and gravity are a natural team of work horses, which when properly harnessed can do a prodigious amount of work. Water and fire make another team, which, being easier to hitch and handle, does more work at present despite its ravenous appetite for coal or other fuel. The water-gravity team requires rather elaborate "stabling" in the form of dams and reservoirs, but it consumes no "feed," and affects thereby a magnificent economy of expendable energy resources.

Hydroelectric power will outlive the mineral fuels

Early American manufacturing depended upon direct water-power developed with wooden (crib) or masonry dams, open flumes, and water wheels. There was neither the need nor the know-how for damming full-fledged rivers. The choice dam sites were on small streams, and there was little necessity for impounding a great water reserve against seasons of slack flow; the streams were more dependable then than now. On such sites sprang up the grist mills, sawmills and hammer mills, magnetic nuclei of many historic villages. Industry was confined to stream banks, and other community appurtenances often gravitated to industry. Onto this scene strode the giant of industrial energy, coal, and released industry from its stream-side bondage. Steam-driven factories arose where transport facilities and other advantages of location favored them. Auxiliary steam plants kept industry going during periods of low water and flash floods. The availability of fuel—coal or wood, not running water—became the decisive factor in plant location, and coal traveled farther and farther as improvements in transportation, among others, asserted themselves.

With the application of the water turbine to generate transmissible energy the water-gravity team surged to prominence again in the form of hydroelectric power; the United States leads the world in hydroelectric production. Water generates about one-third of our nation's electricity (16, map facing p. 59). Transmission losses restrict the economical use of electricity to a radius of about 500 miles from its source at present, but increased efficiency of distribution may be anticipated. Though perpetual as the rain whence it derives, the ultimate potential of water power cannot exceed that portion of the rain that runs off. Indestructible as water itself, water power will probably serve us after all mineral fuels have been consumed. It affords a unique opportunity for conservation, with many attendant benefits co-incident. Though treated here as a singular service of water, hydroelectric power becomes only one among divers gains from unified water management.

The generation of hydroelectric power increased six-fold during the period 1920-1950 (17, p. 6). Hydroelectric installations, public and private, produced in 1951 nearly 100 billion kilowatt hours of electrical energy (17, p. 7). Installed capacity approximates 20 million kilowatts, which is about half of what we might have if all currently feasible power sites were developed (17, p. 74), and a mere fraction of our ultimate hydroelectric power potential. Figure 18 shows both present status and future possibilities in the major drainage regions.

The practice of applying water artificially to land inadequately supplied with atmospheric precipitation began when ancient desert-dwelling peoples developed sedentary agriculture in their limited environment. Water for crops ranked second only to water for men and animals to drink. Irrigation was born of necessity, and its achievement stretched man's wits before it filled his stomach. It did much to advance ancient civilization, and it has

Irrigation creates inflated water values

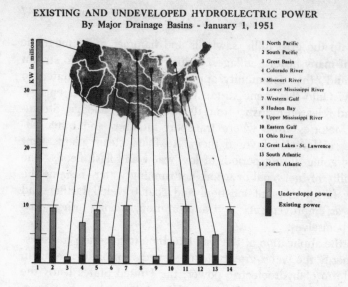

EXISTING AND UNDEVELOPED HYDROELECTRIC POWER
By Major Drainage Basins - January 1, 1951

1 North Pacific
2 South Pacific
3 Great Basin
4 Colorado River
5 Missouri River
6 Lower Mississippi River
7 Western Gulf
8 Hudson Bay
9 Upper Mississippi River
10 Eastern Gulf
11 Ohio River
12 Great Lakes - St. Lawrence
13 South Atlantic
14 North Atlantic

Undeveloped power
Existing power

FIGURE 18. *Potential water power may have a profound bearing on the future of a region. Development of all possible power sites is not yet economically feasible.* (Federal Power Commission map.)

never ceased to challenge human ingenuity. Today its compatibility with good water conservation becomes less apparent but increasingly urgent. Not everywhere does the rich productivity of irrigation justify its extravagant expenditure of water. Irrigation is our greatest consumer of water (13). Many communities in our dry West are entirely dependent upon irrigation, and it is a prominent factor in the regional economy. Cash crops predominate, but in many places, as in parts of Colorado, irrigated forage crops also lend stability to the range livestock industry.

Irrigation exploits adversity, risking heavy capital outlay against a broad margin of profit. Its dividends come from natural paradox. Soils too dry to sustain plant growth do not suffer much leaching by rain water and are therefore generally rich in all the plant nutrients. Many desert soils are indeed so full of certain soluble salts that water renders them toxic to plants (18). Such soils are not suitable for irrigation because the alkaline substances in them tend to be floated out by water and precipitated at the surface in poisonous concentration. Thus water *can* render desert soil even more sterile than it was before water was introduced.

But in many places desert soils need only suitable water to make them abundantly productive. Deficient rainfall means fewer clouds to obstruct sunlight and consequently the receipt of a

48

FIGURE 19. *Lettuce under irrigation in California. Good crisp salad is worth the price, unless its production entails water consumption exceeding replenishment.* (S.C.S. photo.)

higher percentage of possible sunshine. In effect, desert crops under irrigation receive sun and rain simultaneously—an ideal arrangement. The combination of rich soil, full sun, and regulated water promotes luxurious plant growth, high yield of forage or fruit, and uniform, early ripening of a superior product. The warm sunshine which imparts quality to the crop also steals by vaporization much of the water in an open irrigation system, thereby raising higher the high water costs. A warm, dry location means lower water efficiency because of a higher evaporation rate. A good Texan may not admit it, but a gallon of water in Texas will not go as far as one in Montana.

In our humid East irrigation attains increasing importance in the production of certain crop specialties, and as seasonal supplement to rainfall (19), but in the arid West it sustains crop agriculture and thriving communities where the land lay barren without it. West of the hundredth meridian there are only limited areas capable of safe and profitable cultivation without artificial watering. In the vast, dry intermontane region irrigation has converted many a parched valley into a veritable garden spot. Man-made oases produce many of our choice fruits and vegetables (Figure 19), and a variety of such common field crops as cotton, alfalfa, barley, and sugar beets.

In 1889 less than 4 million acres were irrigated, and expansion

49

was slow (20). In 1902 Congress passed the Reclamation Act, putting the federal government into the irrigation business. By 1952 we had extended irrigation to 26 million acres (21), almost 5 per cent of our total cultivated acreage. Relatively very small in area, our irrigated lands contribute, acre for acre, much more than their proportionate share toward our high living standard. Under certain conditions irrigation is certainly consistent with good water conservation; but let us hasten to say that even verdure may be bought over-dear. Remember Tam O'Shanter's mare.

Water provides our cheapest transport medium

Water has carried man and his worldly goods from place to place since the dim dawn of civilization. Boats and rafts served our species long before Noah built the Ark, and were bearing important commerce when Archimedes shouted "Eureka." The story of mankind might be read in the evolution of floating carriers, from inflated animal skins and hollowed-out logs to tankers, barges, and refrigerated, petroleum-powered liners.

The United States was discovered, explored, settled, and developed largely by water. The deep estuaries of the Atlantic coast, the greatest chain of inland lakes in the world, a broad, warm sea—the Gulf of Mexico—and one of the largest rivers—the Mississippi—were the framework for initial strength and progressive westward expansion half way across the continent. Water courses were the highways by which our young nation reached greatness. With few exceptions, our greatest cities began as water terminals of one sort or another.

During the formative period of our nation we were so reliant upon water to carry out growing commerce that inland waterway improvements, such as canals and locks, were promoted both privately and publicly. But the fabulous steamboats of Mark Twain's day were no match for locomotives on iron tracks; and engineers turned to bridging rivers instead of dredging them. Modernization of overland transportation has so facilitated traffic that many canals have fallen into disuse.

In terms of ton-miles, water carried 14.97 per cent of our domestic freight in 1952. At 16.21 per cent, motor carriers were a very poor second to the railroads' 54.91. Oil pipelines moved 13.87 of all freight, approaching the water-borne load. Air freight was only 0.1 per cent of the total. (22)

Under favorable conditions such bulk commodities as coal, iron ore, grain and oil can be shipped by water at a ton-mile rate a fraction as high as by railroad, yet less than 15 per cent of our total domestic freight goes by water. We have more than 28,000 miles of channels authorized by Congress for improvement,

FIGURE 20. *Two large tows meet on the Intracoastal Waterway near Houma, Louisiana. Water transport is economical where nature provides the highway without expensive artificial aids.* (Corps of Engineers, U.S. Army photo.)

of which some 23,000 miles have been improved; to these figures must be added the useful spans of navigable lakes. About three-fourths of the authorized mileage can accommodate craft drawing six feet or more of water (23). Quite unknown to many Americans is the interesting Intracoastal Waterway that extends the length of the Atlantic and Gulf Coasts. It is popular for pleasure cruises, and carries much freight as well (Figure 20). It is neither "inland" nor "ocean," but a cross between the two. Only a few stretches of it remain uncompleted.

Excepting the Great Lakes, whose importance has increased, our inland waterways have lost their pre-eminence. As incidental adjuncts to well planned water development, certain segments will be extended or improved, but there are few water projects that will merit execution for the sole purpose of transportation (24, pp. 1363, 1516-1524). Only in the remote future, when mineral fuels run out, can one visualize any considerable reversion to water transport in America, although increased use of our water courses could divert to other purposes considerable land area devoted to overland transport facilities. For the immediate future the trend is toward air rather than water navigation, toward atomic propulsion rather than sail.

Far from being outmoded by mechanical and chemical innovations, ice continues its time-worn service as refrigerant. Where "moist cold" is required there is no satisfactory substitute for ice. It protects many perishable foods in storage and transit, and renders many more palatable on our tables. Thanks to ice, lettuce from irrigated valleys in the West reaches eastern city markets fresh and crisp. By the aid of ice one may enjoy fresh shrimp cocktail or oysters on the half-shell anywhere in the country—products of salt water delivered in frozen fresh water. In many other ways ice enriches our diet and contributes to good American living.

Water refrigerates and air-conditions

Not so long ago our refrigeration came from an annual ice harvest on northern lakes and ponds. Huge cakes, perhaps 18 inches thick and twice that long, were shipped considerable distances by rail, laid up tier upon tier in storage sheds, and covered with sawdust to insulate them against summer heat. By promptly replacing the sawdust after each removal of ice a calculated supply was made to last out the summer. Many railroads, creameries, packing houses and other ice-using concerns had their own ice-storage; and many a farmer laid up his private supply. Nor has the ice-house departed the American scene. Even now the annual ice harvest enlivens many northern communities in the dead of winter. However, most of our ice today comes from ice-manufacturing plants using water of high quality. Many such plants are integral parts of hotels and other ice-using institutions; and many commercial establishments make ice for sale. Their advent took ice off the luxury list even during summertime in Dixie, and multiplied our use of water in solid form.

As solid or liquid, water is virtually indispensable to modern air-conditioning. Actually most air-conditioning is accomplished with naturally cooled water pumped from wells, though it can be done by costlier artificial means. So considerable has become the use of water for cooling large buildings in summer that it creates a very special water problem in certain metropolitan areas. During one hot day in July 1952, 60½ million gallons of Potomac water were pumped through the Pentagon to keep that colossal building cool (25).

Engineers were not content to use water for cooling alone, so they developed a "heat pump," which cools in summer and heats in winter by simply reversing refrigeration processes. It uses naturally tempered well water throughout the year, and may thereby aggravate the problem of ground water shortage already acute in some places. The recharging well by which water is pumped back into the earth after being used for air-conditioning has become a significant water-conserving device. It appears likely that the use of water in air-conditioning will grow progressively greater as the need for decontaminating air becomes more pressing.

Water determines the abundance of fish and wildlife even more precisely than it governs the pattern of human population. The conservator must not overlook the fact that all wildlife—upland birds and animals as well as water fowl—need water to live, that species can range only a limited distance from water, and that most of them tend to gravitate toward it. Furthermore, wild creatures discriminate in their choice of water. Some prefer it cold; others, warm; some prefer it running; others, quiet. Most of them thrive best where the water is clean and shallow and plant life flourishes. Shore areas are the epitome of habitat; but, unfortunately, they are often affected negatively, even to the point of destruction, by water developments considered by men to be more desirable (26). Wildlife suffers whenever a marsh is drained off, or flooded by a dam.

Water determines the abundance of fish and wildlife

Water affords us many of our most popular and wholesome forms of recreation. Lakes and streams amuse, refresh, and inspire both young and old from all walks of life. Beside them we build parks and camps for public enjoyment, lodges and homes for pleasant living. People travel long distances to enjoy them during a brief vacation. They are the arenas for many favorite outdoor sports, winter and summer—swimming, boating, sailing, fishing, hunting, and skating. Surface waters provide much of the fun and relaxation essential to health and efficiency under the stress and strain of our accelerated culture.

Water affords wholesome recreation

For recreation as for most other purposes, we have increased both our use and our expenditure of water. In the old swimming hole we used water naturally available, untreated, unmetered, and free. We swam in the nude, and carried away no water in wet bathing suits. We were, unwittingly, conservative. But the swimming hole lost its magnetism to the private pool and the public natatorium. Swimming became expensive business, especially in terms of water. A well-patronized public pool requires frequent changes of water to meet acceptable health standards, and one refilling may take hundreds of thousands of gallons of high-quality water. The total United States water bill for swimming pools alone is charged with billions of gallons annually.

It is also old-fashioned to skate on natural outdoor ice on lakes and ponds. Nor do we wait for wintertime to enjoy our ice sports. Winter or summer we flood and freeze indoor rinks, using large quantities of high-quality water. Midsummer "Icecapades" illustrate the greater enjoyment and greater expenditure of water that parallels our technological progress.

As if determined to be the complete servant of mankind, water voluntarily removes the grime and filth which would otherwise so befoul his habitat as to render it ultimately untenable. "Refreshing rain" and "purifying streams" are much more than poetic phrases; they are the faithful janitors in our environment. Anyone who has seen the accumulation of dirt during drought or breathed the acrid air of a tropical desert city, appreciates the cleansing power of rain and run-off. If water did not remove wastes and spent materials from the land and deliver them to the sea, there would be eventually neither marine nor terrestrial life. A fundamental natural cycle would break.

Water carries away more than its share of wastes

Man, the ingrate, while pleased and profited by the manifold services of water, consigns to it his refuse and offal for disposal. Mindful only of its readiness, and ignorant of its limitations, he is inclined to overwork the good servant and jeopardize his own well-being. He has exaggerated the capacity of the greatest solvent.

In the United States we have increased enormously our employment of water for industrial production, domestic comfort and convenience, and other desirable applications; but we have apparently failed to acknowledge that our expanded productivity and elevated living standards, to say nothing of our growing population, expel an increasing volume of wastes that must be removed. By greater expenditure for high-priority uses we have curtailed the water available for waste-removal while constantly augmenting the load of waste cast into it. In effect, we have used so much water about the house that there is not quite enough left for swabbing the back porch.

Much of our domestic water, of potable quality, serves only to carry sewage. In 1950 domestic water carried sewage from 11,800 American municipalities, and dumped most of it untreated into natural surface waters (27). Septic tanks or cesspools and dispersal lines serving rural homes expend only the confined water used, without the additional water wastage incidental to the emptying of sewerage lines. But sewerage is one of our expanding public facilities, and garbage disposals are increasing the burden of household refuse. Continuing industrialization, and especially the emphasis on synthetics, places additional strain on water as a waste bearer. In many places over our fair land streams overloaded with wastes are blighting the landscape (28).

Unequal to all the tasks we would set it, water balks first and most violently against its meanest function, waste removal. Unless water be treated with due respect it becomes an agent of contamination rather than purification. We are delinquent in attending to that obvious threat. Here, as in all too many cases, our abuse of one resource does violence to several others. A polluted stream can injure every resource it touches, and befoul the entire landscape through which it flows.

Water influences every activity everywhere, and concerns every one of us (29). For the country as a whole, we receive about 30 inches of rainfall annually, of which approximately 22 inches return to the air by evapotranspiration (30). Thus, we get each year an average replenishment of 8 cubic inches to every square inch of area. That is our limit of fresh water supply for manipulation, from both surface and underground sources. If we consume more than that, we deplete our stored reserves. If we conserve those 8 inches carefully, they will satisfy our growing water requirements for a long time to come. The choice is ours. The time is now!

CHAPTER 3: REFERENCES CITED BY NUMBER

(1) H. U. Sverdrup, Martin W. Johnson, and Richard H. Fleming, *The Oceans, Their Physics, Chemistry, and General Biology*. Prentice-Hall, Inc., New York, 1942.

(2) "Report of the Water Planning Committee," *National Resources Board Report*, Part III. Washington, D.C., 1934.

(3) Jonathan Forman and Ollie Fink, *Water and Man*. Friends of the Land, Zanesville, Ohio, 1950.

(4) Stephen S. Visher, "Evaporation Regions in the United States," *Scientific Monthly*, LXII, No. 5, May 1946.

(5) Robert DeC. Ward, Charles F. Brooks, and A. J. Connor, *The Climates of North America*. Verlag von Gebruder Borntraeger, Berlin, 1936, pp. J-146–J-160.

(6) "Flood Control Begins at the Top of the Hill," *Tractor Farming*, XXXV, No. 1, January-February 1952.

(7) Oscar Edward Meinzer, "The Occurrence of Ground Water in the United States," *Water Supply Paper 489*, U.S.G.S.* Washington, D.C., 1923.

* U.S.G.S.: United States Geological Survey.

(8) W. Appleton Aiken, "Streams of Culture" (The Heritage of Great Rivers), *The Land,* IX, No. 3, Autumn 1950.

(9) M. M. Ellis, B. A. Westfall, and Marion D. Ellis, "Determination of Water Quality," *Research Report 9,* F.W.S.† Washington, D.C., 1948.

(10) Kenneth A. MacKichan, "Estimated Use of Water in the United States, 1950," *Circular 115,* U.S.G.S., May 1951.

(11) Arthur H. Carhart, "Turn Off That Faucet," *The Atlantic Monthly,* CLXXXV, No. 2, February 1950.

(12) Sheppard T. Powell and Hilary E. Bacon, "Magnitude of Industrial Demand for Process Water," *Journal, American Water Works Association,* XLII, No. 8, August 1950, pp. 777-785.

(13) Jack R. Barnes, "Water for United States Industry," in Materials Policy Commission, *A Report to the President;* V: *Selected Reports to the Commission,* Report 9. Washington, D.C., 1952.

(14) Arthur H. Carhart, *Water–Or Your Life.* J. B. Lippincott Company, Philadelphia, 1951.

(15) Glenn E. McLaughlin, "Water," in National Resources Planning Board, *Industrial Location and National Resources,* Washington, D.C., 1942, Chapter 8.

(16) Senate Committee on Interior and Insular Affairs, "Basic Data Relating to Energy Resources," *Senate Document No. 8,* 82nd Congress, 1st Session. Washington, D. C., 1951.

(17) *Thirty-Second Annual Report of the Federal Power Commission, Fiscal Year Ended June 30, 1952.* Washington, D.C., 1953.

(18) Harold A. Hoffmeister, "Alkali Problem of Western United States," *Economic Geography,* XXIII, No. 1, January 1947.

(19) F. E. Staebner, "Supplemental Irrigation," *Farmer's Bulletin 1846,* U.S.D.A.‡ Washington, D.C., 1940.

(20) "Irrigation Agriculture in the West," *Miscellaneous Publication 670,* U.S.D.A., 1948.

(21) Peveril Meigs, "Water Problems in the United States," *Geographical Review,* XLII, No. 3, July 1952.

(22) Lee R. Nowell, Acting Director, Bureau of Water Carriers and Freight Forwarders, Interstate Commerce Commission; personal communication dated August 27, 1954.

---

† F.W.S.: Fish and Wildlife Service.
‡ U.S.D.A.: United States Department of Agriculture.

(23) Morris Perlberg, Chief, Water-borne Commerce Branch, Statistical Division, Board of Engineers for Rivers and Harbors, Corps of Engineers, U.S. Army; personal communication dated September 13, 1954.

(24) *Domestic Land and Water Transportation,* hearings before the Committee on Interstate and Foreign Commerce, U.S. Senate, 82nd Congress, Second Session, on bills relative to domestic land and water transportation. Washington, D. C., 1952.

(25) Eugene Kafka, Senior Mechanical Engineer, Heating, Refrigeration, and Sewage Disposal Section, Southeast Pentagon Building; personal communication dated August 12, 1952.

(26) *Crisis Spots in Conservation,* pamphlet. Izaak Walton League of America, Inc., Chicago, 1949.

(27) "Water Pollution in the United States," Series on Water Pollution No. 1, *Public Health Service Publication No. 64.* Washington, D.C., 1951.

(28) Bill Wolf, "Running Sores on Our Land: Conclusion—The Remedy," *Sports Afield,* CXXI, No. 3, March 1949.

(29) Federal Security Agency, Public Health Service (in cooperation with the state water pollution control agencies), *Clean Water is Everybody's Business.* Washington, D.C., 1950.

(30) William E. Hiatt, Chief, Hydrologic Services Division, U.S. Weather Bureau; personal communication dated December 10, 1952.

CHAPTER 4

Our Soils:

Basic Wealth

*soil combines air, water,
organisms, and minerals in a
marvelous, life-sustaining medium*

SOILS ARE THE FOUNDATION OF OUR WORLDLY GOODS; A BASIC WEALTH upon which our existence depends. From them comes nearly all the food we eat, much of our clothing and shelter, and most of the materials for our comfort, convenience, and pleasure. Water alone is more important to the viability of resources, and without soil water would be useless. With the exception of water and its life-forms, all other renewable resources come from the soil. The importance of soil as primary producer grows ever greater with the dissipation of exhaustible resources and proportionately increased reliance upon the renewable kinds. Soils must fill in when mineral materials fade out. When we have dug out all our minerals and used them up, we shall need more soil products than ever. Rather than relaxing our dependence on soils, our advancing civilization will reassert it more and more. There is no real evidence that we may some day detach our lives from the soils that sustain us.

He who would call his sustenance "dirt" might well speak softly and conceal his ignorance. Soils are infinitely more than just plain dirt; they are a composite of minerals, organisms, air, and water, so wondrously combined that man has never exactly duplicated their structure and composition. Toward a better understanding of soils he has developed a whole field of inquiry called "soil science," whose teachings are basic to soil conserva-

They are not
"dirt"

59

tion. A quick glance at the nature of our soils is the sole purpose of this chapter.

Soil development begins when simple life forms establish themselves among weathered particles of rock. The organisms help reduce the particles further, hold them in place so they can accumulate, and add their own bodies to the mass as generation after generation dies. When the mantle becomes thick enough, higher forms of life intrude, and accelerate the formative process. The final result is an unconsolidated layer, several inches to several feet in thickness, containing minerals, humus, plant life, animals, air, and water, in mechanical mixtures and in chemical combinations. Under suitable cooperation between sunshine, rain, and life, during hundreds of years, that surface layer becomes soil, a separate entity produced by unique processes.

Most important of these processes is the downward translocation of surface materials by water percolating through the soil section. This process of taking materials near the top and re-depositing them deeper down is the basic producer of soil profiles. Instead of noses, chins, and foreheads, soil profiles have layers called "horizons," identified, top to bottom, by the simple designations, "A," "B," "C," and "D." See the drawing of a hypothetical soil profile (Figure 21).

Profiles distinguish soils

The upper horizon, A, is the one from which percolating water removes fine soil particles, leaving the coarser materials behind. Thus the A horizon has become known also as the zone of impoverishment. Under extreme conditions it becomes so coarse and open that it loses the power to retain humus and other desirable substances, and becomes a leached, sterile body of mineral matter. Its removal may be more desirable than its retention. The pale gray sand that accumulates on certain uplands in the humid East is about as lifeless as any cadaver of similar hue.

Next below lies the B horizon, in which the water deposits what it steals from A, causing the B to become more dense and finer-textured than A. It is referred to as the zone of enrichment, since it gains what A loses. Under certain conditions the precipitated materials develop a layer so compact that it blocks vertical movement of water. Such a hard, impervious layer is called "hardpan" or "claypan," an undesirable characteristic of B in many areas.

The two horizons, A and B, constitute the true soil, or *solum,* our primary concern in soil conservation. The solum contains all the humus and all the organisms that make soil a unique body—bridge between the geologic and biologic, the atmospheric and hydrologic. A good solum is literally crawling with organisms—if

ORGANIC DEBRIS LODGED ON THE SOIL, USUALLY ABSENT ON SOILS DEVELOPED FROM GRASSES.		A$_{00}$	LOOSE LEAVES AND ORGANIC DEBRIS, LARGELY UNDECOMPOSED.
		A$_0$	ORGANIC DEBRIS PARTIALLY DECOMPOSED.
	HORIZONS OF MAXIMUM BIOLOGICAL ACTIVITY, OF ELUVIATION, (REMOVAL OF MATERIALS DISSOLVED OR SUSPENDED IN WATER), OR BOTH.	A$_1$	A DARK-COLORED HORIZON WITH HIGH CONTENT OF ORGANIC AND MINERAL MATTER MIXED.
		A$_2$	A LIGHT COLORED HORIZON OF MAXIMUM ELUVIATION. PROMINENT IN PODZOLIC SOILS; FAINTLY DEVELOPED OR ABSENT IN CHERNOZEMIC SOILS.
		A$_3$	TRANSITIONAL TO Ⓑ, BUT MORE LIKE Ⓐ THAN Ⓑ. — SOMETIMES ABSENT.
	HORIZONS OF ILLUVIATION (OF ACCUMULATION OF SUSPENDED MATERIAL FROM A) OR OF MAXIMUM CLAY ACCUMULATION OR OF BLOCKY OR PRISMATIC STRUCTURE, OR BOTH.	B$_1$	TRANSITIONAL TO Ⓑ, BUT MORE LIKE Ⓑ THAN Ⓐ. — SOMETIMES ABSENT.
		B$_2$	MAXIMUM ACCUMULATION OF SILICATE CLAY MINERALS OR OF IRON AND ORGANIC MATTER; MAXIMUM DEVELOPMENT OF BLOCKY OR PRISMATIC STRUCTURE; OR BOTH.
		B$_3$	TRANSITIONAL TO Ⓒ.
THE WEATHERED PARENT MATERIAL. OCCASIONALLY ABSENT; I.E., BUILDING MAY FOLLOW WEATHERING SUCH THAT NO MATERIAL THAT IS NOT INCLUDED IN THE SOLUM IS FOUND BETWEEN B AND D.		G M C C$_{CA}$ C$_{CS}$	HORIZON Ⓖ FOR INTENSELY GLEYED LAYERS, AS IN HYDROMORPHIC SOILS. HORIZON Ⓜ FOR HARDPANS IN WHICH CEMENTATION OR COMPACTION DOMINATE OVER OTHER CHARACTERISTICS. (MAY BE IN SOLUM). HORIZONS (C$_{CA}$) & (C$_{CS}$) ARE LAYERS OF CALCIUM CARBONATE AND CALCIUM SULFATE IN SOME SOILS.
ANY STRATUM UNDERNEATH THE SOIL, SUCH AS HARD ROCK OR LAYERS OF SAND, THAT IS NOT PARENT MATERIAL BUT WHICH MAY HAVE SIGNIFICANCE TO THE OVERLYING SOIL.		D	HYPOTHETICAL SOIL PROFILE ADAPTED FROM: SOIL SURVEY MANUAL, U.S.D.A. 1951

SUNSHINE

AIR

WATER

THE SOLUM

THE GENETIC SOIL DEVELOPED BY SOIL-FORMING PROCESSES

FIGURE 21. *Soil profile.*

all of them were ever to pull together in the same direction they might drag the solum right off the land!

Under the solum lies the C horizon, also called "parent material" of the soil. It is simply rotten, or weathered, rock, broken down by chemical and mechanical processes. It is unconsolidated, and inanimate except as soil life invades it from above, bringing the soil section down into it, as it were. Soil development, like good stream management, begins at the top and proceeds downward. While the formative process at the bottom goes deeper into fresh material, the spent residue at the surface moves off. One might compare soil formation with the growth of the skin—new tissue building underneath and old tissue sloughing off the surface.

At the bottom lies the unaltered geologic foundation, either loose mineral material or solid rock, often called the D horizon. Its physical and chemical composition has an important bearing on the qualities of the soil that forms upon it because few, if any, of our soils have remained in place long enough for the complete decomposition of their mineral constituents.

Color, texture, and structure of their horizons are the most conspicuous criteria for identifying and evaluating soils. Black and dark shades of brown indicate abundant humus, and conversely light brown or buff indicates low humus content. A pale or ashen A horizon means deficiency of humus just as a sallow, washed-out look indicates ill health in humans. Bright shades of red or yellow in the A or B horizon are deceptive, since they indicate only iron content, not fertility. The more brilliant the color, the less may be the life.

Soil texture pertains to the size of the mineral particles, or grains, that make up the mass. A coarse, or open, texture, as of sand, permits water to pass through too freely and therefore lacks the power to retain humus and plant nutrients. On the other hand soil too fine in texture, such as plastic clay, impedes water movement, lacks proper aeration (air spaces), and holds too tightly any plant foods it may contain. Between the extremes are the desirable loams—various mixtures of sand and clay that can hold air, water, and humus without overdoing it, and respond well to fair treatment.

Soil structure is the arrangement or grouping of soil particles, which may have profound influence on soil quality. Coarse sand lacks structure, being simply an accumulation of grains. Plastic clay may be said to have a massive structure, since the whole body tends to hang together and resist separation. Clay that divides into small loose lumps (i.e., that flocculates), is said to have a granular structure—a most desirable characteristic because it renders the clay friable (crumbly) and more easily tilled.

The feel of soil, when one squeezes a handful, or walks over a field, is a good index of quality. Soil full of humus and life feels spongy in the hand and springy under foot. Dead soil has the cold, fixed hardness of *rigor mortis.*

Many variables influence the rate of soil formation. Some soils have developed in a fraction of the time it took others, but under the most rapid soil-making conditions a century or two might be required. Cool, humid climates are among the fast soil makers, but it appears that they sacrifice quality for speed. They leach the A horizon of its best material, producing podzol soils (Figure 22). Cool, sub-humid climates produce soils very slowly, but their end product is superior. They produce a deep, black or brown A horizon, characteristic of the prairie and chernozem soils shown in Figure 22. When one considers that humus content transmits the dark color, he can appreciate that it represents the annual residue from many, many years of grass—thousands of years might be a conservative estimate.

Soils develop slowly

Soils, like people, age at different rates, and for each, age has a double meaning. Soils old in point of years may be young in profile development, and vice versa. Natural surface erosion keeps many soils perennially young; rapid leaching by water makes others prematurely old. Soil maturity indicates normal profile development; rejuvenescence means its interruption or postponement.

By any interpretation, soil forms so slowly that what we lose will be lost for centuries to come. The fraction of an inch washed off by a summer shower may represent a man's lifetime. Soil loss is more final than most men suspect. That is why it is so vitally important that we conserve what we have left. Age is not necessarily a criterion of soil quality, but environmental factors condition both age and quality of soils.

Local soil variety corresponds with the pattern of environmental conditions. In regions of uniformly heavy rainfall and constantly high temperatures soil processes operate rapidly and continuously, producing deep soil sections except where surface erosion is also accelerated. However, the deep soil may be extremely poor in quality because the same combination of warmth and moisture that developed it causes organic matter to decay and leach out too fast to permit production or retention of much humus. In cold, moist regions bacterial action is so slow that plant remains may

Soil variety derives from climatic differences

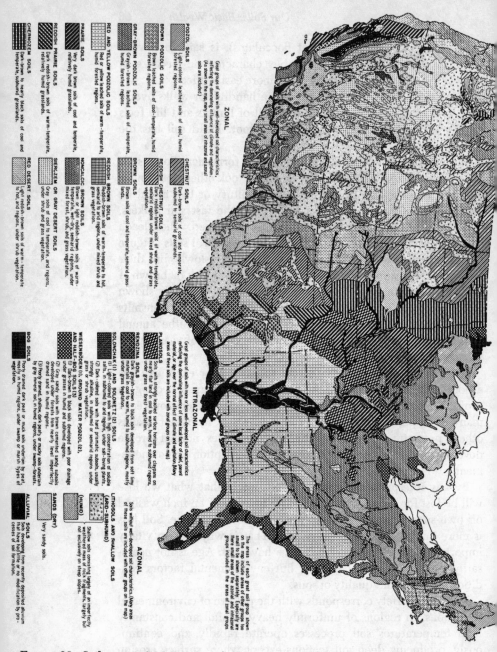

FIGURE 22. *Soil groups.* (U.S.D.A. map.)

accumulate as raw, acid humus. The extensive peat bogs of northern Minnesota developed that way; they show an excess of organic matter and no true soil.

In desert regions soils are inclined to be mineral rather than organic because the deficiency of moisture limits plant growth, which is the main source of humus, and precludes the possibility of vertical soil development by percolating water. The small quantity of humus produced is either lost off the surface or remains near the top of the soil. Under extreme desert conditions the soil, so-called, is simply a loose mantle of rock, its original mineral content largely intact, and its organic content nonexistent. The gray color of desert soil (sierozem) expresses the paucity of humus.

Between the extremes lie the climatic gradations of temperature and rainfall that produce the grand divisions of productive, conservable soils in the United States. Those divisions are shown on the accompanying map (Figure 22). Within those divisions further refinement of soil variety and arrangement derives from differences in parent materials, topographic position, slope, drainage, elevation, and vegetative cover.

Major distinctions obtain between our large region of eastern forest soils (pedalfers) and the region of western grassland soils (pedocals). In the humid East there is enough rain to sustain a forest cover, enough to seep through forest litter, soil, and parent material, and reach the water table. The percolating water, charged with acid from leaves and pine needles, dissolves and removes calcium carbonate so actively that the soils, even those developed upon a limestone base, become acid in their chemical reaction. Called technically "podzolization," the process tends to produce a residual *A* horizon of silica sand and a *B* horizon characterized by iron and aluminum compounds (see Figure 23). An east-west arrangement of podzolized forest soils results, largely, from a progressively warmer climate southward, with an attendant lengthening of growing season and a shorter annual interruption of soil processes, both constructive and destructive. Examine carefully the map of soil groups on page 64 (Figure 22), correlating each group with the legend and with the maps in Chapters 1 and 2. Note that portions of the grassland plains receive insufficient rain to sustain a continuous, permanent, forest cover, and percolating water does not ordinarily maintain contact with the water table, but dissipates in the *B* horizon of the soil. Quite the opposite of acid-making trees, grasses concentrate basic compounds, especially calcium carbonate, and produce humus without an undesirable acid reaction. Water seeping through the sod takes up calcium carbonate in solution and precipitates it in the *B* horizon. Where this process, called "calcification," attains maximum effect—as in the black chernozem soils

Major distinctions obtain between our forest and grassland soils

FIGURE 23. *True podzol under forest of the Northeast. A thick layer of raw, acid humus overlies the soil. The A horizon is white silica sand, thoroughly leached by percolating water. The B horizon is dense and compact, chocolate brown in color from its abundance of precipitated organic matter. Note the location of podzols in Figure 22. (Photo courtesy Charles E. Kellogg.)*

FIGURE 24. *Northern chernozem developed at the eastern edge of the short-grass plains. Two feet of rich soil, black with humus, underlain by a hard, white layer of carbonate (lime). Compare this pedocal with the podzol opposite. Note the location of chernozems in Figure 22.* (S.C.S. photo.)

—the precipitate forms a solid, white layer of lime, inches in thickness (see Figure 24). The grassland soils lie in north-south belts; and their color grades from black in the eastern belt to light brown and gray in the western belt, which is a clear expression of progressively less rainfall, less vegetation, and less humus westward. Another soil forming process, laterization, should be mentioned, although podzolization and calcification evince contrasts as striking as any, and operate over major portions of the United States. Laterization is a tropical soil process, operative in only limited areas of the southeastern United States. Whereas podzolization accumulates silicon dioxide in the topsoil, laterization decomposes and dissipates the silicon dioxide, and forms instead a concentration of iron oxides. Laterites are red in color, with horizons less distinct than in podzolics.   •

Local soil groups accord with topography

Within the great soil regions boundaries and groupings accord with topographic arrangements and relationships. Individual soils follow rather closely the pattern of particular parent materials, and their association with other soils follows the lay of the land. Pedologists have suggested that all soils under a given set of climatic conditions and similar topographic position will, if climate and topography have enough time to assert themselves, become identical despite any variety of original parent materials. Consistent with this theory, our soils have been identified and named on the basis of characteristic soil profiles. However, few of our American soils are so maturely developed that they do not bear strong evidence of their origin. Thus, the Hagerstown "series" came from limestone, the Norfolk from sand, the Memphis and Walla Walla from loess (wind-deposited material), the Fargo from lake bottom mud, the Gloucester from a stony mixture of material deposited by glaciers, the Chester and Cecil from crystalline rocks, the Yazoo from river deposits, and so on. Each series carries the name of the vicinity in which it was first scientifically identified, and several have extensive areal distribution. Everywhere, the particular series has its unique features of identification —color, texture, structure, depth, reaction, and others, including a certain productive capacity. A series may include several "types," the type designation derived mainly from the texture of the A horizon. Locally, type may be just as important as series for practical purposes. The conservator can learn to recognize both series and types in any area with which he may be concerned. He can get the information through the agricultural County Agent or from the District Soil Conservationist. He may also be able to obtain a map showing local soils distribution. A knowledge of

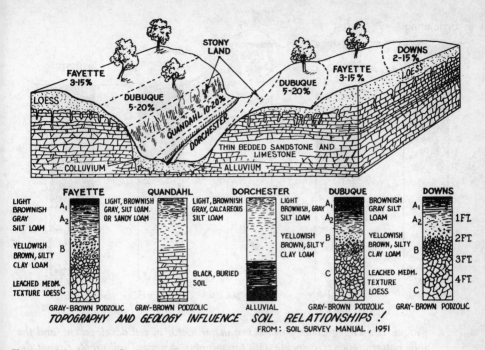

FAYETTE 3-15%   STONY LAND   DOWNS 2-15%
LOESS   DUBUQUE 5-20%   QUANDAHL 10-20%   DORCHESTER   DUBUQUE 5-20%   FAYETTE 3-15%   LOESS
THIN BEDDED SANDSTONE AND LIMESTONE
COLLUVIUM   ALLUVIUM

FAYETTE	QUANDAHL	DORCHESTER	DUBUQUE	DOWNS

LIGHT BROWNISH GRAY SILT LOAM A₁ A₂
YELLOWISH BROWN, SILTY CLAY LOAM B
LEACHED MEDM. TEXTURE LOESS C

LIGHT, BROWNISH GRAY, SILT LOAM. OR SANDY LOAM

LIGHT, BROWNISH GRAY, CALCAREOUS SILT LOAM
BLACK, BURIED SOIL

LIGHT BROWNISH, GRAY SILT LOAM A₁ A₂
YELLOWISH BROWN, SILTY CLAY LOAM B
C

BROWNISH GRAY SILT LOAM A₁ A₂
YELLOWISH BROWN, SILTY CLAY LOAM B
LEACHED MEDM. TEXTURE LOESS C

BROWNISH GRAY SILT LOAM A₁ A₂   1 FT.
2 FT.
B   3 FT.
C   4 FT.

GRAY-BROWN PODZOLIC   GRAY-BROWN PODZOLIC   ALLUVIAL   GRAY-BROWN PODZOLIC   GRAY-BROWN PODZOLIC

TOPOGRAPHY AND GEOLOGY INFLUENCE SOIL RELATIONSHIPS !
FROM: SOIL SURVEY MANUAL, 1951

FIGURE 25. *Most soils reflect the character of their parent material, and their geographic distribution follows the pattern of surface geology.*

soils nomenclature will often help him understand more clearly the practical advice of an expert.

The effects of topography in soil delineation are at least three-fold: (1) the geologic arrangement due to the differential resistance of parent materials to weathering and erosion, (2) the differences between parent soil materials themselves, and (3) the various exposure and drainage conditions imposed by topographic position. In the humid East (Pennsylvania), where resistant sandstone and soluble limestone lie in juxtaposition, the latter has generally become lowland and the former highland. The sandstone begets light, sandy upland soils like the De Kalb, easily tilled but low in fertility. The limestone begets heavy, clayey soils like the Hagerstown, which is highly fertile but more difficult to cultivate. Upland soils are generally more mature than lowland varieties because of better drainage, but it should be remembered that open texture also facilitates drainage, given adequate elevation. Thus soils may be excessively drained by virtue of either coarse parent material or high topographic position, or by both, which is not an unusual combination. They can be made to retain more water by increasing their humus content. Figure 25 shows how the soils pattern coincides with geology and topography in a hilly locality of northeastern Iowa.

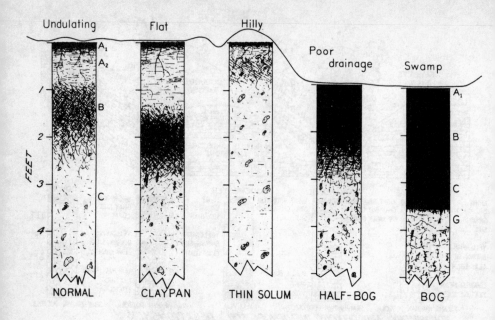

FIGURE 26. *Topographic position is a major factor in soil development, and the soils pattern tends to coincide with topography. A normal soil profile cannot develop on a steep, eroding slope, nor in places poorly drained or recurrently flooded.*

Slope soils tend to remain young or immature in development, and become coarse in texture because run-off removes the finer surface material and leaves a residue of larger particles. In some places the residue takes on the aspects of a surface mulch, and resists the very process by which it came to be. Notable among such slope soils is the stony "phase" of the Gloucester—one reason why Massachusetts has fewer gullies than Mississippi.

In valley bottoms and on other low, flat areas topographic position asserts itself in imperfect drainage and immature or abnormal soil development. Flood plain soils, as in the lower Mississippi Valley, are often without profile, being simply transported and redeposited soil materials (alluvium). On low plains, such as the waterlogged flatwoods of Florida, the high water table obstructs the percolation of water necessary to normal profile development. Instead, organic matter carried through the A horizon becomes so compacted in the B that it constitutes an organic hardpan, blocking both downward and upward passage of water. The Leon and St. Johns series are good examples of this bad situation. Their use capability is extremely limited.

Figure 26 shows various influences of topographic position in soil development.

For purposes of conservation it is not enough to describe a soil as sand, silt, loam, or clay, on rolling upland, steep slope or flat lowland; other less conspicuous characteristics may be equally important in the choice of conservation methods. We have spent much time and money to refine our knowledge of American soils, and much of the information can be useful in conservation. Our soils experts may identify as many as 200 different kinds of soil —types, phases, complexes, and variants—on a detailed map of a single locality. The conservator should recognize the functional groups, at least, because they may be the basis for land-use planning and farm management. Soil maps, soil descriptions, and soil management recommendations are available for much of our land. The conservator should familiarize himself with those aids to agriculture for the same reasons as he should learn to identify the important tree species in forestry or the important grass species in range management. He should know the characteristics of any resource he wishes to conserve.

Turning now from soil genesis and classification to an equally brief outline of productivity factors, let us consider first what a soil must contain in order to support a healthy plant community. Staple foods—the meat, bread, and potatoes—of all common plants are compounds of nitrogen, potassium, and phosphorus, flavored with calcium. But none of the "big three" is palatable or digestible unless it be properly "cooked" and "served." Agronomists learned long ago that soil analysis by chemical test does not always mean that a substance detected is in a form plants can use. Of course, a negative chemical result means that the substance just is not present and therefore cannot be obtained by plants. However, presence of plant nutrients in the soil means little unless they be present in forms *available* to plants. Availability depends upon several factors, among them chemical composition and combination, humus content, organic activity, conditions of moisture and aeration. Modern utilitarian soil tests are designed to show the amounts of nutrients available to plants rather than the amounts that can be detected by chemical analysis. Certain availability tests now common involve testing extracts from the plants grown in the soils, on the logical assumption that these substances would not be in the plant unless available in the soil. However, when the farmer wants a sure index of soil fertility he sows a crop and sees how well it grows. Nature provides the ultimate soil test.

Soil productivity depends upon availability of plant nutrients

Compounds of nitrogen, phosphorus, and potassium furnish the bulk of plant foods in soil; but plants gorged on these can starve unless they have available with the main course a number

Certain trace elements play subtle roles

of side dishes commonly referred to as "trace" elements—iron, manganese, magnesium, copper, zinc, and sulphur—and certain appetizers like barium, boron, cobalt, sodium, chlorine, and chromium. These secondary soil components are comparatively recent discoveries, are only partially understood, and are the objects of intensive continuing research. Several are believed to be essential for normal plant growth, and some are equally essential to good health in animals. The metals have particular soil value in the form of metallic salts. Though one and another serves a specific vital function in extremely small quantity, that same compound in slightly higher concentration may be strongly toxic. A little goes a long way; a trifle more can go entirely too far.

The trace elements probably have less utility as food absorbed by plants than as catalytics that release or prepare other materials for assimilation. Chicken manure, containing 0.001 per cent zinc, acts somewhat like a transfusion to certain sick nut trees (Tung) on sandy southern soils. The trees respond to minute quantities in their diet, and many soils lack even that trace. Zinc seems to prevent specific tree ills much as iodine prevents goiter in humans. Iron and magnesium are considered essential to the functioning of chlorophyll, and others may be found equally necessary. Trace elements in the soil are like vitamins: we know they correct deficiencies, but we know little about their complex operational procedures. Much soil chemistry remains to be learned.

Plant foods must be in solution

Unless they be dissolved in water, plant nutrients in the soil cannot be absorbed and used by the plants. The thin film of water that envelopes each tiny particle of good soil contains all the plant food the soil can supply to the probing root-hairs seeking it. Quantities not in solution are like packs of frozen meat in a freezer-locker, and water is the only key to their release. Furthermore, plants tolerate only a certain concentration or dilution of the food-water mixture, some thinner, some thicker. Soil containing too little water to nourish the ordinary upland plants (mesophytes) is said to be *physically,* or *actually, dry.* Soil containing too much water for such plants is said to be *physiologically,* or *in effect, dry.* Some plants adapted to moisture deficiency can grow in either situation. Water and soil are partners that the conservator must often consider together.

Strong acidity or alkalinity of the soil causes starvation and poisoning of plants when other properties might favor fertility. The soil factor of chemical reaction, commonly referred to as "*p*H," can determine the productive capacity of a soil. To the technician, *p*H is "the common logarithm of the reciprocal of the hydrogen-ion concentration of a system." In plain language a *p*H of 7.0 indicates neutrality, lower numbers indicate acidity, and higher ones alkalinity. Soils with a *p*H of 4.5 or less are extremely acid; those with a *p*H of 9.1 or higher, very strongly alkaline. Soil reaction interests the conservator because a suitable control of *p*H may be the decisive factor in the conservation of certain soils.

*The *p*H must be within a moderate range*

Plants are more generally tolerant of acidity than alkalinity, but extremes of either are toxic. Some plants prefer an acid reaction; others prefer a basic one. Some are specific, others less particular, in their *p*H requirement. Most of our common cultivated plants do best with a *p*H value somewhere between 6 and 8; and the acid forest soils need artificial neutralization to hold their reaction within that range. Application of calcium carbonate (lime) sweetens them much as bicarbonate does a sour stomach. Soils too highly alkaline, such as the solonchak and solonetz shown in Figure 22, require more specific medication, like a prescription to correct faulty metabolism. Correct prescription must be based upon careful diagnosis of a particular situation.

Essentials of soil fertility complement each other, and paucity or defection of a single one can render the entire soil impotent. Like the vital organs of the human body or the players on a baseball team, all components of good soil are integral parts of the total organization, the character and function of each indispensable to the whole. Air, water, minerals, humus, flora, and fauna are merely raw materials, and no matter how precisely they might be apportioned and however thoroughly mixed they would not be soil. They become soil only when the slow, complex, pedologic processes combine them in a balanced, reciprocating union. Unless texture be neither too coarse nor too fine; unless there be enough humus, but not too much; unless the soil section permits water passage, yet prohibits too rapid movement, the soil will not retain the water needed to dissolve and distribute plant nutrients. Unless the solution be neither too thin nor too rich, neither too acid nor too alkaline, the plant cannot get the foods, however abundant they may be. Unless the chemical reaction be about right, bacteria and other organisms cannot continue their work of preparing plant foods and generating soil fertility. They also need air, water, organic material, and warmth in moderate proportions, and every one of these individually plays a double role of cause and effect in soil quality. Physical, chemical, and

Essentials of soil fertility complement each other

biologic characteristics of soil are so intricately bound together that a minor change in one can foment revolt in another. An established balance can be extremely delicate, and those who desire to improve it should proceed with caution.

Good tilth enables high productivity

The farmer who tills the soil summarizes all its qualities of arability and productivity in the single word "tilth," though the word pertains more specifically to the physical state of the soil in terms of its capacity for producing a particular crop. Soil in good tilth breaks and turns from the plow in smooth furrows that crumble and fall together into a friable (loose) mass upon exposure to sun and rain. Friability indicates, generally, desirable texture, structure, content of humus and water, aeration, organic activity, and chemical reaction. Dead, plastic clays that bake into clods after plowing are not only physically intractable but lack several other desirable attributes of friability. One wet plowing can injure them for several years. Compaction of a soil, in most any case, is attributable to poor physical make-up, and compaction renders correction of deficiencies doubly difficult. But good tilth means more than easy cultivation and high productivity; it means responsiveness to practices for maintaining or improving fertility. Tilth is to soil what health is to people, and the two conditions may be closely associated.

The soil processes and characteristics that have been mentioned in this chapter have a direct bearing on conservation, not only of the soils themselves, but also of water and of all the living resources, be they plant or animal. Soil characteristics determine how well, or how poorly, a field may naturally resist the destructive forces described in Chapter 7, and how amenable it may be to the remedies and preventives described in Chapter 8. Soil characteristics and patterns constitute a basic frame of reference in land planning (Chapter 5) whether for a farm or ranch, a community, or a region. They are dominant factors in water management (Chapter 6). The trace elements so vital to soil productivity are minerals, as are also some of our most important fertilizer materials (Chapter 16). Soils produce our important plant resources, and the vegetation (forests and grasslands) can best defend the soil against excessive erosion by wind or water. The soil may be regarded as a main source of food for marine life (Chapter 15); even the wealth of the sea is related to the soils on the land. Certainly wildlife resources on the land are strongly influenced by soil conditions (Chapters 12-13); whether for flora, fauna, or humans the qualities of a habitat are fundamentally soil factors (allowing always that climate governs soil processes). Finally, the entire cultural landscape and many singularly aesthetic aspects of it are clear reflectors of soil conditions (Chapter 14). Patterns of rural land occupance will be more or less in accord with soil boundaries. The prosperity or poverty apparent in a rural scene become, as it were, the development of a basic theme—the soil—which dominates the entire composition. If the scene be faithfully transferred to an artist's canvas, soil qualities may show through even there, often discernible in certain blendings or contrasts of colors. Scenic beauty and soil may be closely related. Thus the chapter here concluded serves in many ways as a background for those that follow.

Land Management—

Approach to Conservation

*land management accordant with land capability
sets the pattern for conservation*

ALL RESOURCES ARE ATTACHED OR RELATED TO THE LAND. THE SOILS
and water resources introduced in the two chapters preceding
are the crucial attributes of land. By their adequacy or paucity
they influence the usefulness of land for various purposes. On the
other hand, the conservation of soils and water depends more on
the use of the land than on any direct manipulation of the soil
or water itself. From the land, its soils, and its waters come most
if not all of our biotic resources.

The land provides the surface space necessary to exploit and
process resources, including the minerals brought up from below.
As container and producer of resources, land holds resource
status in its own right; but more important than that, it is the
frame of reference for understanding and conserving the other
resources. It is the base from which the conservator must work.
It is the map on which we plan the strategy of conservation. It is
our maneuver area for isolating, attacking, and solving a wide
variety of conservation problems.

The apportionment of a land area among particular kinds of
use may actually be a most important conservation measure, but
let us regard it rather as a prelude, or preliminary, to the specific

The land
is our base
of operations

Land use
sets the
pattern for
conservation

77

treatment of resources that pertain to that land. Let us not consider the types and arrangement of land use an end in themselves, but merely an adjustable pattern into which we fit the appropriate conservation measures. This idea should be borne in mind as the reader progresses through the following chapters, because they proceed on the assumption that land management has a further end in view. It is assumed, for example, that soil conservation pertains mainly to cultivated land, that good forestry conserves soil, water, and wildlife incidentally, that reseeding and management does the same for the dry grasslands, and that areas preserved as wilderness are immune to the ordinary ills that trouble us elsewhere.

Whether for the nation as a whole or for an individual farm, the appropriate allocation of space (land) to various uses is a prerequisite to conservation. It is to the conservator as fire protection is to the forester. Unless it be accomplished first, all other measures may come to naught. Only after use-allocation has been made wisely and well can the success of other applications be fully realized. The entity with which we must deal first in conservation is *land*—soil, or water, or anything else takes its place as part of the picture of land use.

There is much land without soil

In the chapter just preceding it was suggested that all *terra firma* is not soil-covered, that the terms "land" and "soil" are far from synonymous. There is much land without any true soil upon it, much that has never had soil, and much on which soil may never develop. When one considers the spread of lands naturally devoid of soil and the extent of others from which the soil has been lost he might become more concerned about land than soil. Certainly land occupies more space, but without soil it is generally neither highly productive nor readily improved. Bread comes from soil, not from land devoid of soil; without bread, who would there be to fret about wasting the land barren of soil?

Soil-less areas are of several different kinds, ranging in composition from the thick organic deposits accumulated in bogs and marshes to the deep, sterile sands of old beaches and dunes. Soil surveyors recognize 34 types of land which must be mapped without any soil designation (1). Certain muck lands can be made highly productive by drainage and specific treatment. From many of them come superior truck crops, especially roots, tubers, and bulbs that prefer soft earth in which to grow.

The sands, on the other hand, are not only naturally unproductive, but lack the capacity for retaining materials that might be applied to make them productive. Some sand areas have more value for glass manufacture or military maneuver than for plant growth. Locally they serve a useful purpose as recharge areas for groundwater.

Where the country rock sticks out of the ground there is, obviously, no soil; and fragmentation, such as in "shoe-peg" shale, does not make it much less barren than if it were solid. The disintegrated material will admit rain and roots, and may sustain a forest cover though true soil be lacking. Trees like the cedar, with extensive lateral roots to support them, take hold where flat rock strata lie too near the surface to permit normal soil development and where inclined strata crop out at intervals with soil pockets between them.

Where loose stone blocks or boulders occupy the ground there is no soil in the ordinary sense, and unless the mantle be completely stabilized the most tenacious plant species survive with difficulty.

Areas of stones or exposed rock have been classified in American soils literature as "stony land" and "rock land" respectively. The sterile, sandy areas have been mapped as "undifferentiated sands and gravels," without soil designation. The literature has dealt more kindly with the more deserving bog and marsh areas, referring to them variously as "organic soils," "muck," or "peat." In the arid West are extensive areas from which winds and torrential rains strip off mineral materials before any soil can form in them. Such bare areas have been described as "badlands." Aridity prohibits vegetation from covering their nakedness. These and other soil-less land types compose a tremendous aggregate area.

Whichever nomenclature one prefers, he should appreciate that, although good land has soil on it, land without soil can also be useful. *Land, per se, holds resource status!* For land that lacks soil, conservation becomes largely a matter of wisely planned, limited utilization. The presence of soil broadens the choice of land use and increases the economic feasibility of other conservation measures. So much has been said about *soil* conservation, and so little about *land* conservation, that the latter might appear to be neglected. However, neglect has been more apparent than real. It has been assumed that most of our land has some trace of soil upon it, that soil and land conservation are too closely allied for separate treatment. The assumption has been confusing. Land and soil may be considered together in planning the use of an area, but each must be treated separately for good management and conservation.

Crops, pasture, and *forest* occupy so much of our land and yield

The land itself holds resource status

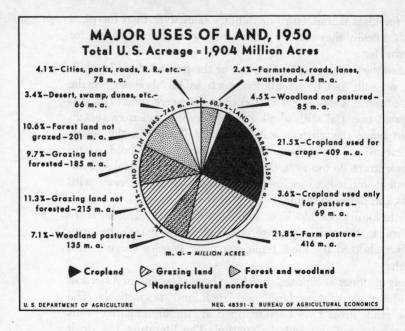

FIGURE 27. *The slices of pie are subject to change, but only gradually. This graph represents the land economy of the United States as a whole.*

The primary land uses occupy most of the space

so much of its produce that they have come to be known as the *primary* land uses. Those three surface adaptations contribute most of our food supply and the greatest variety of our raw materials. Without this *primary* triumvirate on the land all our digging in the earth for minerals and all our fishing in the sea would come to naught. The three are, indeed, primary—fundamental! The proportionate space each occupies in the United States may be learned from Figure 27; their regional importance from Figure 28.

The magnitude and health of our agricultural, pastoral, and forestry industries gage the state of the Union as a whole, and dominate the economy of almost every section of America. The crop-pasture-forest ratio greatly influences the source of livelihood, mode of living, and even the politics, of states and regions. Of course, it determines also the comparative regional interest in the various resources and their conservation (see Figure 29). One should not expect a sheep man in Wyoming to be much concerned about forestry, nor a logger in Idaho to worry about water and forage for sheep. Neither should one suggest that a wheat farmer on the black Dakota plains can apply the same soil

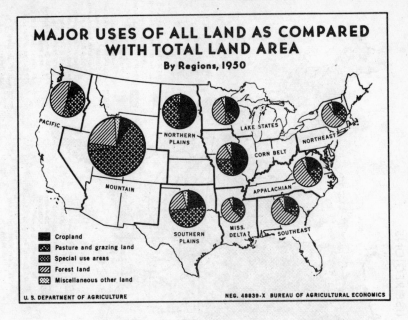

MAJOR USES OF ALL LAND AS COMPARED WITH TOTAL LAND AREA
By Regions, 1950

■ Cropland
▦ Pasture and grazing land
▩ Special use areas
▨ Forest land
▨ Miscellaneous other land

U. S. DEPARTMENT OF AGRICULTURE   NEG. 48839-X BUREAU OF AGRICULTURAL ECONOMICS

FIGURE 28. *Resources and interests of one region may be quite different from those of another. Regional land economy becomes an important index to regional conservation and planning.*

conserving measures as a hog farmer in Iowa or a dairyman in Wisconsin. But one can hope that a furrier in Manhattan who likes butter and biscuits, lamb chops and pork roast, and his kitchen finished in Ponderosa pine, appreciates that he enjoys the fruits of the primary land uses. Our urban population approaches two-thirds of the total—64 per cent, according to the new definition of "urban" used in the 1950 Census (2). It is therefore important that the city dwellers know where and how their bread is buttered. They need reminding that farmers, ranchers, and lumbermen are entrusted with the permanent source of their material well-being —our productive land.

Special cultural developments constitute a fourth major category of surface land use, covering approximately 5 per cent of our total land (3). They compose a long list of divers social and economic demands for space, all indispensable to our culture, some highly productive of material wealth, others creative of less tangible values, but none contriving to bring forth any direct fruit from the land it occupies. All buildings, roads, streets, railways, communication and transmission lines, parks and play-

Special uses aggregate a large total area

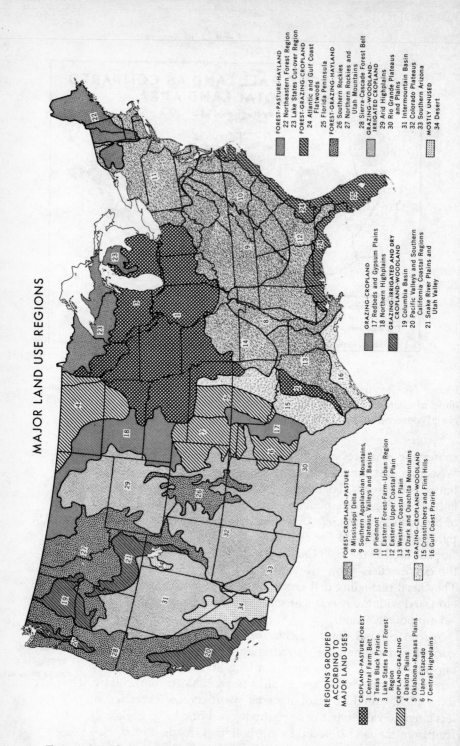

MAJOR LAND USE REGIONS

REGIONS GROUPED
ACCORDING TO
MAJOR LAND USES

CROPLAND-PASTURE-FOREST
1 Central Farm Belt
2 Texas Black Prairie
3 Lake States Farm Forest
  Region

CROPLAND-GRAZING
4 Dakota Plains
5 Oklahoma-Kansas Plains
6 Llano Estacado
7 Central Highlands

FOREST-CROPLAND-PASTURE
8 Mississippi Delta
9 Southern Appalachian Mountains,
  Plateaus, Valleys and Basins
10 Piedmont
11 Eastern Forest-Farm-Urban Region
12 Eastern Upper Coastal Plain
13 Western Coastal Plain
14 Ozark and Ouachita Mountains
15 Crosstimbers and Flint Hills
16 Gulf Coast Prairie

GRAZING-CROPLAND
17 Redbeds and Gypsum Plains
18 Northern Highplains

GRAZING-IRRIGATED AND DRY
CROPLAND-WOODLAND
19 Columbia Basin
20 Pacific Valleys and Southern
   California Coastal Regions
21 Snake River Plains and
   Utah Valley

FOREST-PASTURE-HAYLAND
22 Northeastern Forest Region
23 Lake States Cut-over Region

FOREST-GRAZING-CROPLAND
24 Atlantic and Gulf Coast
   Flatwoods
25 Florida Peninsula

FOREST-GRAZING-HAYLAND
26 Southern Rockies
27 Northern Rockies and
   Utah Mountains
28 Sierra-Cascade Forest Belt

GRAZING-WOODLAND-
IRRIGATED CROPLAND
29 Arid Highplains
30 Rio Grande Plateaus
   and Plains
31 Intermountain Basin
32 Colorado Plateaus
33 Southern Arizona

MOSTLY UNUSED
34 Desert

FIGURE 29. *The geography of land use sets the national pattern for conservation. The boundaries on this map are not static, but subject to considerable change. Future changes should be based on land capability. (U.S.D.A. map.)*

grounds, airports and flying fields, dams and reservoirs, oil wells and tank farms, military reservations, mines and quarries, race tracks and cemeteries are cultural land uses. They are expanding constantly, often usurping space highly prized for primary production. It is estimated that our cities, roads, and airports will claim 15 million additional acres during the next quarter century (4).

Many special uses are only temporary, destined to shift in the course of a few years, but they leave scars that heal slowly. The recovery of abandoned building sites, road and rail beds, mined areas, or even burial grounds, for productive use affords better opportunity to conserve land than many a project of reclamation by drainage. Unfortunately, recovery is often a bigger task than the original conversion of a field to a special use, because soil removed or mutilated incidental to construction work is not so easily replaced.

The four great categories of land utilization, and the numerous classes of use within each, compete for the space they occupy, the most discriminate laying strongest claim to the land. Among the primary uses, cultivated crops take first choice, pasture takes second, and forest retires to areas poorly suited to either of the other two. Ordinarily, a special use prevails against any one of the primary ones because it attaches a higher value per areal unit either in terms of earning power or in special desirability. The most intensive cropping about a city retreats farther into the country with every onslaught of subdivision and suburban expansion. Roses, cows, or asparagus tips cannot resist filling stations, drive-ins, and tourist courts.

Fertility ratings yield to site factors

For special purposes—such as residential, commercial, or industrial use—the location and form of the land become criteria of valuation. Inherent fertility loses its significance as a measure of quality; the space becomes "real-estate," and it yields artificial dividends instead of genuine produce. Special, cultural uses rob the land of its normal resource status, subordinating productive capacity to site factors. Competition for space in our metropolitan areas long since necessitated detailed planning and restriction of land use by zoning ordinances or similar regulations to protect public interests against haphazard private promotion. We have also made good progress toward rehabilitation of land mutilated by mining operations.

However, we have barely begun the scientific, selective, allocation of rural land to primary uses that should precede any application of specific conservation techniques. We have talked much

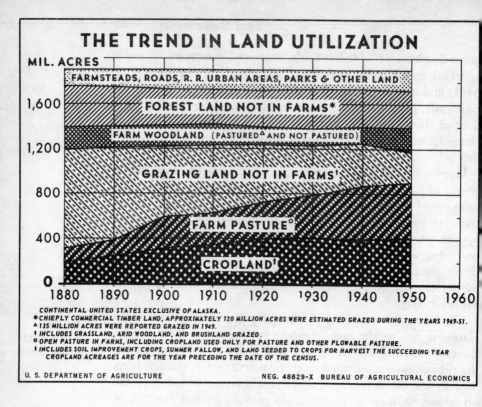

THE TREND IN LAND UTILIZATION

MIL. ACRES

FARMSTEADS, ROADS, R. R. URBAN AREAS, PARKS & OTHER LAND

FOREST LAND NOT IN FARMS*

FARM WOODLAND (PASTURED△ AND NOT PASTURED)

GRAZING LAND NOT IN FARMS¹

FARM PASTURE°

CROPLAND‡

1,600

1,200

800

400

0

1880 1890 1900 1910 1920 ¹930 1940 1950 1960

CONTINENTAL UNITED STATES EXCLUSIVE OF ALASKA.
* CHIEFLY COMMERCIAL TIMBER LAND, APPROXIMATELY 120 MILLION ACRES WERE ESTIMATED GRAZED DURING THE YEARS 1949-51.
△ 135 MILLION ACRES WERE REPORTED GRAZED IN 1949.
¹ INCLUDES GRASSLAND, ARID WOODLAND, AND BRUSHLAND GRAZED.
° OPEN PASTURE IN FARMS, INCLUDING CROPLAND USED ONLY FOR PASTURE AND OTHER PLOWABLE PASTURE.
‡ INCLUDES SOIL IMPROVEMENT CROPS, SUMMER FALLOW, AND LAND SEEDED TO CROPS FOR HARVEST THE SUCCEEDING YEAR
CROPLAND ACREAGES ARE FOR THE YEAR PRECEDING THE DATE OF THE CENSUS.

U. S. DEPARTMENT OF AGRICULTURE   NEG. 48829-X BUREAU OF AGRICULTURAL ECONOMICS

FIGURE 30. *The trend in land utilization. Project a trend, and predict the future! Special land uses are gradually taking more space as the nation becomes more heavily populated. Farm woodland and farm pasture are increasing rapidly at the expense of public grazing land. The term "farm" on this graph should be interpreted to mean also "ranch."* (B.A.E., U.S.D.A. diagram.)

about soil conservation with reference to arable (plowed) land, and said very little about conserving land by changing its use. We have accepted traditional land-use ratings too readily, and observed land-use trends (Figure 30) without thought of interference. But the conservator will not be bound by tradition. He has no qualms about retiring an infertile field from cultivation and planting trees on it. Neither does he hesitate to challenge the validity of acreage trends as land-use criteria unless they are correlated with production trends. Good land conservation does, in fact, cause progressive divergence of acreage and production curves—higher yield from less area.

Quality of use and quality of land tend to coincide

Other factors being equal, *superior land receives the most intensive attention; inferior land, the most extensive.* (Intensive land use applies much labor and/or capital per unit of land—heavy investment in small acreage. Extensive land use involves much

84

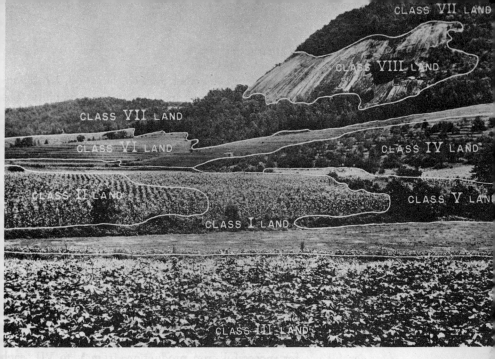

FIGURE 31. *The land shown in this photograph has been classified into eight categories according to its use capability. Mapping and land classification are prerequisites to planning and conservation. Categories are characterized as follows:*

SUITABLE FOR CULTIVATION:
I. *Requires good soil management practices only.*
II. *Moderate conservation practices necessary.*
III. *Intensive conservation practices necessary.*
IV. *Perennial vegetation—infrequent cultivation.*

(S.C.S. photo.)

NO CULTIVATION: PASTURE, HAY, WOODLAND, AND WILDLIFE:
V. *No restrictions in use.*
VI. *Moderate restrictions in use.*
VII. *Severe restrictions in use.*
VIII. *Best suited for wildlife and recreation.*

land and little expenditure per acre.) Good land rewards well the keeper who tends it, but poor land makes less promise of such reward. Land cannot repay tillage costs exceeding its limits of production. Simple economic theory relegates unproductive land to idleness; and practical technology, including conservation, cannot always abrogate the time-worn theory. Conservation relaxes economic restriction on land utilization by physical improvement of the land. It is a moot point whether the elevation of waste land to pulpwood cropping represents better conservation than the conversion of a pulpwood stand to saw timber, or whether pasture land made arable or pasture land simply given higher carrying capacity be the better achievement. In any case, the degree of *increase in productivity attained* should be the criterion. And, unless added production can defray improvement costs the im-

85

provement represents waste rather than conservation, a futile at
tempt to elevate the land above its inherent use capability. The
conservator cannot make fertile crop land out of rough, stony
waste any more than a tailor can fashion a woolen garment out
of cotton shoddy. Instead, each can only do his best with the ma
terial at hand, letting his product conform to the fabric. To the
conservator such conformation means the employment of land for
its optimum productive use, be it crop, pasture, or forest; inten
sive, extensive, or in between. *The first step toward good land
conservation is the classification and use*—the allocation of unit
areas on the basis of capability ratings.

**Land use
according to
capability
improves the
farm, the
region, and
the nation**

The Soil Conservation Service evolved a practical system of
land classification that identifies according to use capability eight
classes of land in farms, as illustrated by Figure 31. The first four
classes are suitable for crops, the next three adaptable to grass
and trees, and class VIII is useless except as wilderness or wild
life habitat. From I to IV, each class demands progressively more
careful use for successful crop production; from V to VII, each
class becomes more limited in its usefulness for pasture or forest
(5). A land-use plan according to land capability may be a farmer's
most constructive conservation measure. Without a good plan,
other conservation practices cannot be effective. Figures 32, 33,
and 34 show the steps by which a farm plan is evolved. Planning
similar to that which improves a farm can be applied, on a grand
scale, to improve the economy of states, regions, and the na
tion as a whole. Whatever its scope, land planning must be based
upon a preliminary classification and inventory of assets in the
area affected by the plan.

Modern land utilization and conservation revise a traditional
connotation of intensiveness. In the "good old days" pasture and
forest were never more than extensive land uses. Stock raising
and lumbering were expansive enterprises loosely attached to the
land. Now much of our beef comes from intensively used land,
from pastures carefully prepared, sown, fertilized; and, in places,
even irrigated with portable sprinkler systems during periods of
drought. We are also developing silviculture to a degree that
intensifies the use of land for producing forest. Eventually land
in saw timber may receive as much attention as land in fruit or
chard. Conservation breaks the old-fashioned parallel between
type of land use and intensiveness of use, and enforces the stronger
parallel between land quality and intensiveness, with less and less
regard for type of enterprise.

Conservation also faces up to the economist's problem of mar-

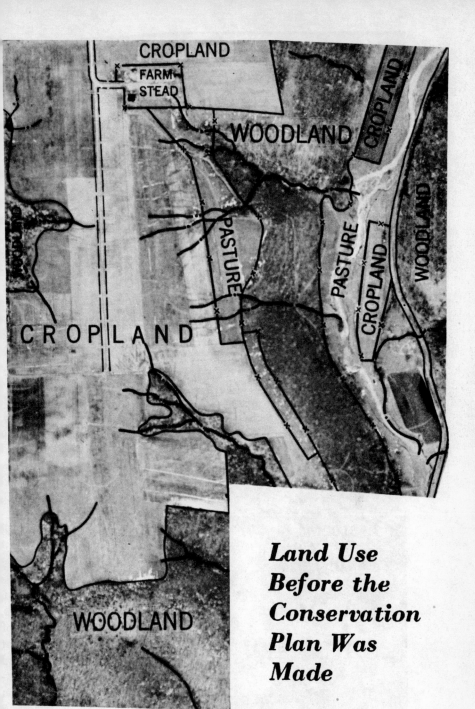

CROPLAND

FARM-STEAD

WOODLAND

CROPLAND

PASTURE

PASTURE

CROPLAND

WOODLAND

CROPLAND

WOODLAND

WOODLAND

Land Use Before the Conservation Plan Was Made

FIGURE 32. *This and the next two photographs show how the land capability idea improves the use of a farm. Each part of the farm is put to the best use it can sustain without damage.* (S.C.S. photo.)

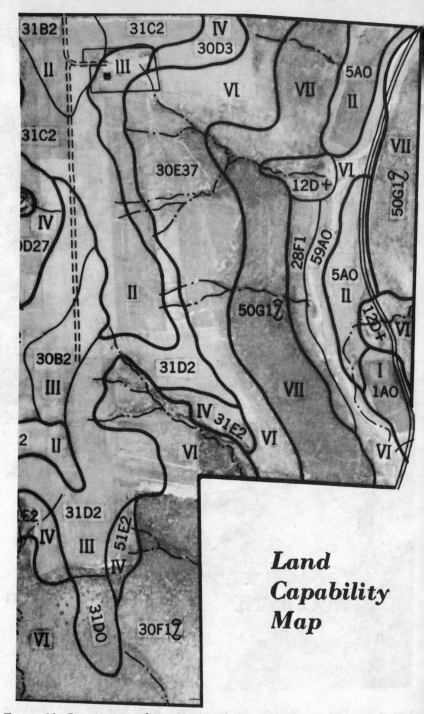

FIGURE 33. *Roman numerals on this map designate the same categories of land as in Figure 31, with area descriptions further refined in coded symbols. How many classes of land does this farm contain?* (S.C.S. photo.)

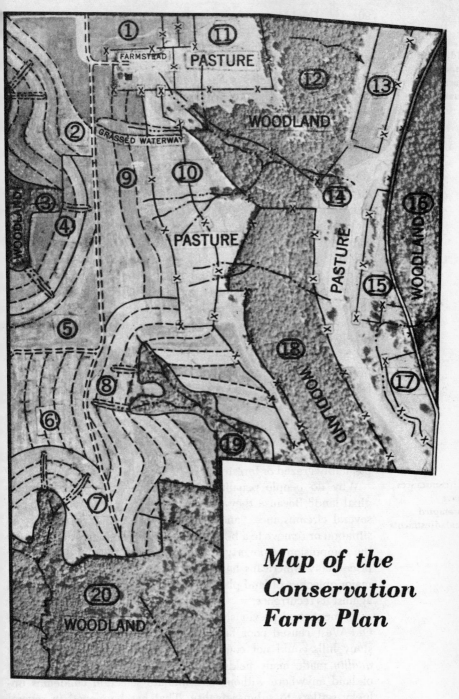

FIGURE 34. *The acceptable farm plan makes reasonable allowance for established adjuncts, such as fences, roads, and so on. In this farm are 20 unit-areas to be considered individually in the total management program.* (S.C.S. photo.)

**Adjustment of
land use
corrects
marginality**

ginal and submarginal land by classification and selective use.
(Marginal land is land that will barely yield its operator a livelihood under prevailing use; submarginal land will not meet his
simplest needs for food, clothing, and shelter.) In this province
the planning aspects of land conservation have special significance. Land submarginal in small cultivated tracts can often be
used profitably for grazing or forestry in larger blocks. Our
legislators acknowledged that fact when they amended the Homestead Act to populate the plains. Their fault when they doled out
our dry grazing lands lay in being too conservative rather than
too rash. They over-estimated land capabilities because they
lacked the experience necessary to judge them. Perhaps they did
foresee that abusive practices would render submarginal a large
acreage of land in the humid eastern portions of the country,
much of it ruined by robber crops, but even more of it damaged
by misappropriation for uses above its capabilities. In any event,
the problem of submarginal land (and submarginal tenants) attained national proportions long before we took concerted action
to solve it.

The urgent need for salvage and reassignment of misused land
invoked our modern planning and conservation movement. We
learned that hunger stalks the man who plants cotton where slash
pine ought to be or wheat where grass ought to grow, that marginality may stem from human error more often than from any
fault of the land, and that self-imposed pain can be self-alleviated.
We learned that much land submarginal under cultivation can be
profitably grazed or forested.

**Circumstances
have
prompted
maladjustments**

Why do people penalize themselves by cultivating submarginal land? Because they are become victims of any one among
several circumstances, and lack the wherewithal to correct the
situation or remove to a better locale. Abandonment of land under
the compulsion of poverty, malnutrition, and disease is the tragic
price many Americans have paid for unwise land occupance. A
major objective of land planning is to salve that misery and guard
against its recurrence.

As mentioned previously, the settlement of better lands in the
Old West caused poor farms in New England to lie idle. The
stony hills could not compete with fertile plains. *Comparative
quality* made many fields in the East submarginal. Settlement
of land anywhere without discriminate selection condemns un-
lucky settlers to submarginality. That has happened in several
places about our country. We condoned, and encouraged, private
ownership of land which could not support the owner. Selection

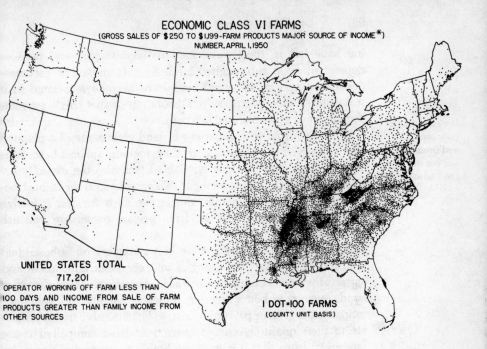

ECONOMIC CLASS VI FARMS
(GROSS SALES OF $250 TO $1,199-FARM PRODUCTS MAJOR SOURCE OF INCOME*)
NUMBER, APRIL 1, 1950

UNITED STATES TOTAL
717,201
OPERATOR WORKING OFF FARM LESS THAN
100 DAYS AND INCOME FROM SALE OF FARM
PRODUCTS GREATER THAN FAMILY INCOME FROM
OTHER SOURCES

1 DOT=100 FARMS
(COUNTY UNIT BASIS)

FIGURE 35. *Land too poor or farms too small, or both—poverty!* (Bureau of the Census map.)

comes by painful trial and error, by forced migration of any residents in excess of the number the land can adequately and permanently sustain. Many of the dots in Figure 35 represent maladjustment to the land.

The Dust Bowl demonstrated conclusively the tragic consequences of wrong land occupance. Abnormally high prices accompanying war pressure for food pushed cereal crops, particularly wheat, beyond their safe limits of aridity. Decline in market demand and price asserted the submarginal character of the "boom" expansion. Price fluctuations have often caused or exposed the marginality of land for a particular use.

Many Americans live on land that became submarginal at their own hands or the hands of their ancestors. Such unfortunates have victimized themselves, but their plight is nonetheless a problem for the planner-conservator. His the task to correct and rehabilitate, whatever the origin of the trouble.

Extractive industries, such as mining and "destructive" lumbering have left in their wake men without wages, and families dependent upon submarginal land. By this and other processes destitution and submarginal land have become associated in a scavenger-carrion partnership. Dissolution of that tragic partnership depends upon planned land use.

We consolidate poor land and intensify our use of good land

Whereas farms with a variety of land classes may be planned and conserved economically if they include sufficient portions of good land, those lacking good land lack also the capacity for significant internal improvement. Their conservation is best accomplished by consolidation into larger units for less intensive employment or by retirement from private ownership and use by public appropriation.

Farm subsidy or bounty that keeps farmers on submarginal land simply prolongs the agony of sane economic adjustment and aggravates a bad condition. Crop acreage restrictions, on the other hand, encourage better tending of select parcels and voluntary retirement of poorer parts of a farm to less intensive use appropriate to their quality. Acreage restrictions have compelled many farmers to learn that it is more profitable to concentrate energies and means on a little good land than to dissipate them over a much larger area of poor land. The curtailment of acreage intended to protect commodity markets has achieved more valuable and permanent results in the realm of land-use improvement.

Public ownership enables special utilization and conservation of land

Land was an abundant commodity during the entire formative period of our great nation, and west of the mid-continent it became freer than water. When the United States had extended its dominion to the Pacific coast the federal government held title to most of the lands west of the Mississippi in a grand "public domain." There followed the phenomenal era of westward expansion implemented by lavish gifts of land under various plans calculated to speed settlement and private ownership. What was the good of land that yielded no taxes?

The Homestead Act of 1862 and subsequent liberalizing amendments, the Timber and Stone Act of 1878, and other legal devices for giving land away brought settlers to the plains and valleys of the West. Liberal land grants encouraged the building of railroads, roads, and canals to facilitate settlement. Swamp and overflow lands were given the states within which they lay. The federal government disposed of the public domain with a vengeance. Not before 1934 was the wild give-away spree checked. There remained very little "open" land upon which a private owner might make a living.

Meanwhile, men of vision had begun a national program of

salvaging and reserving certain lands for permanent public use and administration. In 1872 Congress established Yellowstone National Park—the initial step toward our great national park system of today. In 1891 Yellowstone Park Timberland Reserve was set aside—the forerunner of our national forests. Congress decided that vast areas of our great land might best serve the people if held in public trust, at least for an indefinite period. States, counties, towns, and communities have followed the example until publicly owned lands now aggregate tremendous totals. The public lands mapped in Figure 36 are largely in federal ownership.

With the modern planning and conservation era came a complete about-face in our attitude toward public ownership of land. Public acquisition became the means of removing from submarginal land the unfortunate tenants struggling to live on it, thereby diverting both land and human resources to better purposes. Most of the displaced tenants were relocated on land better suited to their use. The states discovered that tax-delinquent land may not always be "redeemed" by the payment of back taxes, that its repeated resale means repeated human suffering, and that its depopulation and retirement at public expense is good economy. Acting upon this knowledge and for the common weal, we have returned to federal ownership some 50 million acres once privately owned, or held by local governments (6, p. 146). We have abandoned counties and dissolved their governments. We have returned submarginal land to its proper tenants —trees, brush, birds, snakes, foxes, and other wild things, none of whom demands subsidy. Many expansive units of our land have been wisely adjudged most useful in their natural state, and only the public can afford to own and preserve a wilderness. Only public ownership, under democratic government, can hold in trust for future generations the unspoiled, wild lands we want them to inherit. Therein lies a unique governmental responsibility for conservation.

Trends in land economy, by design or otherwise, point the way to future land conservation. Good trends express conservational progress; bad ones foreshadow complication or obstruction. As noted above, there is a trend toward *more intensive use of good land and more extensive use of poor land,* both facilitated by acreage restrictions and government acquisition. The latter is largely an application of land-use planning; the former a by-product of artificial economic stabilization. Both contribute to land conservation. Their constructive results may be inferred

**Trends in
land economy
are guideposts
of conservation**

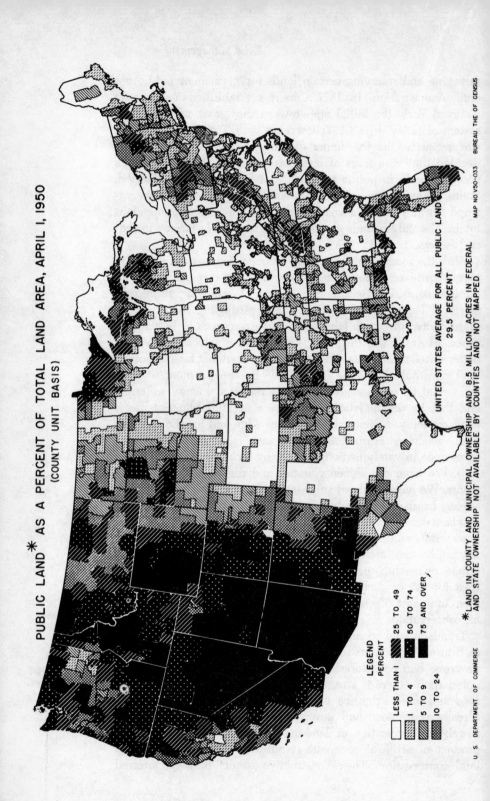

PUBLIC LAND * AS A PERCENT OF TOTAL LAND AREA, APRIL 1, 1950
(COUNTY UNIT BASIS)

LEGEND
PERCENT

LESS THAN 1
1 TO 4
5 TO 9
10 TO 24
25 TO 49
50 TO 74
75 AND OVER

UNITED STATES AVERAGE FOR ALL PUBLIC LAND
29.5 PERCENT

* LAND IN COUNTY AND MUNICIPAL OWNERSHIP AND 8.5 MILLION ACRES IN FEDERAL
AND STATE OWNERSHIP NOT AVAILABLE BY COUNTIES AND NOT MAPPED

U. S. DEPARTMENT OF COMMERCE

BUREAU THE OF CENSUS

MAP NO V50-033

from our substantially increased production during recent years while our total crop acreage remained about constant. Land selection has magnified the advantages of improved plant strains and the application of mineral fertilizers.

Another current trend relating to intensified use of our better land involves the revision of traditional land-use ratings on the basis of enterprise. Local intensification of stock raising and timber growing on good land shifts grazing and forestry into higher cash-yield brackets, elevating them nearer to parity with conventional cropping. It appears likely that the transition will gain momentum as we refine our adjustment to the land. The conservator may wisely anticipate the time when Americans will meticulously regulate cattle grazing, and cultivate timber crops under systems long since perfected by Europeans.

The modern trend of industrial decentralization and urban dispersal makes its own impact on land economy. By cultural expansion horizontally rather than vertically it reduces vulnerability to aerial bombardment, but it is costly in terms of land space. Having first choice of site, cultural uses will further compress our total area available for primary production.

The land planner needs to recognize and analyze all land-use trends with a view toward meeting future land requirements without waste, and without jeopardizing our standard of living and our national strength. We know that our nation has a total land area of about 1,900,000,000 acres, exclusive of some 30,000,-000 acres of inland waters, and that our population exceeds 166 million (3). We know that we are growing crops on just about all the land that can be tilled economically at present—478,000,000 acres in 1950 (3)—and that our population continues to increase. Population grows while land area and potentially arable acreage remain constant. How then may we continue to satisfy the mounting demand for food, to say nothing of other products of the land considered essential? Thus far we have met the challenge with increased yields per acre under scientifically improved agriculture (Figure 37). Conservation, though as yet not fully applied, has contributed much to that efficiency. Estimates of anticipated increase in production per acre between 1950 and 1975

Our population increases while land area remains constant

FIGURE 36. *Much land was reserved or acquired for special public use. Some was retained in public ownership because we could not give it away. Much has reverted to public ownership because private owners could not make a living on it.* (Bureau of the Census map.)

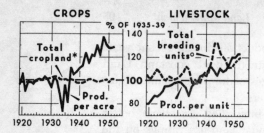

FIGURE 37. *U.S. farm production per acre and per animal unit. Improved management has greatly increased our agricultural production without any significant expansion of cropland area.* (B.A.E. diagram.)

* Indicates the sum of the estimated acreage from which one or more crops were harvested plus the acreage of crop failure and summer fallow.

o Includes all breeding livestock except horses, and all livestock production except farm-produced power of horses and mules.

range all the way from 33 to 75 per cent (7 and 8). Figure 38 gives a conservative forecast for the near future.

We need not fear hunger any time soon, nor even quite remotely, but when our arable acreage has been pressed by mechanization, fertilization, seed selection, breeding, and complete husbandry to yield its utmost—our population still increasing— we shall be compelled to expand our crop area. We could develop for crops some 80 million acres more capable of production than many now cultivated (9), and we could round off the increase to 100 million acres without sacrifice of standards (7). We have no immediate need for expanding our crop acreage, but future food requirements may compel us to do so. Then we may bring water to all the irrigable acres in the dry West and resow to crops those fields once retired from crop production in the humid East. And should the pressure for food be unrelenting, wise men may condone drainage of wet land to avert hunger. The planning against future land requirements must not be ignored by conservators of today, although future procedures may change greatly to accord with changing circumstances.

As our nation fills with people we need ever nicer and wiser

We are far from our limits of production

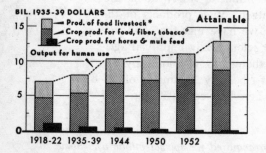

FIGURE 38. *The farm output picture—past and attainable within five years. Conservation will make our farms increasingly productive in the future. Many predictions are much higher than the one shown here.* (B.A.E. chart: data for attainable levels are based on reports of state productive capacity committees.)

* Includes product added and pasture feed consumed.

o Includes feed, except for horses and mules.

cultural adjustment to our land, ever more judicious allotment of space to increasingly competitive uses. Upon planner-conservators devolves the responsibility for progress to the utmost social growth our land resources can sustain without undue sacrifice of the *base*. Their success will be commensurate with the degree to which they keep pace with needs and events. Their ideas cannot be static; their concepts must be continuously adjusted to changing conditions. Their work cannot be done "once and for all" because the very progress they ensure sets them new tasks. Land use and land economics must keep pace with the changing situation, and conservation must be adapted to the new frame of reference.

We must continuously refine our adjustment to the land

CHAPTER 5: REFERENCES CITED BY NUMBER

(1) Soil Survey Staff, U.S.D.A. "Soil Survey Manual," *Agriculture Handbook No. 18,* 1951.

(2) U.S. Census Bureau, *Statistical Abstract of the United States.* Washington, D.C., 1952.

(3) Taken from U.S. Census Bureau Statistics.

(4) John D. Black and Arthur Maass, "Future Demands on Land Productivity," *Report of the President's Materials Policy Commission,* 5 vols.; V: *Selected Reports to the Commission,* Report 7. Washington, D.C., 1952.

(5) "What is a Conservation Farm Plan?" *Leaflet No. 249,* S.C.S., 1948.

(6) Marion Clawson, *Uncle Sam's Acres.* Dodd, Mead & Company, New York, 1951.

(7) "Improving Agricultural Resources," *Report of the President's Materials Policy Commission;* I: Foundations for Growth and Security, Chapter 9. Washington, D.C., 1952.

(8) "United States Fertilizer Resources," *Report of the President's Materials Policy Commission;* V: *Selected Reports to the Commission,* Report 8. Washington, D. C., 1952.

(9) H. H. Wooten and Margaret R. Purcell, "Farm Land Development: Present and Future, By Clearing, Drainage, and Irrigation," *Circular No. 825,* U.S.D.A., 1949.

Water Conservation

*water conservation intercepts the rain
that falls upon the land, regulates its
movement, and gains maximum benefit from it
within the limits of replenishment*

WATER ON THE LAND, ABOVE AND UNDERGROUND, MUST BE ADJUDGED
the phase of the hydrologic cycle most useful to man—without
discounting the role of the sea, the source of all water. In other
words, the water of real service to us is that which, having fallen
upon the land, either soaks in or runs off the surface; it is the
segment of the water cycle that begins with precipitation and
terminates in the sea.

Since our most *useable* water is always on its way to the sea,
it should be possible to magnify its usefulness by impeding its
movement—thereby in effect increasing its volume. Nature demonstrates this fundamental principle of water conservation with the
snows accumulated on mountains in winter and released through
lifegiving streams during summer. Many a valley oasis owes its
verdure to such natural detention of water on the land. Freezing
stores it up when it would otherwise be wasted. Warmth converts
it into useable form and draws it off when it may do the most
good. Exactly so can the practical conservator-engineer (i.e., the
user of the land) store up water by detaining it with dams, or

Crux of the
problem: slower
return to
the sea

99

terraces, or duff, or sod, or other barrier to obstruct its seaward coarse and gain from it much greater service.

However it is accomplished, whether in the ground or upon it, storage increases the total water resource, and by rendering the supply more constant increases its efficiency. Storage derives from slower return to the sea: that is the crux of the problem. Its solution is best assured by enlisting the same tactics as those employed by an infantry commander: attack the enemy before he can assemble his forces, engage him at several points simultaneously, and neutralize his dispersed units before they can mass for concerted action. Intercepted and absorbed where they fall, raindrops cannot join forces in a rivulet, rivulets interrupted and dispersed cannot produce vigorous tributaries, and tributaries curbed with dams and other detainers cannot compose a violent river. If the engineer stands idly by until the waters combine their force—as in a river—his mission is doomed to failure and he should be relieved of his command. He cannot restrain the river without first containing its headwaters (1, 2). Water management must commence where the rain falls, as shown in Figures 39 and 40.

Rain that soaks in does most good

Water conservation begins with the raindrop. If the drop is induced to soak into the ground instead of running off, it escapes evaporation, joins the less fugitive ground water supply, and moistens the soil without eroding it. If the drop be shed into surface waters, it steals a little soil and silts the storage areas. Likely as not, it evaporates before it can reach the sea. All in all, it is short-lived and limited in service. An open body of surface water may lose several inches by evaporation during a summer month (3). Surface water storage is makeshift compared with an aquifer.

Land receptive to rain can absorb it and hold it like a blotter. Loose, deep soil, mulch or litter, grass sod, and best of all a broad-leaved forest with a deep floor covering of duff and leaves, are good absorbers (see Figure 41). Healthy forests are storage reservoirs more efficient than those we build of concrete. They capture the raindrop immediately it begins the useful phase of its life cycle, thus getting maximum work out of water (4). Furthermore, they are immune to sedimentation. It goes without saying that exposed sand or gravel beds may absorb all the water that falls upon them. They are natural manipulators of water much as mountain snow reserves, but whether they store the water or merely drain it off, the conservator can do little more than estimate the consequences and make the most of them. Some gravel beds feed rich aquifers (5, p. 47). Some are useful as media for artificial recharge of ground water supplies.

Raindrop reception and absorption initiate water conserva-

FIGURES 39 AND 40. *Structures such as contour ridges (above) and ponds (below) conserve water by detaining run-off at its source and inducing it to soak in. The new pond shown here needs its banks protected against erosion. It should be fenced against cattle, and the water piped to a tank from which they might drink. (S.C.S. photos.)*

tion; penetration improves water storage with depth. Detention of runoff helps maintain ground water level by inducing soakage, besides performing the more obvious functions of surface water. But none of these operations equals the all important retention of moisture in the soil, without which rains pass through it too quickly to do much good. Without adequate soil moisture neither wild nor cultivated plants can flourish. Desirable as is the percolation of water to replenish underground reservoirs, the storage of soil water is of more immediate and more general importance to resource conservation. It is a primary soil factor, and the basic promoter of all other renewable resources. It exemplifies the complementary relationships that pervade the whole field of conservation.

Humus in the soil acts as a sponge

Plant and animal remains—organic materials—in various stages of decomposition, constitute the sponge that holds soil water. Collectively they are called "humus," a most significant single word, and material, in conservation. By its capacity for holding water, humus renders plant nutrients more easily and constantly available to growing plants, and resists the loss of those nutrients to erosion or leaching. Humus contributes even more toward soil quality than toward water quantity, and we shall consider it again in connection with soil conservation. That it conserves water cannot be doubted by anyone who has seen nursery stock shipped in sphagnum moss or felt the wetness under an old pile of leaves. Soils rich in humus retain moisture and dissolved minerals, releasing them to nourish growing plants. Humus in the soil holds in reserve the surplus moisture of a wet period as defense against seasonal drought and crop-water shortage. In contrast, soil devoid of humus either resists penetration, or releases the water as through a sieve, becoming droughty almost before rain stops falling. Such soil sheds water so rapidly that little can soak into the earth, and the bulk rushes off the land too fast for effective surface use. Soil conditions are potent elements in water conservation (6).

Supplies of ground water are limited

Ground water deserves emphasis in water conservation because it is by nature "conservative." It moves less rapidly, suffers less loss to natural forces, and maintains uniformly high qualities. Certain rock basins and deep aquifers may be almost leak-proof, but most ground water reservoirs release water through springs, streams, or seepage areas, so their storage is not absolutely permanent. Unless they be replenished they would ultimately be empty. Their total capacity is fixed. If all the earth cavities and interstices were filled with water there would be a certain quan-

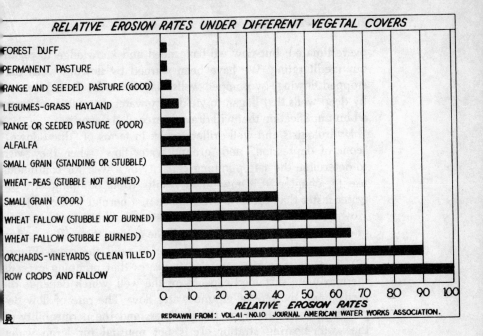

FIGURE 41. *Good vegetal cover on the land serves as a storage reservoir for water, and dissipates the erosive force of run-off. Healthy forest or sod is superior for both water storage and protection against erosion. Inter-tilled crops are the least desirable.*

tity, and no more. Contrary to popular notions, *ground water supplies are limited.* The only way to maintain them is to take out no more than goes in. Unless we do this, we will eventually pump the land so dry underneath that we shall be forced to change our whole scheme of water supply, becoming increasingly dependent upon elaborate and costly surface storage. About one third of our metropolitan water supply comes from wells; and in virtually all the metropolitan areas supplied by wells the draft of ground water is excessive (7, p. 99). Many cities have already constructed surface reservoirs to supplement a ground water supply once adequate, and many others may be compelled to make similar provision. How many acre-feet of surface water would our cities require if all their wells went dry (one acre of water one foot deep is an acre-foot)? Could we devote all that space to water supply at the expense of other land uses? If they are pumped faster than rain can soak into the catchment areas, the wells will go dry!

What are the warnings against overdrawing our subterranean accounts? Can we audit and balance them or must we gamble on credit? Thus far we have spent recklessly from reserves grossly

Beware a
lowering
water table

overestimated; but now we have need and knowledge to regain our credit rating. We have been warned by flowing wells that stopped flowing, by pumped wells that had to be drilled deeper, by deep wells that began to yield salty water. In each case it was a blunt notification that withdrawals exceeded deposits.

Hydrologists and well-drillers speak in terms of "draw-down," "cone of depression," and "ground water flow" when they wish to determine the safe pumping capacity of a well for continuous use (8, chapter 9). Draw-down results from pumping out the water faster than the flow will replace it, a normal well condition. However, if draw-down be so excessive that the resultant cone of depression reaches the bottom of the casing, the well goes dry, at least until natural flow can begin to refill the cone (Figure 42). A steep cone of depression indicates that pumping exceeds the maximum sustained capacity of the well, which depends directly upon the rate of ground water flow. The rate of flow depends, in the main, upon the thickness and the permeability of the water-bearing stratum. It is not unusual for large water users to make several borings in proximity to secure a combined flow adequate for their purposes. If they pump the battery of wells so heavily that the general ground water level under the area sinks deeper and deeper they have committed the hydrological sin called "overdevelopment." They have drained the underground reservoir beyond a safe margin of recovery; they have lowered the water table as shown graphically in Figure 43.

Most regions of our country were naturally well endowed with ground water, particularly the extensive coastal and interior plains with their excellent artesian structures. However, in some of the more richly blessed areas water users have so radically overdeveloped the supply as to lower the water table several feet in a few years. It is estimated, for example, that under portions of the High Plains the water table has fallen as much as 40 feet during the past few years (5, p. 46). Such depression foreshadows regional calamity. The wealth of water under portions of the Gulf Coastal Plain remains a major factor in the industrial development of the South, but even this great wealth could be subjected to overdevelopment.

Be it understood that a lowering water table results from reduced intake as well as from excessive output, though the latter may be more apparent and its consequences usually more immediate. Clearing of forest, breaking of sod, draining of swamps and marshes, and abusive cropping or grazing of the land can reduce absorption materially. Buildings, hard roads, and other

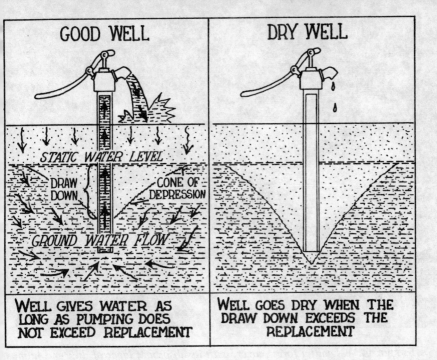

GOOD WELL	DRY WELL
STATIC WATER LEVEL	
DRAW DOWN — CONE OF DEPRESSION	
GROUND WATER FLOW	
WELL GIVES WATER AS LONG AS PUMPING DOES NOT EXCEED REPLACEMENT	WELL GOES DRY WHEN THE DRAW DOWN EXCEEDS THE REPLACEMENT

FIGURES 42 AND 43. *Overdevelopment of ground water invites regional ruin when depression of the water level becomes extreme. When too much water is pumped from too many wells, the general ground water level falls lower and lower until the depth makes further drilling and pumping prohibitively expensive, if not physically impossible.*

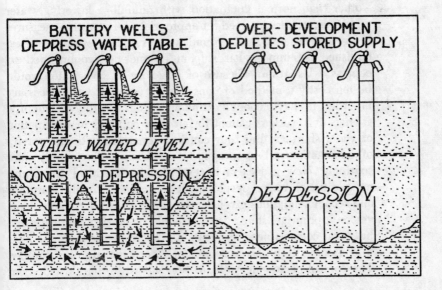

BATTERY WELLS DEPRESS WATER TABLE	OVER-DEVELOPMENT DEPLETES STORED SUPPLY
STATIC WATER LEVEL	
CONES OF DEPRESSION	*DEPRESSION*

FIGURE 44. *A healthy forest cover, with its absorbent layer of duff and humus, is a better flood preventive than man-made barriers. The flick of a cigarette might destroy the incomparable water storage facility pictured here. A forest floor such as this may be worth much more than the trees that produced it.* (S.C.S. photo.)

cultural features constrict the absorbing area. Whatever its cause —other than normal fluctuation with rainfall—a lowering water table indicates urgent need for appropriate conservation measures to prevent exhaustion of ground water supply. Restriction of established uses imposes hardship, and cannot be recommended except as a last resort. Closure of a factory to save water would be too costly a method of conservation unless it were necessary in order to have enough drinking water for the community. Owners and workers cannot forfeit their earnings in anticipation of water shortage. But they can be acquainted with the gravity of the situation and encouraged to use the dwindling supply more sparingly. New users can be excluded from critical areas, and no additional water development permitted. Timely warnings and recommendations given by the United States Geological Survey or appropriate state agencies should be heeded automatically, but legal controls need application in more places than one likes to contemplate (9). Overuse cannot exceed recharge indefinitely. The control of flowing wells to prevent waste, the development

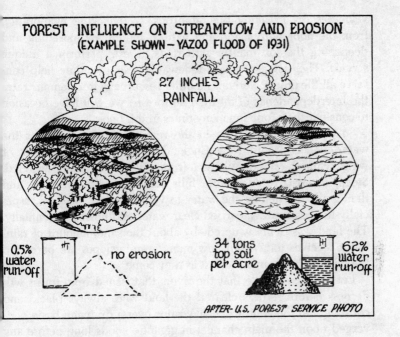

FIGURE 45. *This comparative diagram shows an actual case of forest influence on run-off and erosion. The statistics were obtained by observations and measurements.*

of recharge areas and recharge wells (5, pp. 188-191), the re-use of water when feasible, and other direct water-saving practices have checked much foolish wastage of subterranean waters.

Forests are the effectual regulators and conservers of water by natural means, virtually prohibiting run-off. A dense canopy of leaves can intercept a light rain so completely that the ground underneath gets none at all. Trees in foliage draw back up much of the water they admit to the ground, and give it off by transpiration. From a vigorous forest evaporation and transpiration dispose of 15 to 20 or more inches of water a year (10). How then do forests conserve water? That portion of the rainfall which reaches the forest floor is absorbed by leaves, litter, and humus (Figure 44), whence much of it passes into the ground to emerge elsewhere later on in springs and streams. Some of it passes all the way down to deep ground water reservoirs. Forests stow away water which comes in heavy, erratic rains, and release it gradually over an extended period of time (4). An actual measurement of this forest function is illustrated in Figure 45. By reducing wind

Forests regulate water

velocities, by breaking the raindrops, by checking evaporation from the floor with shade and natural mulch, by loosening and deepening the soil mantle with roots, forests perform a unique service. Themselves a major renewable resource, they help conserve all the others. Perhaps no other resource better demonstrates the interdependence of all than do forests; we will have occasion to consider their function many times in this book.

So proficient are forests in the regulation of water that the water wheels of old New England rarely stopped for lack of water while the slopes upstream from mill sites remained wooded. Steep, forest-covered granite hills could contain a deluge and then gradually deliver the water to valleys below. Streams, especially the headwaters, carried clear water and flowed perennially. The land was richly watered—by about the same amount of rainfall it receives today. But now many granite slopes are bare, and the rains rush off almost as fast as they come.

Settlement magnified river floods

Let no one suppose that the rivers that issued from forest wilderness before settlers cleared the land were always placid and constant. On the contrary, heavy rains over a drainage basin converged upon the main channel in gigantic floods long before any man, white or red, set foot upon our continent. The primeval forests did indeed bridle the violence of rivers, and the floods spent themselves with less apparent destruction, since the valleys contained no man-made "property" to destroy. When white man came and developed his property he unleashed the wild violence of waters that have repeatedly laid waste the river valleys. He made arrangements for disaster, and now he must seek to correct them in some degree, as a concomitant of good water conservation.

So drastically has the denudation of watersheds accelerated runoff that stream flow once highly valuable has in many places become a dubious asset. Streams that once turned water wheels constantly are now only periodically useful for power. The Westfield River in Massachusetts is one among many with such a history. Brooks that once flowed perennially now flow only intermittently, and often with muddy water. Unhampered headwaters rush together so rapidly that the master stream becomes now and again a wild torrent that defies discipline. Floods like that of the Mississippi in 1927, that of the Ohio in 1936, that of the Missouri in 1947, that of the Columbia in 1948, that in Kansas in 1951, and that in California in 1952, to mention a few, have become milestones from which the valley folk reckon years. They have caused tragic losses of life and property. Floods have cost fantastic sums of private and public money; more in a few years than it would cost to prevent indefinitely their recurrence. Kansas is certainly not crowded with urban or industrial development, yet the 1951 flood caused damage estimated at 2 billion dollars (11). Flood waters spread far and wide over the level terrain with consequent damage to crops, soils, homes, and communities in an extensive area. Good soils were buried under sterile sand.

Best defense against floods evolves from wise land use: forest on slopes where trees ought to grow, grass on dry land that ought to be sod-covered, and crop land tilled under good conservation practices. But immediate, emergency, flood defense requires detention of hurried waters behind barriers across the stream. "Flood control" is a major purpose of many of our great dam structures, though they *prevent* rather than "control," holding back waters that would flood if unrestrained. Our nearest approach to flood control has been with levees such as those along the lower Mississippi. Time and again those levees have proved inadequate. We have breached them to disperse floods by releasing the waters through prearranged spillways into broad passes that direct them to the Gulf. Perhaps dissipation of force amounts to control. Confinement has been impossible (12, pp. 169-170).

Whatever their length or height, whatever their material, whoever built them—men or beavers—dams conserve water by impeding it (Figures 46 and 47). Whether confining farm ponds or inland seas, dams reduce flood hazards by impounding water during wet seasons for release during dry ones, and by equalizing stream flow throughout all seasons. Every dam on a river system lightens the task of the ones downstream. A river with regulated headwaters flows more uniformly into the sea. Beavers in Montana build social security for wharf rats in New Orleans.

Dams and reservoirs serve multiple purposes

Hundreds of dams in this country are large enough to perform several valuable functions simultaneously. Each one, large or small, inevitably does something toward flood prevention. Comparatively small dams are used economically for power production where power is needed. Large ones that impound sizeable reservoirs may serve a combination of purposes—domestic water supply, navigation, recreation, industry, irrigation, landscape enrichment, and power—without overtaxing the storage capacity, but in most cases competition limits the variety of uses. Priority of use, and allocation of water among various uses, lie well within the province of water conservation. "Water over the dam" represents outright waste, and water released without doing much work represents waste only slightly mitigated. Figuratively speaking,

Figures 46 and 47. *Above: beaver dam and lodge, with the dam across the foreground, and the lodge to the right of center. Fur-bearing engineers at the headwaters enhance the work of human engineers down-stream. Beavers are more valuable in water conservation than in fur coats.* (Photo by Willis Peterson.)

Below: the high Fontana Dam in North Carolina, a unit in the T.V.A. system. Note its location on the map, Figure 49. (Photo courtesy T.V.A.)

water passed through a turbine to generate electricity has not lost anything except its head (the depth behind the dam that gives the water its power). The body remains intact, and its usefulness below the dam may be quite as great as above it, for certain purposes under certain site conditions. Its utilization for power does not detract from its value for irrigation. An industry using water downstream from a power dam may gain its greatest operational advantage from the regularity of flow ensured by continuous operation of the generating plant above it.

Not all uses of reservoirs or lakes are complementary (13); several conflict with one another. The fluctuation of water level incidental to draw-down for power and flood prevention causes the "shore" to migrate in a manner most disconcerting to bathers, boaters, and fishermen, and injures the wildlife habitat as well. At the same time, the change of water level combats mosquitos and other water-breeding insects—a result pleasing to health experts. High dams across steep-sided, V-shaped valleys produce powerful heads and deep, cool water, but their shores are inhospitable and difficult of access. Long, low dams across wide valleys in flat country produce extensive lakes with shores easily approached and well-suited to beach development. The shallow waters become comfortably warm for summer swimming, but their expansive surfaces lose much of their volume to evaporation.

Aristocrats among reservoirs are the ones that store drinking water for population centers. From them other uses are ordinarily excluded for reasons of sanitation. Capacity permitting, they might be used for power without detracting from their primary function, but other uses involve, at best, additional problems of filtering or other treatment. The highest type of water use asserts its priority in many different ways.

Dams and reservoirs can serve only temporarily because, sooner or later, the storage space fills up with soil and debris washed into it. The process is called "siltation" or "sedimentation" from the terms "silt" and "sediment" pertaining to water-deposited materials. Some silting takes place under the most favorable natural conditions, and no man would presume to stop it. Where soils are protected, as by a dense forest, siltation proceeds at an exceedingly slow rate, and may be almost imperceptible. Thus it would take a millennium to fill our great reservoirs. Unfortunately such conditions do not obtain over any of our major watersheds: none has a continuous, undisturbed forest cover.

Where soils have poor natural cover or are exposed by unwise land use, their erosion and consequent choking of reservoirs

FIGURE 48. *Less than twenty years after construction this reservoir at Arcadia, South Carolina, was rendered ineffective by sedimentation. Soil conservation above the reservoir would have prolonged its usefulness.* (S.C.S. photo.)

(double trouble) can proceed at such fantastic rates that the useful life of a dam may be only a few decades. Readers less than middle-aged bid fair to outlive in usefulness several of our big dam structures. Many dams, big and small, have already been filled to the top, and back up alluvial flats instead of water. One of these is shown in Figure 48. At the rate the mighty Lake Mead has been filling since Hoover Dam was completed in 1935, even it will be brim-full of sediment in less than 500 years (14). In the immediate future, hydraulic engineers will face problems of their own creation: Shall they remove the sediment or raise the dam? When must they yield to the natural forces that carve valleys? How may they abandon a moribund project without destroying cultural adjuncts? All the impending problems must not be blamed on our government or public agencies because more than half of our dams are privately owned. Federal projects generate only 40 per cent of our hydroelectric power (15). Among our large dams are many, well planned and sited, with a life expectancy of several centuries; but even they should be regarded as temporary expedients, lest they instill a false sense of permanent security.

n the United States are some 10,000 reservoirs larger than farm
ponds, with a total storage capacity approximating 200 million
acre-feet. However, sedimentation is stealing about 350,000 acre-
feet of storage per year, varying from a small fraction of 1 per
cent in some reservoirs to more than 3 per cent in others (16).
Thus, a dam whose tributary watershed erodes rapidly may be
defunct about thirty years after construction. The health of the
watershed as a whole determines the longevity of a dam.

The Tennessee Valley Authority demonstrates unified watershed development through the successful execution of regional
planning built around a river system (17, pp. 765-770). Considering the fact that we must become increasingly dependent upon
surface waters for our expanding water consumption requirements, and not only for those water uses peculiar to the surface
such as power and transportation, the yard-stick value of the
T.V.A. for unified water management alone will likely be its
greatest historic contribution. Surface streams should be brought
into service at a rate sufficient to offset the depletion of deep
ground water sources which require centuries to accumulate
(5, p. 46).

The Tennessee Valley was a good place for this great experiment. The Tennessee had been a rampageous stream and a heavy
contributor to Mississippi floods. The valley contained little industrialization that would involve relocation costs. The valley
populace was so hard hit by the national depression that its traditional thrift and self-sufficiency proved inadequate, and potential construction and industrial workers were on relief. This depression emergency reduced local opposition to the project.

The T.V.A. development might have been better than it is had
it more strictly applied the principle of beginning with headwaters and progressing downstream. However, other considerations dictated that the lower dams be erected before the upper
ones. Except for navigation, many small dams might have been
better than a few big ones; and less emphasis on electric power
might have made the Authority a better proving ground for other
regional developments.

Whatever its faults and failures, its successes and achievements,
the T.V.A. has inestimable value as a research laboratory for regional planning and conservation. It is a unique project of profound interest to planners and conservators everywhere. By
scientific selection of sites and designs for a *system* of dams, the
Authority has gone far toward acquiring maximum multiple utility
of an entire watershed. See Figure 49.

The T.V.A. must not be appraised on a short-sighted cost-profit

> The T.V.A.
> demonstrates
> unified
> watershed
> development

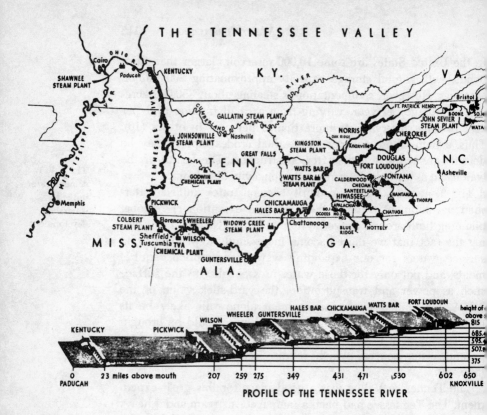

PROFILE OF THE TENNESSEE RIVER

FIGURE 49. *Yardstick for unified valley development. Water management was the main line of approach. Each dam in the lower series backs water to the foot of the one next above it, thus creating a navigable waterway the length of the main stream.* (Courtesy T.V.A.)

basis. Its value as a proving ground for unified watershed development has infinitely greater significance, and its greatest contributions may be intangible. More or less incidental to the primary products of systematic stream management came some 650 miles of safely navigable waterways, dependable water supply, new and varied recreational opportunities, conservation of soils, forests, and wildlife, and vital contributions to our national defense. The modern Tennessee Valley is living proof that all our renewable resources are mutually interdependent, and that their conservation can be best accomplished by careful coordination of selected improvements within a defined spatial unit. One particular resource may dominate the scene, but it should not be permitted to exclude others from appropriate attention. Total improvement must be the main objective whatever the initial line of departure (18).

One cannot question the unique position of water as the fundamental resource, and the T.V.A. has shown how well it serves as he center of reference for regional planning and conservation. A river is simply a distinct unit of circulating water, but all its branches, or limbs, are integral parts of the body. All parts belong, and all must be attended. The primal character of water and the unitary behavior of a stream may well dominate not only the theory, but also the future practice, of conservation in general. Water-divides may well attain much greater importance as boundaries than any arbitrary line between states. Our national domestic economy might some day revolve about river basins. At such time we may turn to T.V.A. and other valley experiments for help with such perplexing questions as these: Should any valley authority be established without the express wish or approval of citizens resident in the area involved? Should the local people themselves organize and operate any such project? Should many small dams be built in preference to a few big ones? What should be the priority of work as between the trunk stream and its tributaries? Should dams be merely sited by the central authority, and the sites leased to private companies? Should structures publicly built be leased or sold to private interests upon completion? Should the power market be held within the minimum seasonal output of hydroelectric plants, or should supplemental thermal (i.e., fuel-burning) power units be installed to absorb the load during periods of slack water? Should any state be deprived of its best (river bottom) land by reservoir flooding in order to protect the land of another state downstream from flood damage? How should costs and indemnities be computed and distributed? In any case, what should be the minimum life expectancy of a project to justify its execution? Is the forty- or fifty-year amortization plan a valid criterion of project feasibility?

The map of principal drainage basins (Figure 50) shows a logical division of our nation into compartments for water management and other conservation programs. In several of the watersheds work is already under way. The Tennessee pioneers the field in both systematic engineering and integrated conservation. Construction has begun in the Missouri, the Columbia, the Colorado, and several lesser basins, but in none of them has there been more than a beginning toward adequate development. Though well planned and constituted, the Tennessee project still awaits much of the land-use rehabilitation essential to its full realization. While forests burn and red clay washes into the reservoirs the plan remains only partially executed. No amount of engineering can conserve a drainage basin without the aid of good land utilization (19).

The idealist might wish all watersheds completely reforested, but the practical conservator must arrive at a workable compro-

National economy might revolve about river basins

FIGURE 50. *Principal drainage regions. Our national economy might revolve about the major drainage basins. In several of them, planned development is well under way.*

mise between water management and land occupance. If we eject farmers from our drainage basins, where will they farm? If there be no food, who will use all the water? In valley bottoms agriculture, grazing, and forestry will inevitably yield space to water storage, but on the slopes that feed the reservoirs they must be reconciled with water "production." Few wilderness areas remain available for water storage, and fewer still lie sufficiently near settlement to render their water presently valuable for controlled use. Highly industrialized valleys, such as the upper tributaries of the Ohio about Pittsburgh, prohibit the kind of watershed development that involves big dams, because it would cost entirely too much to relocate industrial plants and facilities. For the visible future at least, such industrialized valleys cannot be dammed and flooded for water storage as was the Tennessee. Their improvement will be served better by small dams and good land-use management at their headwaters. Conservation of land and soil about its tributaries is in any case the most effective and permanent way of regulating the main trunk of a stream (20).

Extension of unified river basin development depends upon centralized planning and coordination by state and national gencies. Whether we like it or not, certain aspects of water conservation exceed the scope and capability of any private enterprise. Delinquent public action to reduce flood damage and extend vital waterways reflects lack of public understanding. We have just begun flood prevention. We debated for half a century the unique opportunity afforded by the Great Lakes-St. Lawrence System for transportation (21). A threatened shortage of domestic iron ore and increasing dependence on imported ores opened our eyes and brushed aside selfish, sectional interests. The life of our inland steel empire was insured by Congress in 1954 when the St. Lawrence Seaway project was finally approved.

If ever we could develop completely all our drainage basins and pump out ground water exactly as fast as it goes in we should have available *all* the water possible to obtain with the techniques now generally understood. There would be a specific quantity for all purposes, procurement would be competitive, and margins of supply would be sought through artifical precipitation of cloud moisture and the freshening of sea water. The "production" aspect of water conservation would be accomplished, and only the problem of optimum "disposition" would remain. Meanwhile, far into the remote future, we must look to production and disposition (credit and debit) simultaneously. Water conservation is clearly a matter of double-entry bookkeeping, and our ledger has entirely too many red entries at present. Let us examine a few questionable accounts in our record.

None of us would like to do without the lush vegetables and fruits furnished us by irrigation, but we may well be skeptical about the expenditure of scarce water in the West for ordinary field crops that can be produced adequately in the humid East without artificial watering. Federal financing of irrigation projects which increase a crop surplus is certainly preposterous! Neither all the complete irrigation in the West nor the supplemental irrigation in the East can be considered essential to national well-being. However, supplemental irrigation counters drought in humid areas, thus increasing both farm productivity and economic stability. In the dry West complete irrigation is the very life of entire communities and regions. Insofar as the practice of irrigation promotes prosperity and progress its neglect would be waste —a sin of omission—but if the prosperity be bought with overdeveloped water supply it becomes a sin of commission—also waste— and ends in tragedy for the land occupants (22). Irrigation, our most extravagant use of water, can easily be over-done. Areas under complete irrigation are shown on Figure 51.

The stolid Mormons made the desert bloom in the now famed

How much can we irrigate safely?

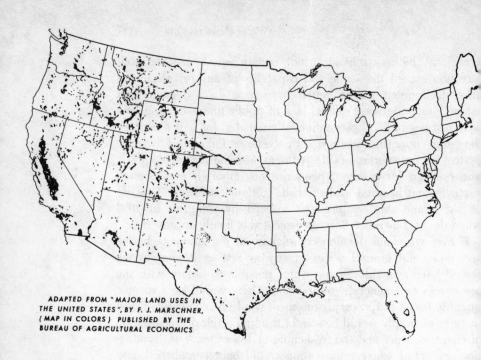

FIGURE 51. *Irrigated land in the United States, 1950. A community dependent upon irrigation must not permit water requirements to exceed natural replenishment of water supply. This map does not show supplemental irrigation, which is becoming important in the eastern United States. Rice is the main crop irrigated in the lower Mississippi Valley.*

Great Salt Lake oasis; and other dry valleys in the West have been similarly transformed into veritable garden spots. However many such communities live precariously, by over-extended application of water, courting disaster. Even public financing under a 40-year amortization plan cannot be accepted as a guarantee of success in the long run. Caution must be the watchword in irrigation, whether the project be old or new. Exhaustion of irrigation water can create ghost towns and communities just as grim as those that die when ore bodies or saw logs run out.

We will probably double our irrigated acreage in the future, but more of our irrigation water will come from storage made primarily for flood prevention. Less will come from wells, because we have learned that a constantly lowering water table is too high a price to pay for lettuce. Waste and evaporation losses of irrigation water can be reduced by transporting it in pipes instead of open canals or ditches, by applying it only when the crop can make good use of it, by applying it at night or during calm days, by releasing it on the ground rather than from overhead sprayers, and by other known means of reducing loss and increasing effectiveness (23 and 5, p. 365). And when we have applied all the science and thrift we can muster, the deserts will still be expansive and forbidding, and the oases few, small, and far between. Of every 100 acres in the dry West only 3 can be irrigated. About 38 million acres is the absolute limit of safe reclamation, and of these more than 21 million are already under irrigation (24, p. 2).

Availability of water has begun to deter American urbanization, and numerous metropolitan districts face grave water problems. Many American cities may find themselves demonstrating the principle that water supply fixes the ultimate limit of population distribution. Water shortage drives industry and people away; the threat of shortage discourages them from locating. Many cities, large and small, are threatened with imminent regression unless acute water deficiencies be promptly and positively alleviated. Brooklyn, Philadelphia, Camden, Los Angeles, Indianapolis, Louisville, Des Moines, Tucson, Minneapolis-St. Paul, and many others have tried and strained the margin of their water resources, either by overdraft or excessive pollution.

Will metropolitan water supply limit urbanization?

Strangely enough, the two regions hardest pressed for metropolitan water supply are located on the seacoasts—at the very edge of our ultimate water source. One of them—New York— is on our northeast coast, and the other—Los Angeles—is in the southwestern corner of the nation in southern California (25). The latter area had a naturally imposed water problem from the beginning of settlement; but the former, located in an area abundantly watered, is a clear case of overdevelopment to sustain an excessive concentration of people. In both regions wells have been struck so deep in pursuit of a receding water table that salt water seeps into many of those near the coast. Damage by invasion of sea water is difficult to correct.

Both regions have long since resorted to surface storage to supplement the dwindling ground water reserves, and each finds its peculiar problem more and more difficult as requirements mount. Los Angeles draws water from reservoirs hundreds of miles away, competing for limited supplies against all needs in a vast water-hungry interior. Silted reservoirs will mean more miles of aqueduct and more fabulous water costs. New York City pipes water from the inland mountain areas of the state to eke out supplies from reservoirs in closer proximity. Near the metropolis other adjacent cities compete for watershed area and storage space, jealously guarding themselves against similar destitution. Here

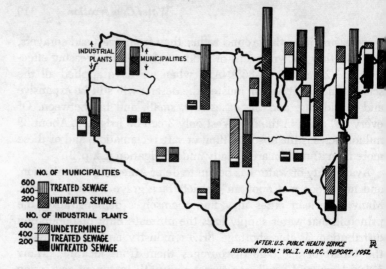

AFTER: U.S. PUBLIC HEALTH SERVICE
REDRAWN FROM : VOL. I. P.M.P.C. REPORT, 1952

FIGURE 52. *How many cities and industries pollute water? No region ca[n]
immune to pollution, but the problem is most serious where people and in[dus]
tries have congregated, as in the Northeast.*

in our northeastern metropolitan region water production for industrial and domestic purposes threatens to dominate the rural
land economy.

Steps have been taken to reduce waste of metropolitan water
supply. Many cities prohibit the tapping of city mains for air conditioning; some impose fines on leaky faucets; some demand specific recharge practices on the part of heavy ground water users.
There is much talk about re-use of domestic water by recovering
it from sewage, treating it, and running it back into the water
mains, though one wonders how that might boost the sale of
bottled drinks and artificial flavorings. Reclamation of used water
for purposes other than direct domestic supply is, indeed, a practical method of water conservation that should have much more
general application at present.

It has been said that nature whispers many hints for the solution of man's problems of adaptation; but concerning deficient
water supply, peculiarly ominous in coastal areas, she fairly shouts
a suggestion that he learn to use sea water. Economical de-salting
can be expected eventually, but in the meantime much more salt
water could be used for cooling and other purposes. Industrial
plants near tidewater could save high quality water by installing
non-corrosive equipment and employing sea water in those processes for which it is suitable. In only relatively few factories is such
water economy effected at present.

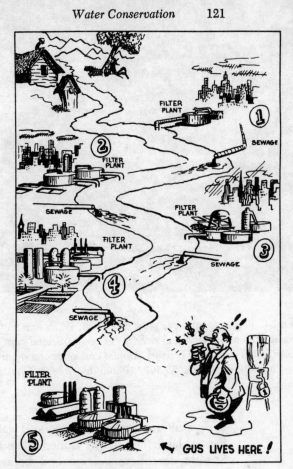

FIGURE 53. *Gus at the water fountain, reminded of his friends upstream.*

Pollution is certainly the most disgusting and perhaps the most dangerous and destructive of all our water abuses. Its detection requires no sense, except of smell, and one's nose need not be keen. Much of it may have resulted from ignorance, but its tolerance must be ascribed to slovenly indolence. It destroys much more than water, blighting the whole landscape it touches. It has ruined scores of our streams and lakes, and many segments of our coasts, killing the fish, driving wildlife away, and discommoding if not actually jeopardizing human society. Its cures are as obvious as its causes, and yet we have done shamefully little about it. Figure 52 indicates the regional severity of the pollution problem.

Water pollution befouls, withers, and destroys

In the early days, when factories and population centers were few and scattered and rivers ran full, it was possible to pour wastes into the streams without much danger. Dilution was adequate then, but growth and concentration of people and industry mutilated watersheds and increased water consumption, simultane-

FIGURE 54. *Sewage treatment plant, Kenosha, Wisconsin. Adequate treatment of metropolitan waste costs only a few dollars per capita. Initial cost of this installation in 1940-1941: $475,000 exclusive of land. Annual cost of operation and maintenance: $82,500 in 1952. Population served: 55,500.* (Photo by Joseph Constanti, courtesy the City of Kenosha.)

ously. Cultural development reduced water "production" by clearing the land. The supply waned while the demand grew larger. Streams shrank in volume and became erratic in flow. The production of industrial wastes and sewage grew progressively greater until many weakened streams became overloaded with filth. Now, especially in the densely populated Northeast, many a river once clear, beautiful, and beneficent has become an ugly, stinking menace. Had the explorers who sailed up the Delaware or the frontiersmen who went up the Schuylkill or down the Mahoning come upon the scene as it is today they would have beat a hasty retreat to warn against a poisoned land.

Polluting matter in our streams comes mainly from soil erosion, water-using industries, mining operations, and city sewerage systems. Worst pollutants are the industrial and metropolitan wastes. Raw sewage is the most objectionable of all because it contaminates water with disease germs far beyond the extent of areas visibly soiled. So common is the practice of dumping raw sewage and factory wastes into a creek or a river that, except in remote wilderness areas, few streams carry clear water. Many are

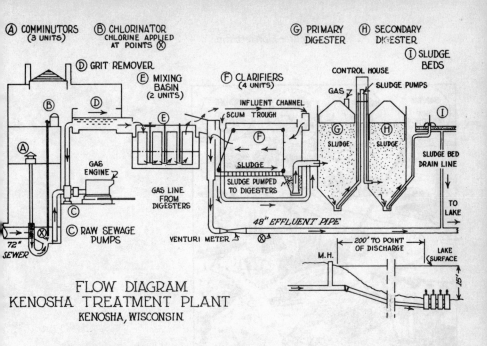

FLOW DIAGRAM
KENOSHA TREATMENT PLANT
KENOSHA, WISCONSIN

FIGURE 55. *Kenosha borrows 8,022,000 gallons of water a day from Lake Michigan. Shown here are the processes by which the city, having used and soiled the water, cleans it before returning it to the lake.* (Diagram courtesy the City of Kenosha.)

open sewers traversing our most populous landscapes. Too many towns and institutions, too many pulp mills, steels mills, chemical plants, collieries, and other industries overwork the streams, using them both for water supply and waste disposal.

When city water systems became practical it was convenient for scores of river towns to draw their water supply from the stream—*above the town,*—and equally convenient to pour their sewage and dump their garbage into the same stream—*below the town.* Of course other towns down-stream complained, but about all they could do was to install better filtering and purifying plants, and drink less palatable water at a higher price (see Figure 53). We have imposed upon ourselves such widespread water adulteration that places with good, pleasant-tasting water are prized by discriminate travelers and home-seekers.

To date we have behaved worse than swine; and it is imperative that we improve our habits. Cannot we, the intelligentsia of the animal world, dispose of our refuse without befouling our habitat? We know the means of preventing or abating pollution, and we are learning the necessity for employing them; but clear streams

Observe the cleanly swine!

FIGURE 56. *A dirty stream degrades the community.* (U.S. Public Health Service.)

are no longer free, and we are reluctant to pay for them. From that attitude has developed our most serious delinquency in water conservation.

Treatment of sewage and industrial wastes must become standard practice

Its remedy should have first priority. The only entirely satisfactory method of handling sewage is to process it in a modern treating plant. Solids must be removed, and the water aerated and decontaminated before release. The recovered solids, also sterilized, have fertilizer value. To waste them is poor conservation. Organic industrial wastes may require treatment like sewage, but most others can be rendered harmless by simpler, special processes to neutralize toxicity. If existing laws were enforced, and water-polluting industries were compelled to put waste treat-

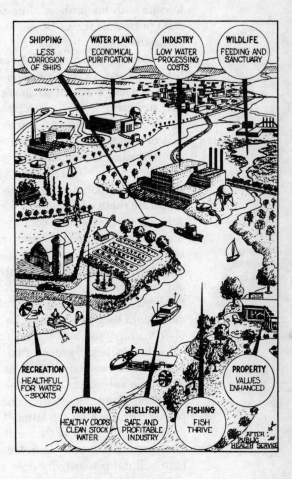

FIGURE 57. *A clean stream promotes health and prosperity.* (U.S. Public Health Service.)

ment into their operating budgets, most industrial wastes might soon be converted into useful by-products (26). Wherever necessary and feasible, public loans should be made available to help finance the required plant modification. We can expect pollution by industrial waste to be very substantially reduced during the next quarter century (27).

The municipalities that choke our water with sewage and other refuse present a less promising outlook. Of some 11,800 sewered municipalities enumerated in 1950, less than 400 had adequate facilities for sewage treatment (28). In other words, most of our cities and institutions continue to pollute our waters, and necessarily continue to expand their filtering and purification facilities to cope with the problem. Figures 54 and 55 show how adequate sewage treatment can be accomplished. Per capita costs are not prohibitive.

Obviously, we are wasting our efforts in attacking pollution at the wrong end. Certainly it would be better to treat the sewage at its source and keep our streams clean than to recover by straining and sterilizing a required supply of water from them *after* they have ruined the landscape through which they flow. The comparative drawings (Figures 56 and 57) suggest how badly pollution can degrade a community and how well preventive measures can rehabilitate the blighted area. Costly as it may be initially, the prevention of polution pays good dividends in the long run (33). There are those who would make it strictly compulsory (29).

Drainage is the most controversial of all our water manipulations. Except in special cases, as on farms in the Midwest and certain muck lands in other places, it has proved more detrimental than beneficial. The term should probably be dropped from our conservation vocabulary, but while it remains it means artificial removal of water from lands naturally too wet for purposes man thinks they should serve. In drainage projects good intentions often miscarry and inflict injury (30, 31, p. 31).

Drainable lands are of two major kinds: those perennially saturated or inundated, such as common swamps and marshes, and those subject to occasional overflow, such as river bottoms and flood plains. Obviously flood prevention, *not drainage,* is the proper corrective for the latter. The protection or rehabilitation of overflow lands, such as the fertile Mississippi-Yazoo Delta, is certainly rewarding and desirable, because their conditioning for high cultural productivity does not negate any other more valuable natural function. However, sure arability of overflow land derives from unified basin development, not from drainage. Drainage is merely a makeshift palliative. The real remedy lies in the regulation of stream flow by the management of tributaries far above the flood plain, by the restraint of headwaters before they can join their forces.

Artificial removal of water from "wet lands" such as swamp or marsh, which is *drainage* in the sense under discussion, violates the fundamental principle of water conservation, *slower return to the sea.* The practice should be discontinued except in particular cases where it may be desirable for rounding out an established farm unit. Drainage lowers the water table far beyond the edge of the drained marsh or swamp, destroying natural water storage. Until the water situation improves or the food situation deterio-

**Drainage
is generally
detrimental**

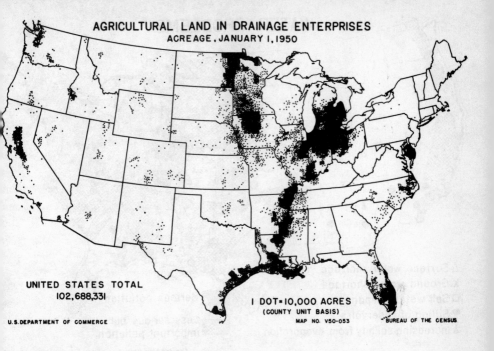

AGRICULTURAL LAND IN DRAINAGE ENTERPRISES
ACREAGE, JANUARY 1, 1950

UNITED STATES TOTAL
102,688,331

I DOT = 10,000 ACRES
(COUNTY UNIT BASIS)
MAP NO. V50-053

U.S. DEPARTMENT OF COMMERCE

BUREAU OF THE CENSUS

FIGURE 58. *Drainage reduces water storage and accelerates water movement. It is generally inimical to water conservation. Its value as a means of reclaiming land for crops may have been exaggerated in many places.*

rates our wet lands may serve us much better as they are than they might if they were drained. Across the nation, from the peat bogs in northern Minnesota to the glades of southern Florida, one may view the sordid exhibits that condemn drainage as a general practice. Much of the black area on Figure 58 represents waste of both natural resources and money. In Minnesota as well as Florida fire has despoiled areas "reclaimed" by drainage. Americans have become less enthusiastic about drainage during recent years, because several drainage enterprises once publicly organized and financed have failed and the land has become tax-delinquent (32).

When in fact we become pressed for food and need additional crop production, we may discover that most drainage projects brought local, temporary gains at the expense of contiguous areas, and that such immediate benefits as accrued to small areas were a drop in the bucket compared with the permanent injury done surrounding regions. In the long run and in aggregate, drainage probably impairs more than it enhances (31). Unless we proceed cautiously we might drain our grandchildren right into a food

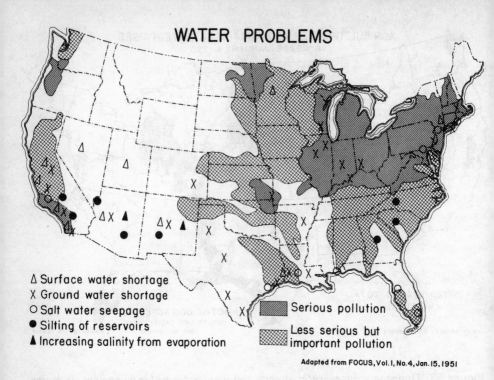

WATER PROBLEMS

△ Surface water shortage
X Ground water shortage
O Salt water seepage
● Silting of reservoirs
▲ Increasing salinity from evaporation

▨ Serious pollution

▨ Less serious but important pollution

Adapted from FOCUS, Vol. I, No. 4, Jan. 15, 1951

FIGURE 59. *Water problems assert themselves most forcibly where they are critical, but no community can afford to ignore its water resources. This map indicates how widespread our water problems have become, although the nation is still young and sparsely populated.*

Ours to choose between conservation and rationing

shortage. Before we dehydrate any more swamps or marshes, let us be sure their yield of corn and hay and other crops will be worth more than their natural production of water, ducks, muskrats, frogs and mystery. We may regret our intervention.

There is no panacea for our bad water situation, no course of action that can quickly and completely revive our dwindling water resources. Certain natural storage facilities have been permanently impaired, and water movement has been accelerated by cultural land utilization. We have reduced the total amount of available water retained on the land—surface and underground— and we are shrinking it more rapidly now than ever before, apparently disdainful of signs and warnings that drain cannot exceed replenishment indefinitely. We will pay for our folly with money, inconvenience, and failure. The accompanying map (Figure 59) shows that large regions are handicapped by water problems and that many localities are threatened with calamity.

We have created a grave water situation, but in the main it is amenable to solution. If we apply to it all the conservation techniques we know, especially those that enlist the most natural assistance, we can avert water famine and substantially enrich our water resources. Good land use, skillful engineering, and public concern must all be brought to bear. We have barely begun to muster those forces. Implementation of Public Law 845 to control pollution will be a major forward step.

Unless the public be stirred out of its apathy, unless we learn to regard a glass of cool, clear water as something that may be precious, and unless we take a cue from legal restrictions already enforced, we invite water rationing. The only alternative to rationing is conservation, and procrastination narrows the choice.

CHAPTER 6: REFERENCES CITED BY NUMBER

(1) H. S. Person, *Little Waters*. S.C.S., R.A.,* and R.E.A.,† Washington, D.C., 1936.

(2) Upstream Engineering Conference, 1936: S.C.S., U.S.D.A.F.S.‡ and R.E.A., *Headwaters Control and Use*. Washington, D.C., 1937.

(3) C. W. Thornthwaite, "Climate and Moisture Conservation," *Annals of the Association of American Geographers*, XXXVII, No. 2, June 1947, pp. 87-100.

(4) "Effect of 15 Years of Forest Cover Improvement Upon Hydrologic Characteristics of White Hollow Watershed," *Report No. 0-5163*. Tennessee Valley Authority, Division of Water Control Planning, Hydraulic Data Branch, Knoxville, 1951.

(5) Harold E. Thomas, *The Conservation of Ground Water*. McGraw-Hill Book Company, New York, 1951.

(6) W. D. Potter, "Rainfall and Topographic Factors That Affect Runoff," *Transactions American Geophysical Union*, XXXIV, No. 1, Febraury 1953, pp. 67-73.

* R.A.: Resettlement Administration.
† R.E.A.: Rural Electrification Administration.
‡ U.S.D.A.F.S. (or F.S.): United States Department of Agriculture, Forest Service.

(7) *Proceedings of the United Nations Scientific Conference on the Conservation and Utilization of Resources, 1949,* 8 vols.; IV: *Water Resources.* United Nations Department of Economic Affairs, New York, 1951.

(8) E. W. Bennison, *Ground-Water—Its Development, Uses, and Conservation.* Edward E. Johnson, Inc., St. Paul, Minnesota, 1947.

(9) C. L. McGuinness, "Water Law With Special Reference to Ground Water," *Circular 117,* U.S.G.S., 1951.

(10) George W. Craddock and Charles R. Hursh, "Watersheds and How to Care For Them," in U.S.D.A., *Trees: The Yearbook of Agriculture, 1949.* Washington, D.C., 1949, pp. 603-609.

(11) Verne Alexander, "The Greatest Flood of History," *Weatherwise,* IV, No. 5, October 1951, pp. 110-111.

(12) Stuart Chase, *Rich Land, Poor Land.* McGraw-Hill Book Company, New York, 1936.

(13) E. Laurence Palmer, "On The Level," *Nature Magazine,* XLIV, No. 3, March 1951, pp. 137-144.

(14) C. P. Vetter, "Sediment Problems in Lake Mead and Downstream on the Colorado River," *Transactions American Geophysical Union,* XXXIV, No. 2, April 1953, pp. 249-256.

(15) Leon M. Fuquay, Secretary, Federal Power Commission: statistics on hydroelectric power, private and federal, generated in the United States, 1951; personal communication dated April 3, 1953.

(16) Carl B. Brown, "Sediment Steals Water Storage," *Journal of Soil and Water Conservation,* Vol. VI, No. 2, April 1951.

(17) *Report of the President's Water Resources Policy Commission,* 3 vols.; II: *Ten Rivers in America's Future.* Washington, D.C., 1950.

(18) Subcommittee on Benefits and Costs, Federal Inter-Agency River Basin Committee, *Proposed Practices for Economic Analysis of River Basin Projects,* report of the committee. Washington, D.C., 1950.

(19) Elmer T. Peterson, "Big-Dam Foolishness," *Country Gentleman,* CXXII, No. 5, May 1952.

(20) Bernard Frank and Anthony Netboy, "Cradles of Rivers," *American Forests,* LV, No. 5, May 1949.

(21) Freeman Lincoln, "Battle of the St. Lawrence," *Fortune,* XLII, No. 6, December 1950, pp. 84 ff.

(22) J. Russell Smith, "Regional Suicide," *The Land,* VIII, No. 3, Autumn 1949.

(23) Allan W. McCulloch and Wayne D. Criddle, "Conservation Irrigation," *Agriculture Information Bulletin No. 8,* S.C.S., May 1950.

(24) Bureau of Reclamation, Department of the Interior, *The Reclamation Program 1948-1954.* Washington, D.C., 1948.

(25) O. O. Winther, "Los Angeles: Its Aquatic Life Lines," *Journal of Geography,* XLIX, No. 2, February 1950, pp. 45-56.

(26) *Proceedings of the Conference on Industrial Waste.* University of Washington Engineering Experiment Station, Seattle, 1949.

(27) Cloyd A. Snavely, "Waste Going into Streams," *Across the Board Studies;* No. 2: *Waste Suppression,* Part A. Battelle Memorial Institute, Columbus, Ohio, 1951.

(28) Public Health Service, Federal Security Agency, "Water Pollution in the United States," *Water Pollution Series No. 1.* Washington, D.C., 1951.

(29) James H. Duff, "Let's Outlaw Pollution," *American Forests,* LV, No. 11, November 1949.

(30) Warren S. Bourn and Clarence Cottam, "Some Biological Effects of Ditching Tidewater Marshes," *Research Report 19,* F.W.S., Washington, D.C., 1950.

(31) National Resources Committee, *Progress Report.* Washington, D.C., 1938.

(32) Leslie Hewes, "Drained Land in the United States in the Light of the Drainage Census," *The Professional Geographer,* V, No. 6, November 1953, pp. 6-12.

(33) Public Health Service, *Environment and Health.* Washington, D.C., 1951.

CHAPTER 7

AGENTS:
—
BLUNDERING MAN
WIND
WATER
GRAVITY

Soil Depreciation

*ravished soil degrades and disinherits
the society accessory to the crime*

WATER AND SOIL ON THE LAND IN BALANCED SYNTHESIS MUST BE regarded as man's most essential material heritage—his bread and butter. To recount our dissipation of the greatest American resource, the soil, becomes the unpleasant purpose of this chapter.

Many soils, like many men, were created poor, but unlike men of low birth, soils born poor have no higher destiny unless they be aided by men. Soil conservation, American style, has long since outmoded the old idea of soil "maintenance," which suffices only for soils naturally fertile. Since such are restricted in area, conservation must be directed toward soil "building," increasing rather than merely maintaining the "given" soil fertility.

Some
soils were
created poor

Our sub-humid grasslands have extensive areas of soils so rich that they can produce many crops without serious impoverishment. For them the maintenance of natural fertility might be a satisfactory objective. But on either side of those grasslands on the "wet-dry" scale, soils are generally so anemic that they need a transfusion after bringing forth a few crops, if not from the very first. Deficiency of humus is symptomatic of soil anemia. Dry lands lack the vegetation necessary for humus to accumulate; humid lands under forest lose both humus and plant food to leaching water. Where there is enough rain to produce forest there is enough to cause considerable leaching of the soil as well. Our pedalfers, inherently low in fertility, can only briefly sustain a profitable agriculture without specific treatment to strengthen them. Our failure to maintain, where in fact we should have im-

133

proved from the very beginning, accounts for much of the lost soil and mutilated land so tragically apparent in the Southeast.

Nor has our ruin of soils been confined to poor ones, or to the South. The soil-mining cotton aristocrats appear less guilty when one remembers that most of the soil they abused was *poor* when they got it. Other men, in other places, have spent *good* soil—i.e., they have embezzled more from larger funds. Wheat farmers have perhaps dissipated more soil riches than have cotton planters.

Other soils have been impoverished by our abuse

When our European ancestors arrived in the New World they set about resolutely to make the virgin soils produce their utmost. First with iron plows, later with steel; first with scythe and cradle, then with reapers, binders, and combines they harvested crop after crop, heedlessly or unwittingly draining the soil of its fertility. They took from the soil all it could give, with little or no regard for its replenishment. They bled it white, depleted its plant nutrients, and complained when yields dwindled. They blamed everything except themselves when worn-out fields could no longer reward their abusive handling. Sons grew poor where their fathers had prospered, because the soil was spent or wasted away. The space was the same, but it was barren space, like the empty drifts in exhausted mines. Only then did the agrarian heirs come to realize that their soil had been impoverished by extractive utilization, that removal exceeding replacement had sapped the base beyond its own capacity to revive, and that their "indestructible" heritage had so gravely depreciated that it must be counted partially destroyed. It was a rude awakening, but it inspired a soil-conserving program which, if fully prosecuted, will spare our nation the disastrous depletion of soil that has ruined civilizations.

By over-cropping our plowed soils, by over-grazing our grass-lands, by over-cutting and burning over our forest areas we have diluted and dispersed our basic wealth for quick gains, creating urgent need for salvage and repair. We spent the base by two means: *exhaustion* in place and physical *removal*. The latter we call *soil erosion;* the former, *soil depletion.* Erosion is more obvious—even spectacular—and cannot go far unnoticed unless one refuses to see it. *Depletion is much more elusive and insidious, because it leaves the soil body more or less intact, though with lowered fertility and reduced powers of recovery.* It steals soil vitality, leaving a sick, empty, body on the land. In some cases the body has been brought so near death that it might well be buried, but more generally the body can be brought back to health with remedial treatment.

Clearly, constant removal of any soil substance faster than the pedologic processes can regenerate it will, inevitably, exhaust the supply of that substance unless positive steps be taken to make up the deficit. That simple fact might be grave enough, but much more serious than the individual loss is its disruption of soil balance and impairment of the entire soil body. From the production viewpoint, the lack of one essential element can negate the effectiveness of others. Abundance of one cannot offset the deficiency of another. Since crops vary in their required proportion of nutrients, repeated sowing of one particular crop on a given plot of soil will first exhaust the nutrient for which that crop has the biggest appetite. The plant will suffer malnutrition when its favorite dish is consumed no matter how much other food is left. Finally, the available diet becomes so ill-balanced that no plant can thrive unless the soil be given artificial supplement—nitrate, phosphorus, potash, or other plant food. If crops are varied from year to year (rotated) they tend to equalize the removal of nutrients, thereby prolonging the life of the soil; but in the end the variety will simply exhaust the soil more thoroughly. Whatever the planting scheme, *crops sold off the land represent soil substance,* and unless out-put be compensated with in-put the soil "goes broke," like a bank whose withdrawals consistently exceed its deposits.

**Poverty
engenders
affliction
difficult to
remedy**

Soils severely worn and depleted become afflicted, as it were. They lose more than the substances removed. They lose the normal health and function of the biotic soil community much as the human body sickens when one or more of its vital organs or glands fails to work properly. Soil poverty is not amenable to immediate alleviation by simply applying measured parts of exhausted elements to replace losses. The soil making processes, the assimilating activity of soil flora and fauna, both normally slow, may be retarded almost to the point of cessation, and soil so nearly lifeless can respond only gradually to good treatment. It cannot recover instantly under any medication, however large the dosage. The malady can be arrested rather quickly, but full recovery takes a long time. If a few high-powered injections could *cure* soil fatigue —or pernicious anemia—neither of the diseases would cause much anxiety.

Were it not for the fact that soil morbidity ultimately infects man we might be unconcerned about it. But *man victimizes himself when he abuses the soil,* and the insidious infection often reaches a stage too far advanced for easy control before the victim detects its presence. This contagion spreads by devious means, and breaks out in various forms. Crop yields decline, the children grow ill and morose, buildings sag and rot, broken implements

**Ultimately,
soil morbidity
infects man**

stand rusting, parents work harder and harder for less and less, often jeopardizing health and being. Necessities become luxuries, homes become squalid, prayers more fervent, and faith less assuring.

Man thus frustrated curses the soil that once he praised, and stands only half repentant when, at last, he sees that its ruin was his own doing. Tragic enough is the fate of him who fails on soil inherently too poor to sustain him; far more pitiable is the plight of him who sinks by slow degrees from prosperity to poverty as the waning strength of soil *once good* compels him to lower his living standards, surrender his fondest hopes and ambitions, and witness in despair the defection and degradation of his children.

By the time a predatory cultivator realizes the measure of destruction he has wrought, he lacks all too often both the moral courage and the material means wherewith he might make restitution. Soil impoverishment depreciates land values and discourages the occupant; and where both confidence and collateral be shaky, who will lend the funds with which to rehabilitate? Soils apparently intact can be so thoroughly depleted by abusive occupance that their renewal cannot be accomplished without public aid. Where there is little evidence that subsidy may be amortized, it is better economy to retire them from private use by public purchase, and endeavor to salvage the people from their self-made destitution. *Disheartened people and the soil they have worn out are a very poor combination.*

There is one consoling virtue of soil depreciated *in situ* (in place): *while the body remains one can hope it will revive,* given proper care and sufficient time. Fortunately, we have learned that soils wear out; we know the signs of weakness; and we have begun to treat the malady before it gets out of hand. Experience has taught us the unmitigated truth that rapacious men who sack and sell the soil condemn their kin to scavenging.

Weakening by one ailment invites infection with another

Serious as they may be, the direct consequences of soil depletion—crop failure, low income, malnutrition, poor plants, poor animals, and poor people—are perhaps less considerable than the concomitant deterioration of soil itself. Man has often more or less damaged the soil where he has cultivated, grazed, or logged it. Rarely has he repaired the damage. Frequently and over extensive areas he has so aggravated the damage that complete ruin resulted.

Depletion invites further injury by erosion or leaching, or both, because loss of humus reduces the capacity for absorbing and retaining water. Without good water storage, artificial application of plant nutrients can be only partially effective, because they are too rapidly carried away—either in percolating water or in run-off, depending upon soil texture, structure, and topographic position. It follows that the production of plants with which to restore humus content will be slow and often costly beyond economic feasibility; and there is no short-cut to renewed soil vigor, no detour to soil fertility without humus.

Farmers, communities, and nations have gone by the board when they lacked the vision, the means, or the food reserve necessary to the replacement of dissipated soil humus. Whether by burning, washing, or blowing away, *loss of humus* is the crucial factor in soil wastage. It has made desert out of grazing land, and ghost towns out of forest villages. It hastened the fading of cultures once effulgent—Cretan, Sumerian, Persian, Athenian, Phoenician—and it scourges with hunger and famine the redundant Chinese and Indians of our modern era.

Depleted, deteriorated soils have little resistance to other destructive forces. Injury tends to become cumulative. *More violent and absolute than exhaustion by wear is the destruction of soil by dissection, dismemberment, and removal that we call "soil erosion."* Soil erosion is an abnormal operation of the natural process mentioned in Chapter 2, whereby high places are reduced and low ones filled up. Infinitely slow if left to itself, the process becomes radically accelerated under man's inept intervention. The activating forces, gentle and restrained on nature's leash, become monstrous and diabolical when man misbehaves and cuts them loose. Indignantly they tear apart and take away what previously they helped construct and ordain. Loosed by man, they dissolve and scar, transport and bury that without which he cannot prevail. He may have inherited the earth, but unless he disciplines himself to better guard the soil, the earth will disinherit him!

Wind and water, erstwhile man's indispensable servants, become his most formidable adversaries when he bares the soil to their attack. The wind, purveyor of water to the land, turns hostile in its absence, and the life-giving water, unbridled, destroys the life it would sustain. Without wind and water man could not exist, but when by his own erring they do him harm, he is quick to place the blame: "Had the wind only slacked during that one dry week," or "That driving rain came just when I had the hill worked for planting."

Man is awed by the power that marches sand dunes across the desert or levels a city, by the relentless attack that moves mountains into the sea. He flees for his life before gale or torrent, but

Erosion tears the soil apart and carries it away

The agents, wind and water, get the blame

forgets that unprotected soil is also defenseless against them. Might a few inches of soil resist what mountains of stone cannot endure? Certainly not! Winds that can plane a rock desert smooth make quick work of loose, dry soil, pulverized by tillage implements, or soil disrobed and trampled by the hooves of hungry animals. Running water, which grooves the rocks and fashions valleys under the restraining hand of nature, makes game of a soft soil mantle exposed to its unfettered caprices.

In a single day of carnage wind or water can carry away the product of centuries, and the soil in dust clouds or muddy streams has lost its usefulness. Perhaps no useable soil, or land, is totally immune to the ravages of wind or water. Indeed many soils, and expansive areas of land, feel the destructive fury of both wind and water, each in its season. Over the United States as a whole, as over the world, water erosion has probably destroyed much more soil than wind, and affects a much larger total producing area. Both of these destructive agents are shown at work in Figures 60 and 61.

The instigators, man and gravity, pass the buck

Vociferous man and his silent accomplice, gravity, are instigators of the criminal plot—the latter mutely constant, the former blindly prodigal and unscrupulous. Man makes the arrangements and gravity does the dirty work. An apple a day—dropped on his head from a considerable height—might keep man reminded that his wilful partner never deserts him, and that the same uncompromising force by which rain falls always speeds water down hill. Had he learned that elementary lesson well enough when first he herded animals or tilled the soil, we could abbreviate this gloomy discourse. Unfortunately, man is not yet fully convinced that the soil he surrenders to gravity inevitably drags him down with it. *When the soil goes man must go too* (Figures 62 and 63). Ours to pity rather than condemn the individual who, seeking livelihood, plows too high on the hill or runs more cattle than the land can carry; ours to examine critically the culture that imposed the need and the society that condoned the act. With malice toward neither, the striving individual penalizes both himself and his society.

Denuded uplands in China and India lie empty while the populace crowds the lowlands in a desperate struggle for food. Through the ages, soils and peoples have gravitated to the river plains, surrendering the barren, rain-repellent uplands to marauding jackals and xerophytes. In these hungry lands man-made wastes dominate the physiognomy of whole regions, and it appears doubtful that the teeming millions can regain what they permitted gravity to steal.

FIGURES 60 and 61. *Soil on the move: airborne above and waterborne below. Water and wind are the carriers, but man prepares their cargo! Above: a dust storm in Colorado. Below: water in action on an eroding field in Oklahoma. (S.C.S. photos.)*

Have we Americans done better than the Indians or the Chinese? We have indeed—from the standpoint of flaunting disregard for gravity. We have perhaps dispossessed more soil in less time than any other people in history, ancient or modern. In keeping with the American tradition of speed and volume, we have undoubtedly dissipated more soil in two centuries than other comparable areas have lost in a millennium. That is a mean boast, but the doing was not really malicious.

Several circumstances contributed to our fantastic wastage of soil. Our initial land occupance was largely by northwest Europeans from lands so low and flat that gravity is almost impotent, lands on which rain falls so gently that run-off cannot possibly attain the violence with which it operates over most of the United States.

In response to a seemingly insatiable market in Europe young America developed a lucrative, commercial agriculture, in which row crops such as tobacco, cotton, and corn were entirely too prominent for the good of the land. (They still occupy much of our land, as may be seen in Figure 64.) Clearing, burning, and planting ensured quick profit, and when the soil weakened there was more to clear. Men prospered by a single cash crop specialty, kept the soil stirred during the growing season and naked to the elements all year. They plowed straight furrows up and down hill, except where slopes were too steep to permit it. They got their wealth, and lost the soil whence it came. Worse still, they inaugurated a sort of land-use psychology that spread westward with settlement and tinges our land economy to this day: the fascination and gamble attendant upon a specialized land-use enterprise. We are justifiably proud of large, square fields, mammoth cattle spreads, and gigantic logging operations. We like to boast about *big* harvests, *big* herds, and *big* lumber stacks, without enough thought for the land whence they must come. Cutting a wide swath is traditionally American, but we need to transpose the tradition into good land management and soil husbandry. Then we shall have something we can always boast about without flinching—record production coincident with increased potential of a permanent base.

Destructive erosion does several kinds of damage

Destructive, or accelerated, erosion takes a variety of forms, and each form does several kinds of damage. Being simply an artificially activated operation of the natural geologic process, every form involves *removal, transport,* and *deposition* of soil materials. Points of origin and destination bear the brunt, with lesser injury along the route. *Wind* steals the soil away from one

Figures 62 and 63. *Eviction is the ultimate penalty for land abuse. The farmer who lived in the shack above (Colorado) was evicted by drought and wind because he plowed the wrong land. (Note the half-buried plow beam, and see Chapter 11). The cotton planter who lived in the house below (South Carolina) was evicted by running water because he plowed the land too much, the wrong way. (S.C.S. photos.)*

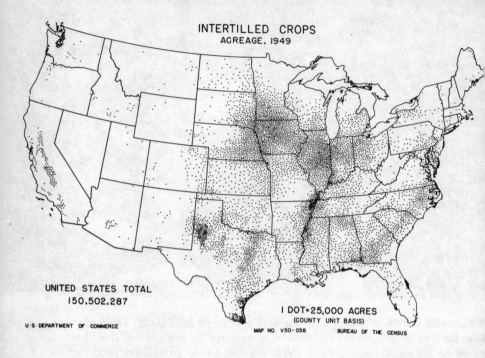

UNITED STATES TOTAL
150,502,287

U·S· DEPARTMENT OF COMMERCE

I DOT=25,000 ACRES
(COUNTY UNIT BASIS)

MAP NO. V50-058   BUREAU OF THE CENSUS

FIGURE 64. *Inter-tilled crops, such as cotton, corn, and tobacco, incur greater erosion losses than close-growing crops, such as small grain or hay. Note Figure 41 again. It is especially important that row crops be grown in relatively narrow contour strips instead of entire fields as was once the custom.* (Bureau of the Census map.)

place and buries other soil when it deposits the debris (Figure 65). It brings injury to plants and animals in the path of blowing dust and grit, increasing the difficulty of re-establishing enough life to stem subsequent attacks. Soil movement by *slipping* down-slope in a mass removes the soil bodily, and pushes it onto the soil below. It leaves raw edges and surfaces at the top, and distorted, hummocky soil at the bottom. *Water* wreaks havoc with soil from the impact and splash of the raindrop to the dumping of mud into the ocean. It robs the upland, scarring what it does not remove, it pollutes the streams and chokes their channels, and it buries under debris the soils and alluvium of valley and lowland (Figure 66). It reduces water storage at its source, it renders water courses inadequate for the discharge of excessive run-off, thereby magnifying stream erosion and flooding; it destroys plant and animal life (including man and his works) from its most inland point of

FIGURES 65 and 66. *Whether wind or water is the agent, erosion involves removal, transportation, and deposition. Where the eroded debris comes to rest it may ruin other soil by burying it under dust, sand, or silt. In dry regions, wind and water take turns eroding exposed soil. Both of these photos were taken in Texas.* (Fig. 65 by Sue R. Ford, from the National Audubon Society; Fig. 66, S.C.S. photo.)

origin to its seaward point of destination. Wash from a corn field in north Alabama can ruin an oyster bed in Mobile Bay more permanently than it affects the meadow immediately below the corn. Wash from their watersheds fills reservoirs with silt, negating the usefulness of costly dams and appurtenances. Wash spread over stream banks and lake shores spoils them for recreational use and wildlife habitat. From beginning to end, in scores of ways, soil erosion by water damages and disfigures our country.

Erosion by surface run-off, the most widespread and destructive, falls into three major categories: sheet wash, slope channeling or rilling, and gullying. It is appropriate that we examine the salient features of each.

Sheet wash
wears bald
spots

Sheet wash wears the soil away on areas inadequately covered. As the term implies, it peels off the top a little at a time, and often goes unnoticed during its initial stages. The process begins with the pounding and splash of raindrops, which suspend fine soil particles in water, clog soil pores with the soupy fluid, and agitate a sheet of the mixture that moves off as surplus.

This sheet erosion is invited by loss of humus, compaction, nakedness, and any other reduction of soil capacity for absorbing and retaining water. A forest floor devoid of litter, a pasture slope too closely grazed, a plowed field left bare, facilitates the process. When tree roots become exposed, or when bare earth shows through grass or grain, the process is well advanced. When the trees appear to have hoisted themselves out of the ground, or the thin spots in field or pasture have changed their hue, the attack has inflicted serious injury. The A horizon, the B horizon, or the entire soil section, may have been taken by stealth. When a farmer observes that fields once of uniform color have become brindled he might mark down in his almanac that sheet wash has robbed him. The clues are very obvious.

Once begun, sheet wash accelerates as the affected area becomes less receptive to water. Run-off from the bald spot tends to cut channels or incipient gullies below it, like infection spreading from an open wound. Here, as with many cases of resource abuse, damage and loss are cumulative and progressive; Figure 67 shows the process.

Slope
channeling
rips the
top soil
away

Slope channeling, technically a form of rill erosion, rips loose top-soil away so swiftly and boldly that its audacity amazes even the trained observer. One heavy shower can literally "cut to ribbons" the freshly-tilled soil on a steep slope, carving channels so deep that they expose the plow-sole as a flight of stairs (Figure 68). Where plow depth equals or exceeds the thickness of the A

FIGURE 67. *Sheet wash has removed the topsoil, and gullies have begun to develop in the subsoil. Soil erosion, once begun, is a self-accelerating process because eroded soil absorbs less water and increases run-off. (Photo courtesy T.V.A.)*

FIGURE 68. *Slope channelling or rilling (Washington). Heavy rain brings disaster to plowed soil on a steep slope. Note how the channels are enlarged toward the bottom, evincing the gathering volume and force of water as it runs down. Length of slope may be quite as critical as steepness of slope as a factor in water erosion. (S.C.S. photo.)*

horizon one does not need calculus to figure out that the loss of topsoil will be proportionate to the part of total surface space occupied by such channels. A thousand years of soil can be half gone in an afternoon thunderstorm, carried away in little rills of water.

Up-and-down farming expedites channeling; contour plowing impedes it. In either case, cultivation that fills the grooves after one rain invites further loss to the next. Many a well-meaning farmer smoothes a carved-up field, oblivious to the fact that the remnants he stirs become *more* vulnerable to attack. He considers the storm damage repaired when the channels are filled, failing to associate with the channeled slope the sediments spread out below it. He may view with detachment the recurrence of sheet wash or rilling until declining productivity precludes the possibility of effectual and economical countermeasures.

Rills are to gullies as acorns are to oaks, but they are seeds of destruction instead of growth. A few hundred millions of years ago a little rill began the world-famed Grand Canyon of the Colorado. There was no man to accelerate the cutting of the Canyon; nature did it unaided, and very slowly. Men have induced canyon-cutting in many parts of our country, and Missouri, for example, is not immune, as clearly evidenced by Figure 69.

FIGURE 69. *This gully in Missouri was later blocked and converted into a farm pond.* (S.C.S. photo.)

FIGURE 70. *Gullied cow lane (Kansas). The wear of animals can initiate destructive erosion. Cow paths may become gullies, as shown here.* (S.C.S. photo.)

Gullying does not stop with the soil, but rends the whole earth mantle right down to bedrock. Unrestrained, it makes of little grooves tremendous V-shaped or vertical-walled trenches that almost defy containment. It can begin with a mere scratch on the surface and produce an excavation in which battleships could be concealed. The scar of a log snaked out of the woods or the rooting of a razor-back hog, the drip from the eaves or the discharge from a spot of sheet wash, or wheel tracks, foot paths, cow trails (Figure 70), or pig pens, poultry yards, cattle corrals, or grading, filling, excavating—every one, and many another, has commenced gullying of titanic dimensions.

Gullying rends the whole earth mantle

Early in their development gullies become "triple-threats" to the land. Removal and deposition are direct damages, but the ditches soon become obstacles to animals and machinery, thereby restricting or prohibiting the use of areas between them. Interdiction defeats farmers much as it does troops on a battlefield. Unless it be accessible for use the best of soil has little value.

In advanced stages of gullying the land lies completely dissected or mutilated. Under certain conditions mature gullies assume parallel courses down-slope, producing veritable badlands of V-shaped grooves and sharp-crested divides, the site entirely stripped of soil and vegetation. Under other conditions, as in the loess bordering the lower Mississippi, they assume forms much more grand and grotesque, with vertical, ragged sides that cave in, tons at a time, like cliffs tumbling into a chasm. In both cases the destructive work proceeds headward and laterally like the spread of a festering wound, gaining momentum as it destroys, until those who began it are helpless to stop it.

Few people see in a gullied landscape the real loss depicted there, the work of millennia wasted in decades. More of us must learn the implications of severe gullying, the most spectacular form of water erosion. With all our technology we cannot rebuild quickly what nature took aeons to create.

Mass movement of soil also accelerates

"What goes up must come down" applies to soil as well as to anything else, and when the translocation involves segments of soil otherwise intact the shift may be identified as *"mass movement."* *Landslides and earth flows are violent and sudden mass movements.* So far as these phenomena are natural we can neither accept blame nor in every case prescribe preventive treatment; but where our use, or abuse, of the land apparently activates or accelerates any of them it behooves us to examine our fault.

Pasture land appears particularly susceptible to soil creep or slipping, and it may be that the weight of the animals and the paths they wear across the slope are contributing factors. Slips are common features on steep pasture slopes in southeastern Ohio and adjacent areas, where smooth rock underlies the soil. They are also common on the gently sloping grazing lands of the Great Plains, in eastern Montana and southward. They may be seen in upland pastures and steep fields most anywhere in the nation. The one pictured in Figure 71 happened in the Northwest.

The *slumps and flows* characteristic of hillsides in Muskingum County, Ohio are probably typical soil slip features. A section of soil breaks away and slips a few feet down-slope, leaving a miniature scarp or series of scarps about its upper side, and pushing the soil up into peculiar hummocks at its lower margin. The scarp may be a few inches to several feet in height; the mass may possibly be an acre in area, though usually much less; and the movement, once begun, tends to recur until it leaves a dent in the hillside and a jumbled mass of soil debris at the bottom. The dent in the hillside loses its soil and becomes droughty, while the billowing area below it loses its normal structure and becomes poorly drained. The "stepped-crescents" of the Plains are similar, but in them the slipped mass is usually thinner and the identifying features considerably subdued. Modifications of *slumping, slipping,* and *flowage* have damaged our soils in many places; but the aggregate consequences certainly do not equal those of run-off water or of wind.

FIGURE 71. *Erosion by mass movement may be induced or accelerated by inept use of the land. This slip occurred in Washington on a slope too steep for cultivation.* (S.C.S. photo.)

Terraces apparently made by animals are probably both cause and effect of mass movement—the indirect results of over-grazing, disturbed water behavior, and rupture or weakening of the binding that healthy sod and deep plant roots maintain.

This is not to say that grazing is the only way by which our use of the soil accelerates soil erosion by mass movement. We jeopardize forest slopes, too, whenever we injure or destroy the mass of roots that secures the soil, or the litter and humus that detain water. We accelerate the caving and slumping of stream banks with every upstream employment of land that hastens run-off. Here is another of the manifold relationships between one conservation problem and another: impaired water storage, which directly curtails soil fertility where it occurs, is indirectly responsible for soil destruction elsewhere.

Much has been said about *steepness of slope,* or grade, in connection with soil erosion, but not enough about the *length of slope,* which may be equally important. Other factors being equal,

Length and steepness of slope gage the vigor of attack

the *length* and the *steepness* of a slope gage the vigor of attack by water.

Perhaps the simplest statement of grade is in terms of per cent a one-foot vertical drop in a hundred feet horizontal distance constituting a one per cent slope. A hundred per cent slope equals the hypotenuse of a right triangle with both legs equal, one vertical and the other horizontal. By plane geometry it equals a 45° angle, by common sense, an incline too great for ordinary cultivation. The southern mountaineer calls it "steep as a horse's face," and he knows that it is physically impossible to plow it up-and-down. With a "hillside" plow that can be flipped over at each end of the field, to throw the furrow down-slope both going and coming, he has always farmed on the contour, often without any thought of employing it to save his soil. Where the soil lasted until modern conservation came along, the hill farmer was a ready convert to a practice he already simulated under compulsion.

A negligible portion of our land surface lies flat enough to escape accelerated erosion under cultural use without specific precautions. Water erosion takes place on slopes of less than one per cent grade, whose incline may be difficult to detect visually except by observing run-off. Wherever water can run off it can also erode! Erosion by mass movement does little damage on slopes of three or four per cent, but on slopes only twice that steep it may be active. *Flatness of terrain saves very few soils from erosion.*

Second only to the grade factor comes the length of the slope, especially as it influences water erosion. Grade lends velocity per se, but *length builds up volume all the way down,* as clearly shown in Figure 68. Obviously, volume incidentally increases velocity, and multiplies destructive capacity by augmented flow and intensified impact. On a uniform slope each unit of area contributes a comparable amount of the run-off. Theoretically, if each acre discharges as run-off ten barrels of water from a rain, then four acres in a row down-slope should discharge forty barrels. Each acre in turn takes a worse lacing than the next one above it, and the lowest one gets the whole attack assembled by the others. That explains how gullying, like the self-made man, begins at the bottom and works up. *The longer the slope, the more severe its erosion by water.*

Wind has less respect for grade

Wind, the horizontal movement of air, while it has little respect for grade, is nonetheless responsive to aspects of terrain. Flatness that stems eroding water gives wind the free sweep it needs to attain menacing force. *Level or gently undulating uplands bear the brunt of wind erosion.* Surface irregularities and lesser obstacles, such as trees, brush, or hedgerows, cause friction and turbulence that moderate the attack. Windward exposures suffer maximum deflation, and sheltered situations receive the wind-borne debris. Wind, too, takes away from one place and deposits in another (Figure 65), but, unlike water, wind erodes up hill more actively than down.

Although wind wreaks more havoc in dry regions, it also erodes humid lands whenever drought affords the opportunity. During dry spells in our humid East considerable soil blowing takes place. Muck on valley floors, where one might think the wind impotent, falls easy prey to wind erosion when the light organic material is dry. The soft material of our Coastal Plains blows quite extensively, not only along the shore, but also on exposed sites far inland.

The dust on a footpath or a dirt road, a playground or cow-lane, may yield to wind when water fails to move it. Sunken roads in loess, whether in moist Mississippi or in dry Mongolia, are at least partially the product of wind erosion. The free air of the troposphere is charged with salt blown off the oceans and dust blown off the lands. If it were not so there should be less precipitation, for lack of condensation nuclei. The dust originates with wind erosion. When it attains a density visibly apparent, land somewhere is losing its soil; when it obstructs vision, soils nearby are in full flight.

As previously mentioned, few areas are entirely secure against water erosion. The same can be said for wind. However, there is much more soil destruction by water in our dry West than there is by wind in our moist East. Predominance of one over the other is a matter of degree, variable from time to time and place to place.

Climatic conditions influence human activities everywhere in many different ways, among them the selection of land use enterprises and the provocation of accelerated erosion under a particular type of land use in any location. Climate is the framework, no less than the land itself, against which we have poorly planned and pursued the employment of our soils. We have failed to comprehend, or refused to acknowledge, the full significance of climatic elements in relation to land use and erosion.

Extremes and vagaries of climate are crucial factors

Averages, or means, most accurately computed, are at best inadequate or misleading for land-use planning. *Departures* from the norm, periodic or cyclic *fluctuations,* erratic *extremes* and *variations,* are the *crucial factors in soil erosion.* A severe freeze in Louisiana can ruin the cover crop intended to protect the unfrozen soil. A January thaw in Minnesota can erode soil that would normally lie frozen so solid, or so deeply buried under

snow, that no erosion would be possible. Soils that can absorb a
monthly rainfall of five inches even when it comes in five days
can erode badly if the total falls in one day. Worse has happened
and the excess is disastrous where the average is harmless.

Spring drought in the wheat country, where spring is ordinarily the rainy season, has ruined both crops and soils when
wind stripped the top off the pulverized fields and exposed the
seed. A series of dry years in that region created the Dust Bowl
tragedy, about which more will be said in the chapter on the
grasslands. Land use geared to the *wet* cycle failed when the *dry*
one arrived.

Too much rain, or not enough, temperatures too high or too
low, heat or cold, wetness or dryness out of season, extremes of
climate and vagaries of weather—these are the recalcitrants that
have eluded our best efforts at control.

**Our losses
are
staggering**

How much has our young nation sacrificed? More than any of
comparable age in history. Many of our good farm lands have
surrendered more topsoil than they retain. Many a present-day
farmer in eroded parts of our Southeast has never tilled any considerable area of *A* horizon. Many are farming the *C* horizon,
parent material deserted by its offspring. Unless they move away
they may never farm anything better than parent material. Many
dry-land farmers are cultivating soil remnants and drifted soil
debris. Correction of past error is impossible, and improvement
of the inhospitable situation is difficult because the means have
been lost or impaired. Nor is there any regional sanctuary from
soil erosion. The deep, rich soils on the rolling plains of Iowa,
Illinois, and Indiana are down to the *B* horizon in many places.
(Indeed, many eroded soils to which the best modern farming
practices are applied produce more than ever before, but how
much greater still might their yield be if those practices could
have been applied to them undamaged?) The general extent
and severity of erosion may be seen in Figure 72.

**Erosion
complicates
our water
problems**

Indirect losses are also great, almost beyond comprehension.
Soil erosion pollutes our streams, reducing their values for water
supply, recreation, and wildlife habitat. By sedimentation it
chokes stream channels and estuaries, rendering them less capable
of discharging the concentrated run-off from eroded lands. It
imposes extravagant expenditures for dredging and other measures to keep our waterways and harbors navigable. It silts our
reservoirs. It increases floods, and decreases our developed and
potential water power. In short, it complicates all the major
aspects of water conservation, and robs us of the wherewithal to
take corrective action.

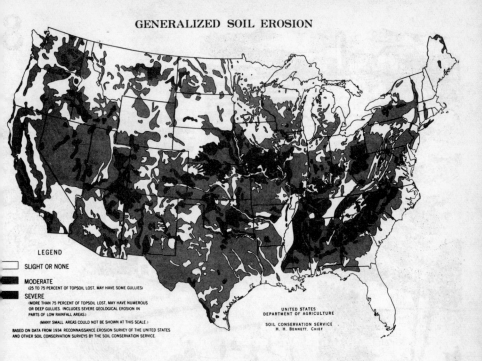

LEGEND

SLIGHT OR NONE

MODERATE
(25 TO 75 PERCENT OF TOPSOIL LOST. MAY HAVE SOME GULLIES)

SEVERE
(MORE THAN 75 PERCENT OF TOPSOIL LOST. MAY HAVE NUMEROUS
OR DEEP GULLIES. INCLUDES SEVERE GEOLOGICAL EROSION IN
PARTS OF LOW RAINFALL AREAS)

(MANY SMALL AREAS COULD NOT BE SHOWN AT THIS SCALE.)

BASED ON DATA FROM 1934 RECONNAISSANCE EROSION SURVEY OF THE UNITED STATES
AND OTHER SOIL CONSERVATION SURVEYS BY THE SOIL CONSERVATION SERVICE.

UNITED STATES
DEPARTMENT OF AGRICULTURE

SOIL CONSERVATION SERVICE
H. H. BENNETT, CHIEF

FIGURE 72. *Mapping of soil erosion revealed a sad state of the Union. Injury in any given locality was largely a matter of degree, because few areas have escaped damage.* (S.C.S. map.)

Worst of all, erosion compromises our enviable American society. It threatens the highest material standards on earth. It humiliates and frustrates our people. The erosion menace is not everywhere equally present, but no region has complete immunity. In some places, as in the "blow" area of the southern plains, its ravages continue almost unabated. The early 'fifties have been a painful reminder of the "dirty 'thirties." Erosion continues to disrupt our regional economies and social structures, attendant upon personal hardship and community distress. Erosion remains a serious national problem, both economically and socially.

Foreclosure, bankruptcy, and forced migration are end products of soil erosion, and emergency relief cannot compensate the victims. We cannot recover personal pride and self-confidence with disaster funds. The by-products of soil wastage—dispossessed, disillusioned, disheartened people—are not always capable of full recovery by any means. Our *real* national strength reposes in the people. Our greatest resources, those for whose aggrandizement we strive to conserve all the others, are *human*. If we would conserve them, let us look well to the defense of our soil.

Erosion
compromises
our
society

Soil Conservation

*soil conservation holds the soil in place,
maintains or improves its health and fertility,
and increases its capacity for sustained production*

OUR LOSSES OF SOIL HAVE BEEN GRIEVOUS, AND THE CONTINUING losses are great; but during two decades of scientifically organized soil defense we have made such gains that many other nations, young and old, look to us for example and advice.

We cannot recover soils eroded away, and we cannot repair damaged soils beyond a degree permitted by situation and circumstance; but *we can hold and fortify those soils that remain.* Couched in military terms: we cannot regain all the ground we have lost, but we can hold the line, and advance rather than retreat. Our tactics, as yet imperfectly developed, have even now such demonstrated effectiveness that we need only apply them more widely and more vigorously to ensure for ourselves and posterity the soils now surviving, with higher productivity and greater resistance. (In Figure 73, see how soil conservation transformed an eroded farm.) Meanwhile we must develop a better *public sense of values. We must learn that soil inches per acre guarantee social security more realistically than dollars per month.*

In Chapter 5 the futility of employing soil-less land for soil-using purposes was mentioned. By the same token, one cannot conserve the soil where none exists, as for example, on certain deep sands of our coastal plains or the bare rock exposures of mountains and deserts. Only if population pressure becomes extreme, as in parts of the Old World, can such sands and slopes

We can
keep and
improve
the soils
that
remain

155

FIGURE 73. *With good treatment we can heal and rejuvenate much of our worn and wounded land. A few years before this picture was made (in North Carolina), the farm at the left was as sick as the field at the right. Conservation changed the scene.* (Courtesy T.V.A.)

be economically covered with soil artificially developed or transported from other areas. Meanwhile, the apparently unproductive spaces may be playing such subtle parts in the total scheme of things that their true worth eludes us.

Time, place and condition indicate the modes of treatment

Time, place, and *condition* must dictate the choices of method and technique. *Condition* means the state of the soil to be conserved, especially its erodability and its relative health. *Place* connotes all the geographic attributes that influence soil development, soil use, and soil erosion—climate, vegetation, topographic position, and so forth. It also involves the established land economy and cultural practices. Applications must be chosen and adapted to suit the situation: wind defense where wind is the miscreant, water defense where run-off does the damage, and so on. Within our space limitations we cannot detail the specially endorsed methods region by region, but we can indicate, now and then, how the general methods discussed have specific pertinence to certain parts of the country.

Time is of the essence! Procrastination has already enlarged the problem tremendously, and every delay makes it greater. But, there are more tangible time factors to be regarded, such as the importance of countering wind injury during a wet cycle when nature lends a hand, or the importance of conducting costly engineering when funds are available. Waiting spreads the malady, increases the cost of treatment, and renders the cure less positive and permanent.

Land-use planning is the first line of defense against soil damage. Had we better arranged our schemes of land use to accord with land capabilities from the beginning our task would have been comparatively easy. But, because we consigned our land to various uses almost haphazardly, and lost or damaged much of the soil, our planning must be remedial more than preventive, applied to soils in all stages of deterioration. We are land planners of necessity, not by choice.

Land-use planning is the first line of defense

Planning for regions, communities or political units is a proper function of groups and governments at the various levels. Execution of any plan depends on public enlightenment and cooperation. Good civic leadership is the key to water-power development, establishment of community parks and forests, and a host of other public improvements. But land planning for soil conservation cannot be implemented without the *participation of private landowners.* They are not only the producers of our crops and animals, but also the *keepers of our soils.* They must be convinced, instructed, and often assisted in the wise use-allocation of the space they own. Consistent with our democratic principles, we have not forced farmers to conform, unless we count the condemnation and acquisition of land for such public developments as reservoirs, roads, communication and transmission lines. Perhaps one of the payments for democracy has been the loss of soil incidental to absolute ownership and almost unrestrained use of the land. If that be true, which it may well be, the costs can be reduced by educating the people for democracy *and* conservation simultaneously. The combined process is implicit in group planning for area improvement.

We formulate and implement our plans without duress

The best laid plans often miscarry or fail of execution when economic necessity or opportunity intervenes. A farmer may be fully convinced that a certain tract should be planted to trees, but he cannot meet next year's mortgage payment with seedlings. A rancher may have to choose between over-grazing or selling his animals on a weak market. A timber grower may be offered so much for one clean cutting that he abandons his sustained-

"The best laid schemes o' mice and men . . ."

yield program. Tempted by high wheat prices, the plains farmer may risk plowing up the grass he sowed to guard his soil against wind erosion. Thus in scores of ways those who live on the land are inclined, if not compelled, to compromise the plans to which they subscribe in principle.

If his first attempt fails—if his trees burn, if his young grass withers, or his range erodes despite carefully regulated grazing, the conforming individual loses heart and confidence. One bad year, one accident, and he bolts the planned program. Short-range reverses can blind him to long-range advantages.

Impetuous, independent men, fluctuating prices, weather, and catastrophes, must be taken in stride by the planner, but he cannot be entirely successful without a checkrein on the human element. Cognizant of that, the Soil Conservation Service, early in its brilliant career, placed its assistance to land owners on a cooperative basis to ensure execution of recommended farm plans. To enlarge the work toward regional scope the Service organized (usually along county lines) Conservation Districts under enabling acts passed by state legislatures. Thus came into being the individual obligation and community organization which gave the movement the latitude and continuity essential to its success. Demonstration farms showed District members the methods and advantages of conservation farming. Many non-member individualists also observed the good work and adopted similar practices on their own land. Many who resisted District organization initially became its staunch supporters when they had proof of its merits.

Management can prevent soil injury

Once the land is consigned to its proper use—be it *crop, pasture,* or *forest*—the next step toward soil conservation is *skillful management under the chosen use or uses.* Unless one follows through, his planning goes for naught. Having determined a pattern, the land operator becomes forester, grazier, or farmer, or any combination of the three. He may abandon or restrict his specialization, and strengthen his economic stability by producing a greater variety of goods. *Variety of produce* and *stability of producer* are a combination conducive to good soil management and conservation.

Continuity of tenure is basic to proper soil management, because a constructive program means several consecutive years of scheduled activities. Immediate gains, this year or next, must often be disdained in order that more substantial ones may accrue later. The vision to defer and the means to sustain the wait must be at hand. Lacking either, especially the latter, the operator can-

ιot be a *keeper* of the soil, but must be instead a scavenger
scratching desperately to exist this year, and maybe next. Men
struggling to survive cannot be concerned about anything be-
ʿond the immediate future. Short-term tenants and sharecroppers
ιre often at once the products and the victims of poor land. Desti-
ιute people on sterile land can improve neither themselves nor
ʰe soil without assistance. Expert advice cannot help them unless
ʰey are also assisted in applying the recommendations. Cogni-
ʐant of these deterrents to soil conservation, Congress has appro-
ͻriated vast sums of money to encourage farm ownership and to
ιssist the owners in converting to good farm management.

The object of management is the maintenance or improvement
ͻf soil health and fertility, and in soil maintenance an ounce of
ͻrevention is if anything worth more than a pound of cure.
ͅkillfully accomplished, the objective may be attained without
ʲerious disruption of productive land use; but if attention be
ʲeferred until health and fertility are impaired the best oppor-
ͱunity has passed, and procedures will almost invariably interfere
ʋith regular production. "A stitch in time" is infinitely more ap-
ͻlicable to the tiller of soils than it is to the patcher of little
ͻoys' breeches.

An ounce of prevention better than a pound of cure

Except in organic soils such as muck and peat which require
ʲpecial treatment, soil maintenance or improvement depends primarily upon *retention and addition of humus,* the vital soil component most transitory under productive soil employment. As
ʳetainer of water and nutrients, and the medium for an active
biotic community, soil humus is the mainstay of soil health and
fertility. Unless humus be present in sufficient quantity heavy soils
become compacted and intractable; light ones, too loose and porous. Without humus, clays lack pore space for air and water,
and sands lack the body with which to resist the leaching-out of
plant nutrients by percolating water. Humus tends to bind the
soil together, thereby increasing its resistance to erosion. Humus
releases available nitrogen as it decays, thereby promoting plant
growth. It improves the physical condition of the soil so that
plants can respond well when other plant foods are added. Humus
facilitates tillage and promotes good tilth.

If the humus naturally accumulated in grassland or even forest
soils were retained, our soil problems would be much simpler.
When we dissipate humus by burning or trampling the forest floor,
by close-grazing the range, or over-cropping tilled areas, we deprive ourselves of the prime factor in soil maintenance. Once lost,
that factor is difficult to re-establish, because the vegetation

whence it must come is retarded. No amount of chemicals or con centrates can substitute (1).

Soil fatigue and soil wear resemble emaciation and infection o the human body. If weakness be detected early and preventiv measures taken promptly the trouble will usually right itsel without specific or radical treatment. Unless it be neglected neither soil depletion nor tuberculosis, neither erosion nor cancer need be fatal. Unchecked, any one of them may be tragic. Goo general care of the body, good health habits, or good cultura practices, are the best protection against serious infection o malignancy. *In early stages many ills respond to common treat ment; care and nourishment rather than medication.* Retainin; health is much easier than regaining it. If a fair portion of so product were always returned, as plant residue or animal waste to the soil whence it came, soil ills would rarely become so grav as to require elaborate and costly palliatives. But too few of ou husbandmen love and understand their soil well enough to guard its health before it has failed.

In early stages several ills respond to common treatment

Advanced organic ailment requires specific medication, and the prescription may be very complex. A tonic cannot cure a dia betic, nor can humus remedy excessive soil acidity. Treatmen generally beneficial may aggravate the particular systemic de rangement. If the soil be too acid one must sweeten it; if the duodenum ulcerates one must soothe it.

Advanced organic ailment requires specific medication

Soil afflictions engendered by abuse are so numerous and variec that all cannot be described here. They fall into three major categories: *physical, chemical,* and *biologic.* There is a degree of reciprocity among the three, but the first demands greatest at tention because it controls the other two, and is therefore of pri mary importance. Physical soil ailment can usually be diagnosed as a deficiency of one or more vital elements, or the wearing away by erosion. Deficiencies may be corrected by incorporating the material in short supply, be it nitrogen, phosphorus, potassium, humus, calcium, or any other. That done, and a reasonable bal ance regained, wear will be less active, if not stopped altogether (2). When diagnosis shows humus content below par, its replen ishment should come first, the better to assimilate any other ad ditions. Early recovery can be assured unless deficiency and wear have proceeded so far that only nature with her infinite means and patience can afford a cure.

Serious physical injury may require surgery

Serious physical injury may require surgery. When the attend ing physician, the land-user, plows around a gullied hillside or abandons a worn-out field he admits tacitly that he cannot suc cessfully treat the injury, and that he is obliged to amputate the

amaged portion. In the case of the exhausted field he turns his
adly handled patient over to rature for such recuperation as
he may ordain. In the case of the wounded hillside he may be
ble to isolate the gangrene and prevent its spread. He may
educe the bleeding by localizing the wound. Our country is
otted with such land surgery. It devolves upon soil conservation,
ursued individually and cooperatively, to defend against further
ajury the soil that remains, and recover or revive wherever pos-
ible that which we have lost or ruined. The need is urgent; the
ask, colossal. We cannot do it quickly, and we cannot do it once
nd for all. We must attack with determination, and continue the
ffort without pause. Tactics employed must be adapted to par-
icular situations; commitments must be commensurate with the
bstacles to be overcome.

Many areas require only slight modification of established
and-use practices; others demand complete revision of utiliza-
ion. In some areas adequate conservational procedures show a
uick profit over and above their total cost; in others adequate
neasures demand an expenditure per acre many times greater
han the highest price quoted by a real-estate agent.

First, the soil or whatever is left of it must be *stabilized,* held
a place. "A rolling stone gathers no moss," and soil on the move
ollects no fertility. The farmer-conservator cannot improve soil
hat is actively eroding—any better than the surgeon can operate
vhile his patient cavorts about the hospital.

First, the soil or soil remnants must be held in place

All erosion preventives are, in effect, soil stabilizers, and in
nany cases several must be applied simultaneously, lest none be
ffectual. Increase of humus content, increase of pore space for
ir and water, a dense, unbroken surface cover, dispersal of run-
ff, and moderation of wind velocity—all contribute toward fixing
rosive soil in place. The function of each, always constant,
aries in relative importance from one situation to another. For
nstance, one might gain nothing by adding humus to muck land,
vhereas its incorporation with salvable parent material where
othing better remains might well be the signal step toward its
onservation.

Unless it is bare and dry and pulverized, soil cannot be very
adly damaged by wind. When the soil is so dry that the wind
an easily remove it, it is too dry to produce a protective vegeta-
ive cover. Conversely, when the soil is moist enough to resist
vind action it has moisture enough to grow protective vegetation
s well. Thus, *defense against wind erosion hinges upon water
onditions* (3, 4).

Soil cannot blow badly unless it is bare and dry

Since soil blowing is a natural hazard to flat lands under low

FIGURE 74. *Contour (horizontal) tillage is a basic application in soil conservation. This farm layout in Pennsylvania shows two additional devices for curbing run-off—diversion terraces and a farm pond. A clean-tilled orchard needs conservation measures similar to those applicable to any other row crop. (S.C.S. photo.)*

and erratic rainfall, it is man-made only to the extent that man breaks or weakens the protective covering and reduces soil capacity for absorbing and storing water. He can correct his error by establishing and maintaining a *cover* as good or better than the original one nature provided, and ensuring that the soil receives and retains water just as effectively as it did before he disturbed it.

Sores of sheet wash heal under a bandage

Sores of sheet wash will heal under a proper bandage (5). Straw, stalks, leaves, brush, sawdust, or other material, spread over the wound to intercept raindrops and prevent the spatter effect that causes irritation, serves in much the same manner as a wet wrapping over a burn. If the gall be large and deep it may be necessary to retire it from use temporarily. The application of a thick blanket initially, and the addition of new layers as older ones decay and settle, can mend a deep sore in a few years. However, results cannot be very satisfactory if the bandage is ripped off annually and the wound probed with a plow. Temporary,

easonal bandaging does well just to reduce festering and
preading.

Horizontal tillage checks slope channeling and incipient gully-
ng by dividing slope length into shorter segments, by breaking
he gradient, or by interrupting both slope and grade. Horizontal,
r contour, tillage means the performance of cultural operations
rosswise of the slope (on the level) instead of up and down (6).
A contour is a line drawn on a map or on the ground, all points
f which lie at the same elevation.) Since water runs downhill,
ny obstruction on the contour impedes its flow and reduces its
rosive power. The principle is as simple as that. Its application
n the land is illustrated in Figure 74.

In practice there are numerous contour tillage devices, some
f them developed to a high degree of technical perfection. Plow-
ng furrows along the contour is the simplest form. Each furrow
cts as a dam against water moving down-slope. Strip cropping
s another simple form. It is a mere matter of alternating contour
trips of close-growing crops such as hay and grain with strips
f row crops such as cotton, corn, and tobacco that require clean
illage. Each close-growing strip, itself receptive to water, dis-
erses the run-off and captures the silt lost from the tilled strip
bove it. Strip cropping is both practical and artistic, as may be
een in Figure 75.

**Horizontal
tillage
checks
slope
channeling**

IGURE 75. *Strip cropping is a special application of contour tillage, employing strips of
lose growing crops (hay) alternating with inter-tilled crops (corn). Run-off from a heavy
ain can cut to ribbons a long slope planted entirely to corn, but it cannot gather great
lestructive force across a few rows. Any wash that does occur will be intercepted and
lispersed by the next hay strip below. The sweeping curves of strip cropping harmonize
ith the natural design of the land. Squares and corners are conspicuously rare in nature.
S.C.S. photo.)*

Another device for controlling slope wash and conserving water is a system of terraces or diversion channels—almost but not quite accordant with contours, so that the slight pitch will lead water off laterally instead of running over the terrace ridge (7). There is no essential difference between a field terrace and a diversion channel except that the latter is a larger structure with a broader trough, to discharge uncommonly heavy run-off. See in Figure 76 how a channel-type terrace catches water, spreads it out, and causes it to soak into the soil.

Terracing has been the object of much experimentation to determine the most effective construction under various conditions of soil, slope, climate and cultural utilization. Early attempts with terracing failed because the ridges were built exactly on the contour, with both troughs and ridges too steep and narrow. Heavy rains broke over the ridges and cut them to pieces. They were obstructions to normal tillage operations, with little compensation in the form of water storage. Field testing evolved the broad "easy" terrace now in vogue, which discharges excess water laterally into pre-planned and permanent disposal channels such as the one pictured in Figure 77 (8 and 9). It has extensive storage and soakage area for water, and interferes very little with mechanized tillage. Terracing has recast the rural scene in many parts of America, and given many communities a new lease on life. The word "contour" has become important in the American language. Many who cannot read it know its practical application. Many others must learn.

Contour tillage serves either preventive or corrective purposes, depending upon the timeliness of its employment. In American history it will rank high among the great scientific achievements of the 20th century. We may add new variants, such as stubble mulching and sub-tillage (10) to take fuller advantage of its soil and water conserving capabilities, but the simple, basic, concept remains constant: *restrain and detain run-off at its origin, and both soil and water will be conserved.*

Gullies respond to blocking and planting

Gullies respond to blocking and planting despite their forbidding aspect. Only against the cavernous kind with precipitous walls are man's efforts to erase often frustrated. Some gullies initiated by men will probably scar the earth long after the human species has departed. About the best we can do with the man-made canyons is to deflect run-off away from their heads so it cannot tumble over the brink and undermine the walls. We can hope to slow down headward destruction and perhaps even arrest it after a time, but to fill in and smooth over all the mon-

FIGURE 76. *The channel-type terrace conserves both soil and water. It impedes erosive run-off and spreads the water over a wide soaking area. It presents no serious obstacle to normal tillage operations, including harvesting. This one was photographed in Louisiana.* (S.C.S. photo.)

FIGURE 77. *In many situations, grassed waterways are the best means whereby converging run-off may be removed without scarring the land. They can be made to produce good cuttings of hay, as shown here on a farm in Illinois.* (S.C.S. photo.)

strous holes already dug would be prohibitive in cost, if no physically impossible.

V-shaped or U-shaped gullies may be arrested and graduall refilled by constructing "check dams" or gully blocks across then at appropriate intervals, closely spaced on steep slopes and far ther apart on gentler ones (11). Each block establishes an artificia base level and causes debris to fill in behind it. For maximum re sults the blocks must be built first across the head of the gully then progressively farther down its length. With gullies as with streams, beheading gets positive results. Figure 78 shows one way of doing it.

Hardy vines, grasses, shrubs, or trees can effectively stop gullying under certain conditions, particularly if active gullying be arrested with dams prior to planting. In the Southeast, kudzu and honeysuckle have stopped many gullies without any aid be yond the planting. Trees wrought the change observable in Fig ures 79 and 80. Either process can quickly blanket a deep earth

FIGURE 78. *Decapitation is the first step in subduing a gully. This conquest was begun by diverting run-off away from the head. Log dams, or blocks, were then built, commencing near the head. Tons of boulders were deposited below each spillway to absorb the impact of water. The sides of the gully were sloped, and planted to black locust, small grain, and lespedeza. The full treatment was completely successful, resulting in a stabilized condition soon after its application. This was a public project near Spartanburg, South Carolina.* (S.C.S. photo.)

Figures 79 and 80. *Quick rehabilitation of gullied land may be prohibitive in cost, but the process of natural healing can be facilitated by planting hardy species. Black locust made the gain shown here in only 3½ years, and the scene continued to improve. This transformation was wrought on a farm in Illinois.* (S.C.S. photos.)

wound, and heal it in a few years. Perhaps honeysuckle is too efficient; farmers who have fought it as a weed have been known to reckon gullying a lesser evil. However, now that they can kill the vine with toxic sprays, they should be less prejudiced.

Repair of dissected land involves engineering

Land completely dissected by gullying is extremely difficult to rehabilitate by damming and planting because each gully requires its own series of dams or blocks, and the intervening raw ridges slough and crumble so rapidly that plants cannot attach themselves securely. Stabilization by vegetation takes a long time.

Only drastic measures can quickly mend dissected, denuded land, and in many cases the costs are not justifiable in terms of recovered productivity. Where remaining earth materials have *substance* to warrant the expenditure the torn land can be contoured and terraced with a bulldozer or other heavy machinery, and stabilized so plants can take hold and begin the slow process of developing new soil in place of that which washed away. Without adequate private means or public assistance, an owner of man-made badlands may either view them with detachment or look the other way. He can help nature bind them with vegetation, but he cannot expect much gain from them during his lifetime. They may not be a legacy for his grandchildren to cherish.

Cultivation should enrich rather than impoverish

Soil abuse was once so nearly universal in the United States that we had almost come to accept shrinking production from aging fields as a foregone conclusion. But now we have determined that the age of a cultivated field has no significance as an index to its productivity. We must revamp our land-use psychology, and there are good indications that we will. No changing current of American thought could possibly be more prophetic. We have begun to employ our soils according to their quality. We have made some produce more abundantly than when they were broken. But we have done it the hard way, with artificial means and narrow perspective. When we learn to enlist the natural forces ready to serve us and view the soil as a sacred trust we dare not violate, then shall we be on the only sure road toward soil enrichment coincident with continuous crop production. Genuine soil conservation cannot be realized without that approach and that conviction.

Replenishment should approximate withdrawal

If enrichment by tillage be temporarily waived, at least replenishment should approximate the withdrawal of essential elements. Anything less than that must be deemed uneconomical and antisocial. Until we know exactly what we take from the soil in each crop we harvest we cannot be sure of restoring the losses entirely, but we certainly can make general restitution insofar as we do know the food requirements of that crop. By scientific analyses of soil and plant tissue we are narrowing the margin of chance (12). In their annual farm operations good farmers place replenishment on a par with yield, knowing that future years will compensate.

Any alert, experienced farmer recognizes the inherent advantages of general farming or animal industry over cash-cropping. He knows that in meat, milk, or eggs he sells less soil off his farm than in wheat, hay, or cotton. One such farmer, on being praised for his lush meadows, explained very candidly, "I sell only what can walk off the place. My biggest loss is the phosphorus in the bones." Of course our friend lost more than phosphorus, but he voiced a sound idea in soil conservation. The waste of energy incurred by converting vegetable calories into animal calories represents economy in terms of soil.

Thorough tillage stimulates soil organisms and soil processes that convert soil material into plant food, thereby promoting productivity. By the same token, good tillage hastens the assimilation and availability of materials contributed to the soil, artificially or otherwise. Unless the supply of raw materials for plant foods be replenished, tillage simply pirates the nutrients until they are exhausted. *Piratical cultivation has exhausted many of our soils.* We have thus overworked one function of tillage and neglected another. Only when we equalize or reconcile the two can we perpetuate the fertility of our crop land; neither theorizing nor experimentation will suffice. Farm owners and farm operators must determine that cultivation "doubles in brass." Else the "orchestra" goes out of tune.

If ever a strong back and a weak mind qualified a man for farming that time has passed long ago. In order to make a fair profit, and at the same time keep the factory (the soil) in good repair, the modern farmer must be intelligent and well-informed. Increased mental requirements have not materially offset the need of a strong back, however. Mechanization has not done away with physical labor on the farm, as anyone who has plowed corn stubble with a tractor can attest. Keepers of arable soil need both brain and brawn to discharge their trust properly. Each must be planner, mechanic, accountant, producer, and conservator, all wrapped up in one. All of us depend upon their versatility, now and for the future.

Crop rotations promote soil balance and economic stability. The "single cash-crop culture" once dominant in several farming regions depleted the soil rapidly and afforded the farmer only one source of income. All the eggs were in one basket, a most precarious arrangement. Whenever the crop failed or the market

Crop rotations promote balance and stability

slumped the farmer had nothing with which to ease the pinch. When his soil weakened under repeated planting to the same crop without respite he found himself in a grave predicament.

A partial answer to both problems lay in *crop variety*—the several crops "rotated" from one field to another in a more or less regular sequence (13). Rotation schemes were nothing new to our "general" farmers, but to certain of the cash-crop specialists, such as wheat growers and cotton planters, they meant complete revision or replacement of the conventional system. Transition has been slow, but few areas remain in which some form of *cropping system* has not displaced the degrading single crop. In many places suitable rotations have become a standard practice. The five-year rotation shown in Figure 81 is only one of many that have become popular.

Diversified crops in well-ordered sequence benefit both soil and farmer in a number of ways, their inherent advantages variously manifest from one place to another. They vary from year to year the drain of any particular plant nutrient, thereby helping maintain better composition and physical condition of the soil. A good rotation helps maintain the supply of humus and nitrogen, keeps the soil protected more, if not all, of the time, and increases total yields. It counteracts the development of toxic substances,

FIGURE 81. *Crop rotations are of many different kinds, but every system helps conserve the soil and gives the farmer a safer economic base on which to operate.* (After F.B. 1981.)

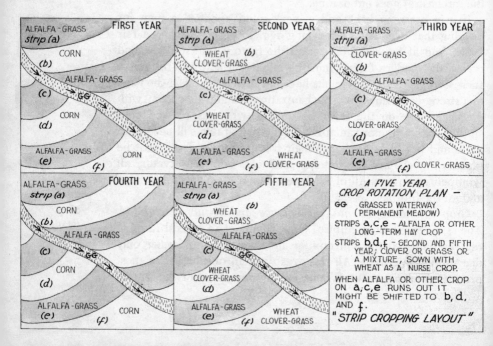

varies the feeding range of roots, helps control insects and diseases, and improves crop quality (14). It affords opportunity for better weed control, better use of fertilizer, and a more equitable seasonal distribution of labor requirements. By all these means, directly or indirectly, crop rotation plays a unique role in soil conservation (15). Aside from its assistance toward holding the soil and maintaining its fertility, it ensures the farmer a more regular income with which to operate.

Especially effective in a soil conserving rotation are the *close-growing grasses and legumes* sown for pasturage or meadow. A thick grass sod protects the surface against baking and washing. Its mass of roots bind the soil in place, open it to air and water, and add humus as the roots die and decay (16). The legumes (clover, alfalfa, lespedeza, and so on) penetrate the soil with their roots, and perform the distinctive service of enriching the soil with nitrogen taken from the air. Peanut or locust, herb or tree, leguminous plants possess special nitrogen-fixing equipment that places them in a class by themselves as soil builders (17). However, when they are grown as field crops in a rotation their full benefits cannot be realized unless they be plowed under or grazed. Good use of a legume may be seen in Figure 82. Harvested for hay and sold, their fixation of nitrogen may be poor compensation for their drain of potash and calcium. Farmers who grow peanuts for soil improvement and sell both nuts and vines cheat the soil and deceive themselves. Attractive prices for peanut oil, peanut hay, and peanut butter have often negated the good intent of peanut growing to conserve the soil.

Grasses and legumes are especially effective

Alfalfa holds top rank among our leguminous forage crops. It is a deep-rooted, hardy perennial that produces highly nutritious hay or silage. It is adapted to a wide range of temperature and moisture conditions, and flourishes for several years from one sowing, under favorable conditions. Its dense, rapid growth requires frequent cutting, making it an excellent weed eradicator. A major detraction from its popularity is its requirement of a "sweet" soil and a generous supply of calcium. It abhors acidity, and will not make hay on acid soil without the application of lime.

Idleness will not energize the soil, nor will soil be idle unless it is too dry or too cold for anything to grow in it. (Summer fallowing to store moisture in dry farming is not idleness in this sense.) Fields left untended get no rest unless they are too weak to support plant growth. Weeds (plants out of place) soon occupy the "idle" space, and draw upon the store of nutrients in the soil. A rank stand of weeds can tax the soil quite as heavily as a crop

Idleness will not energize the soil

grown for harvest. Soil substance given to the production of noxious weeds usually represents flagrant waste of a natural resource.

Something may be said in defense of weeds, because they are not altogether evil. Under certain conditions they are genuine assets. A good weed cover can be a very strong deterrent to erosion, by either wind or water. It can also add considerable organic matter to the soil, particularly if it be plowed under when it is lush and green. A lesser virtue of weeds is their indication of soil fertility. Pity the farmer who has no weed problem, because his soil probably cannot bring forth much of what he sows either.

There can be no vacation for soil during the growing season unless it be kept bare by tillage, a dangerous invitation to erosive forces. Furthermore, such an enforced rest period cannot energize the soil except as it may store needed moisture and encourage the conversion of soil contents into available plant foods. Like a typical vacation, it is often more exhausting than energizing.

Cover crops afford more than soil protection

Problems unsolved by fallowing or idleness are most adequately met by keeping a vegetative cloak on the soil as much of the time as possible. Plantings made for the purpose of protecting the soil are referred to as *cover crops* (Figure 82). When they are sown into another crop being grown for harvest, as between rows of corn after the last cultivation, they are called *catch crops*. In any case, plants that grow quickly and produce a thick, heavy stand are preferable (18). Suitable species comprise a long list, some adapted for winter, others for summer cover. Their service is particularly valuable during such time as a regular money crop does not occupy the space, whenever or wherever heavy snow or deep freezing fails to defend the soil (19).

Cover crops are not only protective while they grow, they are also a valuable source of humus and fertilizer (green manure). A heavy stand plowed under or worked into the soil adds many tons of organic material per acre, an excellent substitute for barnyard manure (20).

Their nitrogen-fixing characteristic makes annual legumes particularly desirable for use as cover crops. A great variety of clovers, peas, and beans have come into popular favor. Many of our foreign plant introductions have gained American citizenship through outstanding service as leguminous cover and green manure crops. Crotalaria, kudzu, lespedeza, and ladino clover are solid though foreign-born citizens.

Organic wastes belong to the soil

Organic wastes are of the soil, and belong to it (21). Unless they be returned to the soil, it loses its power to produce. They

FIGURE 82. *Cover crops protect the soil after clear tillage. Legumes are favored because they add nitrogen while also giving good protection. This vetch in a Texas pecan orchard was plowed under as green manure.* (S.C.S. photo.)

are the vital fiber of the soil, whence, in life, all organisms draw their strength. But in our artificial, mechanized, culture we are liable to overlook that salient fact, and distinguish too precisely between the quick and the dead. We are prone to forget the endless chain of life that transcends our creature existence. Starvation taught the Chinese to respect it. Let us profit by their experience before we, too, feel the sting of that lash.

Organic wastes are of many kinds, and not all are wasted from the standpoint of proper return to the soil. However, entirely too many, defamed as *"trash,"* or *"filth,"* or *"refuse,"* are conveniently disposed of or destroyed, and diverted from their proper destination, the soil.

Organic wastes include the garbage that pollutes our streams, the pile of leaves burned in the alley, the sawdust heaps that smolder at sawmill sites, the straw-piles burned after threshing to destroy weed seeds and clear the space for plowing, and a host of others. The man who buries the garbage in the garden, or makes compost of leaves he rakes, or spreads a straw pile as manure after it has settled and rotted, deserves a badge of distinction as a conservator.

A current trend that bears watching is the "salvage" of crop residues for fabrication into marketable products: wall board from cane bagasse or corn stalks; furfural from corncobs and hulls of oats, cottonseed, and rice; "soft-grit" blasting material of ground-up corncobs for cleaning precision machine parts;

FIGURE 83. *Crop residues belong to the soil whence they came. They help to protect the soil and increase humus content.* (S.C.S. photo.)

plastics from "flour" of straws, stalks, cobs, hulls, or nut shells; corrugated shipping containers from small-grain straws; cigarette paper from seed-flax straw, paper pulp from wheat straw, and many, many others. American farmers produce an estimated 250 million tons of dry residues annually, of which about half may be available for industrial use (22). Can we spare them? Can our soils get along without them? We may discover that residues left on the ground as mulch, plowed under for humus, or used as litter for animals are more profitable in the long run than those sold off the farm for industrial utilization. The organic wastes shown in Figure 83 may be exactly where they belong—on the field that produced them.

Animal manures are the best fertilizers

There is probably no adequate alternate for *stable or barnyard manure as a soil builder and fertilizer,* and we are producing too little of the precious, odoriferous, stuff. When oxen, mules, or horses drew our farm implements we had much more manure and less area in need of it. Now, with autos and tractors replacing work animals (Figure 84), manure has become a scarce and costly commodity while the fields in need of it have expanded. A 20th century dilemma reposes in the fact that exhaust fumes from a tractor have no fertilizer value. The saving of crop area once used for animal feeds may be deceptive (see Figure 85).

More diversification of farming systems, to include considerable animal industry (beef, dairy, swine, sheep, poultry) is a sure way to offset our reduced numbers of work stock. Grazing animals help fertilize their pasture; but stall feeding with abundant litter or bedding to catch and absorb the wastes produces a greater volume of manure with more strength and a slower rate of decomposition and dissipation. The stable variety, spread on the land promptly upon removal from the stall, has no equal for soil improvement (23).

The alert farmer-conservator conserves even the manure with which he helps conserve his soil. He spreads it on the land raw (green), before it loses any of its strength. If he cannot apply it fresh from the stable, he stores it in a roofed, watertight pit until such time as he can best apply it. Manure piles that have lain in sun and rain until they have faded on top and burned (molded) inside have lost much of their power to reinforce the soil. Americans need a finer appreciation for the pungent odor of freshly-spread manure about a countryside. They could take lessons from their European cousins.

Commercial, chemical fertilizers cannot entirely replace manure and other organic material used to enrich and reinforce the soil.

Prepared concentrates resemble emergency rations

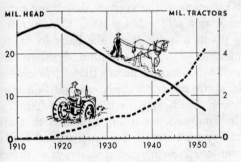

FIGURES 84 and 85. *Left: horses and mules, and tractors on farms as of January 1. Below: major uses of cropland.* (B.A.E. graphs.)

Farm mechanization has saved space once used to produce feed for horses and mules, but unfortunately tractor smoke has no fertilizer value.

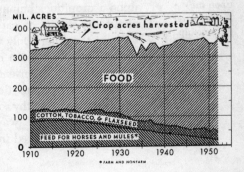

The organics fit better into the natural scheme of things, improving the soil community at the same time as they contribute to soil fertility. Almost squarely in contrast, the prepared concentrates give immediate (artificial) stimulation. They may be likened to the *emergency rations* in a soldier's field pack intended to tide him over when other food is temporarily unavailable. Used in a similar manner, commercial fertilizers serve a most valuable purpose in soil conservation, but when used indiscreetly they can sterilize more than they fertilize (24, 25).

Excessive use of chemicals can distort or destroy the biotic balance in the soil and reduce its powers of recuperation. Repeated applications can make a bad condition even worse, until finally each crop becomes entirely dependent upon a measured dosage calculated to mature it. Soil so abused degenerates into an inert, mineral mass, whence roots struggle to extract their measured rations and hold the plant upright for exposure to sunshine. Soil can be killed, and virtually embalmed, by excessive chemical applications.

Concentrates are invaluable when properly used. Exhausted soil can be helped with injections if the verdure they bring forth be converted into humus, *not* sold off the farm. Concentrates are excellent for giving plants a quick start (like baby foods) to put them ahead of competing weeds. Used cautiously, they can effectively make up specific deficiencies before those deficiencies become so acute that the entire soil is adversely affected. Soil conservation would be seriously handicapped without them (26, 27).

Lest the uninitiate be confused, let it be explained that all bagged and bought fertilizers are not of the concentrated kinds about which we have cautioned. Such natural materials as dried manure, cottonseed meal, bone meal, ground phosphate rock, and many others also come in bags—effective but expensive substitutes for stable manure and crop residues.

All depends upon the humus-water partnership

The success of other soil conserving measures is contingent upon a propitious humus-water partnership. Much has been said about the merits of each partner, but neither can be effective without the other. Only where there is sufficient humus to govern its receipt and release can soil water serve its full purpose as vehicle for plant nutrients; only where water is adequate but not excessive can humus develop normally from organic materials and maintain a healthy soil body.

There are many ways of fortifying the soil with humus. Whether it be worked into the soil or spread on the surface as a

FIGURE 86. *Sub-surface tillage and stubble mulching conserve both soil and water on our dry farmlands. Steel sweeps, drawn through below the surface, loosen the soil without turning it over. The half buried straw (stubble) improves water absorption and reduces the wind hazard. This picture was taken in Montana. (S.C.S. photo.)*

mulch, any kind of organic matter is raw material of humus (28, 29). A flat rejection of one method and acceptance of the other would be wrong because related factors vary widely from place to place. Farmers in the sub-humid and semiarid regions employ an innovation called "stubble-mulch" farming or "subtillage" wherein they loosen the soil by running blades through it several inches below the surface instead of turning it over as with a plow. The stubble, held at the surface and protruding above it, as shown in Figure 86, guards admirably against wind erosion, besides admitting and holding water effectively. The practice may prove desirable in other regions, but it would not be suitable in all areas.

If humus be abundant, how else may one strengthen the humus-water partnership? By *"water-spreading,"* another device which, as the term implies, involves spreading excess water over broader area in order that it may soak in where it would otherwise run off (30). Broad terrace basins and other contour depressions induce water soakage. Farm ponds in dammed-up gullies, or wherever the terrain favors them, accomplish water-spreading by holding back run-off so more of it soaks into the ground. Furrows such as those pictured in Figure 87 can be a crucial factor in stor-

FIGURE 87. *Contour furrows (listing) to catch winter precipitation can be a decisive factor in valleys of the dry West. This is New Mexico. (S.C.S. photo.)*

ing soil water where precipitation would be inadequate without them. Many soil conservation practices, specific in their apparent function, contribute to the dual purpose of enriching soil humus and moisture content, simultaneously *conserving both soil and water*. Those two major resources must be treated jointly, not independently.

For many of our soils the control of acidity is a necessary conservational measure. (Alkalinity is the crucial problem in certain portions of the dry West, and sulfur or gypsum the standard antidote) (31). The eastern forest soils tend to be naturally acid, their soluble alkaline compounds leached out by percolating water. Where the soil material is acid (silicious), and the forest deposits raw, acid humus through which the rain percolates, calcium is rapidly dissolved and carried away. Even soils derived from limestone and resting on a limestone base become highly acid. Fortunately, the condition is easily corrected where there is limestone beneath the soil.

It is a simple process to quarry the limestone, crush it or "burn" it, and spread it on the land. While it dissolves and passes through the soil, it counteracts acidity. That is exactly what is done in practice. Lime (calcium carbonate) is the neutralizer, and the competent land-user tests his soil at intervals to determine how much he should apply (32). He may prefer burned lime for

Calcium carbonate combats acidity

immediate reaction, or raw, ground or crushed lime for longer endurance. He may choose to "lime" with *basic slag,* the black, waste-bearing limestone flux from iron smelters. Thus, a waste that has purified one resource is salvaged to conserve another.

Liming can be a vital operation in the rehabilitation of depleted soil. The organic matter and humus added to give such soil "backbone" are themselves nitrogenous, and tend to be acid. Their beneficence may not be fully realized unless calcium carbonate is also added to complement them and combat acidity.

Last, but probably not least, soil conservation requires attention to the elusive *trace elements* that guard the health and fertility of soils in much the same manner as vitamins guard those qualities in humans and other animals. A perfect ratio of nitrogen, potash, phosphorus, and calcium is no guarantee of high productivity. Deficiency of a single trace element in a soil otherwise rich can cause critical deficiency in plants, and starve the animals that feed on those plants (33).

Study and research magnify our respect for the elusive trace elements

Cows graze themselves thin on knee-deep pasture unless the soil under the grass contains cobalt. Tung trees need zinc; citrus trees, manganese; apple trees, boron. The trace elements influence each other's effectiveness, and that of the major fertilizer materials. They make themselves felt in such minute quantities, and their functions are so delicate, that the novice should not tamper with them. Let the land user call an expert when he suspects "trace trouble." (34).

Since *one objective of soil conservation is maximum and permanent productivity,* the conservator should endeavor to understand the trace elements insofar as the soil chemist can advise him. If all ordinary applications achieve unsatisfactory results, one or more of the minor elements may be at fault. They exact thorough, scientific investigation. They comprise a challenging frontier in soil conservation. In them we may find many answers we cannot now propound.

We have always had among us men with "green thumbs" who, to the limits of their knowledge, would guard the soils they use as the priceless property those soils really are. But green thumbs have never attained a majority; the more numerous "plow-sow-reap" men have dominated our use of the land. From colonial times until recent date such men wasted our soils without restraint, often wantonly, sometimes of sheer necessity.

We have made gratifying progress toward conserving our soils

Soil depletion and erosion became such a menace to national strength and prosperity that the Congress determined to apply positive countermeasures. In 1933 it established a federal agency,

the Soil Erosion Service, to cope with the problem. Soon the name
was very appropriately changed to the Soil Conservation Service
to which we owe such gratifying progress toward conserving our
soils that we proudly recount the attainments. Figure 88 shows
how extensive the organization for soil defense has become.

As of July 1954, 2556 soil conservation districts had been
established in the 48 states. Fourteen states were completely
covered by districts (Figure 88). The Soil Conservation Service
was assisting in 21 additional conservation districts. All those
districts (2,577) contained almost 950 million acres of land in more
than 4,743,000 farms and ranches. About 82 per cent of the land
in farms and 88 per cent of the farms in the United States were
in districts (35). Such achievement, most of it in one decade
merits the acclaim ordinarily reserved for victory in war. We are
winning the soil conservation battle, although erosion still costs
us an estimated $3,844,000,000 annually (36).

Our superb beginning foreshadows ultimate success, but much
remains to be done. Our plans are well projected, but they should
be expanded, both in scope and in vision. Soil conservation on an
annual basis can be little more than pretense; on a ten-year basis
it can do some good; but a life-time is too short to realize its full
accomplishment. Our time concepts must be extended. The Soil
Conservation Service plans to complete the organizational and
technical part of the task by 1970 (36), but our land users must
carry it through to fruition, supported by the American public.

More of our people, urban and rural, must see the intimate
relationship between soil conservation, individual well-being, and
collective security. They must learn that straight rows and square
corners violate the natural scheme of things, that the soil supports all of us, and is, therefore the property of society, despite
its private ownership. Soil abuse must be counted a public affront;
soil conservation, a meritorious public service.

FIGURE 88. *Cooperative organization for soil defense has made phenomenal progress, and the coverage continues to spread. This map shows only the areas under S.C.S. organization. Several states, notably Missouri, have excellent programs of their own.*

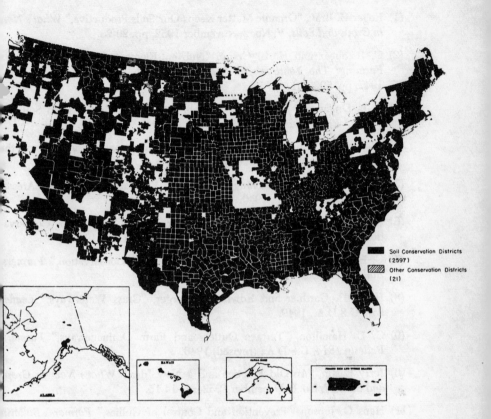

Soil Conservation Districts (2597)

Other Conservation Districts (21)

CHAPTER 8: REFERENCES CITED BY NUMBER

(1) Roger H. Bray, "Organic Matter Keeps Our Soils Productive," *What's New in Crops and Soils,* V, No. 2, November 1952, pp. 20-23.

(2) C. B. Shear and H. L. Crane, "Nutrient-Element Balance," *Science in Farming: The Yearbook of Agriculture, 1943-1947.* Washington, D.C., 1947, pp. 592-601.

(3) F. L. Duley and J. C. Russel, "Stubble-Mulch Farming to Hold Soil and Water," *Farmers' Bulletin 1997,* U.S.D.A., 1948.

(4) Wendell C. Johnson, "Stubble-Mulch Farming on Wheatlands of the Southern High Plains," *Circular No. 860,* U.S.D.A., August 1950.

(5) Sydney Franklin, "Mulching to Establish Vegetation on Eroded Areas," *Leaflet 190,* U.S.D.A., 1940.

(6) Harold E. Tower and Harry H. Gardner, "Strip Cropping for Conservation and Production," *Farmers' Bulletin 1981,* U.S.D.A., 1946.

(7) C. L. Hamilton, "Terracing for Soil and Water Conservation," *Farmers Bulletin 1789,* U.S.D.A., 1943.

(8) Harry H. Gardner and Edwin Freyburger, "Grass Waterways," *Leaflet 257,* U.S.D.A., 1949.

(9) C. L. Hamilton, "Terrace Outlets and Farm Drainageways," *Farmers Bulletin 1814,* U.S.D.A., (revised) 1946.

(10) Jerry Eastin, "An Old Practice and a New Idea," *What's New in Crops and Soils,* V, No. 3, December 1952, pp. 14-15.

(11) Hans G. Jepson, "Prevention and Control of Gullies," *Farmers' Bulletin 1813,* U.S.D.A., 1944.

(12) Michael Peech and Hans Platenius, "Tests of Plants and Soils," *Science in Farming,* pp. 583-591.

(13) Clyde E. Leighty, "Crop Rotation," *Soils and Men: The Yearbook of Agriculture, 1938,* pp. 406-430.

(14) R. Y. Bailey and W. M. Nixon, "Rotations for Problem Fields," *Grass: The Yearbook of Agriculture, 1948,* pp. 195-199.

(15) R. E. Uhland, "Rotations in Conservation," *Science in Farming,* pp. 527-536.

(16) R. E. Uhland, "Grass and the Yields of Cash Crops," *Grass,* pp. 191-194.

(17) A. J. Pieters, "Legumes in Soil Conservation Practices," *Leaflet 163,* U.S.D.A., (reprinted) 1949.

18) Walter V. Kell and Roland McKee, "Cover Crops for Soil Conservation," *Farmers' Bulletin 1758*, U.S.D.A., 1942.

19) J. H. Stallings, "Continuous Plant Cover—The Key to Soil and Water Conservation," *Journal of Soil and Water Conservation*, VIII, No. 2, March 1953, pp. 63-68.

20) A. J. Pieters and Roland McKee, "The Use of Cover and Green-Manure Crops," *Soils and Men*, pp. 431-444.

21) Myron S. Anderson, "Wastes That Improve Soil," *Crops in Peace and War: The Yearbook of Agriculture, 1950-1951*, pp. 877-882.

22) S. I. Aronousky, L. E. Schniepp and Elbert C. Lathrop, "Using Residues to Conserve Resources," *Crops in Peace and War*, pp. 829-842.

23) Robert M. Salter and C. J. Schoolenberger, "Farm Manure," *Soils and Men*, pp. 445-461.

24) Colin W. Whittaker, Bailey E. Brown and J. Richard Adams, "Ammonium Nitrate for Crop Production," *Circular No. 771*, U.S.D.A., February 1948.

25) E. N. Paulson and L. R. Swarner, "What's in the Soil?" *The Reclamation Era*, XXXVIII, No. 1, January 1952, p. 8.

26) F. W. Parker, "Use of Nitrogen Fertilizers," *Science in Farming*, pp. 561-565.

27) W. H. Pierre, "Phosphate Fertilizers," *Science in Farming*, pp. 554-560.

28) "The Use of Sawdust for Mulches and Soil Improvement," *Circular No. 891*, U.S.D.A., November 1951.

29) Robert A. Schrack and Russell L. Albright, "Chips on the Land," *American Forests*, LV, No. 5, May 1949.

30) D. B. Krimgold, "Managing Surface Runoff," *Science in Farming*, pp. 537-540.

31) H. E. Hayward, "The Control of Salinity," *Science in Farming*, pp. 547-553.

32) Emil Truog, "The Liming of Soils," *Science in Farming*, pp. 566-576.

33) Lionel James Picton, *Nutrition and the Soil*, Devin-Adair Company, New York, 1949.

34) Matthew Drosdoff, "The Use of Minor Elements," *Science in Farming*, pp. 577-582.

35) *Soil Conservation Districts: Status of Organization by States, Approximate Acreage, and Farms in Organized Districts*, S.C.S., July 1954.

36) Hugh H. Bennett, *Progress in Soil Conservation*. S.C.S., Beltville, Maryland, October 1951.

VALUABLE MATERIALS

WATERSHED PROTECTION

WILDLIFE HABITAT

ENRICHMENT OF LANDSCAPE

REGULATION OF STREAM FLOW

MODERATION OF WINDS AND TEMPERATURE

INSPIRATION AND RECREATION

Forest Exploitation

forest products and forest influences
are indispensable to our American culture

SOILS HAVE VALUE ONLY IN TERMS OF THEIR PRODUCT—VEGETATION—
and forests represent the most conspicuous vegetative development. They flourish where soil, water, and sunshine in good combination afford a favorable habitat for plants. Trees are the aristocrats of the plant world, and a community of them composes the "high society" called forest. That society claims for itself those environments favorable to it, and relegates to grasses, forbs, and shrubs, those areas climatically or otherwise less hospitable.

Except in rainy tropical regions, where enervating heat and humidity have retarded cultural progress, forest cover generally indicates conditions conducive to a high order of human occupance. Population densities, industrial and commercial developments, in the modern world pattern, show remarkable geographic coincidence with the arrangement of temperate forest regions. Deserts and semiarid grasslands stimulated man's initial rise from barbarism to an advanced state of civilization, but our modern Western culture matured in forests, not by chance, but by the liberal provision of human wants—food, shelter, fuel, and abundant raw materials for manufacture into other necessities.

Forests provide a great variety of useful materials, many of them indispensable to our every-day living. Without the bounty of our forests, we could not have gained the superior economic position our nation enjoys, nor might we envisage maintenance of national prestige in the future.

Out of our woods come tall *poles* on which to string lines for communication and power transmission, *piling* to support wharves

Forests provide a great variety of useful materials

185

and other structures over water or soft earth, *cross-ties* to support railroads and heavy traffic, *logs* for lumber and veneer with hundreds of uses, *bolts* for cooperage, shingles, matches, pencils, and a hundred other purposes. From our woods come *posts* for fences with which to protect our crops and control our animals, *timbers* to shore up mine passages and excavations, *cordwood* for fuel and pulp. From our woods come *bark* for tanning leather, *pitch* for naval stores, *sap* for sugar and sirup, *nuts* for food and feed and flavoring, *raw materials* for goods and services upon which our economic standards and social customs depend.

From wood comes paper, cellulose, cellophane, rayon, explosives, alcohol, dye, medicine, charcoal, acetic acid, tar, plastics, and other industrial products. On paper made of wood we print our newspapers, magazines, books, all sorts of informative and educational matter, our records, contracts, and valuable documents. On wooden railroad ties we travel for business and pleasure and ship the bulk of our domestic commerce, much of it in wooden containers. Wood protects the lives of our miners, knocks all our home-runs in baseball, houses many of our people, adds the allure of rayon fabric to our ladies' attire, helps win our wars, helps furnish our homes, fences the scrubs from our thoroughbreds, and imparts the fine quality that distinguishes a violin from a fiddle.

The virtues and uses of forest products could not be listed, much less evaluated, on the pages in this book. We are constantly making substitutions, but we are even more rapidly developing new uses and greater requirements. We could not live normally and happily without them, yet thus far we have done little to ensure a perpetual supply.

Less tangible forest benefits have untold value

The incidental, indirect, and less tangible forest benefits have untold value, greater perhaps than the entire aggregate of all forest materials. Would any decent citizen, other than the gatherer and the vendor, hang a price tag on a Christmas tree or a wreath of greenery, when its true worth shows only in the sparkle of children's eyes? Could anyone place a monetary value on the aesthetic glory of New England's woods in autumn or the inspirational grandeur of the great trees on the Pacific Slope? Are not trees associated with the fondest childhood memories and the nobler thoughts of most Americans? Our forests would be invaluable to us without any utility other than their sentimental, psychological influences.

Forestry is unequalled as a means of conserving soil and water. Forests on our watersheds, often referred to as *"protective forests,"* prevent soil erosion, *detain surface waters* and release them flowing clear and regularly, and *replenish ground water reserves* by induced percolation. The deep soil under a healthy deciduous forest—may have storage capacity for 14½ inches of rain (1). Our best water reservoirs are those that *grow* about the headwaters; not the ones *built* down-stream. Without *green storage*, be it forest or sod, above them, man-made reservoirs can be only moderately effective and short-lived. A major portion of our forest land needs no commendation to the conservator beyond its function in the regulation of stream flow, the prevention of stream pollution and silting, and the prevention or moderation of floods!

Many forms of wildlife are forest dwellers, and they thrive best where their forest habitat remains intact and healthy. A vigorous forest harbors an abundant population of birds, game animals, and lesser fauna. In clear, cool forest streams and lakes live choice species of fish. In and about those waters live waterfowl and fur-bearers. Bear or beaver, moose or mink, turkey or partridge, fox, deer, or hare—big game and small keep to wooded places more than to the open. Hunting, fishing, trapping, or nature study is generally more challenging and rewarding in the forest than outside it. Woodlands are about as important to wildlife conservation as they are to the conservation of water and soil. For that reason sportsmen are often enthusiastic, if not always proficient, forest conservators. They recognize that forestry improves hunting and fishing by improving wildlife habitats.

Perhaps no other environmental attribute has exerted so potent an influence over American history as have the great forests to which our forest-bred ancestors from Europe laid claim in the New World. Our forefathers virtually wrought a nation out of wood. Trees were to them both help and hindrance. They cut them and burned them to clear land for crops. They built their houses of logs, furnished them and heated them with wood. They bridged the streams with timbers, and floored, walled, and roofed the bridges with planking. They blocked streams with wooden (crib) dams to develop water power with which to saw lumber, grind meal, and forge tools. They traveled in wooden boats and wooden wagons. Their plows had wooden beams, and they drew them with oxen under wooden yokes. Even their household utensils were largely of wood. They hafted with wood the axes for chopping their way into the continent. Wood was both obstacle and facility.

The colonists nurtured our infant nation on wood. The forests yielded the wherewithal to enact the fabulous chapters of colonial

Our forefathers virtually wrought a nation out of wood

Wooden ships
carried wooden
cargoes

commerce and seamanship. From the forests came the timber, and planking, the masts and spars, the pitch and tar with which to seal the seams. Wooden ships carried wooden cargoes, and the European market was America's plum. We shipped masts and spars and naval stores as fast as we could, but demand exceeded supply. We built ships for fishing and whaling, ships to carry a rapidly expanding foreign trade, ships for a powerful Navy, ships to sell to our commercial rivals across the Atlantic.

Before the advent of steam power and steel hulls during the last quarter of the 19th century, our wooden men-of-war, mounting iron cannons, secured our position as a formidable naval power. Our sleek clipper ships outsailed everything else afloat. Even now wooden boats bring in much of our fish, and wooden bottoms carry a considerable portion of our commerce.

The deep,
dense forests
seemed
inexhaustible

To the early settlers along our eastern seaboard the deep, dense forest seemed inexhaustible. They found only limited, scattered clearings, and the pristine wilderness stretched westward beyond the farthest horizon they could comprehend. Who might have foreseen that the tremendous expanse of standing timber would be decimated in a hundred years? (See Figure 89.) Apparently there was wood for every conceivable purpose, and wood to burn! Fire, which has since become a major menace to our forests, was then an effective tool for penetrating and subduing them. Burning was neither malicious nor wasteful. It was an expedient by which men carved fields and farms out of the wilderness and forced the sylvan frontier.

Settlement
chopped,
sawed, and
burned itself
into the
land

Settlement chopped and sawed and burned its way westward into the interior. In many places, notably in the broad-leaved forests of the southeastern highlands, it was convenient to kill the trees by girdling, thus admitting sunlight for crops planted among the weathering trunks. Farms spread westward into the great forest. Crops displaced trees, cows evicted the deer, roosters crowed where ruffed grouse once drummed, men and their tamed retinue dispersed the wild things and usurped their domain. Wild fowl and other game, without which the pioneers would have starved, shrank before the advance of saw and axe and musket. Civilization subdued the wilderness.

Halfway across the continent, settlement was at the expense of forest. Trees and men were mortal enemies, and the human conquest was altogether too thorough. Forests retreated to lands undesirable for cultivation. Game grew scarce, streams waxed rampageous and muddy, and despoliation continued. Halfway across the continent, forests helped and hindered the progress of

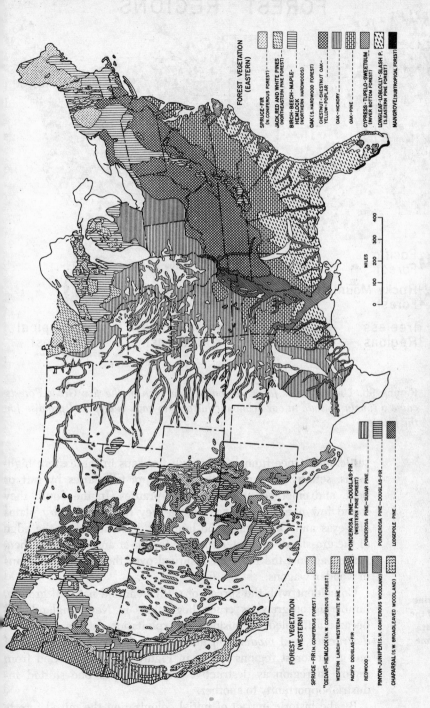

FOREST VEGETATION
(EASTERN)

SPRUCE-FIR (N. CONIFEROUS FOREST)

JACK, RED AND WHITE PINES
(NORTHEASTERN PINE FOREST)

BIRCH-BEECH-MAPLE-
HEMLOCK
(NORTHERN HARDWOODS)

OAK (S. HARDWOOD FOREST)

CHESTNUT-CHESTNUT OAK-
YELLOW-POPLAR

OAK-HICKORY

OAK-PINE

CYPRESS-TUPELO-SWEETGUM
(RIVER BOTTOM FOREST)

LONGLEAF-LOBLOLLY-SLASH P.
(S. EASTERN PINE FOREST)

MANGROVE (SUBTROPICAL FOREST)

FOREST VEGETATION
(WESTERN)

SPRUCE-FIR (N. CONIFEROUS FOREST)

"CEDAR"-HEMLOCK (N.W. CONIFEROUS FOREST)

WESTERN LARCH-WESTERN WHITE PINE

PACIFIC DOUGLAS-FIR

REDWOOD

PINYON-JUNIPER (S.W. CONIFEROUS WOODLAND)

CHAPARRAL (S.W. BROADLEAVED WOODLAND)

PONDEROSA PINE-DOUGLAS-FIR
(WESTERN PINE FOREST)

PONDEROSA PINE-SUGAR PINE

PONDEROSA PINE-DOUGLAS-FIR

LODGEPOLE PINE

MILES
0   100   200   300   400

FIGURE 89. *Forest vegetation of the United States.* (Adapted by F.S. from the Shantz and Zon map, "Natural Vegetation," in the *Atlas of American Agriculture.*)

FOREST REGIONS

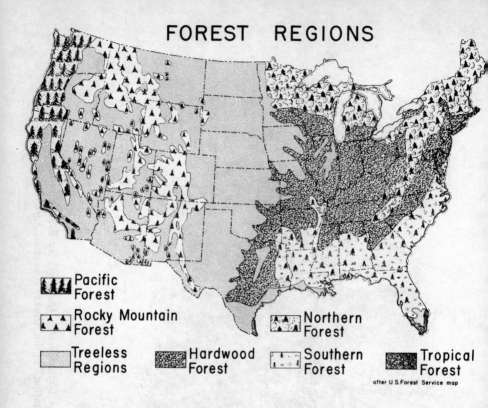

Pacific Forest

Rocky Mountain Forest

Treeless Regions

Hardwood Forest

Northern Forest

Southern Forest

Tropical Forest

after U.S.Forest Service map

FIGURE 90. *United States forest regions. From each of the five Great Forests came a timely episode in our economic history; in each is a special promise for the future.*

settlement. Once funneled through the gaps in the eastern highlands, settlers went down the Mississippi tributaries by raft or boat, and emerged upon the open prairies. In the South they found few natural openings before they reached the dry plains of Texas and Oklahoma. The human tide hesitated at the edge of the grasslands to muster courage for the strange crossing; then, braced against the forest, it resurged over the unwooded plains in wooden wagons.

Lumbering invaded the five great forests one by one

Coincident with the spread of settlement and national growth, lumbering outgrew its crude beginnings in New England and became a full-fledged business of exploitation. It was *extractive, destructive,* and *moderately lucrative;* and it invaded all *five* of our great forest regions shown in Figure 90. It proceeded from region to region as destructive exploitation in one shifted industrial opportunity to another.

By the historic impact of initial colonization the mixed forests of New England were the first to be logged commercially.

American lumbering emerged from the colonial sawmills, commencing with white pine, hemlock and spruce in northerly areas, and yellow poplar and chestnut southward. Then, as now, leading lumber species were softwoods, mainly conifers. Oaks and other hardwoods contributed ship timbers, tight cooperage, furniture and implement parts from the beginning, but their mixed stands and specialized uses spared them from the main assault. The specific gravity of green hardwood logs also discouraged their cutting during the era when logs were almost universally floated to the mill, down the stream that drove the saw. Mean paradox, indeed, that the waters regulated by forest were the prime facility for forest removal! Sawmills were our first commercial application of water power, probably as early as 1631 (2, p. 439), and water power helped make lumbering a top-flight American industry.

Northeastern white pine ruled the shifts and fortunes of American lumbering for more than 200 years (2, p. 438). In quest of that prized species, major logging operations shifted from Maine to New York, to Pennsylvania, and on in turn to Michigan, Wisconsin, and Minnesota.

After the Civil War the famed pineries of the Upper Lakes region dominated the American lumber industry for more than a quarter century. The mythical Paul Bunyan and his great blue ox, Babe, handled huge pine logs like match sticks and sent them down the rivers in gigantic "drives." Bemidji, Minnesota claims Paul Bunyan as a native son and celebrates his fantastic mythical career.

Paul Bunyan logged the North Woods

Cutting was done in winter when the cold north country lay frozen and snow-covered. Good wages lured rough-and-ready lumberjacks away from civilization to the isolation of remote logging camps. During the short winter days they rent the crisp air with the ring of axes, the swish of crosscut saws, the crash of falling trees, loud shouts of "timber," and profanity as keen-edged as the axe bits. The sights, if not the sounds, are preserved in such pictures as Figures 91 and 92.

With large teams of horses they hauled the great logs in great pyramidal loads secured with "log-chains" to wide sleighs with steel-shod runners (Figure 92). They piled them systematically, either on a frozen stream, or on its bank whence they could tumble them into the water after the ice went out. Men called "drivers" rode the logs downstream to the sawmill, guiding them with pike-poles or peavies to prevent stranding or jamming. When jams did occur the drivers broke them up promptly to start the logs moving again before the drive became hopelessly tangled.

FIGURE 91. *Winter logging in the northern pineries, 1904. A team of horses skidding a large pine log on a "go-devil."* (Courtesy Minnesota Historical Society.)

FIGURE 92. *Horse-and-sleigh hauling in the northern pineries, 1892. The load pictured was 21 feet high, 20 feet wide, and contained 31,480 board feet. Jack pine was a weed species when the Upper Lakes Region was originally logged.* (Courtesy Forest Products History Foundation, Minnesota.)

Not infrequently it was necessary to loosen a jam with dynamite. The whole system was "rough"—on both men and timber. Many logs sound on the stump reached the sawmill badly battered or splintered.

Before the turn of the century the South became prominent in lumbering, and by 1910 it outranked the depleted northern pineries as a source of lumber. Southern yellow pine took the place of northern white pine. Longleaf became the leading lumber species, and held sway for approximately as long as had white pine before it. Longleaf and slash (pitch pines) were the source of our naval stores, but lumbering outranked turpentining, and the resinous trees were felled for lumber. Northern capital and equipment invaded the "Piney Woods," took out the finest specimens, and destroyed any others that stood in the way.

Yankees helped slash the southern "Piney Woods"

Never before nor since have men so quickly and ruthlessly "slashed" a forest as they did the southern coniferous forest, the most extensive of its kind. Rebel or Yankee, the southern lumber baron operated under a "cut out and get out" policy. Labor was cheap and plentiful, the terrain flat to gently rolling, and the weather never severe. Techniques of logging and sawing had improved, at least insofar as speed was the criterion of efficiency. Saws were largely steam-driven, the boilers fired with slab and cull logs. (Many logs then used for fuel would be considered high-grade today.) So thorough was the extraction that such a stand of longleaf as shown in Figure 93 is now rare.

The remarkable stands of longleaf, slash, shortleaf, and loblolly were soon cut out, southern yellow pine lost its pre-eminence, mills closed down, and the transient, extractive industry sought new realms to exploit and desecrate. Had not the swamp environment discouraged its logging, the rot-resistant bald cypress would certainly have fared no better than the pines.

Next to bear the brunt of axe and saw was the magnificent, virgin forest of the Pacific Northwest. Douglas fir (Figure 94), in the royal line of conifers, succeeded to the crown relinquished by longleaf pine. In the new "court" were redwood, western white pine, sugar pine, western hemlock, and several other tall timber blue bloods. By 1930 the center of lumbering had shifted diagonally across the United States from southeast to northwest.

Despite rugged terrain and remoteness from market, the Pacific coast forest suffered mass attack while our Doughboys were fighting World War I in Europe. Opening of the Panama Canal in 1914 precipitated full-scale assault against the heaviest stands of timber on the continent. Water transport made western lumber

Despite remoteness and difficult terrain, the Pacific Northwest suffered mass attack

competitive in our eastern markets. Lumber from the Northwest has constituted a major item of Canal freight ever since.

In the Northwest, logging became highly technical and mechanized in order to handle giant trees in rough topography. Tractors and power yarding machinery have all but replaced horses and hand labor; chain saws have replaced the back-breaking crosscuts. Today improvements of techniques and equipment are continually increasing the speed and efficiency of logging operations. The cutting of trees has become big business, involving high finance. From the generations of experience that evolved the modern methods came also a certain respect for conservational applications. The modern logger operates under legal restrictions designed to protect his business against suicide.

The Rockies closed the lumber circuit

Latest contributor to our lumber industry is the Rocky Mountain forest region, yielding western white pine from its northerly areas and the desirable ponderosa pine from widely scattered stands (Figure 95). Logging of the Rocky Mountain slopes completes the regional circuit of soft-wood lumbering in the United States. We have cut a wide swath about the nation; but, the reaping done, we are now concerned mainly with gleaning. To appease our hunger for lumber we have shipped it by sea halfway around the continent and then hauled it overland more than halfway across

FIGURE 93. *Virgin stand of longleaf pine about 125 years old near Hattiesburg, Mississippi. Southern yellow pine held the lumber championship only briefly, but it continues among the "big-time" saw-timber sources.* (B. W. Muir, F.S., photo.)

FIGURE 94. *A centuries-old stand of Douglas fir in the Pacific Northwest. The mature tree crop should be harvested so that a new generation can take its place.* (Photo courtesy Weyerhaeuser Sales Company.)

FIGURE 95. *Mature stand of ponderosa pine, a late addition to the royal line of lumber species. Ponderosa pine is an important species in the Rocky Mountain region, although this stand is in California.* (Western Pine Association—A.F.P.I. photo.)

for delivery. We have so thoroughly exploited our virgin timber that little of it remains anywhere at any price. We have cut out and gotten out until there is no place to go.

From Maine to Washington State the original cut was wondrously rich, and its taking shamefully extravagant as viewed in retrospect. However, from a practical point of view the initial logging of our conifers was simply good business at an opportune time. The trees were ripe, and the demand was strong. Then as now, profit was the motive of lumbermen, and a few of them got rich. However, competition was keen, and the market accepted only the best. The economic climate dictated many wasteful practices; the entrepreneur had little choice if he wished to operate. The old-time logger deserves our praise rather than our blame, for he produced a material that contributed more to the building of America than any other we possessed. Had he been faint-hearted and sentimental our rich stands of virgin timber would have fallen and rotted without benefit to anyone. Was it not better to salvage a portion, even by destructive methods, than to let all of it die of old age?

The timber harvest hastened America's rise to commercial prestige and industrial greatness. It helped build our navy, our fishing fleets and Merchant Marine. It helped bring the fertile Midwestern plains to fruition. It facilitated revival of the South after ravage and economic collapse. It was the dominant factor in the opening of the great Northwest. But the price was high— so high that the consequences cannot be quickly and easily evaluated or corrected. It compelled us to invoke forestry and conservation lest destructive extraction be complete and final. It became possible and necessary to estimate saw-timber reserves by groups and species (Figure 96).

In the wake of the sawmills—north, south, east, and west—lay charred and desolate cut-over lands. Most atrocious was the slashing of the South, where many millions of acres were ruthlessly logged and burned. Burning was not a necessary concomitant of logging, but what with deep pine "straw" on the forest floor, turpentine faces on the trees, wood-burning locomotives on logging spurs, steam engines in the mills, and careless workers smoking tobacco, fire stalked the lumber camps. Many a sawmill closed prematurely because fire claimed part of the cut; none could operate in a fixed location after all suitable logs had been cut within the radius of economical hauling.

When the tributary area had been cut over the operator closed down his mill and moved the "steel" to another site or another

Ripe crops made bountiful harvests

In the wake of the sawmills lay charred desolation

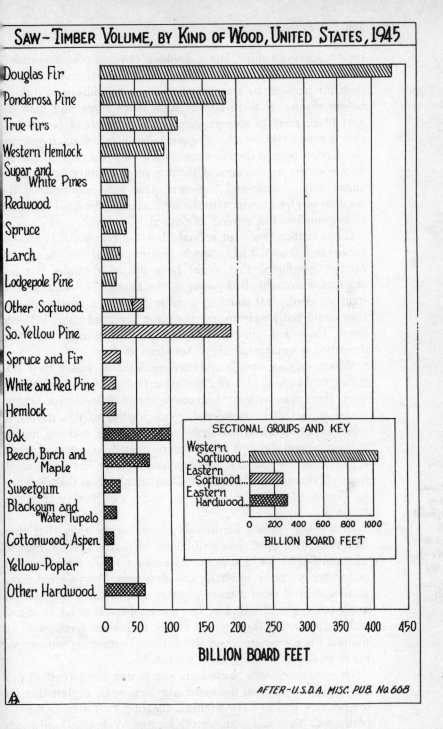

SAW–TIMBER VOLUME, BY KIND OF WOOD, UNITED STATES, 1945

Douglas Fir
Ponderosa Pine
True Firs
Western Hemlock
Sugar and White Pines
Redwood
Spruce
Larch
Lodgepole Pine
Other Softwood
So. Yellow Pine
Spruce and Fir
White and Red Pine
Hemlock
Oak
Beech, Birch and Maple
Sweetgum
Blackgum and Water Tupelo
Cottonwood, Aspen
Yellow-Poplar
Other Hardwood

SECTIONAL GROUPS AND KEY

Western Softwood...
Eastern Softwood...
Eastern Hardwood...

0   200   400   600   800   1000
BILLION BOARD FEET

0   50   100   150   200   250   300   350   400   450
BILLION BOARD FEET

AFTER–U.S.D.A. MISC. PUB. No. 668

FIGURE 96. *Present saw-timber reserves are largely composed of three coniferous species.*

region, leaving behind him a smoking sawdust pile, a rambling skeleton of weather-beaten boards, and several shacks full of destitute families. By arson or accident, many mills burned down before closure. If there be any sight more depressing than the gray-black army of stumps standing as sentinels of barren cut-over it must be the weathered ghost towns in which the monstrous destruction once centered. One cannot view the aspect and reflect upon its implications without a surge of mixed emotions—anger, pity, shame, and contempt. One may countenance the creation of ghost towns with the exhaustion of ore bodies, but he cannot condone the "mining" of timber!

Clean cutting was bad enough, but the burning that accompanied or followed it left scarcely anything alive. The young pine candles (seedlings) that might have flourished under the unobstructed sunlight died young in the flames. The nearest seed trees accidently left standing were so few and far between that they could but slowly re-sow the great, scorched voids between them. How well they *did* repopulate the barrens has been described as a major miracle of American forestry.

Where original stands admitted no light in which their offspring could grow, as under the great Douglas firs of the Northwest, there was nothing destructive about clear-cutting limited areas; in fact, it is considered good practice to this day. But, when an aftermath of fire destroyed forest duff and soil humus it handicapped the next generation of trees. In our epic of forest exploitation the fire that accompanied logging has been much more villainous than the loggers. Desolation such as that depicted in Figure 97 may be found in many localities once richly forested.

Dispersal, mixture, and special utility spared the hardwoods from the main assault

In the big "show," hardwoods played minor roles, but they had their own special contributions to make. Oaks furnished ribs and beams for ship hulls. Hickories furnished tool handles and wagon parts. From birch came shoe pegs. From walnut came gunstocks. And from a score of other species came material for many other specialized uses. But the hardwoods stood so mixed and scattered that the removal of any individual species merely thinned the composite forest stand. Clear cutting for commercial purposes was neither expedient nor feasible.

The central-eastern hardwoods, composing the largest of our forest regions, escaped the systematic large-scale exploitation for lumber that laid low our conifers. Clearing for farms took more hardwoods than did commercial logging. Valuable hardwoods survived the adjacent softwoods because the market demanded a greater volume of pine than of oak, and because the hardwood mixture was difficult to log profitably.

Now steel, paper, plastics and other materials have displaced hardwood for many purposes. Steel drums have largely displaced tight cooperage (barrels and kegs); paper cartons have largely replaced wooden crates and boxes. Plastics have become prominent in furniture and interior finishing. Hickory, once important in the manufacture of wheeled vehicles and horse-drawn implements, has shrunk to the role of handle material and become a "weed" species. Oak retains prominence as flooring; cherry, walnut, birch, and some other species remain popular for furniture and interior finish. Unfortunately the hardwoods take so long to replenish that the remnants of any favored species must be made to last as long as possible.

Soils under the hardwoods are generally more fertile than those under the conifers, and are therefore more desirable for agricultural use. Farmers cleared the hardwoods to get at the soil much as miners strip away the overburden to get at the mineral. The remnants of hardwood left standing are largely in farm wood lots and on land unsuited for agriculture. High unit value now subjects good hardwood specimens of favored species to constant search and collection despite patchy distribution.

When the grand whirl of "quick rich–long poor" lumbering

FIGURE 97. *Cut-over, burned-over area in Colorado. Destructive cutting and burning left an aftermath of murdered forest and crippled land. Each of the forest regions contains similar exhibits.* (S. T. Dana, F.S., photo.)

**Weed species
and second-
growth gained
acceptance**

headed for its last roundup we had to swallow our pride and accept what we had previously rejected. Weed species and second-growth gained favor. Eastern hemlock, southern slash pine, northern jack pine; gum, beech, lodgepole and tamarack; woods that cracked or splintered or twisted, woods full of knots or worm holes; most any lignified stem big enough to make a two-by-four became saw timber. For pulping and synthetics a long list of nondescripts became respectable citizens of the forest community; saplings made as good cellulose as patriarchs. Technology and economics revamped our ideas about forests and forestry. We entered a new era of wood, and 152 different species of trees became commercially important (3).

**We entered
a new era
of wood**

Wood became a primary raw material for a variety of industrial innovations, not simply lumber and timbers. Prices rose and quality fell, but stumpage could be appraised in terms of cellulose (and lignin) instead of board feet. Portable sawmills shifted precariously from place to place about the cut-over lands, cutting scattered patches of trees that had attained merchantable size. Competent lumbermen turned their attention to forest protection and reproduction to ensure the permanence of their operations. Scarcity invoked caution, and logging began to settle down. Notably in the Northwest, where most of our remaining saw timber is located, lumber manufacturers adopted policies and practices whereby their factories might operate continuously and indefinitely. Sawmills became permanent community assets.

Most revolutionary aspect of the "new forestry," pulpwood became a crop, on land abandoned by lumber barons only two or three decades earlier. Fast-growing softwoods stole another march on the hardwoods because the speed of regrowth became a critical factor. Spindly pines, firs and spruces outranked the nobler oaks, birches and hickories. Quantity meant more than quality.

**We have been
cutting our
timber before
it matures;
faster than
it grows**

To meet increasing demands from declining reserves, we have been cutting our young timber before it matures, faster than it grows. We have almost reached a balance between *total* new growth and total volume removed and destroyed annually (4, p. 16). However, as recently as 1944 our *drain of saw timber was 50 per cent greater than saw timber growth* (5, p. 31).

When our forebears began felling trees in the New World that area which is now the United States had almost a billion acres covered by forests (6, p. 2). An estimated 622 million acres of forest land remains, of which 460 million acres are suitable and available for commercial timber production (7, p. 38). Much of the potential area bears only low-grade forest or scrub, cordwood or young growth. Some 60 million acres of it lack organized fire protection (8, p. 40). The entire area of eastern forests contains less saw timber than the Douglas fir sub-region of Washington and Oregon with only six per cent of our total forest area (7, p. 38). We wrought a nation out of wood—well enough, but we also wrought wood right out of the nation. In three centuries we mowed down most of five great forests, and became heavily dependent upon foreign sources for wood with which to sustain our industrial empire.

Self-perpetuation is a fundamental function of all living things, trees included. Given a fighting chance, forests repossess areas from which they have been removed. If we would have clear streams with trout in them, plenty of water and fewer floods, thriving factories and inspiring vacations, books to study and comics to read Sunday morning, we need only give our forests a chance to survive and reproduce their species. We need practice only those forestry and conservation measures which pay their own way. Despite all our past abuse the living trees will continue to serve us unless we exterminate them willfully. All they ask is a fair degree of protection and management.

Trees will serve us if we let them!

CHAPTER 9: REFERENCES CITED BY NUMBER

(1) Bernard Frank, "Deep Go the Roots," *Nature Magazine*, XLV, No. 9, November 1952.

(2) Ovid Butler, Lilian Cromelin, and Erle Kauffman, editors, *American Forests Anniversary Number*, XLI No. 9, September 1935.

(3) William A. Dayton, "Geography of Commercially Important United States Trees," *Journal of Forestry*, LI, No. 4, April 1953, pp. 276-279.

(4) *Forests for the Future*, published by The Conservation Foundation as supplement to *American Forests*, December 1952.

(5) "Forests and National Prosperity: A Reappraisal of the Forest Situation in the United States," *Miscellaneous Publication No. 668*, F.S., 1948.

(6) *Report of the Chief of the Forest Service*, 1951.

(7) "Domestic Timber Resources," *Report of the President's Materials Policy Commission*, 5 vols.; V: *Selected Reports to the Commission*, Report 5. Washington, D.C., 1952.

(8) *Foundations for Growth and Security: Report of the Materials Policy Commission*, I, 1952.

WARNING
FIRES
PROHIBITED BY LAW

Permanent Forests and

Perpetual Timber Supply

*forest conservation perpetuates our abundance
of timber and magnifies the beneficence of forests*

ONE THIRD OF THE UNITED STATES REMAINS IN THE FOREST LAND category, and if we manage that land properly it will grow all the timber we need, with a goodly margin to spare (1). Agriculture will claim certain forest areas with fertile soils, and many acres of poor crop land will revert to forest, but the changes will just about balance each other.

To ensure an adequate, perpetual supply of wood we must apply many practices of forestry in the *production of trees as a crop.* In that application we are sadly delinquent and shortsighted. We know how much timber we have, we can calculate the rate of reproduction, and still we persist in cutting it off somewhat faster than it can mature (1).

Our perspective remains entirely too limited for the good of our forest. More than three fourths of our timber products come from trees of saw-log size. Only half the saw timber cut comes from virgin stands, mainly in the Northwest and predominantly in National Forests, and those stands are dwindling rapidly. Many of them should, actually, be cut faster than is being done because they are overripe, and delay entails waste. Soon we shall be entirely dependent upon regrowth, and our growing stock is

Life expectancy limits individual perspective

miserably poor. Individuals are loathe to wait while softwood
grow to saw-log size, to say nothing of the slow-growing hard
woods. The beauty and strength of white oak are legendary
yet who plants white oak, knowing he cannot live to see it mature
Individuals trade quality for time, often a bad bargain in
forestry program.

Wise men in positions of public trust, cognizant of the inheren
inadequacies of the individual, began long ago a participation c
government in forestry matters. As early as 1817, the Federa
Government established the Santa Rosa Live Oak Timber Reserv
in Pensacola Bay, Florida, to guarantee a source of shi
timber for the Navy. That was our first positive attempt to pro
tect the public interest in forests against selfish, private enter
prise (2, p. 2). The reserve contained only 30,000 acres, and wa
short-lived, killed by narrow politics. Timber reserves for th
Navy came and went, totaling 264,000 acres on the Gulf Coast in
1868. The last of them was not removed from our land offic
records before 1923 (3).

In *1891*, with establishment of the *Yellowstone Park Timberlan
Reserve*, began the great National Forest system which now
encompasses some 180 million acres (4, p. 3). In 1877 Congres
opened certain forest reserves to use, paving the way for scientifi
forestry in America by legal regulation, demonstration, an
experiment. In 1951 our National Forests contributed 4,688,000,00
board feet of timber (5, p. 38), besides providing grazing land
for more than 4,100,000 domestic animals (5, p. 41), protectin
many major watersheds, and harboring an abundant variety o
wildlife and tourists.

Until 1905 the Department of the Interior administered th
forests, and the Department of Agriculture had the professiona
foresters, but in that year the lands were transferred to the De
partment of Agriculture to get the material and the know-how
together (4, p. 2). Since then the Forest Service has pioneered th
conservation of durable resources, very appropriately concernin
itself not only with trees, but also with the grasslands, wildlife
and other resources within its vast and numerous administrativ
units. Figure 98 suggests the magnitude of the task.

State forestry, now an important facet of conservation, bega
in the Colonies with certain fire-prevention measures and penaltie
for timber theft, but did not settle down to serious busines
before 1885. In that year New York began the acquisition of th
Adirondack and Catskill Forest Preserves. During the last hal
century state governments and state police powers have contrib

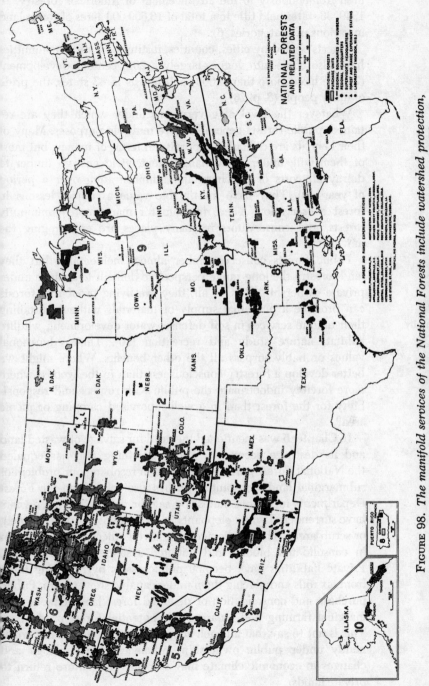

FIGURE 98. *The manifold services of the National Forests include watershed protection, timber production, range and wildlife conservation, forestry demonstration, wilderness preservation (Chapter 14) and others. They contribute to every class of natural resources.*

uted tremendously to the advancement of American forestry. In 1949, 36 states held title to a total of 16,600,000 acres of forest land in various use categories (6).

Forests owned by cities, counties, institutions, and communities have also come into vogue—largely a 20th century development (7). We have more than 3,000 such forests in 43 states, the pride of many people (8, p. 26).

Whatever the level of government under which they are retained, public forests generally serve multiple purposes. Many of their benefits are difficult to appraise in terms of money, but most of them will, under good management, yield enough timber to defray all costs of purchase and administration over a period of years (9). They have inestimable value as object lessons in forest conservation. There is room for many more community forests, and conservators in many places are encouraging the movement.

Public forests conserve timber almost incidentally

Public forests conserve timber almost incidentally, but they lend forestry the long-range perspective difficult to achieve under private ownership. Best of all, they are living proof that forests can produce a perpetual supply of materials without curtailing their unique services in soil defense, water development, wildlife habitat, nature study and recreation (10). Their educational values probably surpass all the other benefits. Where might we better develop a forestry consciousness than in the woods; where more forcibly indoctrinate the public with respect and responsibility for the forest than in a well-supervised camping or picnic area?

In Chapter 5 was mentioned the need for salvage of wasted land and its destitute occupants. Perhaps nothing else has equaled the National Forest purchase program in resolving our problem of submarginal land. Substantial aid has also come from the Forest Departments in various states. By sale or default private owners have surrendered white elephants in the form of cut-over, burned, or scrub areas. The public agencies have gathered them in, often in consolidated blocks, and initiated systematic rehabilitation. Private liabilities have become public assets by removing them from tax rolls and placing them under capable stewardship. Public purchase and consolidation of denuded forest land reduces submarginal farming and enlarges our potential forest production. This is not to say that all such acquisitions should remain permanently under public ownership. Advances in technology and changes in economic climate may warrant their future return to private hands.

Private holdings, large and small, produce the bulk of our present timber supply, and almost all of them serve in some multiple capacity. Whatever its primary purpose, almost every woodland contributes in some degree to the conservation of other durable resources, soils, water, wildlife, and so on. While a few forest tracts are retained privately for recreational or sentimental purposes, woodlands owned by private citizens or corporations must in the main either yield a profit on an investment or produce supplementary income in money or kind.

About one fourth of our private forest land is owned by some 3,600 individuals and corporations. The remaining three fourths belong to 4¼ million owners, with an average of 62 acres each. More than 3¼ million of the small owners are farmers, whose properties constitute about half the aggregate forest area in small holdings (8, p. 14). See the pie graphs, Figure 99.

Forest ownership has special significance in conservation because the owner decides management practices, including manner of harvesting. On public lands our hired foresters prescribe the practices and supervise their application, but for lands privately owned they can only recommend good methods and hope that the owners may employ them. The choice rests with the owner.

Private holdings produce the bulk of our timber supply

FIGURE 99. *Most of our forest land is in farm wood lots and other small woodland tracts. It is therefore imperative that forestry information be widely disseminated.*

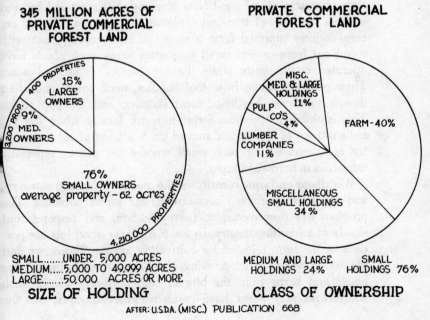

345 MILLION ACRES OF PRIVATE COMMERCIAL FOREST LAND

400 PROPERTIES
15% LARGE OWNERS

3,200 PROP.
9% MED. OWNERS

76% SMALL OWNERS
average property – 62 acres

4,210,000 PROPERTIES

SMALL......UNDER 5,000 ACRES
MEDIUM....5,000 TO 49,999 ACRES
LARGE......50,000 ACRES OR MORE

SIZE OF HOLDING

PRIVATE COMMERCIAL FOREST LAND

MISC. MED. & LARGE HOLDINGS 11%

PULP CO'S 4%

FARM – 40%

LUMBER COMPANIES 11%

MISCELLANEOUS SMALL HOLDINGS 34%

MEDIUM AND LARGE HOLDINGS 24%   SMALL HOLDINGS 76%

CLASS OF OWNERSHIP

AFTER: U.S.D.A. (MISC.) PUBLICATION 668

Industrial
forests are
competitive;
farm wood
lots
supplementary

Private forest ownership is mainly of three kinds: (1) large hold
ings of corporations such as railroads, mining and manufacturing
firms, land and lumber companies, (2) small commercial forests
mostly owned by individuals, and (3) farm forests or farm wood
lots, generally on land undesirable for agriculture.

The first category supports large-scale *industrial* operations, the
prime movers of American forestry. The entrepreneurs employ
many people and big investments against stiff competition. They
must be strictly practical and efficient to show a fair profit. Some
are making their plants permanent fixtures by cropping the forest
instead of mining them (11). They "swing" the big contracts for
cutting publicly owned timber (as on the National Forests) ac
cording to restrictions and specifications laid down by responsible
agents of government. They harvest, process, and sell the major
produce of our forests (12, 13, 14).

The second category comprises the small units in commercia
forestry, operated in a variety of ways. Many owners sell stump
age by the acre, and the buyer comes and cuts it. All too often
anything goes, because the buyer shies away from restrictions on
the manner of cutting. Economic expedience brushes forestry
aside in such cases. Other owners cut their timber and sell the
logs at a mill or plant within market distance. Most interesting
and in many cases most conservational, in this category are the
small owner-operated forests and woodworking plants, particularly characteristic of rural New England, but scattered far and
wide in the wake of transient exploitation. It is true that few are
now entirely supplied from a single woods property, but with
wood cut from several small properties many such plants have
operated continuously while the big "shows" came and went.
Their products range from tool handles, neck yokes, and chair
dowels to staves, headings, meat skewers, and lollypop sticks.
They stabilized American forest industry locally when the big
mills ran out of timber and moved on. Scattered about the country are thousands of such small wood-using plants, especially
numerous in hardwood areas.

Woodland on farms constitutes the most problematic category,
and the most neglected segment of our forest potential. The
problem lies deep-rooted in farm tradition, and responds but
slowly to scientific ministry. In the East, farm wood lots are portions of the farm rejected for cultivation; on the Plains, we find
planted groves of quick-growing, short-lived trees to protect the
house and barns from the bite of cold northerly winds. Such
windbreaks may never have much commercial value, but the

rmer should by good management boost farm incomes and our ational timber crop vastly more than they ever have, or do at resent. Few farmers know how valuable their farm woods might e, because they have regarded them mainly as space for cattle o roam when other pasture needs respite. Figure 100 shows the vide distribution of woodland in farms, and Figure 101 shows hat income from it is much more localized.

Not so long ago, when farmers were less articulate and more ndependent, the farm woods, especially in hardwood country, urnished many materials for the farm establishment. Fuel for toves and fireplaces, rails and posts for fence repair, poles to race haystacks and stakes to hold the tops on grain stacks, ongues and whippletrees for horse-drawn implements—wood for his and wood for that came out of the trusty wood lot. But farm- rs, including those in hardwood country, have modernized, com- mercialized, and mechanized until they buy their fuel, buy the vire and steel for fences, use tractor-drawn implements with teel hitches, and in a hundred other ways shun the use of wood or reasons of economy as well as convenience. Why chop wood vhen the labor costs more than equivalent coal or oil, delivered? Can one neglect his cows and chickens to "lay up" wood when heir regular tending pays more than the price of a wood substi- ute? Not in this age of cash and calculation!

Their *subsistence* functions largely past, farm woods fall from grace unless they too be *commercialized*. The trend is well ad- vanced, but progress is slow because it takes time to sell three million farmers an idea, no matter how good it is.

Pulpwood cutting has become a rewarding off-season activity on many farms, notably in the South where a merchantable crop of pine comes up from seed in 15 to 20 years (15)—profitable tree crops have been grown in considerably less than 15 years. Farm- ers have also learned the high value of saw timber, but too few of them can resist a tempting offer for acre stumpage. They should know that a few selected trees cut now and then bring much more remuneration in the long run than one clear cutting can possibly give.

With forestry as with soil conservation, farmers must *see* the "miracle" before they believe. Once convinced, they find in for- estry a welcome adjunct to other crop systems, a splendid addition to farm diversification, and a steady source of supplemental in- come. Public forest agencies, both state and national, assist the farmers as a matter of good policy for the common weal. Timber operators assist the farmers in the vicinity of their plants as a

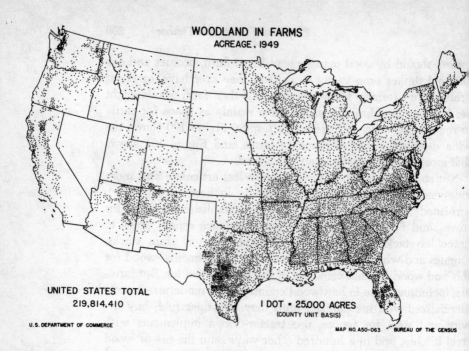

WOODLAND IN FARMS
ACREAGE, 1949

UNITED STATES TOTAL
219,814,410

I DOT = 25,000 ACRES
(COUNTY UNIT BASIS)

U.S. DEPARTMENT OF COMMERCE

MAP NO. A50-063   BUREAU OF THE CENSUS

FIGURES 100 and 101. *Farm woods are the largest single category of forest land. With good management, they would contribute much more to farm income than they do at present. Many farmers have a problem of replacing weed trees with merchantable species.*

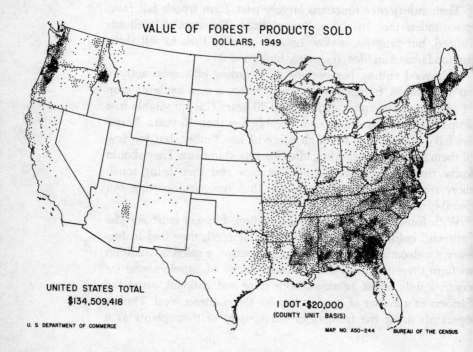

VALUE OF FOREST PRODUCTS SOLD
DOLLARS, 1949

UNITED STATES TOTAL
$134,509,418

I DOT = $20,000
(COUNTY UNIT BASIS)

U.S. DEPARTMENT OF COMMERCE

MAP NO. A50-244   BUREAU OF THE CENSUS

atter of good business, to ensure a better supply of available
w material.

Different kinds of ownership occasion differences in forest man-
gement. Different timber stands, pure or mixed, big or small, or of
arious sizes, demand discretion in the choice of logging and re-
ocking methods. The great variety of forest industries imposes
veral distinct requirements as to modes of cutting and handling.
ood forestry on the part of a farmer with a few walnut logs to
ll may not resemble even remotely the equally good forestry of
timber grower with a large acreage of pine of pulpwood size.
here will also be obvious disparity between the wood-using
lant that works purchased wood and the one that depends mainly
r entirely upon company-owned forests. Conservation cannot
ttain full bloom against the grain of economics, but any detailing
f the economic intricacies influencing forestry in the various
orest regions lies far beyond the scope of this survey. Merely a
rief sketch is apropos here, of *common problems* and *approved
olutions* in forest conservation generally.

Economics must be respected

Fire has probably destroyed more of our forest than we have
ut, and continues to take a heavy annual toll despite our efforts
 prevent it. Great forest fires, such as the Hinckley (Minnesota),
he Peshtigo (Wisconsin), the Tillamook (Oregon), and the Bar
Iarbor (Maine), seared tragic pages into American history. Thou-
ands of little fires gnaw away at our forest resources every year.
During the decade 1940-1950 an average of 21½ million acres of
ur forests went up in smoke *each year*—i.e., we burned annually
n area the size of Maine (5, p. 4).

Fire protection remains the fundamental forestry requirement.
Vithout it all other forestry measures come to naught, like dere-
cts with neither power nor mooring. Unless it be provided first,
very other effort becomes a bad risk.

Fire protection remains the fundamental forestry requirement

None of our forests is fireproof; fires have burned big holes in
very one, even those in cool, moist New England. Drought comes
 all of them, and dry woods are so much tinder. What could be
uch better kindling than dry leaves or pine straw, with dry twigs
nd bark to feed the blaze? What fury can man know more fright-
ning and diabolical than a wind-lashed forest fire? If every Amer-
an could witness just one, close enough to singe his eyebrows,
e fire hazard might be much less.

Seed sowing and tree planting are wasted labors if the resultant
rowth succumbs to fire. No forest industry can attain desirable
ability and permanence where its basic requirement—a contin-
ous supply of wood—may suddenly "evaporate" from the scene.

Will anyone wittingly finance an enterprise whose essential ra
material may vanish before the machinery is well broken in
Forestry without fire protection is about as impracticable as wate
power without watersheds.

**By accident
or intent,
man sets most
of the fires**

Well over 90 per cent of the destructive forest fires are of ou
own doing, either by accident or intent. Carelessness with matche
and cigarettes, failure to kill campfires, trash fires left unattende
and other equally irresponsible acts cause two thirds of thes
Almost one third are set purposely by people who think burnin
improves the range or eradicates pests, by people who war
"clean" woods, and by persons mentally warped who start fire
"just for the fun of it." Less than a tenth can be blamed on train
and lumbering operations. Less than a tenth result from natura
causes, mainly lightning—lightning starts many more, but attend
ant rain puts them out before they can do much damage. The fac
that we ourselves, the recipients of the bounty, put the torch t
our forests is indeed a sorry reflection on our intellectual attain
ment. The pie graphs in Figure 102 are embarrassing to
conservator.

FIGURE 102. *Causes of forest fires, private and state lands. Ignorance and care
lessness cause most of our destructive fires. The frequency of forest fires is thu
a sorry reflection on our intellectual and social attainments. If all young peopl
are taught the real consequences of forest fire, fire protection will become muc
easier and fire losses much smaller.*

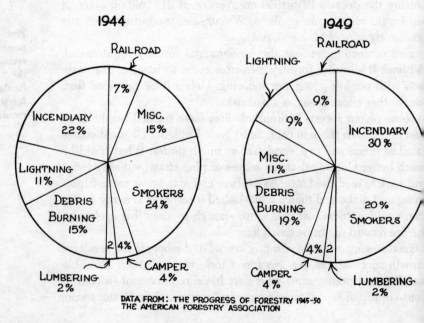

DATA FROM: THE PROGRESS OF FORESTRY 1945-50
THE AMERICAN FORESTRY ASSOCIATION

Woods burning for the improvement of grazing is a major deterrent to forestry in the South. Most of the burning fails in its purpose, because the forest grasses are generally too sparse and too low in nutritional value to afford good range, and at best they have only limited seasonal utility. Good pastures have been developed in the southern pine region, but burning was not the sole means of their improvement. Seeding of suitable forage plants was probably a more important factor. Burning of forest range probably improves it more for quail than for cattle.

All wildfires in the forest are not equally destructive; there are degrees even in burning (16, p. 242). Fire that stays on the floor and lacks the intensity with which to consume tree trunks can run through a forest without direct injury to the main stand. However, such *surface* or *ground fire* destroys litter that shielded the soil, absorbed rain, and would have enriched the humus content. Apparently harmless, the lightest kind of ground fire may do considerable damage to the forest environment.

Wildfire burns soil as well as trees

Another kind of wildfire called *crown fire* takes the roof off the forest, leaving charred trunks and snags in its wake. It can race through a stand of conifers with the speed of the wind that drives it, beheading the big ones as it goes and killing more deliberately anything that grew under their canopy. All crown fires are disastrous, but at their worst they are conflagrations beyond compare, destroying completely the biotic community they ravage and leaving only dead, sterile space behind them.

Those which consume virtually everything combustible we may well call *soil fires* because they destroy the organic matter in their paths, including soil humus, right down to the mineral foundation (Figure 103). They destroy not only present life but also the prospect of rehabilitation for an indefinite period. Soil fires are one of man's most abominable visitations upon his worldly habitat, wiping out, as they do, the entire biotic community and the soil it helped produce through ages of operation. Without life the soil process stops, re-establishment of life forms and redevelopment of a soil mantle become exceedingly slow processes. *Soil fires are the third-degree burns of forest.* They are deep and painful, and difficult to heal. And many of them start with the flick of a cigarette!

The place to stop our great sacrifice of forests to fire is with the cigarette, the campfire or bonfire, the incendiarist, the spark from a locomotive. A single thought of caution can save thousands of acres of forest and soil, millions of dollars worth of property, hazardous man-hours of firefighting, human communities, herds

Precaution and prompt detection are the best firefighting tools

FIGURE 103. *Fire kills the entire biotic community, leaving sterile space to which life returns but slowly. Dead trees and snags left standing are highly inflammable, and a fire menace to new growth.* (K. D. Swan, F.S., photo.)

and flocks of game—whole segments of our environment that we now erase by carelessness or ignorance.

Prevention or "pre-suppression" is the first and best defense against forest fire; prompt detection the best tool with which to combat it. A full-blown raging forest fire almost defies control. Prompt arrival on the scene is the essence of firefighting, and arrival cannot be prompt unless the fire be spotted when it starts and its location reported accurately to the nearest available source of men and equipment. Lookout towers on commanding heights of land, connected by telephone with volunteer crews and equipment stations, stand as symbols of *organized* fire protection; more

cently airplane patrols and radio communications have entered
e spotting service.

Pioneered by the Forest Service in the National Forests, fire pro-
ction now obtains on some 357 million acres of state and private
rest lands, financed jointly by federal, state, and local govern-
ents (8, p. 9). It demands and deserves public and private co-
peration. It must be inclusive in coverage, because no forest
rea can be safe against fire unless adjoining lands on all sides are
lso guarded. It must be an *organized* system; otherwise it be-
omes a piecemeal failure.

First and foremost the system must maintain constant vigilance
henever the forest is dry and easily ignited. Hundreds of "meas-
ring" stations have been established to keep us posted on the
egree of fire hazard at all times (17); through them, inflammability
s scientifically determined and officially reported. The system
ust include emergency crews ready to respond on short notice,
ools and equipment at strategic locations, and vehicles for speedy
ispatch to any detected smoke in the woods.

To improve fire protection, we have spent millions of dollars for
ccess roads into remote areas, as in forests of the Northwest. One
onders ofttimes whether such expenditures are not negated by
heir invitation of deeper penetration of the forest by irrespon-
ible persons who start fires. Perhaps aerial detection and the
elivery of firefighting men and equipment by parachute or heli-
opter, which has proved extremely effective, will become stand-
rd practice in such areas. Though costly, it does not increase the
azard by the very means intended to cope with it. Of course,
ccess roads can be blocked and patroled during fire seasons, but
hat is both expensive and difficult. Furthermore, persons who are
areless with fire in the woods are not likely to respect restric-
ions. Roads for logging and transporting the timber harvest must
e built as necessary, and they serve for fire suppression as well,
ut those built for the sole purpose of access to a fire deep in the
orest may be poor investments.

If we excluded all people from our forests the fire problem
ould be almost nil, but such rigid prohibition would be entirely
oo costly, and would deny us many forest benefits we now
njoy. Education is the more logical approach. People must learn
etter *forest discipline;* individuals must acquire a feeling of re-
ponsibility rather than of detachment. We cannot possibly employ
 sufficient number of fire wardens to protect our forests unless
hose wardens be paid by a public that assists them voluntarily.
Meanwhile, we invoke mandates and impose penalties whenever

guilt can be established. All too rarely can we apprehend th
criminal, and in no case can the legal proceedings recover th
burned forest. In 1949 the states prosecuted 6,880 persons fo
violating state fire laws, and convicted 95 per cent of them (8, p
6). Indictment is much more difficult than conviction in this forr
of crime.

Defense
should be
commensurate
with the
hazard

Defense against forest fire should be commensurate with th
hazard. Weather, forest condition, and terrain are major factor:
Woods drenched with rain or blanketed by snow are safe. Wood
far from the haunts of men are comparatively safe. But dr
autumn woods, infested with excited hunters whose gear include
everything *except* ash-trays, are veritable powder kegs. *Late sum
mer and autumn demand special vigilance.* Fires in flat, oper
woodland are more easily suppressed than those in heavy timbe
on rugged terrain. Prevention assumes maximum significanc
where suppression is most difficult.

Except as parts of a larger area under organized protectior
small groves or thickets of forest cannot repay the cost of defense
whereas an acreage of saw timber or thrifty young growth ma
warrant careful maintenance of a *fire lane* about the periphery t
keep out fire, and *fire breaks* within to limit the spread of any fir
that may jump the outer barrier. Lanes and breaks must be gage
to the particular situation, but in any case they should be broa
enough to ensure a fair degree of security. Plowed strips a fev
furrows wide serve well for seedlings, but they are inadequate fo
stopping a crown fire in tall conifers. A fire break-road combina
tion such as that pictured in Figure 104 serves well both as fir
barrier and logging facility.

No forested
community
can risk
the tragedy
of fire

The fire hazard can be no greater than the extent and value o
the forest. In grassland states like the Dakotas and Nebraska
where forests are limited to planted windbreaks and such volum
teer growth as has invaded the river valleys, any considerable ex
penditure for forest protection would be poor economics and
poorer politics. Grass, not forest, becomes the casualty of wildfir
on our western range lands, and the consequences of range burn
ing are usually less serious and less permanent than those of fores
fire. Not only are the grasses less susceptible to injury than is ;
forest; they recuperate much more quickly.

No forested community can afford to risk the tragedy of fire. A
the forest goes so goes the forest community. A few fatal hour
can reduce to ashes the works of one generation and the hopes o
another. In all our forest regions fire means loss of livelihood, b
the principal income from lumber, as in the West, from pulp, as i

FIGURE 104. *A fire lane or fire break helps protect a woodland against fire originating outside the forest boundary, and helps localize and subdue any fire originating within the forest. This is a carpet grass fire break and road on a commercial timber property in Florida.* (W. R. Mattoon, F.S., photo.)

the South, or from tourists, as in many parts of the North. Forest products and forest services contribute *directly* to the well-being of most Americans, yet comparatively few people pay serious attention to the fire menace before it robs their own pockets or curtails their water consumption. Not until fire burns the economic props right out from under their community do they find time to deplore the lack of foresight that admitted disaster.

Considering the manifold communal services of forest, one observes with embarrassment that in this, the enlightened 20th century, private timber growers are at the mercy of an unconcerned public. That regrettable circumstance prompts the private owner to restrict public privileges. Because a few inconsiderate picnickers, hunters, or fishermen lack decent respect for private property, the owner "posts" his woodland against all comers. In self-defense he excludes many good citizens whose presence in the woods would actually enhance its safety. Sportsmen's organizations all over the country are doing much to solve the problem, by exemplary behavior in the woods and by active participation in defense against fire. Though good hunting and fishing is their objective, they recognize that forest fire kills game and fish, destroys choice wildlife habitats, and may permanently change the wild

Private timber growers are at the mercy of an unconcerned public

population of an area. Chain reactions characterize both natural and social aspects of conservation.

Small owners control a major portion of our forest area and hold the key to the future of our forest industries, but fire loss, or fear of it, discourages many from employing forestry practices they would otherwise prefer. The most enthusiastic tree farmer loses heart when his young planting burns. The East Tennessean who set a large hillside with walnut for his grandchildren and saw the thrifty young planting killed by fire in one afternoon could hardly be expected to plant it over again. Fire is a deterrent to the planting of any species, and more especially of the slow-growing hardwoods. The slower the growth of a tree the longer its exposure to fire and other hazards before it can acquire any value.

Organized fire protection is a sound public investment

Unable to afford adequate precautions against fire on separate, scattered parcels of forest, the individual or corporate owner must look to cooperative organization and governmental support for necessary fire control. The basis for such organization and support dates back to 1911, when the Weeks Act was passed by Congress. The main purpose of that law was to authorize purchase of land for addition to the National Forest system; but it also provided for federal cooperation with states to protect against fire the watersheds of navigable streams. The Clark-McNary Law of 1924 extended the purchase authority to lands primarily for timber production rather than for watershed protection, and also broadened the scope of federal cooperation in fire protection. Later legislation liberalized federal assistance, and states concerned with forestry lent their legislative support and police power. The county has become the standard unit for organized fire protection, which now covers more than four fifths of our total forest area, including the National Forests. Broadly speaking, organized fire protection has reduced the incidence of fire to a third of the rate on unprotected land, and reduced the average area burned by each fire to less than a fifth. While more than 15 per cent of the unprotected area burns over each year, the area burned on protected land has shrunk to a fraction of one per cent (8, p. 8). The investment would pay off in wood alone, given time, but infinitely greater are the savings in the intangible, inestimable services of forest.

Economic irony resides in the fact that the South, where wood grows fastest, is most delinquent in combating fire. Considering that slash and longleaf are the only American pines yielding both pitch and wood, and that they produce pulpwood, poles, and saw-

ogs in less time than northern species, it is most unfortunate that
heir protection against fire has been neglected.

In parts of the Northeast, where forest services frequently out-
veigh the value of wood, fire prevention measures are rigidly en-
orced. The forest-conscious Yankees in Massachusetts mean business when they order that "No bonfire may be built without a
permit from the District Fire Warden." If the clambake is rained
out, which one anticipates in Massachusetts, another fire permit—
and another bushel of clams—must be procured for a future *day
and hour*. Conservative New England is *conservative* in more ways
than one, and forest protection can be calculated to pay off. Who
would render a financial statement on New England's autumn
foliage? How much water power would be lost if the upper Connecticut Valley were burned over? How much tobacco would
floods ruin in the Valley? How many tourists would cancel their
reservations?

Consider the metropolitan nucleus farther south, and the *direct
influence* of *remote* forest fires on it. For example, how thirsty
would New York be if the Catskills burned over? How many
would ski at Lake Placid if the vicinity looked like the Tillamook
Burn? Indeed, organized fire protection defies appraisal, but it is
probably worth more than twice what it costs anywhere. Common sense ought to nettle our delinquent areas to participate. Its
demonstrated merit foreshadows its eventual extension to all our
forest lands. Delay is wasteful, and will surely occasion much regret. We cannot be content with anything short of complete coverage because neglect in one region penalizes another. A fire in
Washington raises the price of houses in Ohio, a fire in Mississippi
increases the cost of *The New York Times,* and a burn in Minnesota can ruin the muskrat "crop" in Louisiana. The annual burning
costs us a billion dollars (18). Losses incurred by delay should convince us that we are delinquent in the extension of organized fire
protection; yet as recently as 1952, 66 million acres of our forest
and watershed lands remained without such protection (19).

To the outdoorsman nothing can equal the mild tang of pine
smoke on crisp autumn air, and it would be unjust to deprive him
of the pleasure. Let him be assured that all smokes in the forest
are not destructive, that fire is also a valuable forestry tool, and
that smoke may be enjoyed without any feeling of remorse.

Controlled burning, prescribed by a competent forester, is a
very versatile aid to forestry. Under certain conditions it is the
quickest, cheapest means of clearing ground for sowing or planting, removing litter that would prevent seeds from contacting the

**Controlled
burning
aids
forestry**

earth, and destroying noxious competitive growth. In trained hands it can be a technique for *selective* forest reproduction a much less expense than by conventional methods.

Travelers to the "Deep South" would be somewhat less revolted by the numerous smokes in the woods if they knew that there where destructive fire is most rampant, *constructive* burning i also exceptionally useful. Fire combats fungus on young pine seedlings, becoming a superior sanitation measure. Run through young growth when conditions are right, fire sorts a mixture o conifers and hardwoods, killing the oaks and sparing the more resistant pines, a practical method of burning for selection o species.

Protective burning has several variations, all of them helpful in averting fire damage. They are a special version of the back-fire the last, desperate resort against a full-blown wildfire. "Once over lightly" causes no injury to longleaf a few inches in diameter, but the same trees, worked for turpentine years later, would be extremely susceptible to injury if pine straw, twigs, and dead grass were permitted to accumulate on the forest floor meanwhile. Thus it is often wise to burn the debris every year or two to prevent fire with dangerous intensity. Burning also serves to maintain fire lanes and fire breaks where general burning is not advisable. Thus for many special purposes, fire can be employed to promote that which it usually threatens.

In harvesting the forest men have been almost as indiscreet as with fire. Logging has left areas almost as devastated as if they had been burned. With heavy machinery and steel cables men have taken what they wanted and knocked down whatever stood in the way. They have left rejected trees and parts of trees scattered about where they fell, like engraved invitations to fire. Nor have they yet mended their ways entirely. Where "big stuff" remains to be logged, as in the West, much destruction often accompanies the taking.

Logging need not be ruinous

Logging need not be ruinous; in fact, it can be beneficial to the forest. Loggers who remove mature trees and culls without damaging the younger, healthy ones improve the forest incidental to its harvest. By taking out the trees that have stopped growing, and releasing the space to vigorous ones that can use it, they accelerate increment (growth of wood) by reducing competition. When a tree in a commercial forest shows little or no annual increment, it is wasteful to leave it standing, but a conservation of space, rain, sunshine, and soil to cut it down.

A step further, and one arrives at the ultimate in good forestry, *selective cutting* and *sustained-yield* management. The two

FIGURE 105. *Slash pine plantation near Homerville, Georgia. Planted during the spring of 1929, the trees were thinned for pulpwood during the winter of 1941-42, when they averaged 7 to 10 inches d.b.h. (diameter at breast height). Thinning yielded 52 cords from 40 acres, worth $7.00 per unit (1¼ cords) loaded on railroad cars—thus paying for the planting as well as improving the stand for future crops.* (Leland J. Prater, F.S., photo.)

phrases may be related—even synonymous—in practice, but not necessarily so. Each has a distinct meaning, and, independently or jointly, neither is as simple as one might suppose.

The ultimate: selective cutting and sustained yield

Selective cutting may entail "selection" on the basis of any one among several criteria, or an appropriate combination of them. It may be done for the purpose of thinning a stand so that the undisturbed trees can grow larger and more valuable (Figure 105), or to remove diseased and decaying trees while they retain some usefulness and before they infect others. It may be done to remove weed trees, deformed trees, and trees with broad crowns (wolf trees) that take up space they cannot pay for. Such *selection* of a stand is aptly referred to as *sanitation* or *salvage* cutting; it is illustrated in Figure 106. Chosen specimens are *not* cut; they are left to grow. It is selective cutting in reverse, as it were.

Selective cutting conventional style, as shown in Figure 107, removes the choice, large trees, leaving the others to mature for a

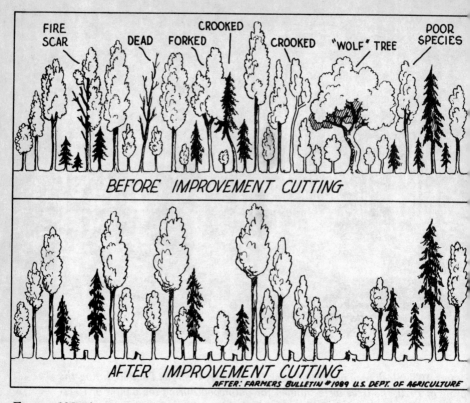

FIRE SCAR   DEAD   FORKED   CROOKED   CROOKED   "WOLF" TREE   POOR SPECIES

BEFORE IMPROVEMENT CUTTING

AFTER IMPROVEMENT CUTTING

AFTER: FARMERS BULLETIN #1989 U.S. DEPT. OF AGRICULTURE

FIGURE 106. *A conservator would not overdo woodland sanitation. He would leave here and there, a hollow tree for squirrels or raccoons and a dead snag for flickers or bluebirds.*

subsequent crop. In mixed stands, with trees of various sizes, selection can be extremely complicated, especially when culling for stand improvement and *harvesting* for maximum market value are accomplished in the same logging operation.

Selective cutting constitutes a form of perpetual *forest cropping* conducive to maximum, sustained-yield production under the most varied forest conditions and economic circumstances. Cutting a few trees per acre one year, a few the next, or several years later, one species or several as the mixture affords and the market demands, brings continual income without depleting the stand or selling at a disadvantage. Except where peculiarity of species or uniformity of stand, or both, favor another plan, selective cutting ensures optimum sustained yield and superior forest conservation. It is the only practice whereby one can take crop after crop of timber without deterioration of the forest environment and curtailment of multiple forest services.

However, nature and economics often indicate or dictate *clear cutting* of timber much as a Kansas farmer reaps wheat. Complete

222

FIGURE 107. *Selective cutting of ponderosa pine in Oregon. Removal of mature trees gives younger ones the space they need for vigorous growth.* (Ray N. Filloon, F.S., photo.)

clearing of patches or strips, while it may be somewhat adverse to other forest functions, may show the best profit from forest products. Commercial logging as commonly done requires costly preparation for efficient felling (cutting down), bucking, skidding logs out of woods, loading, and hauling. Anyone who assembles all the necessary machinery and gear for economical operation must have a "cut" of sufficiently large volume. In uniformly *large* stands, as of virgin Douglas fir in the West, the added cost of selective logging is not ordinarily justified because all the trees are mature. Any left standing would soon depreciate in value. Furthermore, Douglas fir fails to reproduce itself satisfactorily except in clearings. Block, or patch logging, as shown in Figure 108 has proved advantageous. Clear cutting may under certain operating conditions be advisable also in uniform second growth, as of slash pine grown for pulpwood in the South. The southern pines need sunshine for satisfactory restocking, and give way to the more shade-tolerant oaks and other deciduous trees unless openings be large enough.

FIGURE 108. *Block or patch logging of ripe forest. Patches cut out will be sou by seed blown from blocks left standing. The land produces timber perpetuall see also Figure 113.* (Weyerhaeuser Timber Company—A.F.P.I. photo.)

Where it is economically feasible, as in mixed farm woods in high-grade mixed timber, selective cutting tree by tree is th best guarantee of sustained yield, but sustained-yield managemer need not be abandoned just because one must resort to clear cu ting. A sort of crop rotation becomes the alternative. Theoreticall an owner of land that produces a merchantable crop of pulpwoo in fifteen years can get a crop every year indefinitely, if he divide his property into fifteen blocks, and clear-cuts one block eac year. By careful attention to reproduction, natural or artificial, th first block harvested should be ready to cut again in its turn, fiftee years later.

In practice several variations of management secure the ol jectives of sustained-yield forestry—continual cropping, perpetu: restocking, maximum dollar yield, and minimum interference wit protective values. If all our forest land were under such systemati management, we should have more wood than we would knov what to do with (1); but now only about a half of our *commerci* forest area has any management at all (Figure 109). The Norri:

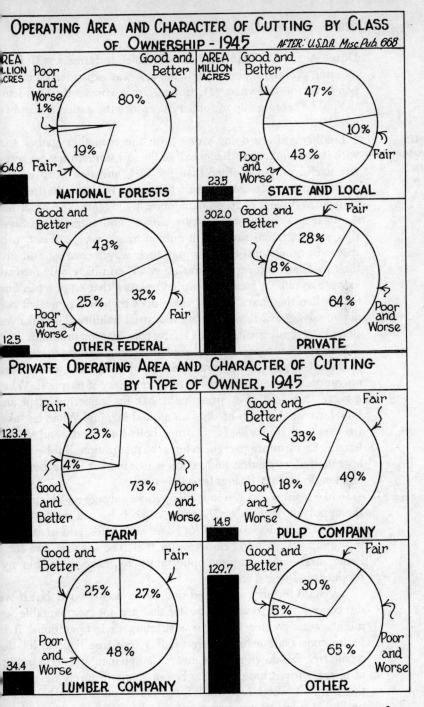

OPERATING AREA AND CHARACTER OF CUTTING BY CLASS OF OWNERSHIP - 1945 *AFTER: U.S.D.A. Misc. Pub. 668*

AREA MILLION ACRES

NATIONAL FORESTS — 64.8
- Poor and Worse 1%
- Good and Better 80%
- Fair 19%

STATE AND LOCAL — 23.5
- Good and Better 47%
- Fair 10%
- Poor and Worse 43%

OTHER FEDERAL — 12.5
- Good and Better 43%
- Fair 32%
- Poor and Worse 25%

PRIVATE — 302.0
- Good and Better 28%
- Fair 8%
- Poor and Worse 64%

PRIVATE OPERATING AREA AND CHARACTER OF CUTTING BY TYPE OF OWNER, 1945

FARM — 123.4
- Fair 23%
- Good and Better 4%
- Poor and Worse 73%

PULP COMPANY — 14.5
- Good and Better 33%
- Fair 49%
- Poor and Worse 18%

LUMBER COMPANY — 34.4
- Good and Better 25%
- Fair 27%
- Poor and Worse 48%

OTHER — 129.7
- Good and Better 30%
- Fair 5%
- Poor and Worse 65%

FIGURE 109. *Our National Forests set a good example, but private owners learn slowly. Sale of stumpage by contract stipulates minimum size of trees that may be cut, maximum stump height, and proper handling of logs and slash to minimize injury to the young growth and the forest floor.*

225

Doxey Act of 1937 provided for assistance to farmers with fore:
planting problems, and in 1951 the law was expanded to includ
non-farm forest owners (8). Congress has constantly broadene
the public sponsorship of forestry to ensure the nation a supply c
wood.

Slash, slab, and sawdust: liability, waste, or salvage?   Lumbermen are doing worse with the crop they gather tha
with its growing. Less than a half of the saw timber they cut serve
any useful purpose, other than for fuel, and one third of it :
wasted completely. Almost half the waste is *slash*—the trees de
stroyed, and parts of trees abandoned, by loggers. The other ha
results from *primary manufacture, sawing,* and *pulping* (20). Slasl
slab, shavings, and sawdust, a million tons a year, are not to b
sneezed at; but until they can pay their way to market and giv
their handler his hire, they are "no good" and have only *intrinsi*
value, like sails in a calm or buried treasure that no one can finc
Only when they have market value does their loss represent *ecc*
nomic salvage waste rather than industrial liability. Their conver
sion to *economic* goods poses a knotty conservation problem.

The solution reposes in *integrated logging* and *integrated us*
of the cut—logging for several species and grades of timber in on
operation, and supplying materials for a variety of purposes. Whe:
a logger cuts, out of a mixed stand, oak for a flooring plant anc
pine for a lumber mill he does integrated logging. When he take
from one oak tree a log for flooring, bolts for barrels, and shorte
lengths for furniture parts he refines the integration. But he canno
operate that way unless he has access to a market for each qualit;
and length he cuts; he logs for a living.

In like manner can the sawmill operator salvage materials whe:
the opportunity affords. Given the market, he can convert slab:
into dimension stock or parts for boxes and crates, and press shav
ings and sawdust into briquettes for fuel. The sawyer saws for ;
living, and welcomes any opportunity to make a salable by
product of salvaged waste.

We could forbid loggers and sawyers to waste wood, but if we
did compel them to salvage wastes that are not merchantable we
might cause greater waste by restricting their operations; it i:
better conservation to use even half a ripe tree than to let the
whole tree fall down and rot away. Complementary organizatior
of primary forest industries has begun, and will surely develop a:
the price of wood increases. By-products plants are becoming
profitable adjuncts to permanent wood-using factories much a:
the recovery of sulfuric acid complements copper smelting, gas
and volatile oils the coking of coal. Technical advice and public

ssistance can achieve much more than all attempts to *prohibit waste* by legal mandate. Sustained-yield and integrated use are ogical, economic partners. One implements the other, and both re gaining prominence. Liquidation cutting and one-product perations have made of themselves forest scavengers, and praccal considerations are starving them to death. One-product orest industry parallels single cash-crop farming. Both systems estroy the base upon which they depend, and cannot long ndure. Integration is to forestry as diversification is to agriculture.

Taxation can be a potent instrument for conserving our forest esources, but we have not employed it skillfully. Certain states ave literally taxed their forest right off the land by neglecting to dopt tax laws in support of deferred-yield forestry. A tax on tanding timber compels the owner to cut enough of it to defray hat tax. Where land under reforestation bears a tax assessment he owner is almost forced to commence cutting as soon as the nost vigorous trees attain minimum merchantable size. If *disarity* of levy obtains between commercial and noncommercial orest land the commercial category is penalized for being productive. Taxation of standing timber can tax it right off the land.

Intelligent taxation encourages forest conservation

Inept taxation has been a serious deterrent to forest conservaion, notably in "conservative" New England. Forests in various rowth categories occupy 77 per cent of New England's land. New Hampshire recently passed constructive forest tax legislaion that her neighbors might well copy. Meanwhile, depletion ontinues faster than reproduction in New England forests gen-rally (21, pp. 188-190). Many of our forest states actively encourge good forest management with constructive taxation (22). Tax xemption for land under forest reproduction and *deferment of ax on standing timber until it is cut* have gotten good response. The collection of a tax when timber is sold (severance tax) has roved difficult and costly, but it has brought benefits beyond its ntended purpose, the inducement of owners to grow mature timer. It has exposed many cases of timber "thieving," a particularly oxious form of larceny that hinders forestry in many places.

Unless the tax system favors him, the ordinary private owner annot hold on to cut-over while it restocks. He surrenders title to he state by tax delinquency. In due time an enterprising scaven-ger with a portable sawmill redeems the land by paying the back axes (often partially remitted), cuts it over as thoroughly and quickly as he can, and lets it revert to the state again. The vicious circle continues, serving badly both private and public interests, until such time as the state either assists the private owner by a

FIGURES 110 and 111. *Cattle and trees are poor partners in most cases. Above: healthy ungrazed oak-hickory wood lot in Illinois. The floor is a living reservoir for water, but very poor pasture.* (B. S. Meyer, F.S., photo.)
Below: overgrazed hardwoods in North Carolina. Understory and duff have been destroyed by the hooves of animals. The result is neither pasture nor forest (E. A. Johnson, F.S., photo.)

eral tax policy or retains title to the land indefinitely. Tax re-
sion can stop the scourge of recurrent tax reversion.

To a country boy, grown and far from home, the clang of a
wbell brings acute nostalgia. He recalls how sweet was its
usic when he, all alone in the dark, found the cows at the far end
the woods. But cowbells do not harmonize with forestry as they
o with boyhood recollections. The bell-cow with her following
ets little grass for much roaming, and, by passive "brute" force,
owly thins the green canopy above her.

**Cowbells
do not
harmonize
with
forestry**

Grazing and forestry are two primary land uses much better
vorced than combined. When they are mixed the forest usually
ffers. Since half of our forests are on farms, and most farm woods
e grazed much more severely than is good for them, the grazing
roblem looms large in forest conservation. Strictly man-made, the
roblem is readily soluble by man's own adjustment of land use.
f course, the carefully regulated grazing in our National Forests
on open areas within the forest rather than among the trees.

Large herds or flocks in the forest trample the duff and litter to
ieces, pack the soil, destroy young growth, and impair conditions
enerally (compare Figures 110 and 111). They restrict or elimi-
ate altogether all the normal services of forest, such as water stor-
ge, soil defense, wildlife habitat, and wood production. Only in
pecial situations is their presence beneficial. They can turn the
de of battle where pine seedlings wage a losing fight with oaks
prowsing goats are especially efficient). Of course, they can re-
nove the fire hazard by wearing the forest floor clean and hard,
ut such conditions are almost as bad as the consequences of
urning.

As a general rule, the farmer who would grow timber should
ence livestock out, and not in. If he wishes some shade for his
nimals, let him fence into his barnyard or pasture a part of his
voodland, and cross that part off his forestry ledger. If he be a
outherner concerned with pine growing he may need a rifle to
rive off rooting razorback marauders that kill young seedlings
nd lay the soil open to erosion. However, wild hogs are not
asture animals in the normal sense. Figure 112 indicates that
armers have begun to distinguish between pasture and forest.

**Modern
turpentining
practices
minimize
forest
damage**

Two species of southern pine—longleaf and slash—play a dual
ole in American forestry, yielding a major portion of our pulp-
vood crop and almost all of our naval stores. Popularly known as
he pitch pines, they are the species worked for turpentine. In the
varm southerly climate, where men take life "tolerably easy," the
rees have a longer growing season and produce wood at more
han twice the rate of their northern cousins (1, p. 40).

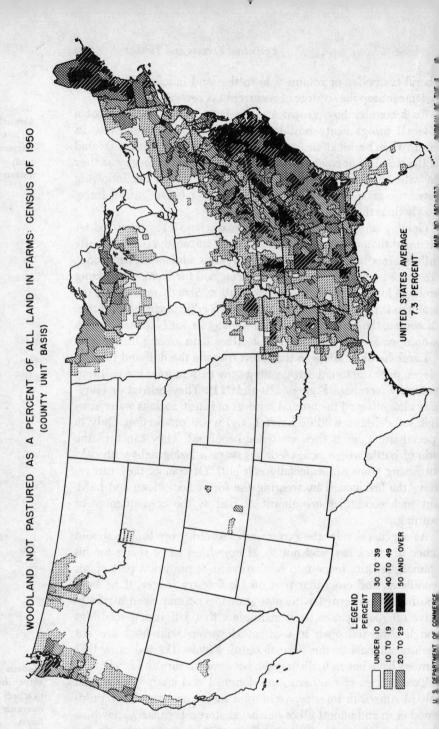

WOODLAND NOT PASTURED AS A PERCENT OF ALL LAND IN FARMS: CENSUS OF 1950
(COUNTY UNIT BASIS)

UNITED STATES AVERAGE
7.3 PERCENT

LEGEND
PERCENT

UNDER 10
10 TO 19
20 TO 29
30 TO 39
40 TO 49
50 AND OVER

U. S. DEPARTMENT OF COMMERCE

FIGURE 112. *Light grazing of forest may be permissible, but the marriage of cows and trees usually leads to divorce on grounds of incompatibility. One or the other gets the contested estate in a condition favorable to neither. A map like this for 1960 should have more dark areas on it. (Bureau of the Census map.)*

The history of turpentining carries the same stigma of waste and destruction that has characterized our exploitation of forests for lumber and timbers. The old methods of tapping were "extractive." Great wounds were cut into the trees, much of the resin was left on the trunk, or in the "box" gouged into the base of the tree to catch it, fire ignited the bleeding wound and burned it deeper, and bugs and decay completed the mayhem. Trees tapped for gum resin lost their value as saw timber because the choice log, the bottom one, was ruined for lumber. Young trees were bled to death, and many stout patriarchs died of torture.

When the original stands had disappeared it became necessary to use a new device for catching the resin; the second-growth trees were too small in diameter to permit cutting out an adequate "box." Thus came one step toward conservational turpentining—gutters and cups were attached to the tree. By experiment and demonstration the "streak"—the diagonal wound—has been reduced gradually to a fraction of its original depth and width. Acid applied after shallow (bark) chipping stimulates gum flow so one streak lasts two weeks instead of one, thus producing as much, and as long, from half as high a "face" (the entire chipped area on one side of a tree). By narrow streaking, by beginning the face low on the trunk, and by working a new face on the other side of the tree instead of running the original one twice as high, timber values are not seriously curtailed. Trees are less subject to fire damage or wind-throw, and live to a ripe old age.

Improvement of gathering and distillation has greatly reduced waste. Gum spirits of turpentine and gum rosin have become permanent crops in all our southeastern states, from North Carolina to Texas. The industry reached its peak about 1909, and was expected to die about 1930, but the regrowth of the pitch pines has exceeded all expectations. In anticipation of its demise we developed the wood naval stores industry, which extracts the pitch from old stumps and dead "lightwood," a unique form of salvage. More recently technology points to recovery of spirits from the liquor discharged by pulp mills.

Boiled down to a thick tar, the gum from pines was originally used to preserve ropes and to caulk the seams of ships. Hence the term "naval stores." Today a major use of turpentine is in paints with which to protect (conserve) wood and other materials. The United States remains the world's leading producer of naval stores, and we need not relinquish that leadership unless we revert to slovenly habits. The Federal Naval Stores Conservation Program initiated in 1936 encourages good behavior (8).

Up to this point we have dealt with problems of forest conser-

Insects,
diseases,
parasites:
the most
destructive
forest
enemies

vation largely man-made, and therefore nicely within our province to correct or arrest. We venture now into a brief exposition on a major forestry problem essentially natural in origin, and less amenable to specific correction. *Insects and diseases take a heavier toll than forest fires* (5), but while we have substantially reduced fire loss, and may almost eliminate it, we have made only limited gains against pests, and cannot be confident of thwarting their future inroads. The myriads of bugs, bacteria, and fungi that infest his realm try the forester's mettle much as the trace elements in soils try the pedologist's. Minute forms of life can steal us blind in the forest before we see them, and when their work becomes apparent it is often too late to apply effective countermeasures. They are the *most insidious and elusive* and the *most destructive* enemies of our forests.

Beetle, caterpillar, worm, or sawfly—a single species of insect on a rampage has damaged seriously, and even killed outright, tremendous stands of choice timber (23). The spruce budworm in the North, the Englemann spruce beetle in the Rocky Mountains, the Douglas fir tussock moth in the West, and many other infamous "bugs" have, time and again, made the most ruthless logging operation look like a Sunday-school picnic. Locally, a bug often has cheated the worst of all forest enemies, man himself.

Wilts, blights, rots, galls, cankers, and other infections are more insidious than the insects, and equally ruthless. Traveling by wind or water, carried by insects, birds, and other forest creatures (even by man himself), they are extremely difficult to contain, and no easier to exterminate. The chestnut blight spread the length of our eastern hardwood region from New England to the southern Appalachians, killing virtually every American chestnut tree. We were unable to check it. The oak wilt, first detected near the northwestern edge of the Central Hardwoods Region, threatens the life of a choice hardwood family. Many fungi are essential to the health of the forest, and we should protect them. How shall we destroy the bad ones without also destroying the good ones?

Various parasites cause serious forest damage by weakening and deforming their host trees and exposing them to more dangerous infestation and infection. Perhaps the worst parasite is the dwarf mistletoe (five species), which does great damage to our western conifers, more especially in ponderosa pine of the southern Rockies.

Did we intimate that we, the people, have little to do with the incidence of forest pests? We spoke too glibly. Several tree killers have been brought to America from overseas, among them the chestnut blight, which all but wiped out one of our most durable and versatile hardwoods, the Dutch elm disease, that threatens several species with a similar fate, and the white pine blister rust, that jeopardizes a chosen species in eastern forest reproduction. Through forest exploitation we have often upset the natural balance that held the pests in check. By poor housekeeping we have bred pestilence. By bruising and burning we have exposed the trees to attack. We have violated the communal organization of forests, and may stand to pay dearly for the offense.

Our campaign against forest pests follows two lines of action: direct (frontal) attack to stop or prevent an epidemic, and the enlistment of natural forces (grand strategy) to oppose any threat of violence. The latter technique depends mainly upon *management* that maintains natural forest conditions and healthy, vigorous growth. It is the forester's "cold war," the safe, sure way to victory without shooting. The former technique involves armed combat to subdue a hostile enemy; DDT sprayed from an airplane is one example. But in a "hot war" we cannot always kill the enemy without also striking our own "guerrillas" and potential collaborators. Let no one but a trained forest pathologist or entomologist declare this kind of war, and let him do so only as a last resort. As with any war, victory may be more apparent than real.

To maintain reasonable security against the ravages of insects and diseases we need public enlightenment and area organization much as for fire protection. Just as with fire, detection and prevention are better than costly suppression, and every forest area is a potential threat to others in the neighborhood. Against either fire or epidemic, cooperation is essential and should be inclusive. But the novice cannot spot an impending disease as he can a fire; that is for the trained scientist. Continuous research, systematic survey, and improved silvicultural practice are urgent needs. The Forest Pest Control Act passed by Congress in 1947 authorized necessary surveys in both public and private forests. It made forest pest control, officially, the national problem that it is. As later implemented, that Act provides for an Annual Pest Survey in order that epidemics may be detected before they reach disastrous proportions.

Wild denizens of the forest perform acts both beneficent and injurious to the vegetation that feeds and shelters them. Terrestrial and arboreal creatures—feathered, furred, or hooved—disperse seeds as if in payment for those they eat, but in their regular round of activity they also carry diseases from one benefactor to

Forest wildlife performs both constructive and destructive functions

another. Birds that sow cherry pits miles from the tree may carry diseases even greater distances. Squirrels plant nuts, but also eat buds and spread fungi. Mourning doves destroy many noxious seeds, but also eat the first, tender shoots from pine seeds. Rabbits and other bark eaters injure or kill young saplings by girdling them. Deer and other browsing animals (leaf and twig eaters) can be so destructive of young hardwoods as to eradicate them. Mice and other seed-eating rodents can be a grave handicap to reforestation by seed-sowing. In actual cases reproduction of certain conifers by sowing has succeeded only when poison was sown beforehand to decimate the rodents (24).

Cooperation with nature reproduces forest better than sowing or planting

One cannot review even casually the contradictions in animal behavior without pondering the ruling force of nature's balance and asking himself whether man, the superior species, is not most frustrated by his own failure to conform. A case in point is artificial sowing and planting where nature, given the initiative, would do the work better free of charge (25). Had men more fully comprehended that fact during the initial stripping of our forests, and made only moderate provision for its normal operation, reforestation would have been spontaneous and our present forest situation would be much more favorable. Where forest once stood it would have risen again, quite promptly, had Paul Bunyan and his breed been content to chop somewhat smaller holes in the mantle or at least left a few more scattered remnants. Where forests have once prevailed they seek to return without our solicitation—quickly to sites unimpaired, and slowly to places from which, in our destructive exploitation, we caused the soil or its substance to escape. In the East, North, and South the deed was done before we knew the error of our ways. We learned in time, however, to save seed blocks or strips (seed-producing trees) in parts of the virgin forest in the West, and thus secure natural restocking of intervening clear-cut areas (12). Figure 113 shows the seed-block system in operation.

Natural reproduction is by far the cheapest and surest means of reforestation. With selective cuttings reproduction takes place continuously even under very light cropping, and requires no special attention if the grower will be content with a future preponderance of shade-tolerant trees (broad-leafed species, mainly). If he wishes to retain certain sun-loving conifers, either in pure or mixed stands, he must so manage the present forest that adequate openings admit sunshine to the floor. Excepting a few, such as hemlock, conifers are intolerant of shade, requiring more or less direct sunshine for healthy development. Unfortunately the

FIGURE 113. *Seed block left standing when a mature, even-aged forest was logged scientifically in the Pacific Northwest. On high ground, which ensures maximum seed dispersal, individual trees would be subject to wind-throw. Natural reseeding of certain pines, as in the southeast, can be accomplished by a few, scattered seed trees per acre. A 300-foot spacing of cone-bearing culls may be adequate.* (Photo courtesy West Coast Lumbermen's Association.)

shade-tolerant species are not generally discouraged by abundant sunshine, and being more versatile they often tend to overwhelm the more sensitive needle-leafed species where the two types are mixed. To secure coniferous reproduction from such admixture may entail special measures against hardwood sprouts. Goats have been employed, but selective toxic sprays are likely to be the best answer. In pure coniferous stands where clear cutting and *seed blocks* are advisable, suitable ground conditions may be the main reproduction problem demanding attention. The tiny, featherweight seeds must be given access to the soil. Very often enough surface is laid bare by logging operations, but some kind of mechanical stirring, or burning, may also be necessary. Volunteer reproduction for sustained yield under clear cutting is best ensured by systematic logging of alternate checkerboard "blocks" (Figure 108), or parallel "strips." The patchwork system for quick, natural restocking, while most economical and profitable, is also nicely compatible with protective forest functions.

Where for any reason natural reproduction fails, the timber grower has a choice between the direct sowing of seed and the planting of nursery-grown seedlings. In large operations successful reproduction has been accomplished by seeding from an airplane, which is much cheaper than planting, but also less certain to produce a suitable stand. The development of tree planting machines gives promise of economical planting on large properties, just where we are now most delinquent. Mechanical tree planting is becoming a custom business much as grain threshing used to be (8). Such planting is transforming many ghastly cut-over areas, notably in the Upper Lakes Region.

Meanwhile, many large wood users, such as lumber and paper companies, while necessarily avoiding the risk of heavy capital outlay for planting their own holdings, have established nurseries to supplement those maintained publicly, in order that small, private forest owners might have good planting stock at very little, if any, cost. This has been one of the most reassuring developments in American forestry, its intrinsic value probably surpassed by its promotion of desirable social attitudes. Tree planting has made America forestry conscious, because a planted area is the most obvious evidence of forestry, even to the casual tourist who drives by it smoking a cigar. The planter was probably more firmly impressed by aches in his back and blisters in his hands. The diagram series in Figure 114 shows how he might have done the job.

By the end of 1951, we had almost 8 million acres of planted forest (26), half of it on farms and private properties, the keys to our future wood supply. Most of this planting was done by hand, and most of the trees are conifers native to the areas. True, many plantings are of poor quality, on worn-out or eroded soil, on sand so deep or rock so bare that the hardiest species cannot produce a timber crop of high quality. But most of them occupy land otherwise wasted, saving soil and water as they grow into useful, serviceable forest.

Intensive silviculture may gain greater prominence in the American scene

Silviculture, the science and practice of growing trees as a crop, will probably be an every-day word in American conversation before our grandchildren manage our affairs and formulate our policies. All the planting and management to date are a mere beginning compared with what can be done under intensive silvicultural practices. Tree farming has barely begun in America; our forestry remains largely haphazard and halfhearted. We are inclined to plant trees where nothing else will grow, ignoring the fact that many species demand comparatively good soil for satisfactory development, that many areas lack even the meager substance to keep alive those species least exacting.

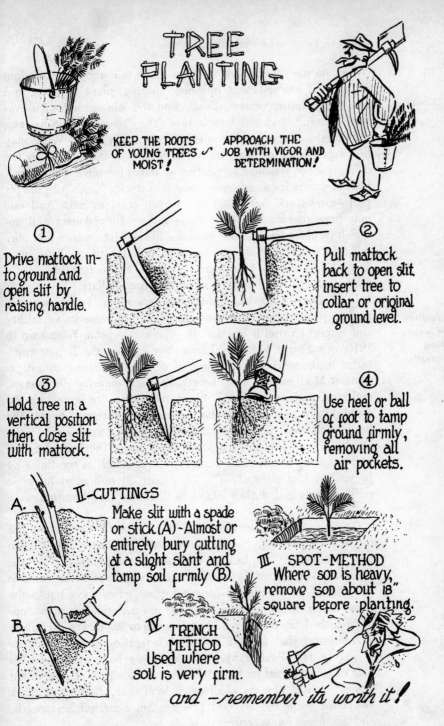

TREE PLANTING

KEEP THE ROOTS OF YOUNG TREES MOIST!

APPROACH THE JOB WITH VIGOR AND DETERMINATION!

① Drive mattock into ground and open slit by raising handle.

② Pull mattock back to open slit, insert tree to collar or original ground level.

③ Hold tree in a vertical position then close slit with mattock.

④ Use heel or ball of foot to tamp ground firmly, removing all air pockets.

A.

II - CUTTINGS
Make slit with a spade or stick (A) - Almost or entirely bury cutting at a slight slant and tamp soil firmly (B).

B.

III. SPOT-METHOD
Where sod is heavy, remove sod about 18" square before planting.

IV. TRENCH METHOD
Used where soil is very firm.

and — remember it's worth it!

FIGURE 114. Commercial tree planting is not always economically feasible, but in many situations planting is the best means of reforestation. Supervised tree planting by school children or college students should be more productive of future conservators than of timber.

But, on the other hand, we hear much talk about the wisdom of soil and site selection, optimum spacing, plant breeding and selection, planting season, disinfection and immunization, cultivation, pruning, and soil fertilization. The "tree farm" movement promoted by large lumber companies, initially in the West, may be prophetic of genuine timber cropping in the future. In the offing one can visualize turpentine orchards for pitch and lumber, walnut groves for nuts, veneer, and gun stocks, "fields" of pine for pulp—grown and harvested like wheat, corn, or oats. And one may hope that there will be those sufficiently visionary and unselfish to plant acorns, that someone in the 21st century A.D. may sell white oaks for several hundred dollars apiece. Even now a good, big one on a northerly exposure and reasonably near a market may be worth more than one hundred dollars.

Wood preservatives might better be called "conservatives"

Increasing scarcity and rising prices encourage forest *conservation by preservative treatment* of wood to increase its versatility and extend its useful life. Established at Madison, Wisconsin in 1910, our Forest Products Laboratory is now the largest institution in the world for the study of wood and its uses. Investigations at Madison and elsewhere have made amazing discoveries, and perfected, among many others, techniques for increasing the durability of timber products. Preservative treatment triples the life of a railroad tie, and does about as well for a telephone pole. Of the 230 million wooden fence posts set in the United States each year the life of some is multiplied as much as ten times by prescribed treatment (1, 27). Of almost 30 million railway tie replacements laid during 1953 less than two in a hundred were untreated (28).

Coal-tar creosote, the old stand-by, and pentachlorophenol are the leading preserving materials to date. The latter, being clean and odorless on application, and permitting painting of the treated wood, has the advantage over creosote of being suitable for interior use. Both are most effective when forced into the wood under pressure. More than 200 pressure-treating plants operate in the United States, adding from 20 to 30 years of usefulness to the timber they treat (27). One such treating plant is pictured in Figure 115. Paul Bunyan would surely have swallowed his bale of tobacco had he been told that a fence post of pine might be made to last 30 years, challenging white oak, chestnut, or black locust for endurance. Wood preservation accomplishes specific and significant forest conservation.

While our annual per capita consumption of lumber declines as scarcity of saw timber raises the price, we multiply our total

FIGURE 115. *Preservation is a form of conservation. These tram-loads of ties, poles, and posts are going into pressure cylinders for treatment with creosote at a Charleston, S.C., wood preserving plant.* (Photo courtesy the Koppers Company, Inc.)

equirement of pulpwood (19). For paper, plywood, plastics, and aminated structural members our use of wood has increased substantially. For fuel it has declined most conspicuously, though we still burn as fuel approximately 50 million cords annually (1). It is estimated that between 1900 and 1950 we reduced our direct waste of wood by almost one half (2), but we persist in the extravagant habit of making matches, pulp, and fuel out of saw logs.

Timber-based industries and trade employ about six per cent of our manpower, and pay almost as big a portion of our wages and salaries. Our average annual gross value of all timber products since World War II has been estimated at 15 to 20 billion dollars (29). And those figures take no account of protective forest values.

We have enough forest land (Figure 116) to produce all the timber we need, and incidentally to protect the watersheds involved. But 75 or perhaps 100 of the 624 million acres need planting (8, p. 24), and most of the remainder must be better managed than heretofore. Through numerous public agencies and private organizations forestry advice and assistance are available to

Through conservation we can have all the wood we need

everyone. Forestry programs such as the "Tree Farm" movement are gaining momentum (30, 31), and a comprehensive plan for American forestry as a whole (32) may eventually get the necessary group support for effective application.

Our schools and other social institutions, already actively assisting, can do much more to conserve our forest resources. If every school child could be privileged to plant one forest tree our forest problems might dissipate in a generation. With no other natural resource does our entire citizenry come into such direct, conscious contact as it does with the forest, and to no other natural resource is public interest and responsibility more vital. Let the public be adequately informed of the contributions forests make to our individual and national well-being, and the forests will prosper. Unless we be fools, we shall never be short of wood. Our forest lands have such potential productivity that, should trade relations permit, we might soon export paper pulp instead of importing it. Late in 1955, the Forest Service announced that total growth actually exceeded the total amount of timber cut (33). The American forest industry, as a whole, can operate on a sustained-yield basis long before the year 2000 if we apply zealously the practical conservation measures now at our command. Other forest benefits can be magnified in direct proportion to the yield of timber.

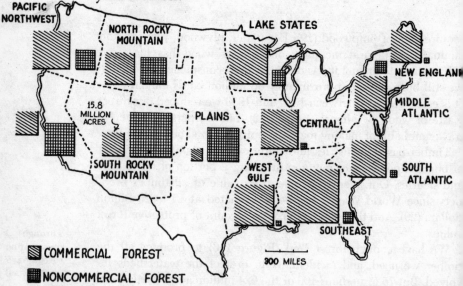

FIGURE 116. *Forest lands of the United States by regions. Properly protected and managed, our remaining forest lands will produce all the wood we need besides performing other important functions.*

CHAPTER 10: REFERENCES CITED BY NUMBER

(1) "Domestic Timber Resources," *Report of the President's Materials Policy Commission,* 8 vols.; V: *Selected Reports to the Commission,* Report 5. Washington, D.C., 1952.

(2) Robert K. Winters, editor, *Fifty Years of Forestry in the U.S.A.,* Society of American Foresters, Washington, D.C., 1950.

(3) William B. Greeley, *Forests and Men,* Doubleday and Company, Inc., Garden City, New York, 1951.

(4) Forest Service, U.S.D.A., "Our National Forests," *Agriculture Information Bulletin No. 49,* 1951.

(5) *Natural Enemies of Timber Abundance: Report of the Chief of the Forest Service, 1951.*

(6) Stanley G. Fontanna, "State Forests," *Trees: The Yearbook of Agriculture, 1949,* Washington, D.C., 1949, pp. 390-394.

(7) George A. Duthie, "Community Forests," *Trees,* pp. 394-398.

(8) *Cooperation in Forestry: Report of the Chief of the Forest Service, 1950.*

(9) C. M. Granger, "The National Forests Are In the Black," *American Forests,* LVIII, No. 1, July 1952.

(10) *Forests, Fish, Wildlife: Their Development in the Tennessee Valley,* Department of Forestry Relations, T.V.A., Norris 1946.

(11) Erle Kauffman, "They Had Faith in the Land," *American Forests,* LVI, No. 3, March 1950.

(12) Harold Bradley Say and Nort Baser, "They Plan By the Century," *American Forests,* LVIII, No. 2, February 1952.

(13) James B. Craig, "What's New on the Horizon?" *American Forests,* LXI, No. 3, March 1955, pp. 24-27, 91.

(14) J. P. Weyerhaeuser, Jr., "Answering the Threat of Forest Depletion," *Ou Renewable Resources Can Be Sustained—A Symposium,* The Chamber Commerce of the United States, Washington, D.C., 1949, pp. 21-24.

(15) R. D. McCulley, "Management of Natural Slash Pine Stands in the Fla woods of South Georgia and North Florida," *Circular No. 845,* U.S.D.A 1950.

(16) A. F. Gustafson, C. H. Guise, W. J. Hamilton, Jr., and H. Ries, *Conserva tion in the United States,* Comstock Publishing Company, Inc., Ithacɛ New York, 1949.

(17) George M. Jemison, A. W. Lindenmuth and J. J. Keetch, "Forest Fire Danger Measurement in the Eastern United States," *Agriculture Hana book No. 1,* F.S., 1949.

(18) "Fabulous Bear, Famous Service Fight Annual Billion-Dollar Fire," *News week,* June 2, 1952.

(19) "Making the Most of Timber Resources," *Report of the Materials Policy Commission; I: Foundations for Growth and Security,* Chapter 8.

(20) "A Reappraisal of the Forest Situation," *Wood Waste in the United States* Report 4, F.S., Washington, D.C., 1947.

(21) *The New England Economy,* a report to the President, transmitting ɛ study initiated by the Council of Economic Advisers, and prepared by itɛ Committee on the New England Economy, Washington, D.C., July, 1951

(22) Ralph W. Marquis, "Forest Yield Taxes," *Circular No.899,* U.S.D.A., 1952

(23) Arthur H. Carhart, "Mass Murder in the Spruce Belt," *American Forests* LV, No. 3, March 1949.

(24) W. E. McQuilkin, "Direct Seeding of Trees," *Trees,* pp. 136-146.

(25) Irvine T. Haig, Kenneth P. Davis, and Robert H. Weidman, "Natura Regeneration in the Western White Pine Type," *Bulletin (Technical) No 767,* U.S.D.A., May 1941.

(26) Erle Kauffman, editor, *The Conservation Yearbook, 1952,* The Conserva tion Yearbook, Washington, D.C., 1952.

(27) "The Technology of Forest Products," Report of the Materials Policy Commission; IV: The Promise of Technology, Chapter 10.

(28) *Cross Tie Bulletin,* Railway Tie Association, St. Louis, July 1954, p. 13.

(29) Edward C. Crafts and Martha A. Dietz, "Forest Resources and the Na tion's Economy," *Trees,* pp. 721-730.

(30) Alfred Toombs, "Money Grows on Trees," *Collier's,* October 21, 1950.

1) William D. Welsh, *Growing Paper on Tree Farms,* Crown Zellerbach Corporation, Seattle, 1951.

2) "A Program for American Forestry," *American Forests,* LX, No. 9, September 1954, pp. 43-50.

3) *Timber Resource Review,* preliminary report, F.S., October 1955.

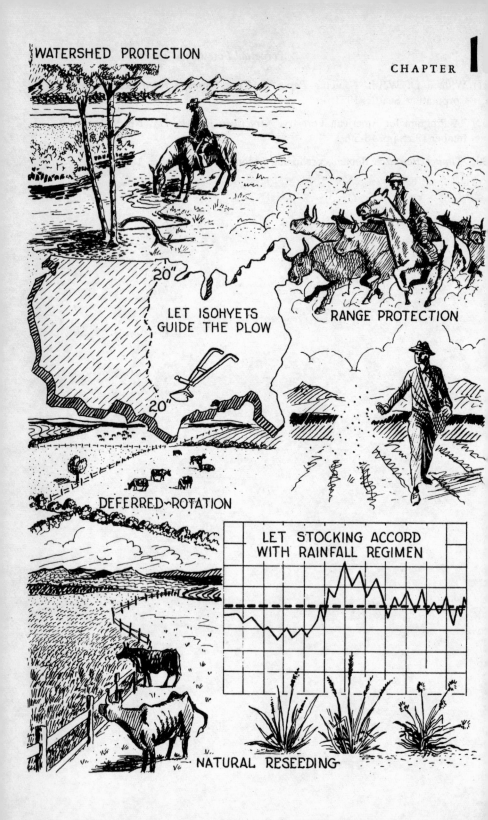

WATERSHED PROTECTION

CHAPTER 1

LET ISOHYETS GUIDE THE PLOW

20"

20"

RANGE PROTECTION

DEFERRED-ROTATION

LET STOCKING ACCORD WITH RAINFALL REGIMEN

NATURAL RESEEDING

poliation and Restoration

of our Dry Grasslands

*nature demands that we mend and maintain
the protective grass cover
to conserve our dry grasslands*

ᶠOURTH AMONG OUR REGENERATIVE RESOURCES WE SHALL CONSIDER
he great, natural pastures that dominate landscape, philosophy,
nd economic history from the Hundredth Meridian westward,
rom our northern to our southern boundary (1). Before the advent
f white men, grazing land of various types occupied an estimated
rea of 850 million acres (2, p. 71), including almost all of the
Great Plains region east of the Rockies, and large portions of that
ast complex west of the Rockies known as the Intermontane
Basins and Plateaus.

In nature's arrangement, satisfactory to the Indians, only forested slopes and a few spots of barren desert interrupted the
great expanse of dry grasslands. White men have dotted the realm
with forest cut-over and irrigation projects, assaulted it with
plows along its entire eastern "front," and gnawed holes in its
cover with excessive herds and flocks. They have respected and
understood the grasslands no more than they have waters, soils,
and forests (3).

A natural grass cover is fairly indicative of climatic limitation that inhibits forest growth by dearth of moisture or warmth,
or both—but the frontiersmen were stayed by neither climate nor
plant ecology. They learned by trial and error, erring magnifi-
cently and learning indignantly.

Where grasses and shrubs or forbs prevail against trees—as on
the Plains and in the western mountain valleys—there is barely

enough occasional rain to keep those plants alive, and not enough to sustain a natural succession of ordinary trees. From approximately the Hundredth Meridian westward, the plains, plateaus and valleys receive less than 20 inches of rainfall annually on the average, and in many places less than 10 (4, 5). (See Figure 4 on page 13.) If those 20 inches—or even those 10—came without fail marginality might admit some compromise, but it happens climatically that *where the least rain falls it is also the least reliable.* Departures from the "normal" are the rule rather than the exception; where the balance is most delicate, it is most frequently upset. The 20-inch isohyet (rain line) oscillates radically eastward and westward; life on the plains blooms and withers as the rainfall waxes and wanes (6). Droughts come so frequently (Figure 117) that they should be anticipated by the land user and accepted by all residents as a regional handicap.

In good years the grasses flourish, producing abundant seeds, deep roots, and strong bulbs and crowns. Those plant parts can survive extreme drought by remaining dormant, and burst into verdure and bloom when the rains come again. Grasses and forbs with such special equipment as bulbs and rhizomes that survive drought in dormancy bridge the gap between forest and desert. Giant cacti go them one better by storing up water when it comes, but none of our ordinary trees can compete. The lowly grama grasses hold their ground where the mighty oaks must yield (7, 8); recurrently decimated by drought and wind long before man's intervention magnified those hazards, the surviving grasses possess amazing powers of recuperation (Figure 129).

From Indiana westward the pioneers to the Northern Middle West sailed veritable seas of grass in prairie schooners to a region where by some strange quirk of fortune needle grass, blue stem, and other stalwarts had driven a deep wedge of *tall grass prairie* eastward into the forest. Many dropped anchor in the rich, black soil, and when the Homestead Act of 1862 gave each wagon's "skipper" a quarter section for the asking, settlers soon filled the billowing prairies and broke the sod to sow wheat. That episode was not inconsistent with natural attributes—in fact, it fashioned our bountiful "bread basket"—but west of the prairie, west of the Mississippi, the schooners ran into cross-winds and shoals. Many ran aground, others went adrift, and our grassland problem began because they had crossed the western boundary of *tall* grass and invaded the *short* grama and buffalo grasses without thinking anything of it (Figure 118).

Nor can we blame the pioneers; experts today cannot quite

(left margin notes:) Grassland makes the geographic transition between forest and desert

The prairie schooner sailed broad seas of grass

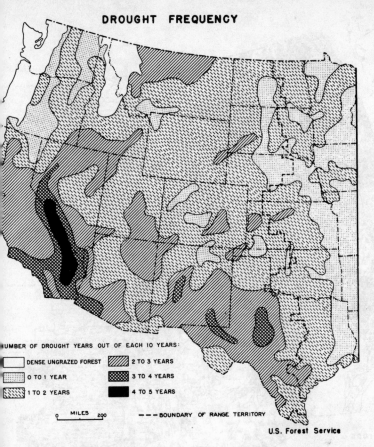

NUMBER OF DROUGHT YEARS OUT OF EACH 10 YEARS:

DENSE UNGRAZED FOREST		2 TO 3 YEARS	
0 TO 1 YEAR		3 TO 4 YEARS	
1 TO 2 YEARS		4 TO 5 YEARS	

MILES 0 200   — — — BOUNDARY OF RANGE TERRITORY

U.S. Forest Service

FIGURE 117. *Erratic rainfall is a natural characteristic of the dry grass-lands that men have failed to respect. Deficient moisture means that land utilization must be restricted accordingly. Rainfall averages cannot be used as criteria of land capability, because the recurrent drought years fix the limits of productivity.*

agree on the location of that boundary, except to say that it is a transitional, shifting zone rather than a precise, fixed line. Nature does not draw many sharp boundaries. Be that as it may, when Americans occupied the short-grass plains and the more dessicated shrub and bunch grass country farther west, they collided head-on with *arid* and *semiarid* conditions, entirely lacking in experience to cope with them (note the complex pattern of range types in Figure 118). They did not know that sod-making grass species tighten their belts and disperse themselves in bunches where moisture is insufficient to sustain a complete cover. They knew not how thin the ice they trod in their westward race for riches (9).

The race began promptly upon cessation of domestic hostilities in 1865, and in a few years there developed in the dry West

Cowboys and
cattle made
a brief bid
for water
and glory

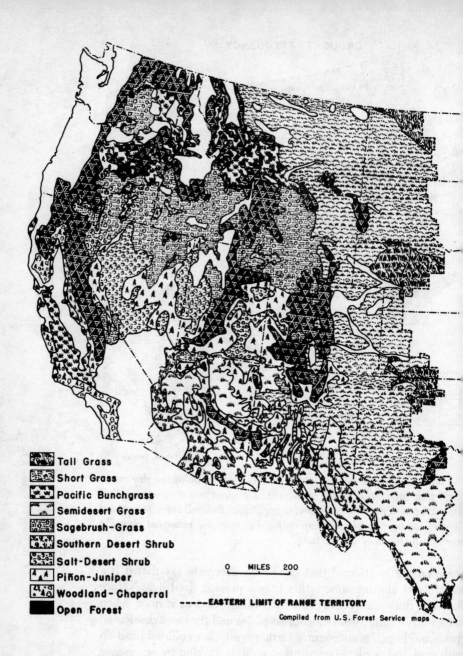

Tall Grass
Short Grass
Pacific Bunchgrass
Semidesert Grass
Sagebrush-Grass
Southern Desert Shrub
Salt-Desert Shrub
Piñon-Juniper
Woodland-Chaparral
Open Forest

0   MILES   200

-----EASTERN LIMIT OF RANGE TERRITORY

Compiled from U.S. Forest Service maps

FIGURE 118. *Principal range types. Vegetation reflects the degree of natural limita-*
tion and indicates the use capability of an area. In many places natural range condi-
tions can be improved artificially, as by clearing and seeding, much as certain
soils inherently poor can be made productive by appropriate tillage and
fertilization.

...at "leather-pounding" six-shooter era of American history that, ...r good or ill, holds our schoolboys entranced in TV and Satur-...ay movies—Hollywood has capitalized where many stockmen ...ent bankrupt. The great cattle empire was short-lived, for the ...attle man lived violently in a violent land. Nature plagued him ...ith scorching droughts and freezing blizzards (10, 11), which ...ften took ruinous toll of his herds. The range was open, public, ...nd Colt's "equalizer" was his best claim to water holes and grass. ...heepmen, "nesters" (farmers), poachers, and rustlers were the ...ane of his existence. Fortunes were quickly made and as quickly ...st, grasses dwindled and markets slumped, railroads, home-...teaders, and prairie dogs encroached upon the cow-puncher's ...ide open spaces. Settlers chose land with water on it, and every ...ew farm deprived the stockmen of a grazing area tributary ...hereto often several times as large as the farm itself. And the *...tronger land bond* would not be denied: the plow unhorsed the ...addle.

Coincidence made doubly tragic our peopling of the dry grass-...ands. Settlement advanced upon them when a cycle of wet years ...ave them extraordinary powers of deception. Nature played a ...ean trick on the rough-and-ready cowboy who in righteous ...rath defended the range as it was, and died without knowing ...is wisdom.

But the temporarily lush and fertile areas could not be with-...eld from the land-hungry people desirous of plowing, fencing, ...nd establishing permanent homes. They came, and plowed up ...he incomparable native grasses, many species of which possessed ...he remarkable faculty of curing on the root and retaining con-...iderable nutritional value where they stood, making hay gratis ...or winter feeding (12, 13). Not only did we permit settlement—...ve encouraged it; and when climatic reverses exposed the true ...arginality of this land, the Congress sought to conceal rather ...han correct its stupendous error. In 1911 it passed the "Enlarged" ...Homestead Act, allowing the grassland settler 320 acres; and ...when even a half-section proved inadequate for the support of a ...amily, it doubled the ante again with the "Stock-Raising" Home-...tead Act of 1916 (14). Even then, Congress was too conservative, ...s may be seen in Figure 119.

At first thought, 640 acres of land might be regarded a fine ...ift, but in the drier, more westerly range lands whole sections ...did not always suffice, especially as they were doled out in rec-...angular pattern without regard for streams or other water sup-...ly. Many areas remained unclaimed—parts of the Public Domain

we could not give away; until Congress passed the so-called Tay
lor Grazing Control Act in 1934, these were grazed without di
cretion by any rancher who could drive his animals to them
"First come, first served" was the maxim of competing graziers
In order to maintain their operations, especially in dry season
they over-grazed the public range (and their own too, for tha
matter) and denied it the respite essential for recovery. Th
weakened cover gave way to erosion by wind and water, weed
overwhelmed more palatable species, and forage values dwindle
to a fraction of their original carrying capacity.

**Barbed wire
and the steel
plow disrobed
the plains**

Barbed wire, patented in 1874, foreshadowed the end of th
Great Plains cattle empire, and when in 1886-87 a combinatio
of drought, blizzard, and over-grazing brought disaster to flock
and herds, the steel plow resumed with renewed vigor its empt
campaign against spurs, saddles, six-shooters and branding iron
Big farmers took over where bigger graziers had failed, ap
parently blind to their own impending failure. They plowed unt
virtually nothing plowable remained unturned. They brough
bigger and better machines to pulverize more thoroughly soil
never intended to know anything more mechanical than th
hooves of a cow. From gang plows and six-horse teams they pro
gressed to steam engines and gasoline tractors, the more quickl
to turn the soil after each successive crop of wheat or cotton. The
cut a broad swath for big stakes; and those who "hit it right" go
rich (9).

Sobered by drought, wind, and crop failure, many adopted dry
farming methods to store two years' moisture for one crop; man
a wheat farmer in Kansas, the Dakotas, and the Palouse of easter
Washington owed his survival to clean fallow and dust mulch
Others elected to "stir it all every year, and hope for enough rai
to make a crop." Those wishful thinkers cursed the drought si
days of the week and prayed for rain on Sunday, and despite thei
most fervent pleas they were the first to feel the pinch whe
drought persisted. Even he who practiced dry farming expose
his soil to wind erosion during dry spells and to water erosio
when the torrential rains came; to exercise caution on the on
hand he incurred a risk on the other, and in his attempt to stor
moisture, he forfeited the soil he was trying to moisten. Eve
"dry farming" failed when extreme dessication persisted. (Im
proved soil conserving techniques have by now rehabilitated man
farms that once literally blew away.)

What with drought and deluge, wind and flood, blizzard, dust
hail, and grasshoppers, farming of the dry grasslands has alway

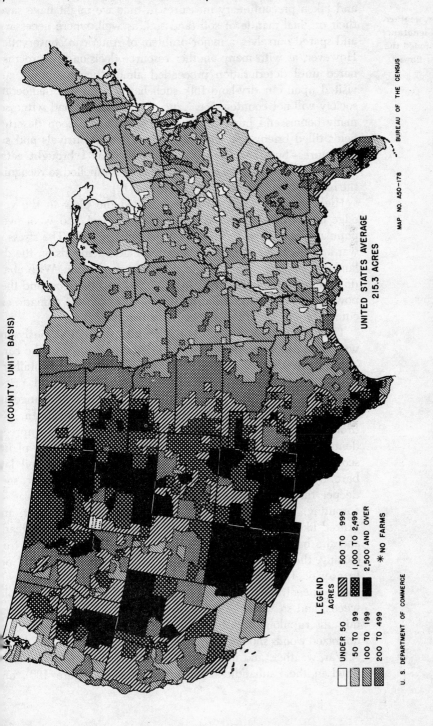

FIGURE 119. *Apparently Congress was too conservative even when it increased the homestead unit to a whole section. Many modern ranches contain several square miles of land. (One section = one square mile = 640 acres.)*

(COUNTY UNIT BASIS)

BUREAU OF THE CENSUS

MAP NO. A50-178

UNITED STATES AVERAGE
215.3 ACRES

LEGEND
ACRES

UNDER 50
50 TO 99
100 TO 199
200 TO 499
500 TO 999
1,000 TO 2,499
2,500 AND OVER
* NO FARMS

U. S. DEPARTMENT OF COMMERCE

been a precarious business. Had we but known their limitation and taken precautionary measures in time we might have saved their original mantle of soil (and sod, as well, where necessary) and spared ourselves a major problem of American conservation. However, as with many another resource decision, we procrastinated until deterioration proceeded almost beyond repair and visited upon our dry-land folk such hardship as our democratic society will not countenance. True, the grasslands had witnessed many booms and busts before—homes built and soon deserted, fields tilled briefly and then abandoned, happy arrivals and sad departures—but the aftermath of World War I brought catastrophe on such a scale that we were finally compelled to recognize the inherent marginality of the grasslands (2).

High wartime prices for wheat invited the plow to the very edge of the desert; comparable prices for beef and wool over-populated the abused, constricted range (2, p. 130). The stress of war and the fever of postwar inflation made demands on the dry lands far beyond their limits of sustained production. With abandon unforgivable even under stress, we sapped them beyond their powers of recuperation, during the most auspicious climatic circumstances they can experience. We spent them.

Then came drought and depression almost simultaneously and with tragic consequences. The cattle market crashed in the early 'twenties, making many stockmen war casualties, while rainfall and wheat prices continued favorable to agriculture. Land prices soared and farming expanded, almost unopposed by range interests. But the ill-founded prosperity was short-lived. In 1930 drought announced its return, and in 1934 it reached unprecedented severity (15). Hot, dry winds lashed the open plains, scorching the remaining grasses and ripping into the soil laid bare by plowing or over-grazing. Farmers drilled their seed deeper than usual, and it "blew out" of the ground instead of sprouting. The soil took flight in billowing clouds of dust, and drifted like snow along the ground, engulfing fences, farmsteads, and the barren stream courses. As double punishment for trespassing, the angry winds sought to bury the soil they could not tear away. The scourge drove eastward with moderated intensity as far as central Minnesota, bringing a brief visitation of tumble-weeds, and so weakening heavily grazed oak woods that a certain unscrupulous bark beetle took the opportunity to kill them; ungrazed woods showed only slight injury.

War, weather, and ignorance had fashioned the so-called Dust Bowl in the Panhandle-West Kansas region (Figure 120), and

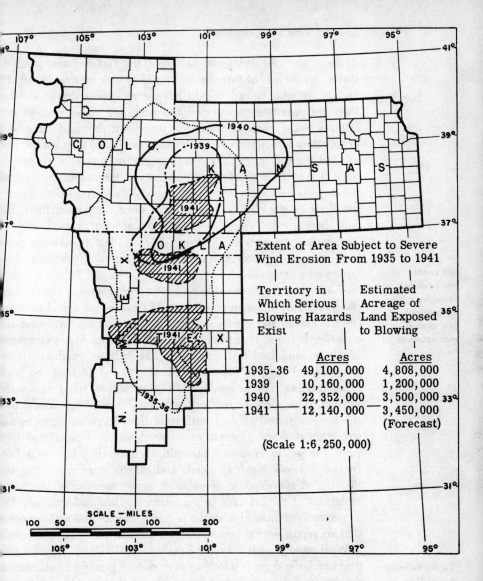

Extent of Area Subject to Severe
Wind Erosion From 1935 to 1941

Territory in
Which Serious
Blowing Hazards
Exist

Estimated
Acreage of
Land Exposed
to Blowing

	Acres	Acres
1935-36	49,100,000	4,808,000
1939	10,160,000	1,200,000
1940	22,352,000	3,500,000
1941	12,140,000	3,450,000 (Forecast)

(Scale 1:6,250,000)

SCALE — MILES
100   50   0   50   100   200

FIGURE 120. *Blow area map, Southern Great Plains. Wind fashioned the Dust Bowl at
our invitation, and we put the blame on drought. Soil drifting and dusting scourged the
grasslands long before they were plowed or grazed; but their inept appropriation by
white men exposed them to hazards against which nature had previously afforded a
goodly degree of protection.* (S.C.S. map, 1947.)

damage was also serious in Nebraska, the Dakotas and other dr states. An exodus of farmers and families was inevitable (16, 17 and many who stayed should have gone. Some departed whe their soil went, some needed the prodding of successive cro failures. Some gave up when the well went dry, and some wei expelled by foreclosure. Many "stuck it out" until they had nothin left but the mortgage. The forced migration was of such propo: tions that in 1934 the federal government intervened to mitigat the tragedy and prevent its recurrence. We determined to recloth the drier of the dry grasslands with grass, and keep them tha way henceforth. There were many cases of backsliding fc "quick-rich" wheat during World War II, but regulatory meas ures and rain prevented repetition of the post-World War I ca lamity on a general scale.

We could not prohibit drought, so we passed a law against its consequences

Shocked by the destitution and forced migration of people fron the interior of our own country, the Congress set about to exam ine the causes and devise corrections. It made embarrassing dis coveries. It found that the portion of the United States compose of range land had lost something like half its productivity, a shown graphically in Figure 121. Uncontrolled grazing and craz homesteading had surrendered the best soil to wind and wate erosion. Denuded watersheds poured devastating floods ove the lowlands, and choked with mud the life-giving streams an irrigation projects. Decimation of predators had permitted thei prey, the prolific rodents, to multiply until they menaced both forage and soil. Noxious weeds and insects were spreading anc thriving at the expense of valuable grass species. In short, ou violations of the delicate balance between life and moisture had so seriously damaged a major segment of our national econom· that its repair would be extremely slow and costly (2, pp. 19-25)

Taylor Grazing Act of 1934

With passage of the Taylor Grazing Act (1934) we began a pro gram of federal proprietorship over public grazing lands outsid· the National Forests somewhat similar to that previously demon strated by the Forest Service on range lands within the Nationa Forests. Under that act, as amended, the Bureau of Land Manage ment supervises the use and administers the rehabilitation of some 180 million acres of range land federally owned (18, p. 148), anc promotes conservational management on millions of acres in othe: ownerships. Homesteading was stopped, and much of the aban doned farm land was recovered by the government. The Bureau has endeavored, by purchase, sale, leasing, and trading, to con solidate range areas into large blocks for economical adminis tration and efficient use. It has endeavored to assist the private

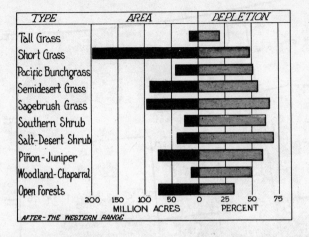

TYPE	AREA	DEPLETION
Tall Grass		
Short Grass		
Pacific Bunchgrass		
Semidesert Grass		
Sagebrush Grass		
Southern Shrub		
Salt-Desert Shrub		
Piñon-Juniper		
Woodland-Chaparral		
Open Forests		

200 150 100 50 0   25 50 75
MILLION ACRES   PERCENT

AFTER-THE WESTERN RANGE

FIGURE 121. *Area and depletion of range types, 1936. Drought and economic depression during the early thirties climaxed range despoliation, and threatened with disaster the entire range economy. This graph is from a comprehensive study of the problem made by the Forest Service at the request of Congress. That study was a basis for important legislation affecting the range resources.*

ranch owners by granting them grazing privileges (usually under a ten-year lease or permit) according to their particular needs, and by advising them in the management of their own lands. The Bureau wields broad regulatory powers, and is strictly charged with the *protection and rehabilitation of our range lands,* and the conservation of resources attached thereto. The task is complicated by many different sizes of units, by the variety of range quality and seasonal usefulness, and by a maze of ownerships—private, county, state, and federal. The actual planning of land use, land apportionment among users, and regulation of grazing comes from elected advisory boards representing the various interests within established *districts* (Figure 122). Ranchers, farmers, and others concerned make their own decisions—subject to the approval of a state board and the federal agency. District advisers make recommendations to the Bureau in Washington. The *democratic process* thus protects our grassland resources much as it does our waters, our soils, and our forests. *Cooperation is our best assurance* of their reconstruction and permanence, although it may be difficult to achieve where public and private interests often conflict. Progress has been made, despite the many complications inherent in the range economy.

A few illustrations may indicate the complexity and complication of problems that confront us in range conservation. To begin

Complexity and complication of the range problem

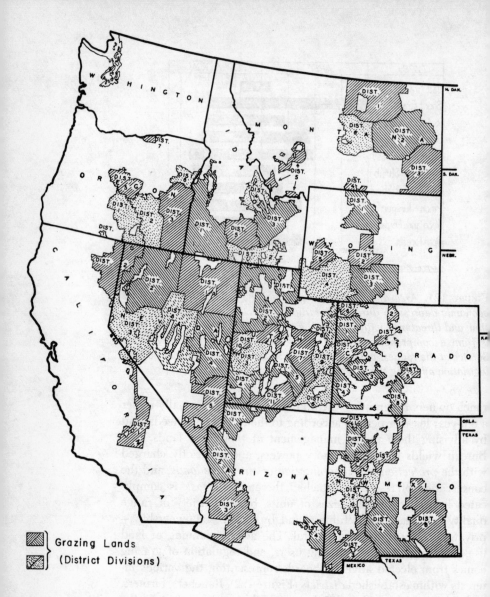

Grazing Lands
(District Divisions)

Bureau of Land Management

FIGURE 122. *Organized Management Areas. For conservation, experiment, and demonstration the Federal Range serves purposes comparable to those of the National Forests. The Bureau of Land Management is charged with the administration and conservation of our range lands. Grazing Districts might be compared with Soil Conservation Districts, although the two types differ in their respective resource emphases.*

with, the geographic diversity of the range land itself is extremely great. Twelve major range types compose our dry grazing lands, with many local variations of plant ecology, carrying capacity, seasonal usefulness, reliability of year-to-year forage production, and so forth. The relative importance of grazing in the total economy varies widely from one locality to another. Graziers adjacent to farms or irrigation projects have ready access to supplemental feed and forage, while those far removed from any considerable cultivated area lack the stabilizing margin of supply thus afforded. Seasonal ranges complement each other, and are often indispensable one to the other, in grazing systems long established. To gain maximum benefit from seasonal ranges their use must be properly integrated—mountain pastures for a part of the year, and open lowland pastures for the remainder. Graziers who use seasonal ranges must be afforded access to them, with the privilege of moving their animals (trailing) across intervening areas. Trailing creates special problems of conservation because the transit area is subject to excessive grazing and wear by the many herds or flocks that traverse it.

Most perplexing from the standpoint of range management and policy are areas in which lands administered by divers federal agencies are intermingled, as in central Utah. There, range administered by the Bureau of Land Management lies wedged between National Forest ranges, with a generous mixture of state and private land thrown into the bargain. Whenever any difference of policy (grazing fees, for instance) obtains between the agencies involved in such a confused situation, the disparity generates controversy that adds to the confusion. Closer coordination of all federal activities in the range country would improve the regional economy and increase its value to the nation.

A unique federal project inspired by the "Dirty Thirties" was the planting of a gigantic windbreak the length of the Plains, from North Dakota to Texas. Young men in the famed Civilian Conservation Corps, under Forest Service supervision, planted 35 million trees and shrubs of species selected by experts as most resistant to the harsh conditions, and set out in north-south strips, athwart the westerly winds (19). A good specimen of tree strips may be seen in Figure 123. By skillful arrangement of species (20 and 21) east to west, so that the shorter, hardier ones bear the brunt of the wind, and by careful attention in the early years, a high percentage of survival has been obtained. The comparative suitability of areas for such shelter-belt planting is shown in Figure 124.

We could not legislate calm, but we did plant a shelter-belt

FIGURE 123. *A ten-row shelterbelt, ¾ mile long, six years old, in Seward County, Nebraska, along U.S. Highway No. 34.* (S.C.S. photo.)

The shelter-belt idea was not new, but its demonstration in America had been limited to farmstead windbreaks. The planted strips have proved locally effective in reducing wind velocities, but many more are needed if they are to moderate surface winds over any considerable area. Wet years and prosperity returned before the Prairie States Forestry Project could be completed. World War II came along, and there was no time for planting trees in the grasslands.

Since the war, the planting of farm windbreaks has continued, largely under the sponsorship of the Soil Conservation Service. In our erratic dry regions, where wet years bring the opportunity for improvement, farmers must be encouraged to exercise better prudence than the man who ignores a hole in the roof when the weather is fair. Field windbreaks, such as those pictured in Figure 125, are effective deterrents to wind erosion during drought, but the trees should be planted during a wet period.

Restrict the plow and return the grass!

Specific procedures for conserving the grasslands cannot be recommended with the same degree of confidence as those mentioned in connection with forestry, because our grassland economy

258

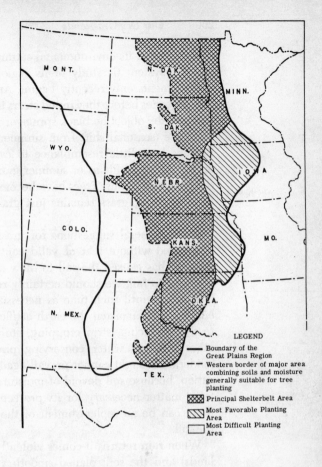

FIGURE 124. *Great Plains Region: major areas of practicable tree planting. Where trees will grow they can be planted to reduce wind hazards.* (F.S. map.)

LEGEND

— Boundary of the Great Plains Region
-·- Western border of major area combining soils and moisture generally suitable for tree planting

▨ Principal Shelterbelt Area
▧ Most Favorable Planting Area
☐ Most Difficult Planting Area

FIGURE 125. *A partial pattern of field and farmstead wind-breaks in eastern Foard County, Texas. The light-colored field in the foreground is exposed and blowing; fields with trees around them show little wind damage.* (S.C.S. photo.)

is very young, its environmental setting extremely heterogeneous, and the systematic study of its regional attributes and cultural developments only recently begun. Americans sawed lumber for two centuries before they roped steers in Texas. Logging is logging, whether the object be black spruce or white oak; sheep and trans-humance (seasonal shift from summer to winter pastures) in the Rockies bear little resemblance to cattle and year-long grazing on the Southern Plains or summer grazing and winter feeding on the Northern Plains. Trees have become veneer and cellulose, but, to most of us, grass remains just grass, without qualification or dignity.

A few general suggestions for grassland conservation may be postulated without fear of valid contradiction. Where recurrent drought has caused the soil to blow away and repeated farming ventures to fail, we should certainly restrict the plow, or exclude it entirely, until such time as necessity requires and technology enables us to moisten the earth artificially whenever it threatens to fly. Terracing, strip cropping, stubble mulching, and all the other soil and water conserving practices that suffice against moderate drought cannot prevail against severe, protracted dessi-cation, because soil devoid of moisture cannot produce the vege-table matter necessary for its protection. Where no plants grow there can be no replenishment of the stems and roots that bind the soil.

When rain returns it comes violently (dry lands are cloudburst lands) and the soil, planed smooth and hard by wind, absorbs but little, suffering severe erosion by the excessive run-off. The comparative flatness that facilitates wind action would deter water action were it not that showers are usually torrential. Where drought and wind fill and level works designed to hold water when it comes, the conservator has only one safe and sane al-ternative—*return of a permanent grass cover* (22, 23, 24).

Farmers have repeatedly pushed dry, upland agriculture too near the desert, and been pushed back in the lean years. Many farms that failed have reverted to public trust, and many more may revert with future droughts. It is quite appropriate that the precarious establishments should be added to the Public Do-main, because private owners cannot ordinarily afford to rehabili-tate them even with the liberal public aids available. Re-grassing by sowing, like reforestation by planting, requires considerable outlay without immediate returns (25). Native grasses, like native trees, will reclaim their own province, given time, but they would take a quarter to a half century to cover certain galls left by the plow (26, p. 71). We prefer to protect the remaining soil more

FIGURE 126. *Results of good and bad management on Southwestern Grassland range type, New Mexico. The range in the foreground was damaged by over-grazing and improper seasonal use. The five-strand barbed wire fence protected the adjoining range from similar abuse.* (Photo from Bureau of Land Management, Department of the Interior.)

promptly, by artificial seeding to hardy species, preferably those native to the area (27). We have begun to salvage abused areas by "sowing them down" permanently.

Many areas never plowed have been badly depleted by running too many animals on them—by grazing them so closely and continuously that preferred forage species could not maintain normal vigor and reproduction, and by trampling them along trails between pastures and around over-used bedding or watering places. The wear of too many animals has broken the cover, compacted and exposed the soil, thinned and weakened—even exterminated—the desirable grasses, and encouraged weeds and rodents. It has caused such general deterioration in many places that natural recovery cannot come about unless the number of animals be drastically reduced or the grazing system be modified to give depleted areas "sabbatical leave" for recuperation. System modification usually boils down to some form of regulated or controlled grazing, which has in fact largely replaced the old catch-as-catch-can that once prevailed. Management of grazing produced the spectacular contrast shown in Figure 126.

Range management for sustained yield is often more complex than sustained-yield forestry, and differs widely in practice as between the fenced ranches common to the Great Plains and the more extensive unfenced ranges prominent in the intermontane regions. Especially on the Northern Great Plains, stock-raising has become a semi-agricultural enterprise, with hay and feed crops produced for wintering and fattening the cattle. Where the quality, or potential quality, of the range warrants the expendi-

Damage by over-grazing responds to "under-grazing"

FIGURE 127. *Arrangement of watering places can be used to get better distribution of animals and more uniform usage of the range. Stock tank or farm pond impoundment conserves both land and water, as demonstrated by this example from Sandoval County, New Mexico.* (S.C.S. photo.)

ture, fencing solves the control problem (Figure 126), but on ranges of low carrying capacity, public or private, less costly methods must be employed. One shepherd can control a tremendous band of sheep (1000-plus) and a man on horseback can ride herd on many cattle. A high degree of control can be achieved by systematic arrangement and timely relocation of "salting" and watering places (28, pp. 241-244). Salt attracts all kinds of range livestock, and cattle cannot roam far from their drinking water (29). Artificial ponds (tanks) such as the one pictured in Figure 127, piped to watering places, can help distribute grazing pressure as desired.

Several systems for grassland conservation have evolved, all conceived to recover depleted areas and maintain the range in a high state of production, without drastic curtailment of the established economy. Temporary removal of all livestock would solve the whole problem, but it would waste the resource and ruin a valuable industry. *Deferred grazing,* the exclusion of animals from an area until the grasses mature their seed and send out new rhizomes, permits reproduction of species where early grazing would preclude the possibility. *Rotation grazing,* the timely shifting of animals from one pasture or tract to another, gives each area in turn a period of rest during which to regain its strength. The two systems are often combined in what the experts call *deferred-rotation* (Figure 128), a very popular and economical system in practice (30, pp. 288-295; 26, pp. 268-274). In some places, *alternate grazing* to sheep and cattle yields maximum proceeds with minimum drain because sheep and cattle have different tastes, the woolly animals selecting grasses and forbs less palatable to the bovines, and vice versa.

Mechanics can help the grass

Where the need is apparent and land values permit, the range stockmen may well employ certain soil and water conserving measures that serve on steeper land in the humid regions, such as contour terracing or ditching and water spreading (31). He may bandage a wind gall or "blow-out" as if it were a spot of sheet wash. But his real objective must be to make whole, and keep whole, the protective, productive grass cover that fits his locality. Grass must be his *means* and his *medium* for conservation and continued prosperity (32).

Health and balance suppress grassland pests

Management that maintains health and balance suppresses grassland pests that can otherwise attain destructive proportions. Prairie dogs and jack rabbits seem to thrive on depleted range where weeds have successfully invaded the grasses. If 15 jack rabbits eat as much grass as one sheep, 75 of them equal one animal unit (30, p. 456). (Carrying capacity of pasture or range is usually stated in terms of animal units, acres, and months, one

FIGURE 128. *Deferment of grazing permits the grasses to mature their seeds and reproduce their species. Animals are kept off the late-grazed pasture until desirable grasses have matured their seed and reseeded themselves naturally. Thus at completion of the rotation the entire area involved has been rejuvenated.* (Redrawn, and reproduced with permission, from A. W. Sampson, *Range Management*, copyright 1952, John Wiley & Sons, Inc.)

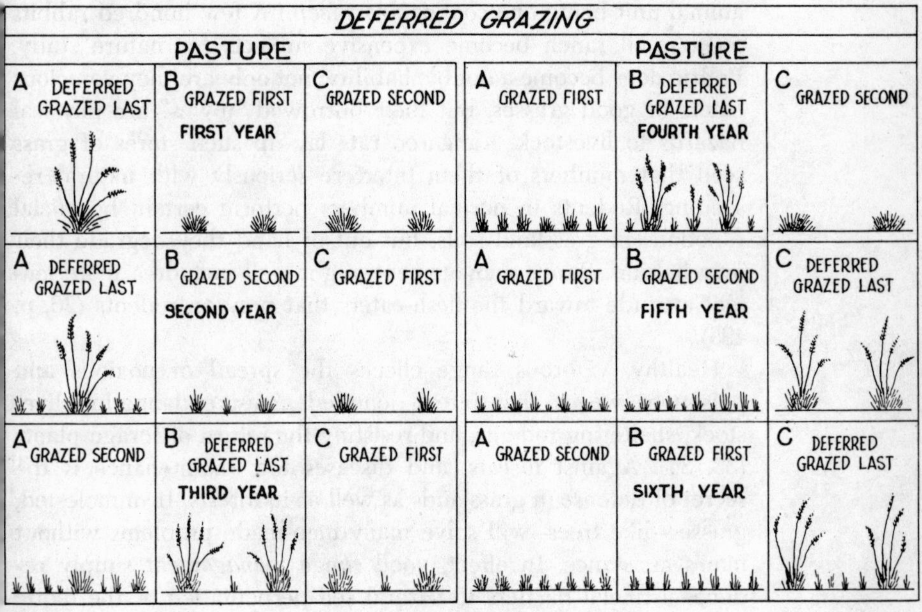

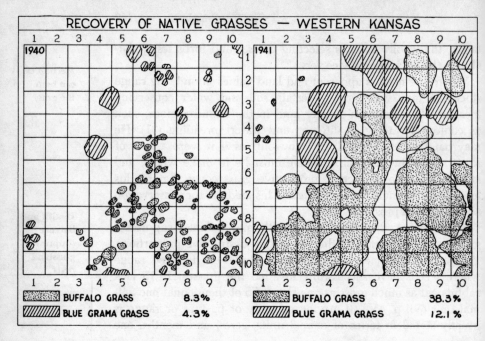

| | BUFFALO GRASS | 8.3% |
| | BLUE GRAMA GRASS | 4.3% |

| | BUFFALO GRASS | 38.3% |
| | BLUE GRAMA GRASS | 12.1% |

FIGURE 129. *Under favorable conditions a depleted grass range recovers quickly. One year of good rainfall made this difference on a meter quadrate of pasture near Ness City, Kansas. Heavy grazing and protracted drought had reduced the basal cover of forage grasses to only 12.6 per cent of area in the fall of 1940. A year later the grasses covered more than half the square.* (Redrawn from Ecological Monographs, 14: 1-29, January 1944 [Albertson and Weaver.])

animal unit being *one cow* or *five sheep*.) A few hundred rabbits on a small ranch become expensive subjects for nature study. Prairie dogs become a double liability; not only are they voracious eaters of good grasses, but their burrowed "towns" are physical hazards to livestock. Kangaroo rats lay up such stores of grass seed that numbers of them interfere seriously with natural reseeding. Rodents in normal numbers perform certain beneficial functions in grassland soils, but out of hand they degrade their own habitat. Range management might well include a more lenient attitude toward the flesh-eaters that prey on rodents (26, p. 493).

Healthy, vigorous range checks the spread of noxious and poisonous weeds that infest denuded areas, endangering livestock, sheltering rodents, and resisting the return of forage plants (33, 34). Against insects, and diseases too, maintenance is the secret of defense in grasslands as well as in forests. If unmolested, grasses—like trees—will solve many man-made problems without man's assistance. In effect, good *range management* simply reduces artificial barriers to natural self-perpetuation of the biotic

:ommunity. Figure 129 shows how quickly a depleted native pas-
ure can recover.

As the tree farmer needs advice from a forester, so the grazier
needs advice from an agrostologist (grass expert). The forester has
he advantage of big subjects, but the agrostologist deals with
plants so small and so numerous that his observations and con-
:lusions are less easily understood by the novice. Even when the
grazier becomes something of an agrostologist himself, he may be
sorely tempted to run his animals onto the young, tender grasses
when his better judgment tells him grazing ought to be deferred.
Sacrifice of superior forage in order that the grasses may reproduce themselves requires stronger will power than the leaving
of valuable trees in selective logging. But stockmen are learning
that deferment in grazing as in forestry pays high dividends in
the long run.

**Mind the
agrostologist!**

On our public ranges least of all can we afford any compromise
of grazing restrictions. Let no blustering rancher or politician
embarrass the inspector who orders animals off knee-deep pasture.
The inspector has probably determined that the tall stuff is
avoided by the animals, that the desirable species at the bottom
need rest in order to hold their own in the competition (35, 36, 37).

The dry grasslands contribute much of our meat, fiber, and
leather, but their annual production must conform to the vagaries
of their marginal climate. Flocks and herds must be adjusted to
the limitations of moisture—not to deceptive *averages* of rainfall,
nor to the good wet years, but to the frequent crucial years and
seasons when drought rides the range (38, 39).

**Climatic
marginality
must be
respected**

He who stocks to capacity in favorable years risks the loss of
both livestock and range during lean ones. Better that he "waste"
some forage one year than that he starve his animals and kill his
grass the next. If he grazes his range to 75 per cent of its capacity
in "normal" years and 50 per cent in bumper years, his operation
is probably as big as it ought to be for a fair degree of stability
(2, p. 507, 6, p. 469, 26, Chap. 17). If he narrows the margin he
gambles with climate, and climate deals the cards.

When by reseeding, caution, and patience we recover the millions of acres now denuded, and prohibit henceforth such
wanton abuse, we shall have solved a most pressing problem in
American conservation. Our grassland economy may never enjoy
the stable security of general farming in the humid East, but as
meteorologists and climatologists become more proficient at long-
range weather forecasting, we can increase total production and
anticipate hazards. Not by environmental *control*, but by careful
adjustment may we better utilize and conserve our valuable

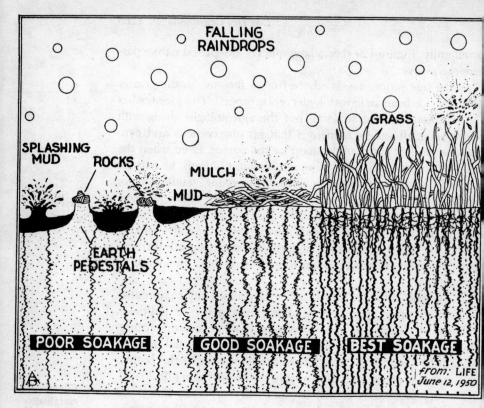

FIGURE 130. *Grass compares favorably with forest as a conserver of soil and water. Grass protects important watersheds where water is a critical resource.* (Diagram courtesy of the artist, James Lewicki.)

grassland resources. We cannot control the cycles of climate.

Much more grassland research of many kinds is needed to discover and improve conservation practices. Improved fire protection is needed on some 170 million acres. Improved range management should be extended to an additional 90 million acres, and watershed treatment work applied to a comparable acreage. Some 22 million acres need revegetation, but this is being accomplished at the discouraging rate of only 40,000 acres a year (31).

The range will pay dividends on our timely investment

The Bureau of Land Management has estimated that our federal range could be rebuilt in twenty years if we would invest 400 to 500 million dollars in the total program (31). The completed program would probably increase carrying capacity 30 per cent or more, with a proportionate gain in our production of meat, wool, and leather. It would contribute to the protection of important watersheds. It would conserve critical water resources, increase the useful life and value of expensive down-stream developments for irrigation, power, and other purposes (Figures 130 and 131). It would rehabilitate desirable wildlife, and enhance

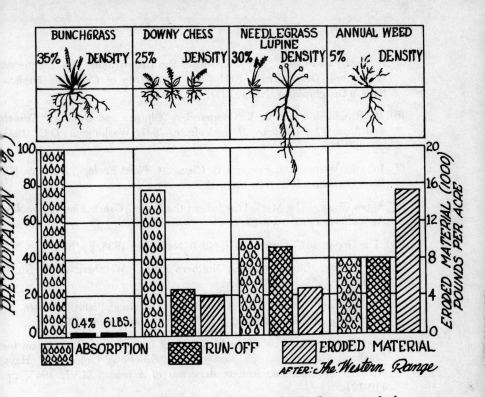

FIGURE 131. *The most desirable plants are commonly the best watershed protectors. Water conservation becomes a free bonus for good range management.*

the recreational values of a vast and interesting landscape. Altogether, the accrued gains would be worth many times the investment.

CHAPTER 11: REFERENCES CITED BY NUMBER

(1) H. L. Shantz, "Natural Vegetation," *Atlas of American Agriculture*, Part I, Section E., U.S.D.A., 1924.

(2) *The Western Range*, Senate Document No. 199, 74th Congress, 2nd Session, 1936.

(3) F. W. Albertson, *Man's Disorder of Nature's Design in the Great Plains*, Smithsonian Institution, Washington, D.C., 1950.

(4) J. E. Borchert, "The Climate of the Central North American Grassland," *Annals, Association of American Geographers*, XL, No. 1, March 1950, pp. 1-39.

(5) Richard Joel Russell, "Dry Climates of the United States, II: Frequency of Dry and Desert Years, 1901-1920," *University of California Publications in Geography*, V, No. 1, 1931, pp. 1-41.

(6) W. R. Chapline and C. K. Cooperrider, "Climate and Grazing," *Climate and Man: The Yearbook of Agriculture, 1941*, Washington, D.C., 1941, pp. 459-475.

(7) John E. Weaver and Frederic E. Clements, *Plant Ecology*, McGraw-Hill Book Company, Inc., New York, 1938.

(8) Agnes Chase, "The Meek That Inherit the Earth," *Grass: The Yearbook of Agriculture, 1948*, pp. 8-15.

(9) "The Grasslands," *Fortune*, XII, No. 5, November 1935, pp. 59 ff.

(10) Roy L. Fox, "Blizzards of the Northern Plains," *Weatherwise*, V, No. 6, December 1952, pp. 123-126 f.

(11) Wesley Calef, "The Winter of 1948-49 in the Great Plains," *Annals, Association of American Geographers*, XL, No. 4, December 1950.

(12) Noel R. Runyon, "The Effect of Season of Growth and Clipping on the Chemical Composition of Blue Grama (*Bouteloua Gracilis*) at Hays, Kansas," *Transactions, Kansas Academy of Science*, XLVI, 1943, pp. 116-121.

(13) Harold H. Hopkins, F. W. Albertson and D. A. Riegel, "Ecology of Grassland Utilization in a Mixed Prairie," *Transactions, Kansas Academy of Science*, LV, No. 4, 1952, p. 404.

(14) E. Louise Peffer, "Homesteading the Arid West," *The Closing of the Public Domain*, Stanford University Press, Stanford, California, 1951, Chapter 8.

(15) John C. Hout, "Droughts of 1930-34," *Water Supply Paper 680*, U.S.G.S., 1936.

(16) "The Dust Farmer Goes West," *Land Policy Review*, B.A.E.,* I, No. 1, May-June 1938.

(17) Lois Olson, "Migration and Economic Opportunity in the Great Plains," *Geographical Review*, XXVI, No. 4, October 1936, pp. 670-672.

(18) Marion Clawson, *Uncle Sam's Acres*, Dodd, Mead and Company, New York, 1951.

(19) *Trees That Temper the Western Winds* (Pamphlet), Prairie States Forestry Project, F.S., Washington, D.C., 1938.

(20) Ernest J. George, "Tree and Shrub Species for the Northern Great Plains," *Circular No. 912*, U.S.D.A., January 1953.

(21) "Windbreaks and Shelterbelts for the Plains States," Extension Service, Forest Service, and Soil Conservation Service, *Leaflet No. 276*, U.S.D.A., 1950.

* B.A.E.: Bureau of Agricultural Economics.

(22) C. K. Pearse, "Regrassing the Range," *Science in Farming: The Yearbook of Agriculture, 1947*, pp. 897-904.

(23) Evan L. Flory and Charles G. Marshall, "Regrassing for Soil Protection in the Southwest," *Farmer's Bulletin No. 1913*, U.S.D.A., 1942.

(24) C. A. Rechenthin, "Potential 'Dust Bowl' in the Making," *Journal of Soil and Water Conservation*, VII, No. 3, July 1952, pp. 111-112.

(25) C. Kenneth Pearse, A. Perry Plummer and D. A. Savage, "Restoring the Range by Reseeding," *Grass*, pp. 227-233.

(26) Arthur W. Sampson, *Range Management, Principles and Practices*, John Wiley and Sons, Inc., New York, 1952.

(27) Max M. Hoover, James E. Smith, Jr., A. E. Ferber and D. R. Cornelius, "Seed for Regrassing Great Plains Areas," *Farmers' Bulletin No. 1985*, U.S.D.A., 1947.

(28) B. W. Allred, *Practical Grassland Management*, Sheep and Goat Raiser Magazine, San Angelo, Texas, 1949.

(29) C. L. Hamilton and Hans G. Jepson, "Stock-Water Developments: Wells, Springs, and Ponds," *Farmers' Bulletin No. 1859*, U.S.D.A., 1949.

(30) L. A. Stoddard and A. D. Smith, *Range Management*, McGraw-Hill Book Company, Inc., New York, 1943.

(31) *Rebuilding the Federal Range—A Resource Conservation and Development Program*, U.S. Department of the Interior, Bureau of Land Management, Washington, D.C., 1951.

(32) W. R. Chapline, F. G. Renner and Raymond Price, "The New Range Outlook," *Farmers in a Changing World: The Yearbook of Agriculture, 1940*.

(33) W. A. Dayton, "Poisonous Plants," *Grass*, pp. 729-734.

(34) J. F. Pechanec, C. E. Fisher and K. W. Parker, "How to Control Noxious Plants," *Grass*, pp. 256-260.

(35) E. J. Dyksterhuis, "Condition and Management of Range Land Based on Quantitative Ecology," *Journal of Range Management*, II, No. 3, July 1949, pp. 104-115.

(36) David F. Costello and George T. Turner, "Judging Condition and Utilization of Short-grass Ranges on the Central Great Plains," *Farmers' Bulletin No. 1949*, U.S.D.A., 1944.

(37) M. W. Talbot, "Indicators of Southwestern Range Conditions," *Farmers' Bulletin No. 1782*, U.S.D.A. (revised), 1947.

(38) Leon C. Hurtt, "Managing Northern Great Plains Cattle Ranges to Minimize Effects of Drought," *Circular No. 865*, U.S.D.A., 1951.

(39) Tom Dale, "When Drought Returns to the Great Plains," *Farmers' Bulletin No. 1982*, U.S.D.A., 1947.

Wildlife:

Functions and Abuses

we have often maligned and abused the fellow creatures that render our environment tenable

BROADLY INTERPRETED, "WILDLIFE" EMBRACES ALL NATIVE LIFE forms, both plant and animal, which are not domesticated or cultivated, but survive in their wild state (1). Plants grown as crops and animals raised for market or to produce a marketable commodity fall outside the pale. The term "wildlife" connotes freedom and not captivity, independence rather than helplessness.

Wildlife resources are renewable, or perpetual, because, being alive, they renew themselves as long as they can reproduce. The powerful instincts of survival and regeneration place wildlife resources in a unique category. Given half a chance, they multiply and retain their respective positions in the total landscape. However, those which have been exterminated are more completely expended than an oil pool pumped dry, and those which have lost the capacity to survive without special attention or care have also lost the most distinctive characteristic of wildlife, namely *wildness*. Herds of game fed like cattle lose their wildlife status much as soil loses its true character when its upper horizon washes away. Prairie grasses lost their durability when the plow turned them upside down, and remnants of the rich plant community that was once true tall-grass prairie are now a rare sight. Thus some wildlife resources have already been expended, some have lost their natural character, and still others stand in imminent danger of one of these fates. Let us say that wildlife resources *should* be perpetual, and would be so but for our inept or abusive treatment.

Broadly
interpreted,
"wildlife"
embraces
all native
plants
and
animals

The criterion
is "wildness"

271

This chapter, and the next as well, treats of wildlife in accordance with a somewhat restricted and popular definition: "fishes, birds, mammals, and the related association of fields, forests, and waters" (2, p. 1). Emphasis will be on animals rather than on plants, although the two primary divisions of life cannot be divorced. We shall further limit our discussion by excluding the biota which support our commercial fisheries; those will be treated in Chapter 15. Thus the two chapters now at hand deal primarily with land animals and the animals of little inland waters, with attention also to the plants upon which the animals depend. And let us remember that all live in a competitive world. More than any other resource, wildlife depends upon natural balance and delicate adjustment to persistent cyclic change. The conservator treads lightly where fools rush in with hobnailed boots!

Animal resources are part and product of the basic resources

Animals are both part and product of the basic resource complex: water, land, soil, and vegetation. Their category is high man on the environmental totem pole—an integral constituent of the landscape. Animals assist with the formation of soil, which produces plant growth, upon which animal life depends. Therein lies a fundamental natural cycle that must be respected in wildlife conservation. We are here concerned mainly with the higher animal forms—the vertebrates, especially mammals, fishes, and fowls.

For the first time in this volume we are dealing with resources capable, within certain limits, of adjusting to a changing environment or moving to one more suitable. For the first time we deal with resources that participate actively in their own conservation —now cooperative, now reticent, but always responsive to the skillful conservator. Animals are often more helpful by instinct than are their would-be benefactors by artificial means.

As the product of other resources, animals are often best conserved by conserving those resources upon which they depend. *A healthy combination of water, soil, and vegetative cover is our most positive assurance of a healthy wildlife community.* Herbivorous species (vegetarians) thrive when their favored plant association remains intact, carnivora (meat-eaters) thrive on fat vegetarians, and omniverous kinds, who take meat with their potatoes, do well when either flesh or vegetable foods are readily available. Mutuality permeates the good biotic community, and if one constituent be lost the others suffer.

By the same token, one of the basic resources cannot alone sustain a healthy wildlife; all must be in as good balance as possible. Being farther up the resource scale, wildlife demonstrates more positively than any other the interdependence of renewable resources and the unity that must pervade their conservation. Wastage of other resources is usually inimical to wildlife; conservation of other resources usually most beneficial.

During many centuries preceding the advent of Europeans, Indians and wild animals lived in ecological harmony on the North American continent. Animals supplied many needs for food, clothing, and shelter, and the red men usually killed no more than they could use. There were few Indians and many animals, so neither jeopardized the other's existence. Wildlife habitats remained almost undisturbed, and natural increase exceeded the kill (3, pp. 2-3).

To this savage serenity came predaceous white men with lethal firearms and burning ambitions; and the 'scene changed. They found wildlife of such variety and abundance as they had never imagined, and could not possibly foresee the decimation that would result from three centuries of "civilized" settlement on the land. Old men now living have seen in their youth such numbers of fish, fowl, and grazing herds that their assertions lend credence to earlier records of flocks that darkened the skies, herds that dotted the plains, and fishes so crowded in shallow creeks that one could catch them with his bare hands. The land in many areas fairly crawled with life, and it is almost incredible that civilization could so quickly threaten the survival of many species.

The rich fauna of continental United States numbers 2,368 vertebrate species, including 670 mammals, 811 birds, 149 reptiles, 138 amphibians, and 600 freshwater fishes (4, p. 6). Among the mammals are 116 fur bearers (4, p. 6); and of all the reptiles, only seven species are poisonous (5). Species classed as "game" constitute only about ten per cent of the total; species of commercial use only about seven per cent (4, p. 7). Most of the others are beneficial to us, or at least harmless.

Without abundant wildlife the sturdy pioneer would have been hard put to it for meat as he pushed back frontiers. Powder and shot were his shopping money; with them he got food and clothing when no other source availed. They provided him with roast fowl, steaks, moccasins, jerked venison, candles, robes, window panes, buckskin shirts and breeches, and grease with which to keep his musket oiled. More as provider than protector he treasured his trusty musket above all other possessions. Neither plow nor axe surpassed the muzzle-loader as an implement for taming the wilderness. Its rank is well symbolized in our cherished tradition of Thanksgiving turkey.

It was most fortunate that our frontiersmen could live "off the

A rich fauna inhabited the American wilderness

His musket meant food and clothing to the sturdy pioneer

land," but it is tragic that they unwittingly instituted a "scorched earth policy." Quite innocently and to good purpose they initiated many of the problems we are here concerned with solving, but some things that they had in untold numbers have now vanished from the land.

Food and raiment for its conquerors were not the only contributions of wildlife to formative American history. The fur bearers lured trapper and trader across the continent in quest of the pelts that constituted one of America's first great export commodities. The demand for furs made Indians commercial trappers. Trading posts for gathering in the pelts became vanguards of civilization and the basis for political claim to territory. Beavers probably did more than statesmanship to secure our hold on the great Northwest. Astor and other Americans outmaneuvered the Hudson's Bay Company before the 49th Parallel became an established boundary. American fortunes famed to this day were built on the lucrative fur trade. St. Louis became renowned as a fur market long before the birth of the "blues."

Fine furs gave the United States prestige in world trade, but trappers took the skins faster than the animals could multiply and produce them. Men over-trapped the fur resources in much the same manner as other men over-cropped, over-grazed, over-fished, and over-logged other assets that also could have been self-perpetuating.

The fur business swept across the country far ahead of systematic land utilization. Fur bearers felt the sting of civilization long before the main force of mankind arrived. Then, with the advance of settlement, wildlife generally shrank and retreated. Man was the master. He converted the land to his own use without regard for those creatures he dispossessed. He felled the forest, broke the sod, drained the marshes, and flooded the stream bottoms, that he might raise cultivated plants and domesticated animals. It was well and good that he should adapt to his purposes the land suitable for them, but tragedy it was, indeed, that he cleared and burned, plowed and drained many areas that would have served him much better in their natural state and as homes for wildlife. By drainage alone he ruined the wildlife habitat and water storage capacities of some hundred million acres (3, p. 8). Perhaps our greatest attrition of wildlife has been passive and unintentional, by usurping or ruining every sort of natural habitat.

But much of our destruction was willful; some of it so shameful that one hesitates to mention it. We became killers by ignorance,

Fur bearers lured trapper and trader across the continent

Wildlife shrank with the advance of settlement

We became killers through ignorance

without qualms or conscience. We killed as if impelled by some diabolical obsession to destroy every wild thing. We killed for sale and we killed for sport, just to see the fur or feathers fly. We killed on suspicion and on prejudice, and we killed without pretext or provocation; and there are those who continue the wanton slaughter even now.

Being conspicuous by their size, and often too bold for their own good, the ungulata—hooved mammals such as antelope, elk, and bison—were primary targets in the war of destruction. In the eastern forests they had some concealment, even after farmers moved in, but on the prairies and plains, with no place to hide, the wild beasts stood little chance against armed men on fleet horses.

On the open grasslands one of the most shameful atrocities in American history was perpetrated against the magnificent bison. His very usefulness condemned him. Pony-riding Indians of the plains put up a formidable defense of their heritage against designing white men until the white men decimated the animals upon which the Indians depended. Cut off from their "base" of supplies, the Indians were soon routed, and the land secured for settlement. Hunters and soldiers killed the bison and ousted the Indian to appropriate for crops much land that plowing and cultivation exposed to ruin. The abuse of land discussed in Chapter 11 began with the passing of the emblematic beast of our grasslands. Of an estimated 75 million bison that roamed in great herds when colonists first saw them on the Atlantic slope, only a few hundred survived the carnage (3, p. 6). Doubly tragic was the fact that Indians themselves sold for a pittance the hides of animals upon which their very lives depended.

Predators—such as wolves and foxes, owls and hawks—have been pursued relentlessly to protect domesticated animals. Men have indicted them on suspicion, convicted them on circumstantial evidence, even put a price on their heads (bounty) when, in fact, few have been "guilty as charged," and many should have been awarded medals for outstanding service. Farmers with half the wisdom of an owl and much less cunning than a fox are now glad to sacrifice a few chickens to marauders that also take burrowing rodents. Figure 132 indicates how badly certain hawks have been maligned.

Killing of wildfowl for food markets flourished after the Civil War, probably reaching its peak in the '80's, and continuing past the turn of the century. Shooting and snaring went on most of the year, and markets were almost constantly glutted. The busi-

FOOD of HAWKS and FOOD for THOUGHT ! (%)

BROAD-WINGED HAWK

INSECTS	FROGS SNAKES	RATS & MICE	SMALL BIRDS	AQUATIC	GAME BIRDS	RABBITS
39.7	30.9	23	3.4	2	.5	.5

RED-SHOULDERED HAWK

INSECTS	RATS & MICE	FROGS SNAKES	AQUATIC	SMALL BIRDS	POULTRY	GAME BIRDS	RABBITS
32	28	25	5.3	6.5	1.4	.9	.9

RED-TAILED HAWK

RATS & MICE	INSECTS	RABBITS	SMALL BIRDS	POULTRY	FROGS SNAKES	GAME BIRDS	AQUATIC
55	10.5	9.3	9.2	6.3	6.1	2.1	1.5

ROUGH-LEGGED HAWK

RATS & MICE	RABBITS	INSECTS	SMALL BIRDS	GAME BIRDS	AQUATIC	FROGS SNAKES
72	8.6	6.5	4.3	4.3	2.2	2.1

SPARROW HAWK

INSECTS	RATS & MICE	SMALL BIRDS	FROGS SNAKES
63.5	20.3	8.4	7.8

COOPER'S HAWK

SMALL BIRDS	RATS & MICE	GAME BIRDS	POULTRY	INSECTS	RABBITS	FROGS SNAKES
55	17	12	10	3.3	1.7	1

SHARP-SHINNED HAWK

SMALL BIRDS	RATS & MICE	INSECTS	FROGS SNAKES	RABBITS	POULTRY
96.4	2.6	.7	.1	.1	.1

MARSH HAWK

SMALL BIRDS	RATS & MICE	RABBITS	GAME BIRDS	FROGS SNAKES	INSECTS	POULTRY	AQUATIC
41	33	9	7.2	4.1	3.3	2.3	.1

FROM CIRCULAR 25 NATIONAL ASSOCIATION OF AUDUBON SOCIETY, NEW YORK 28, NEW YORK.

FIGURE 132. *Food for hawks and food for thought. Figures show per cent of diet.*

ness was badly organized, refrigeration was elemental, handling so slow and crude that much of the game spoiled in transit. Birds that did arrive in good condition sold for a few cents a pair. Such was the ignominious fate of millions upon millions of passenger pigeons, prairie chickens, grouse, ducks, geese, upland plover, snipe, woodcock, quail, and other equally desirable game species (3, p. 5). Market shooting brought nobody much profit or benefit, but it brought disaster to wildfowl.

Some creatures were killed because they looked menacing or because they seemed too numerous. Bears and wildcats that never invaded man's province were killed in their own haunts because men feared they might become hostile. Fish by the tub were fed to swine or spread on fields—away from the captor's domicile to spare him the annoyance of their stench. Untold numbers of pike and other species prized both for sport and flavor were so disgraced.

Wholesale slaughter, coupled with destruction and constriction of habitats, must inevitably lead to extirpation. And so it has. For a few species it is an accomplished fact. The passenger pigeons that once darkened the skies have vanished. So have the heath hen and the Labrador duck. The Carolina paroquet, the only species of parrot once at home in the United States, has gone. The Cape Sable sparrow probably went with the 1937 hurricane. The whooping crane, the trumpeter swan, the bald eagle (national emblem), the California condor (largest American bird), the ivory-billed woodpecker, the everglade kite, the prairie chicken, and others are so near extermination that their survival is in doubt. Once extinct, they are lost forever.

Some species have vanished; others may go

Human depredation has been no kinder to the mammals. The Maine mink, the Gull Island meadow mouse, the eastern puma, the big plains wolf, the Arizona elk, the Dakota bighorn sheep, and several types of grizzly bears have gone the way of dinosaurs and mastodons. The Florida Key deer, the Florida manatee and crocodile, the fisher, the martin, the wolverine, the black-footed ferret, and the kit fox have three feet in the grave (except the sea cow, who has no feet). Many of them will probably disappear despite our best efforts to save them (6). Their pathetic remnants are not likely to survive the natural hazards of a biotic community in which they were once numerous or dominant. Even brutes are overwhelmed by the social persecution visited upon minorities. We have exhausted living resources that should have been permanent.

Extermination is not the only consequence of killing and en-

Results of
abuse: tame
game, planted
fish, synthetic
habitats, and
domestication

croachment. Abuses have reduced many remaining species to a
pitiable state of dependence on the human society that maligned
them. Tame game, planted fish, and domesticated fur bearers are
not our preference. They are substitutes; self-imposed penalties
for waste and transgression. While it is rarely possible to restore
a wilderness as we might wish to do, it is often possible to restore
erstwhile wilderness residents so they can simulate normal functions, or preserve in a semi-wild state a few specimens for our
curious grandchildren.

Big game animals, herded and fed like so many cattle, have lost
their true wildlife value and acquired closer kinship with a pet
goat or the old brindled cow. Their dependence on man, especially for winter feeding, has almost tamed the elk in Jackson
Hole, Wyoming.

Because we ruined our lakes and streams or fished them dry, a
substantial percentage of game fish are now hatched and reared
from incubators and brooders like so many chicks. A few years
ago it was customary to stock waters with fingerlings (minnow-
size fish) and let them mature on their own. However, so many
of them died soon after liberation that for such species as trout
it was found more economical to rear them to legal size and then
plant them where they would get caught before succumbing to
natural causes. Perhaps the fly-caster with fancy gear takes more
pride in catching really wild trout, but if he does his angling near
any populous area he is likely to catch only those reared and
planted for him. But he seems to find it quite easy to flavor his
pride with pan-fried trout and swallow the two together.

Hand feeding of big game, artificial propagation of fish and
fowl, artificial defense against natural enemies and diseases are
tacit admissions that the natural habitat has deteriorated so badly
that the only apparent expedient is artificial correction. Wildlife
so pampered and protected has about as much wildness left in it
as a caged canary in his old age.

The lowly
muskrat has
dethroned
furred royalty

Wild fur bearers still contribute about 85 per cent of our annual
fur crop (7), but the composition of the crop has changed greatly
since the days when trappers and traders scoured the country for
beaver, otter, martin, and other hairy aristocrats. The lowly muskrat has dethroned furred royalty and become far and away the
most important American fur species. Some 20 million of the amphibious rodents give up their skins each year (7).

About two-thirds of our domestic peltries come off the industrious, prolific muskrats. Most of the remaining one-third come
from opossums, skunks, raccoons, foxes, minks, and weasels. Two

million trappers, many of them farmers and farm boys, catch about a hundred million dollars worth of raw furs a year, a valuable harvest to reap without sowing or tending (7).

Center of the wild fur crop has shifted toward southeastern coastal marshes in which muskrats abound. Louisiana leads the nation in fur production and in conservation of fur resources. The state realizes about 5 million dollars annually from its raw fur crop and collects more than $200,000 a year in fees and dues of various kinds for use in maintaining the fur business. Notable among the collections is a severance tax (7), an adaptation of the device used by Louisiana and other timber growing states to promote good forestry.

Commoners tolerant of man have gained prominence as others less sociable quit his presence. The ubiquitous cottontail rabbit, the odoriferous skunk, and the slovenly opossum accepted the human newcomers and found them to be fairly decent neighbors. Men planted whole fields of food where there was little before. They raised flocks of gullible chickens, and trained them to roost regularly in the same place for easy stealing. They laid culverts in the ground like prefabricated dens, and they built barns and sheds under which families could be reared. They provided places of concealment under piles of brush, stone, or wood, and they erected barriers that stopped or confounded the canines. Except for their guns and traps they were most neighborly.

Commoners tolerant of man have gained prominence

Undaunted by human occupancy of the land, the cottontail has multiplied in the time-honored tradition of rabbits and risen to top position among American game animals. He attracts more hunters than any other species and provides our children one of their earliest contacts with wild creatures. Unless he disappoints us, he will still be the first game stalked by farm boys when they carry ray-guns instead of air rifles.

We saw in Chapter 11 that grassland rodents prosper under abusive land utilization. On the other hand many upland species, both mammals and birds, are benefited by good land use. Productive, cultivated fields provide certain kinds of wildlife much more food than did the same areas in their natural state. Land abuse invites vermin, but good land use enriches desirable wildlife when the creatures are given an opportunity to live and raise families. Upon that singular land-life relationship we must base most of our plans and projects for wildlife conservation.

Attempts to conserve selectively and eradicate those thought inimical to the chosen ones have complicated our wildlife problems. People have been prone to classify all wild things as either

"Judge not, that ye be not judged"

desirable or undesirable, without qualification or compromis
They have branded whole groups as good or bad without dete
mining the innocence or guilt of individual species (Figure 13:
To protect domestic livestock against predators, states have vote
large sums of money for bounties when it would have been mu
cheaper and more practical to pay for all the losses. In mar
quarters, the bounty system is, in fact, falling into disfavor. Mo
naive of all our *selection* blunders has been our habit of denoun
ing a given predator wherever found, although the stigma mig
not be applicable away from the region that attached it. We d
not display much brilliance when we kill predators where the
prey does more damage than they do. The coyote (Figure 133) w
persecuted for killing lambs, but more recently he has gained fav
as a killer of rodents that ruin the range on which the lambs fee

Animals, like men, are neither wholly good nor wholly bad. On
may be more inclined to be good than another, but the best
liable to sin if the temptation is strong enough. None has im
munity to the forces of circumstance. A fox in a steer pasture ma
be as innocent as a freshman at his fraternity initiation, but tl
same fox in a sheep fold and the same freshman at a sororit
dance may be "wolves" as fierce as any. A vixen with a family
a menace in a poultry raising community, but only a curiosity o
a cattle ranch. Circumstance makes the difference.

Animals are partly good and partly bad by human standard.
Probably none is entirely undesirable, but very few are withou
fault in relation to man's economy. The apparently harmless co
tontail can be ruinous to fruit trees and berry bushes. When snov
covers other food, and orchards stand in deep drifts, bunn
girdles the branches where they protrude through the snow. Afte
the ladder he climbed has melted away the damage is so high o
the tree that a novice would never identify the criminal. He i
not a predator, yet he preys on fruit growers.

Mistaken identity has been a costly error. Many useful specie
have suffered because they resemble destructive ones. Owls an
hawks are excellent examples (Figure 132). Because one or two o
their kind affect man's interest negatively he has condemned all o
them. Had Kipling meted out similar justice, the entire regimen
would have hanged for Danny Deever's crime. The great horne
owl and the Cooper's hawk are notorious killers of domestic fow
and small game, but most of their relatives are strictly honorable
and have value for the control of mice and other rodents. Screec
owls are such diligent mousers that they have been referred to a
"self-setting mousetraps" (8, p. 46). Other owls and several hawk

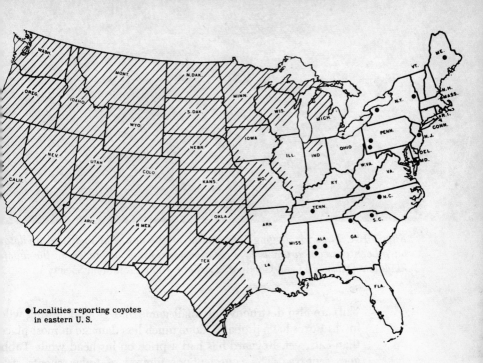

● Localities reporting coyotes
in eastern U. S.

FIGURE 133. *Distribution of coyotes, 1940. Despite bounties and persecution,
the coyote has extended his range. His services as a rodent eradicator are being
increasingly appreciated, and states are lifting their bounties. (F.W.S. map.)*

have comparable merit (9). They deserve to be protected by law,
as in Connecticut and Michigan, with a vigor equal to that which
has been exerted to destroy them. Farmers and sportsmen are
making an about-face. An orchardist plagued with rabbits might
profitably raise a few pullets for the sole purpose of attracting a
great horned owl to his orchard. Perhaps even that silent marauder
does more good than evil, generally.

Foxes and other wild predators have often been convicted for
crimes committed by house cats, which, when abandoned and
become feral, are among our worst destroyers of birds and upland
wildfowl. Reynard was the bird hunter's "public enemy number
one" until it was discovered that he may prefer mice to quail, perhaps because of an aversion to a mouthful of feathers (Figure 134).
Tabby on the prowl hunts birds both on the ground and in trees,
and her mousing services may be inadequate payment (Figure
135). In the "Deep South" where tenant farmers move frequently
and carry with them more superstitions than furnishings, it is a
"bad sign" to move a cat. So the cat stays behind, often becoming
a menace to wildlife. (Stray dogs, and dogs permitted to roam at

Figure 134. Gray fox digging out meadow mouse nest. The maligned predator have been persecuted unwisely. Predation is an essential process in the anima kingdom. (Maslowski and Goodpaster, from National Audubon Society.)

will, are also destructive of small game and ground-nesting wild fowl.) Foxes have probably done much less damage in most place than cats; yet, Reynard has had a price on his head while Tabb goes scot-free. The conscientious nimrod of today shoots stra cats on sight, as a sort of community service in appreciation o hunting privileges.

When predators are exterminated their prey often multiplies s rapidly that starvation finally checks its number. We protect scav engers like turkey buzzards who clean up the remains, and kil the predators that would obviate most of our need for the clean up service. Since the weak and sick are most easily killed, "surviva of the fittest" tends to improve the stock upon which predator feed. Eluded by the more vigorous survivors, the killers rais smaller families to stay within the budget. With less carrion about, the scavengers also thin their ranks, and a balanced ratio c

FIGURE 135. *Tabby may be a respectable member of the household, but she is also a cousin of the tiger.*

ll becomes more or less stabilized. The human hunter might well onder more deliberately his hostile attitude toward brute competitors. His may be the choice between sharing a few live deer nd quail with other predators or consigning many dead ones to cavengers. His blind selfishness has favored sneaking coyotes and tinking buzzards over haughty cougars and magnificent birds of rey (10, 11). Errors of human judgment have created many wild-fe problems that only the animals themselves can solve. (One of their standard methods may be seen in Figure 136.) Passive toler-nce can accomplish more, in many cases, than the most deter-mined attempt to regiment. Nature has its own system of selection 12, Chapter XIV), and nature's system has been working a long, ong time.

All creatures have some function in the complex operation of natural biotic equilibrium, though many, such as reptiles and odents, are repulsive and despicable in the eyes of some humans. Snakes give some people goose pimples, and rodents are known to arry dread diseases transmissible to humans, for example, bu-bonic plague and tularemia. But our contempt for these groups has been no more discriminating than our hostility toward preda-ors. We have permitted individual species and isolated misde-meanors to incriminate a whole genus or family without weighing the merits of an individual member in a particular set of cir-umstances.

Kill the snake, and avenge Mother Eve!

We are not snake haters by instinct, nor snake killers by re-igious conviction; but most of us have been taught to kill a snake on sight. Our acquired aversion is certainly impractical, if not sacrilegious, because many snakes and other reptiles are, indeed, not enemies, but servants of man, living in mortal fear of their master.

Snakes are active destroyers of rodents, and many a southern farmer keeps a pet blacksnake about his place or a pair of rat snakes in his corn crib to discourage vermin. This is not a plea for the protection of snakes, which most of us abhor, but merely to illustrate that even our most despised creatures do have merit, and fit into the scheme of things somehow.

Rodents and other little mammals have been broadly maligned because a few here and there have become a local nuisance. In most such cases man's own abuse of the biotic community invited the trouble. In this and preceding chapters we have mentioned several instances: eviction of predators from fields and orchards, depletion of the range, and disruption of forest society by clear cutting the timber. In each case certain rodents multiply beyond

Mice bother men when men invite them

their normal abundance and become destructive pests; mice become menacing under poorly laid plans of men. Prairie dogs mutilate the range when it has been over-grazed and cleared of coyotes; rabbits girdle fruit trees and mice injure the roots, when hawks, owls, foxes, and weasels (Figure 136) have been routed from the orchard; squirrels, chipmunks, and mice devour the seeds and seedlings that would make them a new home when natural enemies quit the scene and normal food supplies fail. In a deranged environment the little fellows can be extremely detrimental to the basic resources upon which they and all higher animals depend.

A gardener sees little virtue in moles and shrews when they furrow his beautiful lawn or when one of the busy little beasts tunnels the length of a newly sprouted row, leaving the young plants suspended in air. A farmer condemns the pocket gopher for every mound that dulls his mower sickle, and has equal contempt for ground squirrels that steal his seed corn right out of the hills as if schooled in geometry. An apple grower loses patience with mice when they accept the mulch about his trees as an invitation to set up housekeeping among the roots. And the keeper of chickens maligns the mouse-killing weasel when that sly hunter trespasses in the hen house. Yet all these industrious culprits have hidden virtues that may exceed their vices.

Our field mouse population has been estimated at 21 billion, which is quite reasonable when one considers that a female mouse will breed at the age of four weeks, and may have 17 litters a year, with five or six babies in each litter (13). A few happy families in a field of grain can destroy 20 per cent of the crop (13), which should be ample reason for a farmer to encourage both feathered and furred predators that might reduce his loss.

Even the mammalian "underground" has virtue

The insectivorous mole in his ceaseless toil to satiate a voracious appetite consumes vast numbers of grubs and worms that might otherwise plague the gardener. All burrowers—be they moles, gophers, ground squirrels, mice, rats, or prairie dogs—perform a unique and valuable function in soil development and maintenance. While they live, their nests and mounds add vegetable matter, and after they die their bodies make further addition to organic content. Their burrows improve aeration, facilitate the infiltration of water, and increase the capacity for water storage. Any country schoolboy who has enjoyed the sport knows that it takes considerable water to "drown" a ground squirrel out of his hole. However, unless he be taught, the boy might overlook the implication that ground squirrels improve water reception and increase water storage. To see the good in some of our fellows one

FIGURE 136. *Predator and prey: weasel and meadow mouse. Predation is a major factor in the maintenance of biotic balance.* (Karl H. Maslowski, from National Audubon Society.)

must look beneath the surface, and he may have to look twice to establish the guilt of a suspect. Many a mole has been wrongfully accused of eating holes in roots or tubers, when in fact a mouse got into his run and did the damage. The poor, blind mole was merely an accessory before the fact, or so hungry for meat that, when he found no grubs, he reluctantly settled for potatoes.

Birds are not all song and plumage, not all purity and innocence. Many have neither beauty nor musical talent. Some serve us with distinction, and others are apparently useless, if not actually harmful.

Birds are not all song and plumage

Purely aesthetic and sentimental values place birds high on our wildlife list. Their intangible enrichment of our lives would be sufficient reason for protecting them were more concrete justification entirely lacking. The cheering song of the cardinal on a balmy morning in spring, the reassurance of the robin after a rainstorm, the liquid notes of the meadow lark from far across the pasture on a bright summer day, the excited scolding of the catbird when an intruder approaches its nest, and the angry chatter of the saucy little wren under similar circumstances, the demonic scream of the mischievous bluejay, the haunting staccato of an owl, or the brave call of a whippoorwill in the stillness of night— mere sounds, but sounds associated with a thousand cherished memories, these would be reason enough for counting song birds among our natural resources.

Nor must they make noise to be esteemed. Who would discount the worth of the swallows who plastered their mud nests on the great hewn beam in the old barn, of the robins who reared a brood

FIGURE 137. *Sometimes a bird in the bush is worth two in the hand!*

in the box elder by the kitchen window, or of the wrens who appropriated grandma's clothespin bag for half a summer. Such values defy auditing, and enviable is the man who has known them.

While most of us view a pretty bird with admiration, others see in handsome plumage a marketable commodity. In the past many non-game species died that their feathers might decorate millinery. Many egrets, herons, grebes, terns, and gulls gave their lives to "feather merchants" who supplied ornament for ingenious contraptions worn on ladies' heads. Egrets and terns were almost extirpated for the purpose before laws restricted feather traffic and forbade the killing of the birds (12, pp. 170-171). Recovery of plumage birds under legal protection first demonstrated the effectiveness of such measures. In the case of gulls protection appears to have been overdone (12, p. 171).

Birds have considerable functional significance, the value of a given species reflected mainly in its choice of foods (14). Insect eaters, such as bluebirds, swallows, wrens, titmice, and meadow larks are definitely useful, as are also the seed eaters, such as sparrows, finches, and red-winged blackbirds.

Considering that birds are heavy eaters, one must acknowledge their unique service in combating weed and insect pests (Figure 37). Examination of stomach contents has revealed that birds consume prodigious quantities of insects and seeds, much of their diet noxious. However, there is less evidence to prove that birds actually prevent infestations of weeds or mass invasions of harmful insects. The bird enthusiast may be prone to give our avian folk more credit than they deserve. Here again arises the pertinent question of biologic balance and environmental unity, to which an adequate answer still lies beyond our poor powers of perception. As with predator control, the most obvious interpretation may be the one utterly wrong.

A bird in the bush, worth two in the hand

From the standpoint of direct economic liability many of our fine, feathered friends often provoke persecution more than they elicit praise—always according to the circumstances. Bobolinks in a ricefield, linnets in an orchard, or robins in a strawberry patch can be intolerably destructive. Crows in a young cornfield pulling out the sprouts, or blackbirds in a ripe field of grain can ruin the crop and cause heavy loss to the farmer. This despite the fact that the same birds may have rendered yeoman service in another season or another place (15). Broad generalizations do not fit birds any better than they fit quadrupeds or men. The insect eaters destroy good insects along with the bad ones. A main course of weevils may be followed with ladybirds for dessert. The seed eaters frequently fill up on cultivated crops and ignore the weeds. Furthermore, while destroying some seeds they spread others by voiding them undigested, while combating plant parasites they also carry plant diseases. The sapsuckers, maligned members of the woodpecker family, may cause some injury to trees, but who can say positively that their taste for hickory sap has no desirable influence in the long train of forest succession? Certain it is that their cousins, the woodpeckers, combat destructive forest insects (16).

One need not exaggerate their virtues to accord song birds resource status. No other resource is more universally appreciated. In city, town, and country their company is enjoyed. Their services to land use are invaluable, probably indispensable. As noted, sportsmen are beginning to learn that there can be no game without conservation of the fundamental resources—water, soil, forest, and grassland; if game can sell the idea to sportsmen, perhaps song birds should be employed to sell nonsportsmen the critical concepts of conservation. Birds take wing when soils and water fail. Their songs are audible evidence of a tenable environment. Even the least of our fellow creatures have their places in na-

Bugs, worms, and spiders have their places

ture's plan (Figure 138). Insects, worms, and spiders serve uniq purposes in the total environment, although an adequate explan tion of their virtues would go far beyond the scope of this volum Neither can we attempt an objective appraisal of handson butterflies, musical cicadas, or fascinating lightning bugs exce to observe that their advertisements may be deceiving. The butte flies lay eggs that hatch into worms, the musicians have voracio appetites, and, though they set nothing afire, the torch beare have destructive propensities. To say that grubs are mole foo earthworms robin food, and spiders humming bird food would pointless, except that those tidbits furnish energy for more usef

FIGURE 138. *"It takes all kinds to make a world." All creatures live in cooperative-competitive society.* (After a drawing by Felix Summers

inctions—to the mole for soil-working, to the robin for bug-atching, and to the humming bird for pollen distribution.

Most important, perhaps, is the function of one in control of nother, so that all together maintain a healthy, balanced, environment. The prey-predator concept holds for large and small like, right down to the spider and the fly. That is one reason for he controversy in scientific circles provoked by our increasing use f selective toxic sprays to kill injurious organisms, inevitably kill-ıg some good ones along with the bad. It is conceivable that we nay initiate a biotic chain reaction fraught with danger (17, 18, 9). If by killing one pest we encourage another until that one nust also be eradicated, and we then eradicate each one in turn as t becomes a threat, we should finally have no life at all, but a terile void instead.

More practical than theoretical is the work of ants and earth-vorms in soil development, the work of bees, moths, and wasps n plant fertilization, and the work of other legions in converting rganic matter into humus and plant nutrients. It would seem nly fair that ants should pasture their aphids on plants grown rom soil the ants helped to build. They become enemies only vhen they herd their "cows" to the wrong pastures, such as chrys-inthemums, roses, and fruit trees. The best have some evil in hem; the worst, some good. Conflict and contradiction run the ;amut of wildlife behavior, from bears and birds to bugs and)ees. Human regulation demands extreme caution. Patience, olerance, and careful research can more surely conserve wildlife han hasty interference and regimentation. One group of crea-ures cannot be modified without influencing another.

CHAPTER 12: REFERENCES CITED BY NUMBER

(1) V. E. Shelford, "Conservation of Wildlife," A. E. Parkins and J. R. Whitaker editors, *Our Natural Resources and their Conservation,* John Wiley and Sons, Inc., New York, 1936, Chapter 19.

(2) "The Status of Wildlife in the United States," *Senate Report No. 1203,* 76th Congress, 3rd Session, 1940.

(3) "History and Significance of American Wildlife," *Wildlife Leaflet 282,* F.W.S.,* Chicago, Illinois, 1946.

(4) Leonard W. Wing, *Practice of Wildlife Conservation,* John Wiley and Sons, Inc., New York, 1951.

(5) David A. DaLie, "Poisonous Snakes of America," *Journal of Forestry,* LI No. 4, April 1953, pp. 243-248.

(6) Sam Matthews, "Birds, Animals are Vanishing," *Science News Letter* LVII, No. 23, June 10, 1950.

(7) Frank G. Ashbrook, "Fur—An Important Wildlife Crop," *Wildlife Leaflet 314,* F.W.S., 1948.

(8) Wallace B. Grange and W. L. McAtee, "Improving the Farm Environment for Wild Life," *Farmers' Bulletin No. 1719,* U.S.D.A., 1934.

(9) "Food Habits of Common Hawks," *Circular No. 370,* U.S.D.A., 1935.

(10) Weldon F. Heald, "The Case of the Cougar," *Nature Magazine,* XLVI, No. 1, January 1953.

(11) Paul V. Errington, "A Closer Look At the Killers," *Audubon Magazine,* LV, No. 1, January-February 1953.

(12) Ira N. Gabrielson, *Wildlife Conservation,* The Macmillan Company, New York, 1941.

(13) Ellsworth D. Lumley, "Save Our Hawks: We Need Them," undated leaflet, National Council of State Garden Clubs, Inc., New York.

(14) H. W. Henshaw, "Does It Pay the Farmer to Protect Birds?" *Yearbook of Agriculture, 1907,* pp. 165-178.

(15) F. E. L. Beal, "Some Common Birds Useful to the Farmer," *Conservation Bulletin 18,* F.W.S., 1948.

(16) Harold Olson, "Beetle Rout in the Rockies," *Audubon Magazine,* LV, No. 1, January-February 1953.

---

* F.W.S.: Fish and Wildlife Service.

7) Alfred G. Etter, "The Danger of Weed Killers," *The Land*, VIII, No. 2, Summer 1949.

8) J. P. Linduska, "Wildlife in a Chemical World," *Audubon Magazine*, LIV, No.'s 3 and 4, May-June and July-August, 1952.

9) William R. Hanson, "Effects of Some Herbicides and Insecticides on Biota of North Dakota Marshes," *Journal of Wildlife Management*, XVI, No. 3, July 1952, pp. 299-308.

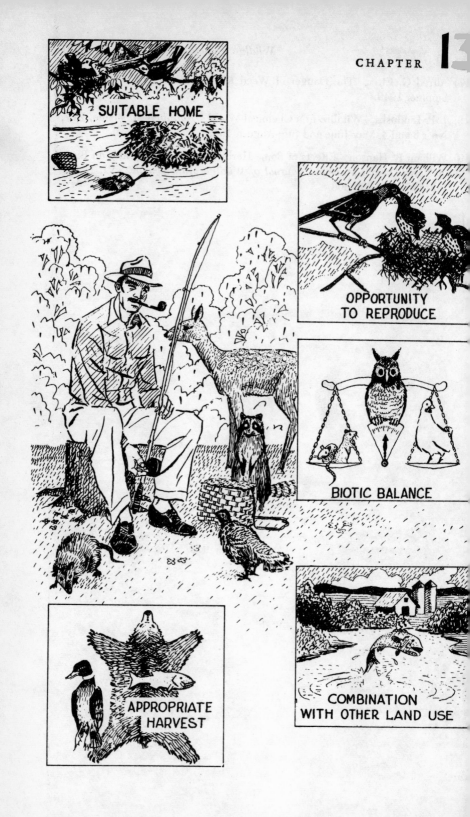

SUITABLE HOME

OPPORTUNITY
TO REPRODUCE

BIOTIC BALANCE

APPROPRIATE
HARVEST

COMBINATION
WITH OTHER LAND USE

Wildlife Conservation

*man improves his own estate by better behavior
as a member of the animal community*

N WILDLIFE CONSERVATION WE HAVE THE ADVANTAGE OF DEALING
ith resources that live and move, with a certain capacity for
daptation to environmental change, and a strong, instinctive
aculty to fend for themselves. Being mobile, animals can seek and
elect new habitats when old ones become untenable—a power
enied forest and grass resources, and bestowed on fishes less
iberally than on land creatures. Only the living resources can
eact to a situation; only the animal kinds can cooperate actively.
Given a modicum of habitable space, with food, water, and shel-
er, wild things take care of themselves. All that need be done to
ave desirable populations of them is to allow them necessary
pace (some require very little), spare enough of them to breed,
nd prevent their increase beyond the capacity of the allotted
abitat.

We cannot pretend to restore the wildlife environment that
vas the American wilderness. Only a few scattered remnants
emain essentially intact, mainly high among our western moun-
ains, and their wildness is not everywhere "primitive," but rather
a matter of degree. We cannot hope to restore to its original abundance the wildlife our country once knew; nor would we wish to
do so if we could. We do not intend to consign much land to the
sole occupance of wild things, though some portions might better
be so utilized. Neither do we intend to regain or retain, except in
a few "wild" areas, the *natural* biotic balance that once prevailed.

Wildlife conservation need not conflict with other more productive resource developments. It should be a part of them. It

Can we regain
a favorable
balance and
truly conserve
our wildlife
resources?

must impose no obstacle to economic gain or cultural progress, bu should enhance both. It must not interfere with the use of lan for crops, pasture, and forest, though it can materially enrich a three (1). In general, wildlife production must be incidental t agriculture, grazing, and forestry, a by-product of good land man agement and conservation (2, pp. 42-47f). The establishment o balance compatible with human occupancy of the land becomes fundamental object of the wildlife manager. His is the problem o adjusting wildlife to a habitat dominated by man, to an environ ment radically modified by human enterprise. Basic requirement for food and fiber have first claim on space. Wildlife must b secondary—now favored, now handicapped by the primary lan function.

Wildlife management reconciles animals and people in joint tenancy

The procedures whereby men rebuild and stabilize wild popula tions in harmony with human socio-economic patterns have be come known, collectively, as *wildlife management,* a major phas of resource conservation with guiding principles only recently evolved. Its development has been impeded by our failure to com prehend the involved organization of animal societies, our tardy acknowledgement of their disruption and constriction by civiliza tion, and our reluctance to interfere further with groups already jeopardized by inept interference in the past.

Our wildlife manager of today builds on many trials and errors accepting his raw materials as he finds them, however deplorable their state. He knows he may appropriate very little land ex clusively for wildlife—say, 1 per cent of our total land area (2, p 45). He knows that one species may depend upon a chain of others and that blunders in selection can break vital links in the chain And he knows painfully well that broken links cannot always be quickly or easily mended, that many gaps may never be repaired. Where predators have lost their normal function he must initiate substitute measures. Where predators, including man, become too destructive he must take steps to control them. For the most part, he deals with public property on privately-owned land, and he must please the public without infringing upon private rights. Quite often he is obliged to get quick results to satisfy an ignorant clientele when he knows that the hasty expedient demanded is absolutely incompatible with sound long-range development. His problems are often more complex and infinitely more delicate than those confronting conservers of land and water, yet his labors produce much less than theirs from a materialistic point of view.

Exotics are a sorry solution

Loss or threatened loss of indigenous species has prompted the importation of exotics to fill their places, and the importations of wildlife are subject to the same challenge as the importations of foreign grasses to reclothe the Plains. Are the ones introduced so much better that we wish them to replace completely the native ones? Should we hazard permanent loss of a native species by introducing an alien species that may not succeed, or may succeed too well?

We brought ring-necked pheasants from China and Hungarian partridges from Europe to make up our loss of prairie chickens, and thus far the newcomers have pleased us. Both have become splendid "American" game birds. However, our sorry experience with English sparrows and European starlings prompted legislation to exclude such opportunists in the future.

Indigenous species ask very small favors to stay with us. All they ask is their elemental needs for food, water, and living space. Many have quickly repopulated places from which they once departed and occupied places not previously inhabited when those three simple requirements were available. However, all three conditions must obtain—one or two will not suffice. And all three must be within reasonable distance of each other and safely attainable.

Requirements differ widely according to size and habits of individual species (3, pp. 400, 401). The ungulata need more space and food than song birds. Aquatic mammals and waterfowl make demands quite different from those of their upland counterparts. Resident species need only one set of facilities, while the migratory kinds need several.

A multiple function is also commonplace. Racoons find food where deer come only to drink. Fish live permanently where ducks stay only briefly. A single bush may contribute to both food and cover for deer, birds, and small mammals. A permanent home for muskrats may be a winter resort for geese, affording both the resident and the visitor his special choice of food and cover. But, if animals shall thrive the three essentials must be present. Those three together constitute wildlife habitat, and since habitat is the most important consideration in wildlife conservation, let us take it apart and look at it right here.

Cover is to wildlife as housing is to people, and wild creatures do no better in slums than do humans. While we have degraded many of our citizens to slum living we have literally razed the living quarters of wildlife. The greatest single need for the conservation of wildlife is the provision of places to live (2, p. 210).

Habitat requirements differ as widely as do the inhabitants.

Indigenous species ask only food, water, and cover to stay with us

Cover takes top priority

Figures 139 and 140. *Above: Mother bob-white with a family just hatched. Homes and families are essential to wildlife conservation.* (Hugo Schroder, from National Audubon Society.)

Below: sweet little darlings of a mother skunk. For most wild creatures, home requirements are very modest. (Maslowski and Goodpaster, from National Audubon Society.)

Deer need a forest, but robins ask only one leafy tree—safe from cats. Canada geese need one marsh in the south for winter vacation and another in the north for rearing a family in summer. Bobwhites need only a neglected field corner on an annual basis to produce many more children than the geese can boast (Figure 139). Some live better by the square rod than others by the square mile. A tuft of grass, a thorny bush, a tangle of vines, a clump of trees, or a patch of briars may be Home Sweet Home to a happy family (Figure 140).

Some forms of wildlife demand standard design, others accept a variety of architecture. If he loses his den tree, a raccoon can be expected to quit the neighborhood and remove to another suitable tree somewhere else. Gray squirrels and bluebirds are almost equally set in their ways, desiring hollows with a small entrance to exclude uninvited company. A mink will not live far from water, nor will a trout live in water that is not cool and clean. Others are less exacting. A woodchuck is equally at home be his "summer cottage" a stone wall in New England, a rockpile in Iowa, or a hollow tree in West Virginia. When he digs in for the winter it bothers the chuck not in the least if a cottontail moves into his attic while he sleeps in the basement. The cottontail borrows any burrow at hand unless the owner objects, and if no hole is handy a brush pile or briar patch serves him quite as well. Muskrats are also adaptable, tunnelling into the bank to supplement their huts in the water (Figure 141).

Cover is not adequate unless it gives a fair degree of protection for all essential activities of the tenant. The best rockpile fails a woodchuck if all about it stretches bare ground or close-cropped meadow. The touted weather prophet is safer to vacate the premises than to expose himself dangerously each time he goes for food or water. Lacking speed, he must live where cover screens his travel between home and the grocery store. A rabbit could more safely occupy the isolated rockpile, and for a skunk, who sleeps by day and digs his grubs at night, the rockpile could be highly desirable. A safe place to live and rear a family, a safe place to feed, a safe place to hide from enemies, a safe place to play and sleep, and a place for shelter against storm or cold— all these are necessary. But they cannot attain full value unless passage between them is also guarded.

Connecting cover is the vital link often overlooked by the would-be conservator. He can learn its importance by observing how consistently wildlife uses it. Another kind, also neglected, is the haven of retreat from danger—*escape cover*. Both travel

FIGURE 141. *Sunset over a muskrat marsh in Missouri. Drainage has ruined many similar communities. Muskrat mounds have special significance to amateur weather prophets. If the muskrats build low in the water, the coming winter will be severe, they say. However, muskrat architecture is probably determined by such factors as the availability of materials and the number of workers.* (John H. Gerard, from National Audubon Society.)

cover and escape cover are illustrated in Figure 142. In this category is the clump of briars that saves a rabbit from the pursuing fox, the matted grass under which a mouse escapes the hawk, the thorny bush or tangled vine that spares a bird from violent death, and the bushes or trees that come between a hunter and his quarry. Nature endowed some with protective coloration, but its value is often negated by environmental change. It is never entirely adequate without the help of protective vegetation. Color loses effect when the creature moves, and it is no defense against the elements.

Food and drink make the home tenable

A house without food and drink has only the semblance of a home, and shelter devoid of food and water makes no habitat for wildlife. However, vegetation that provides shelter may also produce food for its tenants (4). Therein reposes a natural nicety that simplifies the rehabilitation of wildlife areas. The hollow oak in which a squirrel resides may also yield a store of acorns. The mulberry or dogwood tree in which a robin builds contributes berries to his diet. The leafy shrubs that best hide a deer are also his browse. The weed patch to which quail escape may also be a good seed producer. Thus it is that by selection of shrubs, forbs, or grasses, either by sparing the desirable volunteers or by

298

FIGURE 142. *Escape cover and travel cover are essential parts of the wildlife habitat Wild creatures need ready refuge from pursuing enemies, and covered approaches for food and water.*

planting those of proved worth, the two prime essentials of wildlife habitat—food and cover—can be developed simultaneously (5, p. 4). In the humid East natural revegetation is often quite satisfactory without artificial improvement.

Animal tastes differ exceedingly, and many species vary their diets with the seasonal availability of food. Some prefer seeds or insects, others prefer forage or browse, and still others prefer flesh and not much else. Whatever their preference, it comes directly or indirectly from the plant cover, for meat is plant tissue transformed. Vegetable-eating insects become food for birds in summer, but plant parts become their mainstay in winter when the insects are gone. Green foliage and grass keep deer in summer, but bark, buds, and twigs fill in when the plants are dormant. Seeds, berries, nuts, buds, flowers, leaves, stems, and even roots contribute to the dietary requirements of wildlife.

Food supply to be satisfactory must always be sufficient, *within the foraging radius* of a species, to keep that species alive and capable of reproducing. An abundance in summer may be much less important than the smaller, more critical supply during winter shortage. The least bountiful season fixes wildlife populations in exactly the same manner as drought years limit range carrying capacity. If artificial feeding must be resorted to in any but the most unusual season the natural food supply is not sufficient for the population dependent upon it. Supplements doled out regularly to keep animals alive are futile attempts to offset deficiency of habitat or to maintain an abnormal population. They are dangerous palliatives in either case. Doubly blessed are those creatures that fatten when food is plentiful and hibernate during the slack season. Commendable are those that lay up stores to tide them over, or migrate with the sun. Our chief concern here is for those that remain in permanent residence, lay nothing by, and seek their daily bread within a narrow orbit instinctively defined. Research has shown the lifetime cruising radius of bobwhite quail to be less than half a mile (6).

Water supply is often the only limiting factor of wildlife habitat. However, its importance in the total picture evinces many gradations as between different species and different climatic regions. Fish live in it, ducks live on it, and other birds bathe in it and drink of it, while certain upland species are virtually "camels," taking only what they get in their food (3, p. 401). Mallards need an area of standing water, trout need it running, deer need it clean and in quantity, and quail can get by on dew. Water must be available in one form or another if wildlife shall inhabit an area. In its absence food and cover lose their value. Furthermore, it must be near at hand and attainable by a covered approach.

Our waste and abuse of surface waters by drainage, pollution, accelerated run-off, and siltation have imposed a major obstacle to wildlife conservation. Conversely, good management of water resources will probably contribute more to the enrichment of wildlife than any other measure. When water and land are properly conserved, wildlife benefits inevitably.

Habitat is the approved solution

Habitat is the approved solution of wildlife problems. A combination of cover, food, and water to equal or approximate the natural arrangement favorable to a given animal society goes farther toward perpetuating its component species than any number of more specific devices to increase them. Without reasonable habitat other measures are futile; with good habitat conditions many of them may be quite unnecessary. Biologists tried many direct methods of increasing desired species before they learned that none does much good unless it is coupled with suitable habitat. They tried protective measures against excessive capture by humans, they persecuted predators, they established special reservations and refuges, they introduced exotics, they propagated and planted, hatched and released what was wanted. Finally they discovered that the objective hinges upon habitats, and these not in a few isolated places, but throughout the country—maintained or restored on farms, ranches, and forest areas, on lands both public and private. They adopted nature's method and now they get real results.

In typical American fashion, we have often over-done our beneficence to wildlife. We have killed with kindness. In a favorable habitat some species are capable of such rapid increase that they eat themselves right out of house and home unless they are checked by natural enemies or their human guardians (7). Too many can be worse than too few, a fact amply proved by the overpopulation of deer in Pennsylvania and the growth of big-game herds in parts of the West beyond the carrying capacity of their consigned ranges. Whether we blame the problem on faulty favoritism or limitation of space makes little difference. The fact remains that the quickest way to readjust a manipulated environment is to manipulate it some more, as by controlling the number of its inhabitants. We could breed and plant cougars or import packs of wolves to reduce certain game populations, but it is much easier to kill any surplus by encouraging, or even hiring, hunters to do so. Common stumbling blocks in wildlife conservation have been regulations based on inadequate knowledge or on prejudice and public ignorance of a problem. Once established, protection has often become too strict and been continued too long.

Big game is not the only wildlife that needs harvesting to prevent excessive increase. Many other types, similarly favored, need similar control. Waterfowl, upland game birds, and small mammals can become too numerous for their own good unless countermeasures be applied. An un-fished lake may provide poor fishing because fish cannot grow large when too many compete for a limited food supply. Too many song birds in a small backyard become a menace to each other through infection and disease. *Increase of numbers is only one facet of wildlife conservation. Control of numbers at a conservative level can be even more pertinent.*

Suitable habitat is one thing, suitable population another. A population greater than the habitat can support brings disaster to itself and damage to the habitat. Starving animals can so severely overtax their food supply during a season of drought or

Too few are better than too many

cold as to curtail its normal replenishment when favorable weather returns. Such depletion during bad times indicates over-population, which, unless promptly cut down, leads to progressive degradation of the environment. In some places carefully restored to wildlife we have permitted the process to frustrate our efforts. Unless we harvest the wildlife crops we produce with proper regard for their habitat limitations, we lose not only the crops but also the facilities with which to produce them (1). If the population controls shown in Figure 143 become inoperative or inadequate, direct measures should be applied accordingly.

Artificial
propagation
fails when
habitat is
lacking

We have already mentioned the futility of propagating game, fish, or other wildlife without providing a habitat for the incubated, hand reared product of hatchery or breeding station. We have wasted much money, time, and energy to produce game and sport fish for release in places where they could not long survive, much less assume natural functions of food-getting and reproduction. Animals born and bred in captivity, grown with medicated water and vitaminized feeds, are at best ill equipped to fend for themselves in the cruel world outside. If their first adversary is a

FIGURE 143. *Factors that hold down wildlife populations.* (After a drawing by Felix Summers.)

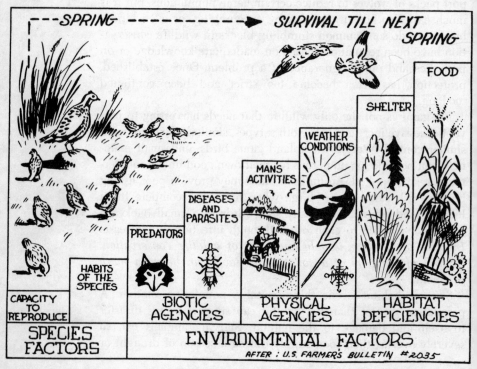

icensed hunter or fisherman they serve some purpose, otherwise hey die to no avail.

Released in a hospitable environment, pen or pond reared stock 1as been the means of re-establishing wildlife in areas whence it 1ad been expelled and of introducing it to new areas made 1abitable in advance. The population distribution of fowl and ish has been remarkably extended by brood stocks transplanted rom game and fish rearing establishments. Less has been done vith mammals, including big game, but phenomenal results 1ave been achieved by capturing them in the wild and planting :hem where desired. To this method we owe the return of beavers o forest streams deserted since Astor salted away his first nillion, and deer to where none lived when "buck" and "doe" 1ecame synonyms of "money." In many cases man's use and 1lteration of the land has materially improved it as a home for 'epatriated species.

All other measures prove inadequate for maintaining wildlife 1opulations unless men exercise judicious restraint against killing 1 species faster than it reproduces itself. Extinct and vanishing :orms bear mute witness to the result of unbridled destruction. To avert recurrent disaster, to regain and retain a desirable 1bundance, we have imposed many legal restrictions conceived to 1rotect wildlife against ourselves. Most familiar of these are the state game laws, but there are also federal prohibitions, including nany rules to safeguard non-game species. Enforcement is costly 1nd difficult, and violations numerous despite the severe penalties imposed on persons found guilty of infringement. Punitive measures often provoke more resentment than cooperation because the offender is either too ignorant to understand or too selfish to appreciate the bio-social purposes of the law he has violated. Protective regulations would be infinitely more effective if all our citizens understood their implications.

Our laws are to protect wildlife against ourselves

Our self-imposed restrictions are intended to save rare species from extinction and to reserve from the annual increase of those more numerous a breeding stock estimated to make maximum use of available habitat and produce the largest possible surplus for capture each succeeding year. The laws are intended to save from each *crop* enough *seed* to ensure a *harvest* the following year. Abiding by such laws, we treat wildlife much as we handle any other crop produced by the land.

Fixed bag and creel limits, daily and seasonal, are arrived at by gaging surplus game and fish against the anticipated numbers of hunters and fishermen who will pursue them. It is often desirable to make the rules adjustable on short notice to suit an available crop rather than fixing them far in advance of the harvest season. While a crop is growing it may be difficult to estimate how much it will yield.

Restrictions on weapons and gear have been imposed to prevent wholesale slaughter of wild creatures and give them a "sporting" chance instead; also to afford sportsmen more equalized opportunity. The taking of sport fish with a net or the shooting of game with a machine-gun cannot be condoned by an informed citizenry. The public has registered its collective objection to carnage by imposing statutory prohibitions. Implements of war and military tactics are not generally approved for use against wildlife.

A most fruitful device, the "closed season," has divers uses in the conservation of wildlife resources. Its most obvious application, of ancient origin, is for the safety of creatures during periods of reproduction or regeneration. It gives creatures a sort of diplomatic immunity while they rear their families or, if inadvertently decimated, until they regain a desirable population. The logic is very simple. He who shoots a duck when she is incubating a clutch of eggs or while the brood needs her care causes the family to die. He who takes a fish full of roe or a muskrat full of kits kills the unborn generation. He who kills a doe from her fawn, a she-bear from her cub, or a whale from her suckling calf causes the helpless offspring to die of hunger. The closed season means sanctity of the home and safety of the family while the young grow up. Since offspring are more dependent on the mother, she is ordinarily given more protection than her mate. It is often permissible to kill buck deer, bull seals, or cock pheasants when similar treatment of the females would curtail reproductive capabilities.

Mobility poses problems peculiar to wildlife

The mobility of wildlife poses peculiar conservation problems. Other appurtenances of land remain in place unless man abuses them and causes their removal, but animals move from place to place of their own volition, and cannot be conserved unless their travels be taken into account. The conservator must consider their itineraries as a whole, not in detached segments. This unique characteristic of wildlife requires for its conservation community interest of local, regional, or even continental scope. No other resource, with the possible exception of ocean fishes, is so reliant upon regional cooperation between places remotely distant from each other as well as between contiguous areas. A farmer cannot conserve quail if his neighbor shoots them whenever they run across the property line. Wisconsin cannot conserve deer if they stray across the state boundary and get killed in Minnesota. Canada cannot conserve geese without the cooperation of Louisiana and the other southerly regions to which they flock in winter.

On the basis of travel or stay-at-home habits, wildlife may be separated into two categories, *resident* and *migratory*. Permanent residents may "round out" their existence within a very limited radius, living and dying where they were born, while the most adventurous migrants make an annual circuit the length of the Americas.

The mammals, including big game, the reptiles, inland fishes, upland game fowl, and several species of birds remain in their respective vicinities throughout the year. Pressed for food, they move indeed, as when deer and elk quit snow-covered mountain slopes to seek food lower down, or when grouse and quail scour the countryside for meager winter fare. But the ruminants return to the slopes in spring, and the feathered beggars starve to death unless they find enough to live on within a few miles of home.

Most of our feathered folk are seasonal migrants. With few exceptions, waterfowl, shore birds, song birds, and birds of prey make long seasonal journeys, and like "rich folks" summer in the north and winter in the south. The rich migrate for comfort, the birds, probably, for food and survival. Some birds migrate within the confines of the United States only. Others spend summer in the United States and winter in Latin America. Still others spend winter in the United States and summer in Canada. The last category includes the greater number of our ducks and geese. To a few rugged individualists, such as the arctic tern and golden plover, the United States is simply a transit area between northern and southern residence (8).

Migratory species need special provisions

From the above it is apparent that many birds and wildfowl are in fact international resources, requiring for their effective conservation the cooperation of all nations they frequent. Toward that end we have signed Migratory Bird Treaties with both Canada and Mexico, and given the migrants federal protection within our own country. Several other American republics have registered interest in the joint program, which should ideally be hemispheric in scope (9).

The migrants fly many different routes and make their flights on many different schedules, but all move northward with the advance of spring and return southward after their summer

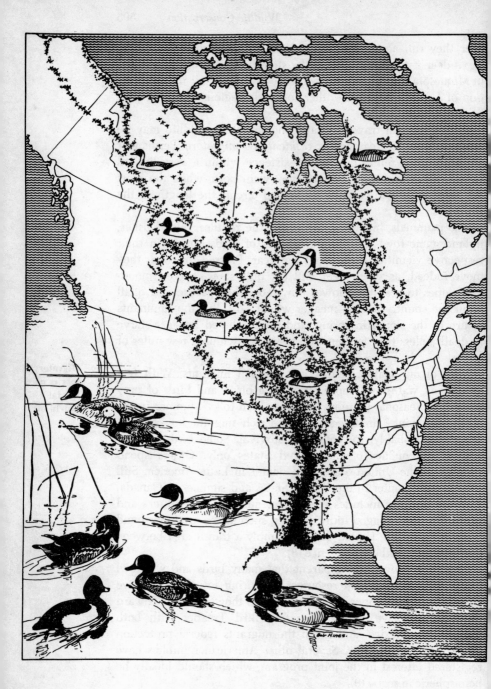

FIGURE 144. *The Mississippi flyway, reputedly the world's busiest natural airline.*
(Drawing by R. W. Hines, F.W.S.)

breeding season. Some turn southward early, while others delay until snow or cold drives them. Ornithologists have not yet determined whether light, temperature, food, sex, or some hidden instinct is the strongest stimulus to seasonal migration; but they have deduced from banding records that species and individuals tend to follow the same route and maintain the same schedule year after year. Consider the amazing punctuality with which the swallows are reputed to return to Capistrano.

The great flocks of ducks and geese that pass twice each year between breeding grounds in Canada and the northern United States and wintering grounds about the Caribbean follow four distinct routes called "flyways": the Pacific, the Central (High Plains), the Mississippi, and the Atlantic, as shown on accompanying maps (Figures 144 & 145). Most traveled of these, the Mississippi flyway, is probably the world's busiest aerial highway, carrying the greatest variety of feathered traffic—birds of land, shore, and water (8, p. 60). Well wooded and watered, flat and free of obstruction, the broad Mississippi Valley affords easy, direct passage between northern and southern habitats (Figure 144). From a bird's-eye view its only serious handicap is the army of hunters that intercepts the autumn traffic. But for the

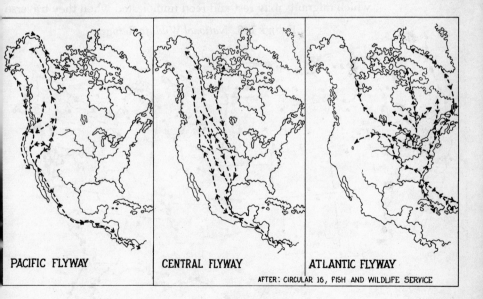

PACIFIC FLYWAY   CENTRAL FLYWAY   ATLANTIC FLYWAY

AFTER: CIRCULAR 16, FISH AND WILDLIFE SERVICE

FIGURE 145.   *Other principal migration routes.*

several restrictions we have mentioned the gunners would soon still the cackling V-formations that forewarn us of winter and in good time herald the return of spring. Pity him whose sensitivities are so elemental that he would rather gorge himself on roast goose than listen to an excited parade of honkers winging their way far overhead on a clear, calm evening in spring!

Refuges, preserves, and sanctuaries

The establishment of refuges, preserves, and sanctuaries, public and private, has greatly advanced our conservation of wildlife. Governments on all levels, many private agencies, and uncounted individuals have become participants in a program of reserving for wild creatures enough suitable space to ensure their self-perpetuation (10). Asylum from human persecution, legal or otherwise, appears to be the most promising means of carrying certain species through the era of public ignorance and apathy that must give way to better understanding and more considerate treatment. Had the sanctuary program been instituted earlier we might have saved several species from oblivion.

Our great Federal Wildlife Refuge system, begun in 1903, has grown until we now have some 300 land units, approximating a total of 18 million acres (Figure 146). More than two thirds of these federal refuges were created specifically for waterfowl—summer nesting grounds, wintering areas, and places between at which migrants may rest and feed unmolested when they traverse

FIGURE 146. *National Wildlife Refuges.*

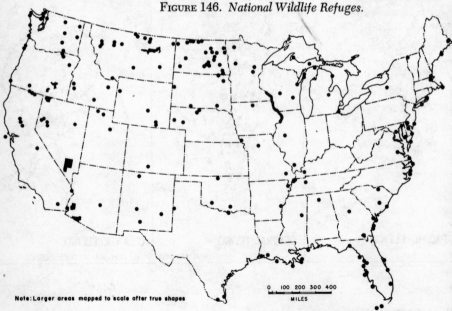

Note: Larger areas mapped to scale after true shapes

0 100 200 300 400
MILES

after maps by National Park Service
and U.S. Fish and Wildlife Service

the country (9). Lakes and marshes from which hunters are entirely or partly excluded become the certified tourist courts of flyway travelers. Other federal refuges are mainly for big game, though less exclusive than those for waterfowl. The survival of bison, elk, and several other large animals may be attributed to their timely management on reservations. National parks and monuments are inviolate sanctuaries.

The states have made tremendous contributions—twice that of the federal government—to the total refuge system, by setting aside parks and preserves in which wildlife may not be molested. The entire District of Columbia is by act of Congress a wildlife preserve.

Cities, towns, and minor civil units have provided further sanctuary and retreat for wildlife. The confines of entire cities have been designated bird sanctuaries, and since cities generally prohibit the use of firearms except to maintain law and order, urban areas can be excellent homes for birds and other wildlife.

Nature lovers and independent wildlife conservators have devoted a very considerable aggregate of land and water area exclusively to wildlife defense. A grove of trees, a pond or slough, even a vacant city lot can be converted into a refuge. Any habitat area becomes a sanctuary when man denies his own kind the privilege of disturbing it.

It will probably be impossible to appropriate for the sole use of wildlife sufficient area to maintain desirable animal populations. Wildlife production must therefore be a part of other land uses. Refuges must be regarded as preventives of exhaustion rather than producers of abundance. Overflow of animals from reservations to circumjacent areas will occur, but one acre cannot be expected to populate a hundred acres about it. Furthermore, the spread of wildlife to private land, as when elk invade farms or ranches, is frequently so destructive that it cannot be tolerated. It means that the refuge is too small for its population. If wildlife production were made the primary function of all publicly owned land (more than a quarter of our total area) we might still lack desirable abundance and distribution of species. Furthermore, established use of public lands rules out even this thesis, most such areas being devoted to services with which wildlife cannot economically compete—roads, cities, timber, range, and so forth (2, p. 45). Rather must wildlife be a secondary product of land, whether it is owned and used publicly or privately. It is estimated, however, that there are in this country a hundred million acres inherently unsuited to any use other than wildlife production (2). Much of this is too poorly drained for agricultural or pastoral

, ideal for water storage and wildlife. As population pressure ~~reases~~ land-use competition and refines our land selection we ~~y~~ expect that 5 per cent of our total space shall be used pri-~~rily~~ for wildlife, but we cannot expect so small a fraction to ~~populate~~ the remainder.

The users of our land are also the keepers of our wildlife

Wildlife conservation devolves upon the users of our land— the farmers, graziers, and timber growers. Most reassuring is the plain fact that good farming, good forestry, and good range management are also most productive of desirable wildlife, that wildlife becomes, as it were, an unearned dividend from conservation of soil, water, forest, and grassland (11). Conversely, wildlife suffers from the wastage of other resources. Land mutilation and inept manipulation of water handicap both human and animal residents. Over-grazing or burning that ruins forest or range spells disaster to useful wildlife. Since the primary land uses occupy most of our space (Chapter 5) it is logical that their production of wildlife as a supplemental crop is our only sure way to abundance (2).

The farmer surpasses everyone else as keeper of our wildlife. Ask him, and he will tell you that he feeds, not only cattle, swine, and poultry, but also the multitudes that fly, swim, or crawl. It is estimated that farmers produce 80 per cent of our wildlife (9, p. 23). As keeper of wildlife the farmer produces public wealth on his private property. He raises animals over which he has no legal jurisdiction (in the case of protected game) on land for the use of which he pays a tax to the owner-administrator of the animal wealth. He becomes a unique public custodian, and we must learn to respect him as such.

Odds and ends of land—a home for wildlife

Every farm is a potential home for wildlife, and almost every consideration for wildlife can make it a better farm on which to live. Somewhere on almost every farm is space better relegated to wildlife than employed for other use—a rock outcrop or a stony knoll that costs more in wear and tear on machinery than it can possibly repay in crop yield, a washed slope or gully in need of healing, a woods corner or slough too small or too inconveniently located for more profitable use, a steep declivity or stream bank that sloughs and crumbles under cattle hooves. Odds and ends big and small, grassy, weedy, brushy, or wooded become good wildlife habitats when machinery and livestock are kept off (12). Sheer economy commends them to wildlife; often, as from fur bearers or fish, yielding a tangible return (13, 14). See in Figure 147 how good farm management can accommodate wildlife.

POOR MANAGEMENT

GOOD MANAGEMENT

FIGURE 147. *Odds and ends of farmland can be homes for wildlife. On a well-managed farm, problem areas, such as rock exposures, gullies, and eroding stream banks become attractive and valuable wildlife habitats. (No extra cost!)*

Waste patches need not be the only farm areas productive of wildlife. A farm so uniformly fertile that it includes no waste land can, consistent with superior management, afford ideal habitat for a rich variety of wild creatures. Any farm anywhere can produce an abundance of wildlife without curtailment, but rather with increase, of its major products. This is an idea on which American thinking must be revised; herein may lie our greatest future promise for wildlife.

No farm is without boundaries, which are often precise lines between it and adjoining lands. Such property lines are customarily secured by permanent fences jointly built and maintained by the two owners whose farms meet along the common demarcation. On most farms is also a fence or two, permanently separating from the fields a woodlot or barnyard or both, frequently a fence along a road or a stream, and likely as not an enclosure about the farmstead (home, barns, garden, lawn, and so forth). It may be safe to estimate that a square quarter-section farm (160 acres) has or might have at least 2 miles of permanent fence.

The primary function of a farm fence is the confinement or exclusion of livestock, with the concomitant function of making good neighbors or providing grouchy ones with something to quarrel about. Fences are no barrier to good will or gossip, but serve well as a prop for both. They are objects of grave concern to the breeder of fine cattle. They climax the adventure of boys stealing melons. They are to birds a perch on which to sit, to the hired man a nuisance to be repaired on rainy days. They can be, by slight modification, splendid homes for wildlife. The New England stone wall and the old-fashioned snake fence (rails) of eastern forest regions have some value to wildlife, for concealment and escape if nothing else; but the straight, clean, wire fence that we have accepted as an indication of good farming is a barren symbol of backwardness. The electric fence is no better because its proper functioning requires that it be kept clear of growing vegetation capable of short-circuiting the current.

The living fence, guardian of wildlife, has until recently found little favor in America. True, grassland settlers made considerable use of it initially, as many overgrown hedgerows of Osage orange attest, but when wire and steel posts became available, most of the troublesome hedges got the axe (a laborious task). The trees grew so tall that they shaded adjacent field borders, and they spread so vigorously that they were difficult to control. Most farmers were happy to root them out and replace them with conventional fencing. With their removal went miles upon miles

[margin note:] Clean, wire fences are ugly, barren sentinels

of wildlife cover in the kind of open country where it is particularly critical.

With the soil conservation era came a reappraisal of farm practices generally, including those standard, bleak fixtures—fences. Americans rediscovered the merits of the hedgerows and fence rows so prominent in European landscapes, and concluded that clean fences, permanent ones in particular, represent a waste of energy and a practical error in farm management. Farmers pondered the unconventional idea that a fence grown up with bushes, briars, and vines confers multiple benefits without detracting from its primary function. Whereas a naked wire fence stops only animals, a densely vegetated fence row serves as a barrier to wind and a trap for snow, thus conserving soil and water. Best of all, it makes an ideal home for desirable wildlife, and lends rustic beauty to a landscape otherwise dull and monotonous (Figure 148).

Living fences are homes for wildlife

Contour farming brings added merit to living fences because it demands that field divisions follow curves instead of straight lines. To swing a taut wire fence about a curve calls for an inter-

FIGURE 148. *Compare sod with shrub fencerows for useful wildlife.* (After a drawing by Felix Summers.)

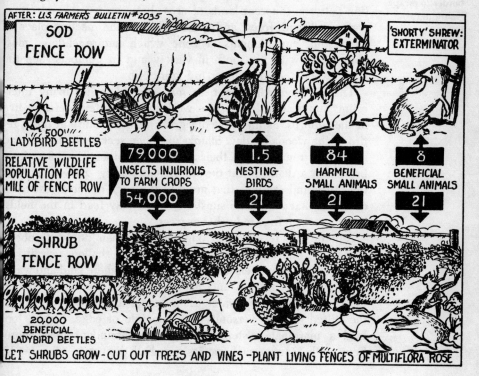

minable amount of bracing to hold the posts upright, but the
planted fence grows equally well curved, crooked, or straight
A thick hedge along a slope retards runoff, catches silt, and combats erosion generally. It need not be so wide as to use much
land (6 to 8 feet), and it need not be so tall as to deprive adjacent
crops of sunshine. Plants available for the purpose live indefinitely,
and, once established, require neither care nor control (5). Contour hedges are gaining favor, and with each one planted, wildlife
gains a residential subdivision.

We have disproved the fallacious idea that clean, straight fences
evince the diligence and proficiency of a farmer. We have
learned that the density and uniformity of hedgerows are more
valid criteria. As that truth gains wider acceptance and application
our countryside will be more beautiful, more prolific, more hospitable to wildlife, and more satisfying to people (15, 16). The
transformation is well under way, but its consummation will take
many years.

Fence rows and hedgerows exemplify the principle of "edge" ir
wildlife management. Being long in proportion to their width,
they present much edge and little depth, an arrangement favoring
wildlife. Edge is the periphery or border, the boundary or transition between different kinds of area—between woods and crops,
water and land, forest and grassland. It is the meeting place of
contrasting environments, a zone which nature endows most
abundantly with life, both in variety and in numbers. See the
marsh-woodland edge shown in Figure 149.

The border environment, or *marginal edge*, has many interesting ramifications. Men who work in town often prefer to live
in the suburbs. Skunks that dig grubs in the pasture at night retire to the woods by day. Skunks and men seek their daily bread
in one environment and their shelter in another. Deer find little
browse in a dense forest devoid of under-story. They must seek
the brush and saplings that grow at the edge of the forest or in
openings that admit the sunshine. Birds may feed in the fields,
but they take refuge in bushes or trees.

Aquatic life responds to edge no less than do landlubbers.
Waterfowl and aquatic mammals prefer the shallow margins to
deep, open water. Their food and shelter are where land and water
intermingle or overlap and fixed vegetation flourishes, though
they may take to deep water when danger threatens. Shore birds,
the stilted waders, personify the principle of edge. Fishes, too,
lead a marginal existence, being most abundant near shore.
Few of the commercial species we shall discuss in Chapter 15

Wildlife chooses the edge or border to escape "marginal" living

FIGURE 149. *The most prolific life zone is the margin, or ecotone, where one kind of environment meets another. The richest edge is the shore or the amphibious transition between land and water, such as this marsh margin in St. Charles County, Missouri.* (John H. Gerard, from National Audubon Society.)

inhabit the deep sea; they prefer the shoal waters on the continental shelf. The sea coast, the transitional zone from land to ocean, is perhaps the very epitome of marginal edge.

Discussion of borders and edges takes us back to the farm, where the most intricate pattern of wildlife environment results from good, diversified land use. Field borders (Figure 150) and woods borders, stream banks and drainage ditches, marsh, pond, and slough margins, hedges, shelterbelts, and brushy fence rows, protected waste areas, ungrazed farm woods opened by selective cutting—all these details of cultural landscape lend the *proximate variety and interspersion* that can sustain a thriving biotic community.

Wildlife and farm economics fit well together

Most of these farm features suit wildlife best when they are best arranged and managed for good conservation farming. The farmer need not take special pains to attract wildlife, although there is many a one who does. Ditch banks covered by grass serve wildlife admirably, at the same time keeping the ditch clear of obstruction that would interfere with drainage. Turning space at the ends of a field (Figure 150), wider now for big machines than

FIGURE 150. *A row of brush and weeds around a field may be as good a marginal edge as any. A quail food strip was sown along the edge shown, originally bare turning space for this field in Alabama.* (A. M. Rearson, F.W.S., photo.)

when horses and mules did the work, becomes wildlife border when sown down against erosion, its quality as habitat dependent upon the choice of cover crop. The sown border conserves both soil and wildlife (12). A farm woodland selectively cut for sustained yield admits enough sun for undergrowth to shelter animals. Its protection against burning and grazing enhances its value as wildlife habitat while also magnifying its forestry values (17, Chapter 12). A farmer need not deviate from good land management to produce abundant wildlife. Figure 150 shows how easily he can entice and retain wild tenants.

Wildlife and social relations have lacked harmony

Farm wildlife is a free crop, requiring no outlay of money or labor except as the farmer may be inclined. He who would have an abundance may invest in fences and planting to improve habitats, or leave patches of grain for winter feed, but even such concessions need not be costly. Wildlife on the farm is no luxury, though game or sport fish can cause a farmer such inconvenience as to discourage him from harboring them (18). Inconsiderate hunters and fishermen have caused much antagonism against the objects of their pursuit by leaving farm gates open, damaging fences, starting fires, trampling crops, or by outright vandalism. In self defense the farmer either posts his land against trespass or destroys the game that attracts the miscreants. This social conflict has retarded wildlife conservation in many places, and true sportsmen, who respect the rights of fellow men (including farmers), are endeavoring to relieve the tension. The respectable sportsman takes no game on private land without permission, and no game anywhere out of season. Instead, he helps the farmer produce game, and pays for the privilege of taking it. Sportsmen's organizations have in many places become active participants in farm improvement and wildlife management. For a little game they do much good, lending assistance with habitat and landscape problems far beyond their immediate interests. Many sportsmen are conservators, not poachers. They acknowledge and demonstrate the inseparable relationship between wildlife as a land attribute and wildlife as a recreational resource.

Wildlife belongs to everyone, benefits everyone, and can be conserved by everyone. In many ways we have made it a public trust, but its conservation depends upon our personal responsibility. Laws fail unless they be coupled with understanding.

That everyone has a stake in wildlife is well evinced by our public concern for its welfare, and by our public investment in it. Every level of government contributes toward its protection and propagation, and every taxpayer supports the program.

Everyone benefits from wildlife, and everyone can help conserve it

But public action cannot succeed unless it is scientifically sound. Thus far we have acted too much on hearsay and snap judgment. Sportsmen have counted themselves conservationists when they propagated game artificially and captured it immediately upon release. In fact, their contributions to conservation in the form of licenses, fees, and so forth have been, and are, extremely important. Politicians have initiated programs known by biologists to be entirely wrong. We have spent public funds to satisfy notions and whims more harmful than helpful.

The scene is in transition. With the efficient leadership of the Fish and Wildlife Service at the national level and many competent state agencies the prospect looks good. People are learning that wildlife legislation must be based upon scientific knowledge, that the politician must be advised by the natural scientist. The trend is toward more biologists and fewer campaign managers in fish and wildlife work—a very good departure.

There remains a great need for informing everyone of his stock in wildlife and his personal responsibility for its conservation. With better understanding will come necessary individual participation. Everyone can help, and everyone will profit. When *values* and *needs* of wildlife are more universally recognized its conservation may be assured.

CHAPTER 13: REFERENCES CITED BY NUMBER

(1) Durward L. Allen, "Wildlife History and The Soil," *Soil Conservation,* XVIII, No. 6, January 1953.

(2) Edward H. Graham, *The Land and Wildlife,* Oxford University Press, New York, 1947.

(3) Charles A. Dambach, "Conservation of Wildlife," Guy-Harold Smith, editor, *Conservation of Natural Resources,* John Wiley and Sons, Inc., New York, 1950, Chapter 18.

(4) William R. Van Dersal, "Native Woody Plants of the United States, Their Erosion Control and Wildlife Values," *Miscellaneous Publication 303,* U.S.D.A., 1938.

(5) W. L. McAtee, Plants Useful in Upland Wildlife Management, *Conservation Bulletin No. 7,* F.W.S., 1941.

(6) Dean A. Murphy and Thomas S. Baskett, "Bobwhite Mobility in Central Missouri," *Journal of Wildlife Management,* XVI, No. 4, October 1952, pp. 498-510.

(7) Frank Dufresne, "Too Many Moose!" *Field and Stream,* LVII, No. 5, September 1952.

(8) Frederick C. Lincoln, "Migration of Birds," *Circular 16,* F.W.S., 1950.

(9) Rachel L. Carson, "Guarding Our Wildlife Resources," *Conservation in Action No. 5,* F.W.S., 1948.

(10) Jack O'Connor, "Desert Revival—The Bighorns Are Back," *Outdoor Life,* CVIII, No. 10, September 1952.

(11) Ben East, "Quail On the Side," *Outdoor Life,* August 1952, CVIII, No. 9, p. 38.

(12) Wallace L. Anderson, "Making Land Produce Useful Wildlife," *Farmers' Bulletin No. 2035,* U.S.D.A. (S.C.S.), 1951.

(13) J. Paul Miller and Burwell B. Powell, "Game and Wild-fur Production and Utilization on Agricultural Land," *Circular 636,* U.S.D.A., 1942.

(14) Verne E. Davison, "Farm Fishponds for Food and Good Land Use," *Farmers' Bulletin 1983,* U.S.D.A., 1947.

(15) Wendell H. Harmon, "Hedgerows," *American Forests,* LIV, No. 10, October 1948.

(16) Wallace L. Anderson and Frank C. Edminster, "Multiflora Rose—For Living Fences and Wildlife Cover," *Leaflet 256,* U.S.D.A., 1949.

(17) R. H. Westfeld and Ralph H. Peck, *Forestry in Farm Management,* second edition, revised, John Wiley and Sons, Inc., New York, 1951.

(18) Durward L. Allen, "Wildlife and the Business of Farming," *Journal of Soil and Water Conservation,* VII, No. 5, November 1952, pp. 223-226, 245.

Resources for Recreation,

Inspiration, and Instruction

*above material wealth let us treasure and preserve
the gifts of nature which exalt man's inner self*

THIS CHAPTER TREATS A SUBJECT THAT DRAWS FROM ALL THE
material resources but proceeds beyond them; a subject which
invites both levity and gravity of treatment. Here we deal
with human happiness, with occasions when people shed their
cares and quit for a time the stress and strain of making a living.
We deal with the surge of reverence and awful humility with
which we view God's handiwork manifest in natural wonders. We
deal with escape from toil and care. We deal with pleasure and
beauty, with love and romance, with science and art, with
health, inspiration, and faith. We extol American pride, American confidence, American energy and drive, American democratic freedom.

We shall not attempt any strict differentiation of resources
that please, inspire, or instruct, because a single resource group
or area often serves all three purposes. Every one of our national
parks, for example, is endowed with recreational, inspirational,
and educational properties, all wrapped up in a single area or
even in a single natural feature. We are further discouraged from
cataloguing these resources by the fact that they serve different
people in different ways. Some people get their recreation from
viewing beautiful scenery, from nature study, or from exploring
wilderness; and others see nothing recreational in such activities.
A singular experience can impart physical refreshment, intellectual

321

stimulation, and spiritual uplift. How, then, can we segregate these sources?

Not by bread alone . . .

Man cannot live by bread alone; and in this chapter we consider the natural resources whence come the wine and diversion to flavor the bread. We shall not elaborate upon man-made facilities and social institutions, since they do not qualify under the term "natural." Neither shall we quarrel with definition lest thereby we sour the wine. Let us strike no discord for him who hears music sifting through pine trees, nor admit obstructions to him who sees the beauty of cathedral spires in mountain peaks. Let each be inspired in his own way, but let him furnish his own church or choir, since such are not of nature.

There is no denying that a theater supplies recreation, that there may be inspiration in a good sermon, and a modicum of learning in a classroom; but we are here concerned only with such properties in their rudimentary state, transmissible to man directly from natural sources. The quickening of the pulse when a hunter squeezes the trigger, the quiet serenity transmitted from placid water through a line and a bamboo pole, the fresh, earthy smell of wet woods when sun follows shower, the startling whirr of a frightened grouse, the invigoration of swimming, hiking, or skiing, and the satisfying rest earned by the exertion, the intimacy with creation in forest solitude, the chastening of false vanities in the presence of majestic mountains, cascading streams, or ancient canyons, the glimpse of infinity in a flaming sunset, the inspiring beauty of autumn foliage or the forbidding aspect of winter wilderness, the communion with God and Nature through intimacy with sun, wind, rain, and snow away from the frail edifices and the confused strife of men—these are a few of the priceless gifts we would cherish in our time and transmit to posterity undefiled.

Are we to presume that abstractions may be conserved, like quick-freezing faith, hope, or love? Perhaps not. But we *can* conserve those material attributes of environment whence the abstractions "emanate." This chapter is perforce one of idealism and altruism, quite in contrast to all the others, but even so, as we shall see presently, it has its materialistic and pecuniary aspects.

"Life, liberty, and the pursuit of happiness"

Among the inalienable human rights espoused by our founding fathers are "life, liberty, and the pursuit of happiness," and our conservation of recreational resources is peculiarly pertinent to the last of these. The espousal of rights would mean little were it not implemented, but American wealth and enterprise have brought it to rare fruition. From our fabulous natural resources we have, by diligence and ingenuity, achieved a high standard of living. With production and efficiency have come progressively higher wages and shorter working hours until most of our people have both time and money for fun and travel. The 40-hour week, long weekends, and paid vacations afford the leisure with which to explore the rich aesthetic resources of our expansive and varied national landscape.

The pursuit of happiness has been further aided by the increasing speed and comfort of carriers—streamlined trains, air-conditioned busses, and luxurious skyliners—to say nothing of the comfort and convenience of traveling by private automobile on paved highways with facilities and conveniences available almost everywhere. We have so effectively shortened distance that scenes utterly remote by horse and buggy are now a few hours distant.

All these cultural advances—higher incomes, faster travel, and more leisure time—have given us unsurpassed capabilities for using natural resources that refresh, inspire, and instruct. Let us hope that our capacity to utilize has been paralleled by a growing appreciation of their worth and a stronger determination to conserve them. What was once for a chosen few is now enjoyed by many, and the more numerous clientele should assert a proportionately stronger influence. The more there are who enjoy a resource, the more champions ought there be to defend it.

Improvement of body, mind, and soul

The promotion of human well-being is an object of all conservation, and the "athletic-aesthetic" resources contribute very directly to the program. They are not essential in the same sense as water and soil, but they enrich even further a people possessed of abundant water and fertile soil. They make of men better conservators by strengthening their bodies, sharpening their wits, and refining their sense of values. Outdoor recreational resources improve the bodies of persons who enjoy them, thereby fitting such persons for greater application to their work and more constructive citizenship generally. The same healthful relaxation promotes mental alertness as well, soothes frayed nerves, and makes of the participant a more agreeable associate.

A clear mind may be counted a physical quality, improved by contact with nature, but the great outdoors also bestows intellectual and psychological benefits of a higher order. Wild areas afford opportunities to study our environment as it was before we disturbed it. To him who can hear, they whisper hints on how we may mend our abuses. They have incomparable scientific value. On a mental plane still higher they challenge, and extend, our limited powers of comprehension. If we but see, they show the inescapable unity of earth and life. They breach the flimsy barrier between instinct and intellect and test the veneer we call culture. They bring our thinking down to earth, on solid footing.

Perhaps the greatest of all human benefits from outdoor experience are spiritual, though such defy measurement, and may reach the recipient without his conscious knowledge. Many a believer feels closer to his Creator amid His handiwork—trees, cliffs, or wide and windy spaces—than in the best appointed and solemnly dedicated chapel. In nature one can pray and meditate without distraction. Nature assists man with the conservation of his immortal soul. Could any earthly resource have nobler purpose?

Not all recreation areas are natural

Choice of outdoor recreation and taste in scenic beauty differ as widely as temperament and social heritage, but none can be indulged without the requisite land area. Space allocation for recreation may be based upon needs rather than any particular attribute of the land, as when a city *develops* a park or playground; but an area of special scenic or scientific interest must be reserved where it happens to be, no matter how remote its location. The conservator should distinguish between natural resources and artificial developments, because the latter concern him only as they occupy space. Many parks developed to meet the recreational needs of a city, community, or metropolitan area have nothing natural about them except their location, the land upon which they are situated, and the elements that impinge on the surface. Selection of site is dictated by population density, accessibility to users, and availability of sufficient space. If a site suitably located has natural beauty or interest as well, so much the better, but proximity is more important than natural attributes. Playgrounds, amusement parks, golf courses, swimming pools, athletic fields, and other *constructed* recreational facilities lie so near the fringe of our subject that we shall say little about them. *Recreational* they are, yes; *resources* they are too—but they can scarcely be called *natural*.

Monopoly of space is not an absolute criterion

Monopoly of space is not necessarily a requisite for recreation, many outdoor activities being compatible with, or even favored by, other uses of the land. If farm land produces most of our small game and logging increases browse for deer, it follows that farmers and lumbermen are patrons of hunting, unless they deny the hunter access to the game. To hunters game is the thing, although the enjoyment of space may be their most important gain. The sport would be exclusive, indeed, were it limited to public lands and others retained exclusively for shooting.

Hunting, fishing, skiing, camping, picnicking, and many other forms of outdoor recreation may be enjoyed wherever conditions favor them, on private land or public, if the participants behave decently and respect the rights of others. Unfortunately, some of our fellow citizens are so retarded socially that they may not enjoy themselves except on public land or on land operated expressly for pleasure. Their slovenliness will not be tolerated on private property. Thus a crude minority has prejudiced the decent majority.

Recreational activities that require exclusive and extensive area, or the provision of considerable facilities, must be either publicly or commercially sponsored. Not many individuals could bear the cost of a water supply for a roadside camp, nor even of a fireplace or latrine, and only by a public agency can such a stopping place be properly policed and maintained. No individual, however wealthy, can adequately conserve a wilderness, because one lifetime is too short! Thus, it does devolve upon the public, through government, to conserve natural resources for citizens to enjoy. Public ownership is a strategic advantage; public maintenance a necessity—one of our worst failures has been the inadequate financing of supervision and maintenance.

Does public ownership mean space monopoly by one exclusive use? By no means. Our National Forests are also national playgrounds. In them are many of our best hunting and fishing lands; yet the same areas yield valuable timber harvests. The public range is for grazing of cattle and sheep, but a pack trip need do the grass no harm. Dude ranching might even be supplemental to stock raising. However, the dude ranch is ordinarily a business enterprise, a recreational land-use specialty. It serves paying guests and shows a profit from land that might be marginal or submarginal for other purposes. It is thus a form of private conservation. Our attention must be focused on public recreation areas and private land with recreational aspects supplemental to its primary use. On the latter, recreational values are secondary, on the former they are primary. The two together constitute our major thesis.

A nationwide survey completed before World War II showed that touring and sightseeing, fishing, picnicking, and swimming were the most popular outdoor American pastimes (1, p. 14). Camping, hiking, boating, nature study, sports and games, and horseback riding stood high in popularity. Hunting, photography, arts and crafts, sketching and painting, and other interests brought many enthusiasts to the great outdoors. Since the advent of atomic energy, prospecting with Geiger counters has attracted a following, but in general our recreational preferences have probably not changed greatly. This partial listing would suggest that our outdoor activities developed without pretentious claims on area and without serious obstruction by private land ownership.

Many may be enjoyed without infringing upon property rights, and others require only the privilege of access. However, as our population has grown, as more and more people have been able to travel and enjoy themselves, and as our land has become more thoroughly utilized, it has become necessary to guard private rights in land more jealously, and therefore incumbent upon us to reserve for public enjoyment areas desirable and available for the purpose. Increasing population pressure proves the wisdom of such public land acquisition, and demands also that governments at the various levels promote supplemental recreational use of private land consistent with both private and public interests. The latter is probably the larger task and certainly the one least advanced. Our national parks and our public game laws, respectively, represent the two programs.

The vulgar corrupts the sacred

While we would exclude from our discussion artificial arrangements for physical exercise, group games, and other amusements contrived to meet purely recreational needs, we may not ignore them as conventional adjuncts to areas of genuine natural merit. We have often mixed the facilities for brute animation with natural resources for spiritual uplift, an incongruous formulation of secular and sacred ingredients. In many places we have constructed recreational facilities amid splendid natural scenery, and their incompatibility has provoked controversy; perhaps we have violated good conservation practice by such mixing. There are combinations we can endorse, such as a golf course or tennis court, camp ground or picnic area in a rich natural setting. A golfer's exercise need be no less invigorating because he admires the landscape between tees, and picnic gossip need be no less sensational if it is punctuated with praises of a beautiful view. However, we shall not attempt any justification for combining recreational and aesthetic resource except incidentally. Each function is probably best realized by separating the two.

The picnic area a natural resource?

The plain, rustic picnic spot familiar to the average American is the smallest, albeit not the least important, recreational unit of the type we wish to conserve. With some such spot, somewhere in the United States, are associated treasured memories of friends and events that have enriched our lives. The lake shore or beach, the deep, cool woods or the bright, sunny glade, the mountain side or stream bank, the roadside park or the quiet, secluded place off a little country lane—each gave its share to our social heritage. Who can forget the last family picnic grandpa attended? Which grandmother has forgotten the time little Annie fell into the river, or the time little Willie strayed off and got lost? Who can recount his happy experiences without including the glow of a campfire on familiar faces?

Indeed, sandwiches, hot-dogs, and marshmallows are symbols of an institution that Americans could ill afford to lose, one they can foster by reserving and maintaining for public use attractive nooks and corners here and there and affording access to them without trespassing. We need more picnic areas even now, and many more for the future. They are the least imposing of all the recreational resources, but they will not be adequately conserved without public action on their behalf.

To go from picnic areas to National Parks may seem like jumping from the ridiculous to the sublime, but let us assume that editorial liberty. Our National Parks embody the ultimate in natural resources for refreshment, inspiration, and instruction.

In them one may know the magnificence of natural scenery, the ordered association of native plants and animals, and marvels wrought by natural forces. In them we would hold inviolate certain segments of primitive America as a legacy from one generation to another.

We wrote our will a little late, after some prizes had been lost, to us and all posterity; but we have salvaged enough outstanding areas to compose a National Park System of unique quality and variety. That system is the pride and property of every American, and every loyal citizen should defend it against compromise. Any unit diverted to another use would be lost forever as a natural exhibit, exactly as our wildlife species have been lost. A natural area is not renewable; it must be preserved as it is.

In 1872 a few wise, unselfish men persuaded Congress to withdraw from entry and preserve for the use and enjoyment of all the people that wonderful part of public domain known as the "Yellowstone"—our first national park. Since then we have added other distinctive areas until we now have 28, comprising more than 8 million acres (2). The map of National Parks and National Nature Monuments shows where they are located (Figure 151). Unfortunately, few are in the East where most of our people live, not only because the natural grandeur of the western United States is more spectacular, but because the eastern lands were largely either privately owned or commercially used before the park movement began. However, every advance in transportation and ease of travel counters the regional disparity.

Under the Antiquities Act passed by Congress in 1906 we have reserved 36 National Nature Monuments, areas of unique scenic or scientific interest in the western half of the country. The same

Our National Parks—nature's masterpieces in public trust

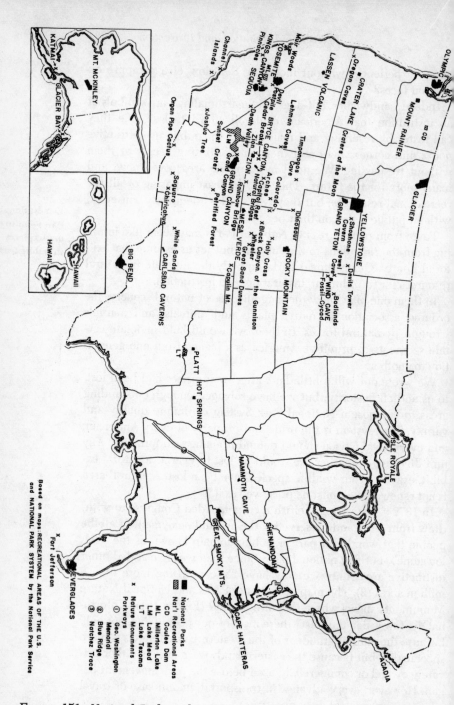

FIGURE 151. *National Parks and Nature Monuments. The National Park Service also administers many areas of scenic and scientific interest not shown on this map.*

map shows their locations, and their names indicate in most cases the features or properties to be preserved. Their focal interests virtually run the gamut of earth sciences, challenging the scholar and fascinating the casual visitor.

In 1916 the National Park Service was established to administer the entire system of national parks and monuments; and an excellent job the Service has done with very limited appropriations. Under the Service come numerous national historical parks and historic sites, military parks and battlefields, memorials, cemeteries, parkways, and recreational areas (3, p. 7) most of which lack the *natural* quality of a natural resource except as they preempt land area.

Our main interest is in those federal reservations more definitively referred to as National Primeval Parks (3, p. 266) in which we condone a minimum of artificial meddling, for the safety and convenience of visitors. These are our great, natural wonderlands, to be enjoyed in our time and conveyed to posterity unspoiled. Their aggregate area takes less than 1 per cent of our total land surface, a trifle we can well afford to dedicate to so high a purpose.

Every one of them is a wildlife sanctuary. Hunting and trapping are prohibited, as is the gathering or mutilation of native plants. Many are final retreats for remnants of big game and rare species (4). They are living laboratories for the study of geography, geology, botany, zoology, and ecology. The geographer finds in them a wide sampling of climates, land forms, vegetation types, and environmental composites. Tropical to sub-polar climates, coastal marsh to alpine meadow, desert to temperate rain forest, highest (Mt. Whitney) to lowest (Death Valley), wettest to driest, flattest to steepest—the Parks present variety. In the walls of deep canyons they show the geologist a complete rock sequence from most ancient formations to recent. They hold remnants of Pleistocene ice and great scars of severe glaciation. They display the gigantic upheaval of volcanoes, and reveal the herculean powers of moving water. In them the geologist reads earth history through hundreds of millions of years. They afford the botanist, the zoologist, and the ecologist unequalled opportunity to observe and study indigenous plants and animals, including the oldest living and the most ancient dead. Such scholars may examine, on the ground, zonal distributions and regional associations nowhere else observable. For scientific values alone our National Parks would be worth many times the cost of preserving them.

Perhaps the greatest educational value of the parks is to those numerous visitors who get their first taste of nature study from a ranger-naturalist. That first true glimpse of nature can stir the imagination more profoundly than systematic research, and leave an indelible, sobering impression. Who can look at the Grand Canyon and trace its physiographic history without pondering immortality? Who can gape up at the "big trees" and feel himself terribly important (Figure 152)? Who can view any of the natural wonders we guard without becoming a bit more tolerant of his fellows and a shade less satisfied with himself? Even the least thoughtful and impressionable park visitor is bound to gain higher national pride and some respect for resource conservation. The parks are veritable classrooms for resource education, a function which, in the long run, may be their most valuable contribution. Common amusement does not become them. In 1950 almost 14 million visitors attested the aesthetic importance of Primeval Parks; in 1951 they numbered more than 15 million. All areas under jurisdiction of the National Parks Service attracted well over 32 million people in 1950, and 4½ million more in 1951, according to the Director's Annual Reports.

State park systems complement the national

Supplemental to the national parks are the several state park systems. The states own more than 1700 separate tracts of land, with a total area of about 4½ million acres (5, p. 9). State park standards vary in some degree between one state and another, and are generally less exacting than those laid down by the National Park Service. Not all the state parks are natural, many of them being artificially developed, with more emphasis on active recreation than on aesthetic values. However, many compare favorably with the national ones in scenic beauty or scientific interest. Many, such as Itasca in Minnesota, headwaters of the Mississippi, the Adirondacks and Catskills in New York, several "Groves" of big trees in California, and a few beaches in Oregon have national interest. As game refuges or nature preserves, most of the state parks contribute to our national program for wildlife conservation.

By their greater number and wider geographic distribution, state parks are accessible to many people unable to visit a national one. (State park attendance in 1950 reached well over 114 million, more than nine times the number of visitors to national parks.) In the populous Northeast they make up for the dearth of national areas, and get heavy wear from city folk in search of fresh air. In the South, national forest areas supplement them, but in the south-central plains they serve without benefit of federal space. In the mountain states they supplement the elaborate national system, and on the Pacific slope they are generously interspersed with it. The combined pattern of state and national areas makes available

FIGURE 152. *Among the oldest living things the egotist sheds his cloak of vanity. This is the Garden Club of America Grove, in Humboldt Redwoods State Park, California.* (Photo courtesy Save-the-Redwoods League.)

to almost everyone a place to relax tensions and regain perspective away from the dull routine or strenuous hustle of making a living. No land has a higher yield.

Much could be said here about the lesser lights of parkdom—the numerous county or community reserves, the metropolitan or suburban parks and playgrounds—but, as previously suggested, few such areas qualify as natural resources. They interest the conservator, however, as *special land uses.* Those in rural communities are generally conservative of land, often putting to good use spaces poorly suited to other employment. Many areas otherwise wasted serve both for recreation and wildlife habitat. Those in urban vicinities are generally spaces appropriated for recreation in competition with intensive land uses. Patches of trees and grass where land sells by the foot instead of by the acre are concrete evidence that open space is almost as essential to health as safe drinking water. Their scarcity evinces poor conservation of space exactly where space is most precious.

The colonists transplanted to the New World the idea of a town common or village green, but the idea was apparently lost in the rush of westward expansion and the erection of vertical cities. We

We need more roof-gardens on the ground

neglected to reserve adequate space for escape from jostling crowds, incessant noises, and gasoline fumes. We built skyscrapers without reserving enough horizontal distance between them to refresh their occupants. We ignored the object lessons taught by such great and ancient cities as London, where spacious parks, "greenbelts," and open squares have been strictly maintained for the people's enjoyment (6, p. 75). Our errors are costing us dearly in condemnation of properties, clearing, rebuilding, and landscaping. City dwellers need many more roof-gardens on the ground, and if they will plan wisely for future urban expansion, they can have them without exorbitant cost. The city planner, through appropriate allocation of coveted space, doubles in brass as conservator.

The vulnerability of tall buildings and compact city blocks to aerial weapons should encourage horizontal expansion of cities. The same dispersal that renders them less remunerative as targets will automatically leave more open space than has been customary. The same adjustment that promotes passive defense will also promote the welfare of urban residents when no attack threatens. Under the lash of danger urban uses will occupy more land, but land devoted to health and security may be adjudged well used. It is, indeed, an ill wind that blows no good; fear provides needed recreational space where deliberate choice failed to do so.

In Chapter 9 we mentioned recreation among the multiple services of forests. Now we are ready to elucidate the idea. Forests are, indeed, among our most valuable recreational resources, their intangible benefits rivaling their value for wood production. More often than not, our outdoor experiences are associated with trees, whether in a picnic grove, a thicket with birds and berries, a farm woodland where squirrels and rabbits live, or a real forest of tall timber, with deep shade by day and heavy silence at night. Neither area nor ownership is a reliable criterion for evaluation, because a mere clump of trees favorably situated, though privately owned, can be enjoyed by more people than square miles of forest fastness, publicly owned but out of reach. The eternal problem of access, which hinges upon public decency, is the main deterrent to recreational use of private land, forested or otherwise. Since right of access remains highly subjective, we shall devote most of our discussion to public forests wherein we, through government, determine our own privileges.

Forests are important recreational resources

National, state, and community forests afford exceptional opportunity for a variety of outdoor activities. In the national forests some 4,500 camping and picnicking areas have been equipped with tables and benches, fireplaces, safe water supplies, latrines, and garbage-disposal facilities. Hundreds of swimming places have been improved, and some 230 winter sports areas developed. In the national forests are more than 400 organization camps, with dormitories or cabins, mess halls, and other appurtenances for group outings, 137,000 miles of scenic roads, and 140,000 miles of trails for hiking or horseback riding. They contain 81,000 miles of streams and thousands of lakes for fishing, boating, or canoeing. Game is abundant in most of them, and may be hunted in accordance with regulations laid down by the state within which the particular area happens to lie, excepting areas designated federal or state wildlife refuges (7). For those who shoot with cameras the forests excel as hunting grounds.

The number of recreational visitors to national forests has grown to almost 30 million annually (1951), more than 4 million of them hunters or fishermen. In addition, an estimated 50 to 60 million motorists enjoy the forest scenery just driving through (8). Provision for sundry sports and other activities is more consistent with national forest policy than with our national park standards. Rules of behavior can be somewhat more lenient in the forests, excepting, of course, a strict fire discipline. Sports that would deface natural exhibits or alter biotic communities may not be detrimental to forestry.

One should be reminded that in neither the forest nor the parks do artificial developments and construction occupy more than about one per cent of total acreage. Service areas and camp sites are simply bases of operation, as it were. The parks excel in scenic grandeur and scientific interest; the forests, our greatest playgrounds, also include areas that rival the parks in aesthetic aspects. Within our national forests are no less than 236 popular skiing areas (9).

State, county, and other public forests are in most cases desirable and useful for recreation. Many were reserved or acquired to fill specific recreational needs, and are maintained primarily for recreation. Some combine forestry with recreation, producing valuable timber crops co-incidental with their service as playgrounds. Some contribute materially to our forest resources and relatively less to the recreational ones, but very few lack entirely those attributes desirable in a recreation area. They lie within easy reach of many more people than the national forests and, within their limitations of size, afford similar opportunities for sports and other outdoor activities. Many units, or parts of units, are distinguishable from parks in name only.

Our evaluation of forests as recreational resources would be badly distorted if we failed to mention farm woodlands and other privately owned forests. They are much more numerous than public forests, and almost every one of them has recreational potential. Whether as places to observe wildlife or places to indulge in more active recreation, they are resources of more than economic significance. Many affluent sportsmen who underwrite private hunting or fishing grounds today shot their first game in a farm woodlot and caught their first fish in the creek that ran through it when they were barefoot boys without money and without business problems. The importance of small woods as wildlife habitats was pointed out in Chapter 13. The preponderance of small holdings in the total forest picture was indicated in Chapter 10. Their proportionate contribution to recreation is probably even greater than their contribution to timber supply. Those that occupy land too poor for more intensive use, or land that needs their protective covering, require no other justification for being. Almost without exception, they add charm and interest to the landscape. They have aesthetic and recreational values that merit greater recognition than is ordinarily accorded them.

Shores and beaches have special appeal

Shores and beaches stand almost as high as forests and mountains on the preferred list of scenic and recreational attractions; yet they have been almost ignored in public conservation programs. In the zone of contact between land and water, man himself responds to the principle of edge that influences so strongly the distribution of wildlife (Chapters 12 and 13). A modified response it is, perhaps, but most of our water recreation depends upon "edge," be it active pleasure such as fishing, swimming, and boating, or passive enjoyment of amphibious scenery. Gunning for waterfowl adheres closely to the land-water edge, and even deep-sea sports fishing depends upon it. Boat docks, bath houses, and other shore facilities for recreation are exploitations of edge. Whoever owns the edge controls the recreational use of the water. That is a fact we have almost missed in public conservation of recreational resources. However, our neglect is moderated by many desirable commercial developments and a favorable evolution of policy.

Except on public reservations such as parks, forests, and refuges, our use of stream banks, lake shores and ocean beaches has been largely private or commercial, without public intervention on behalf of the resources. The Public Domain included no ocean beach that might have been set aside as a national park, but the deficiency has been partially corrected by acquisition of such

FIGURE 153. *Impoundment of water for power, flood prevention, and other uses, has brought new recreational opportunities to many people. As on the "Great Lakes of the South," planned development and high standards of maintenance have been the rule. This boat dock and swimming area are in Kentucky Lake State Park.* (Photo courtesy T.V.A.)

coastal areas as the Cape Hatteras dunes, the Channel Islands off Los Angeles, the Everglades of Florida, and Acadia National Park on the coast of Maine. The last is a nature area of "stern and rockbound coast." The Islands have beaches from which human swimmers might wish to evict the sea lions if park policy permitted. The Park Service is not an amusement agency; beach development for swimming and other sports has been incidental. On the Cape Hatteras acquisition recreation and nature sanctuary occupy separate areas.

We have made substantial contributions to lake shore recreation on the national level in connection with reservoir construction for such purposes as flood "control," power, and irrigation. Federal planning and supervision assures optimum recreational use of the T.V.A. lakes (Figure 153), and the Park Service does similar work around the waters impounded by the Reclamation Service for irrigation and other uses.

Pollution of streams, lake shores, and ocean beaches has become so extremely detrimental to recreation that it constitutes a major conservation problem. Waters too toxic for fish and too filthy to swim in have obviously lost their recreational value and become a menace to health instead of the boon they should be. We considered this grave problem in Chapter 6, indicating some progress toward its solution. Many of our recreational resources are completely dependent upon water conservation. They illustrate once again the inescapable unity of natural assets.

States well endowed with lakes and beaches have generally

neglected to conserve them. They have permitted private purchase of shore properties until public access to the water has been blocked, and condoned such conglomerations of nondescript architecture as would cause every ripple to cringe if it could see them. Homes and cottages, two and three deep, line the best places around beautiful glacial lakes, and a non-owner can barely see the water without trespassing. Shacks, "joints," and dilapidated firetraps degrade many of our finest beaches on the Atlantic and Gulf coasts into a revolting clutter of trash that must shame Old Man Sea himself. Such blighting of natural beauty by cheap commercialization has created many problems for the planner and the conservator.

All beaches have not been divested of natural charm and diverted from wholesome public use. A few of our coastal states, notably those on the Pacific, have reserved and maintained for the public choice stretches of beach. Facilities and services are either state-operated or state-supervised in the public interest. Many commercial beach developments are also examples of good conservation, protecting the natural resource and catering to "solid" citizens who come to enjoy the beach environment.

The highest type of recreational or scenic resource is the primeval wilderness, though we have only recently acknowledged the fact. Its conservation is first of all a matter of preservation. Any idea of direct profit or common amusement defeats its purpose. Its conservation demands an immunity from cultural modification even more absolute than that prescribed for the national parks as a whole, and a longer vision and greater altruism than for any other class of resource, though some of our best wildernesses are actually within National Parks. The value of wilderness as a natural resource depends, not upon development, but upon strict prohibition of development—retention exactly as nature made it. To have genuine wilderness one must begin with a "mature, balanced community of plant and animal life" as it was before man arrived on the scene, and protect it, consistent with its recreational use, against every sort of human intervention (10, p. 46). Some areas, such as the Adirondack Forest Preserves, have reverted to wilderness after serving other useful purposes.

Primeval wilderness is our highest type of recreational resource

A person who has done field nature study as student, teacher, or researcher can readily subscribe to wilderness conservation, but the average "materialistic" American, seeing no practical advantage in it, is more inclined to ignore it than to support it. Public apathy born of ignorance and private selfishness born of greed constitute the major problems. The conservator must instruct the public, and the public must restrain obstructive, private motives.

Why save wilderness? For its unique recreational, aesthetic, and scientific values. The last one mentioned is probably the most important, although wilderness affords the only complete escape from civilization and the only opportunity to commune with nature in her own ageless solitude. The scientific values have many ramifications, both academic and practical. Their importance is probably best evinced by the fact that naturalist groups have most actively and effectively spread the wilderness concept. The wilderness is, obviously, a complete field laboratory for the study of earth sciences. It shows what the environment was before man intervened, and reveals the wisdom (or lack of it) with which he adapted it to his use. Wilderness serves as a point of departure for determining our use and abuse of durable resources. If we save it now, it can do the same for future generations. If we delay, or admit compromise, some future geographer will be unnecessarily handicapped in his interpretation of environmental influences and adaptations. If we disclaim all interest in posterity, the immediate, practical value of wilderness to land-science is in itself more than adequate justification for conserving it (11).

Federal agencies charged with the administration of public lands have responded favorably to the wilderness movement and reserved under various designations many areas of wilderness quality. The Forest Service, our greatest guardian of wilderness, established two major categories: 1. *Wilderness*—single tract of 100,000 acres or more—and 2. Wild Area—single tract between 5,000 and 100,000 acres in area (10, p. 25). The national forests contain 78 units in the two categories, approximating a tenth of their total area, and distributed as shown in Figure 154. In a recent year 200,000 people spent an average of 2½ days in one or another of these wilderness areas (10). Many of the national parks, several of the national nature monuments and federal wildlife refuges, and a few state reservations qualify for designation as wilderness or wild areas, or include large portions that do.

The ideal wilderness system would include a suitable unit to represent every physiographic region and every ecologic association in the country before settlement. But we cannot attain the ideal. Particularly in the East, representative areas of sufficient size are difficult to find. The Linville Gorge Wild Area, established in 1952, was the first area so designated by the Forest Service east of the Mississippi (12), although the Superior Roadless Areas in northern Minnesota are indeed part of the National Forest wilderness system. In non-forested regions a type unit should probably

be at least 500,000 acres in area (10, p. 18). Such a block of un-
modified grassland is a thing of the past, so we shall have to be
content with smaller units.

Recognition of *wildness* as a resource has encouraged the
preservation of many lesser "nature" areas. Michigan, Wisconsin,
and Iowa are reserving primeval ecological remnants on a state-
wide basis (13). Numerous other agencies, institutions, and citizen groups are protecting an untold number of natural areas, every
one of which has some scientific value (Figure 152). We have well
over 600 "Nature Sanctuaries" officially reserved. Every state has
at least one. California alone has forty-four (14). It is too late to

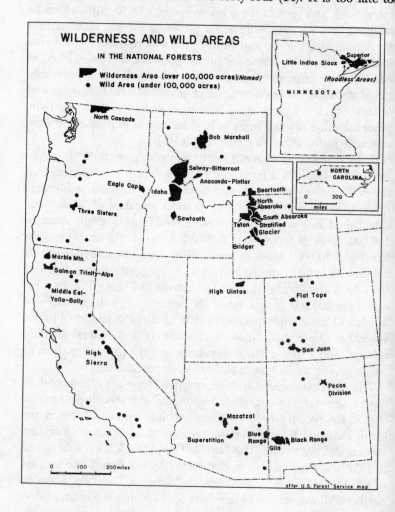

FIGURE 154

ecure a complete set of museum pieces, but let us make sure that
ve do not lose any remaining exhibits that should be added.

Resources such as scenery, wilderness, and natural wonders,
vhich have intangible values, are extremely difficult to defend
gainst selfishness and vandalism because they cannot be appraised in materialistic terms. They might be likened to a family
eirloom that lacks intrinsic worth and is nonetheless a prized
ossession.

Intangible values are difficult to defend against selfish pressure groups

If we assume that a resource is secure when it is publicly owned
ve are deceiving ourselves. Not even the national parks, reserved
nd dedicated by Congress, are inviolate. On the contrary, they
re threatened recurrently, if not continuously, by groups and
gencies with special axes to grind, axes that would chop our parks
o pieces if we did not parry their blows.

To the engineer a deep, narrow canyon is a sculptured invita-
ion to build a dam; to the lumberman a forest is something to be
cut down and sold, at a profit; to a stockman grass is the stuff
rom which cattle and sheep make money. They see these things
rom a limited perspective, and when bureaucracy or sectional
politics supports their aims they become a menace to national
nterests.

Hydraulic engineers flooded a portion of Yosemite National
Park when they built the Hetch-Hetchy Dam, and they have the
plans drawn whereby other park areas would be devoted to water
storage (15, 16). Only by constant vigilance will the American
people prevent wasteful appropriation for the temporary benefit
of a few certain natural treasures that should be the permanent
property of all. Only by national referendum should it be permissible to dam the Grand Canyon and fill it up with silt (17).

Timber and grass above ground and minerals underneath are
as dangerous to public lands as potential dam sites. Selfish interests ferret out every statutory loophole through which they may
work, and our statutes have many loopholes (18). No public area is
secure, be it park, forest, or wilderness (19). Lumbermen would
cut the "big trees," stockmen would over-graze the last remnants
of native meadow (20), and miners would tear up both earth and
vegetation for the purpose (or even pretence) of recovering critical
minerals (17). Certain laws for the encouragement of mineral
exploration and recovery on public lands have jeopardized other
values.

If we were desperate for material resources, we might condone
their procurement at the expense of the intangibles, but while we
revel in abundance we have no reason for such sacrifice. If ever
we permit ourselves to become so destitute that we must scrape

every vestige of wealth off the land in order to prolong our survival, we may find that it would have been preferable to have perished a bit sooner amid more pleasant surroundings. For the interim we should exclude from our nature preserves every common use, such as logging, mining, or grazing, that detracts from their higher purpose. We should not permit sectional or bureaucratic pressure groups to make spoils of our rarest public possessions.

Public property gets public abuse

More disconcerting than selfishness is the wanton abuse of public property and public privileges without *any* apparent motive. Perverse vandalism and human slothfulness curtail public enjoyment of aesthetic and recreational resources by defacing and befouling them, and even destroying them outright. Here we face the embarrassing fact that places for public enjoyment need protection against the very public that frequents them. The United States has its share of people who lack respect for public property, perhaps because they have little of their own to care for or have got what they have too easily. These inconsiderate, unprincipled persons are the bane of a conservator's existence. They leave camp sites and picnic areas littered with garbage. They start destructive fires by leaving camp fires smoldering or by tossing lighted cigarettes away. They shoot holes in signs and markers. They collect forbidden souvenirs, a crime called larceny. They soil and mutilate public structures and facilities until decent people cannot use them. They are like a scourge of human locusts that ruin, not crops and meadows, but priceless public possessions and costly public conveniences (21). One of our greatest needs is the adequate financing of patrols to discourage slovenliness in park and recreation areas.

Vandalism is very difficult to curb by punitive means, because the guilty person is often of the strain that resents suggestion or correction and takes pride in breaking the law. The apparent need is for education that will reform the vandals. Education and information are important to the conservation of any resource, but for conserving those with intangible values they are the primary tools (22). We must teach our citizens the value of natural beauty and wildness, and the very areas we wish to protect may be the best classrooms for the instruction. Well-conducted field trips and group outings for our youngsters will ensure better and easier conservation in the future.

Commercial conservation of recreational resources

Several times we have alluded to selfish interests inimical to the conservation of aesthetic or recreational resources, and have said very little about circumstances under which private interests are desirable. The fact is that opportunities for outdoor recreation would be sadly inadequate without those provided by private enterprises operated for profit. Private capital exploits scenic and recreational resources just as legitimately as it exploits soils and forests, with comparable degrees of care and abuse. We mentioned the case of beaches, some disgraceful and others commendable. The same holds for swimming pools, ski slides, tourist courts and hotels, lodges and rental cabins, and a variety of other facilities, including exclusive resorts for seasonal residence. Many represent desirable resource development and conservation. They are valuable additions to the American scene. We are improving their quality by granting to private companies the recreational and tourist facilities on public reservations under a franchise or concession contract with provisos written in to ensure high standards of operation (Figure 153). Tourist accommodations in our National Parks and in such recreation areas as those on the T.V.A. lakes are privately operated, subject to governmental supervision and inspection. The half-and-half arrangement is advantageous both to the entrepreneur and his patrons, producing private profit and public economy. Condemnation of commercial development of aesthetic or recreational resources on general principles would be quite wrong, because many such resources would be wasted had not private enterprise grasped an opportunity. The conservator applauds those operators who maintain standards commensurate with the quality of the resource they utilize.

Commercial development can also be commercial desecration (recall the beaches again). Juke joints and hot-dog stands that cheapen a grand view are to aesthetic resources as gullies are to soils. They are wasteful abuses of natural beauty. Such commercial blights the conservator cannot condone. He counts them a form of vandalism—crimes against both nature and the American public. When planners "zone" them out of the scene they conserve aesthetic resources, hand-in-glove with conservators.

The favorite outdoor sports of hunting and fishing have risen to singular commercial stature despite the precarious conditions of game resources and the shrinkage of land areas on which to hunt or fish. We mentioned the sportsman's dilemma in Chapter 13, but refrained from analyzing it because game and game lands have become so distinctly recreational and commercial as to be almost divorced from wildlife conservation. Especially is this true insofar as wildlife conservation pertains to migratory waterfowl. The maintenance of duck populations depends quite largely upon our control of hunting pressure, whereas genuine wildlife conservation remains a matter of suitable habitat and favorable biotic balance.

The big business of hunting and fishing

Evicted by drainage from many of their breeding grounds, highly esteemed by gunners, and subjected to mass-murder the length of their seasonal flights, migratory waterfowl became a special conservation problem. Cognizant of this, the Congress placed them under federal jurisdiction in 1916 (Migratory Bird Treaty with Canada) to check their threatened extinction by killing, and began in 1934 under the Migratory Bird Hunting Stamp Act the collection of money with which to recover and rehabilitate nesting and resting grounds. The federal government collects two dollars each year from every licensed hunter of ducks, geese, or brant (23). The money goes into federal waterfowl refuges. The annual sale of "Duck Stamps" (2,296,628 during the year ending June 30, 1953) gives an index to hunting pressure and necessary control of the harvest to maintain desirable reproductive capacity. The recent Federal Aid in Fish Restoration program serves in a different way with the conservation of sports fish. This businesslike system for fish and waterfowl conservation is achieving good results, with funds collected as a sort of tax on one segment of a major industry, namely hunting and fishing. An excise tax on firearms and direct or indirect taxes on other sporting equipment take from the big industry tremendous sums for game and wildlife conservation. Let us take a quick look at the pecuniary stature of the "industry."

It has been estimated that more than 33 million individuals enjoyed hunting and fishing in the United States during a recent year, and spent in the pursuit of these sports well over 9 billion dollars (24). They bought more than 28 million licenses, thereby putting a very tidy sum directly into public coffers. They paid out for goods and services more than our total receipts from swine and cattle sold for slaughter, twenty times our receipts from sheep and wool. They spent for dogs alone more than all gate receipts for spectator sport events (24). Certainly such comparisons should convince us that hunting and fishing are not only recreational, but also very important to our national economy. Many landowners are realizing a supplemental income from hunting leases or permits. Farmers are becoming conservators of game for direct profit, and benefactors of other wildlife inadvertently. We said earlier that this chapter has its materialistic aspects. That is one of them.

Hunters who sight through binoculars and shoot with cameras far outnumber those who employ lethal weapons. Each of the viewers spends at least half as much money as the killer (25), and takes none of his quarry away with him. This admirable breed of hunter contributes substantially to the national economy without the least detraction from our natural resources. He is the unsung

ero of wildlife conservation. He gives much, takes nothing, and
rakes no noise about it.

The enjoyment of our great scenic and recreational resources,
a the highest sense invaluable to us, may nonetheless be ac-
ounted a major American industry with a tremendous money
alue. Touring to "See America First" has attained full commercial
atus, and assumed a prominent place in American business.
Color-page advertisements in a score of national magazines indi-
ate how important it is to state finances. "Tourist farming" and
ue "tourist crop" have become definitive phrases in economic
eography.

Tourism has attained the rank of a major industry

Of course all recreational travel is not directly related to natural
esources, but a very substantial part of it is. Comparatively few
eople spend their vacations in cities; most of them seek open
ountry with beautiful scenery (26). Perhaps as many as three-
ourths of them spend all or part of their vacations traveling and
ghtseeing, and half of these go more than 500 miles from home
26). Over 85 per cent travel by automobile, and a national park
their favorite objective (27). In 1950 about 72 million Americans
ook travel vacations, spending an estimated 10 billion dollars.
More than one-third of the states ranked tourism one of the three
op-flight industries. Florida and New Mexico placed it first on the
st (27). Would anyone deny that scenic and recreational resources
ave material values? Would he question the wisdom of conserv-
ug them when they can by intelligent management yield a big
rop of dollars every year indefinitely without impairment? If one
ust stoop to dollars and cents in order to conserve aesthetic and
ecreational resources, he can stoop with confidence.

The phenomenal growth of vacation travel in recent years—
nore than 50 per cent during the decade 1940-1950 until almost
alf of the national population participates (27)—has profound
mplications for conservation generally. Travel acquaints our peo-
le with their great country better than any other medium could
oossibly do it. They see for themselves the scars of abusive ex-
oloitation and the demonstrated methods of healing them. They
ee how good the land can be when it is cared for and how ill it
an get when mistreated. They must inevitably gain some impres-
ion of our prodigious waste of natural wealth, and the urgent
eed for conservation. Certainly they cannot miss entirely the
triking contrast between healthy communities on well-kept land
nd the cadaverous neighborhoods whose resource base has with-
red or worn away. Even the least observant traveler must be
omewhat annoyed by stinking streams and roadside slums, and

the most casual observer must surely sense the human competence and security reflected in a clean, harmonious landscape (Figure 158). In the long run, public consciousness thus aroused may be worth much more to our nation than the ten billion dollars the travelers spend each year.

Conservation of beauty deserves attention

If travel is so valuable as a source of revenue and so potent a medium for shaping constructive public opinion, and if much of the traveling is in search of beauty, it should be an incentive for all of us, collectively and individually, to make our own surroundings more attractive and wholesome. Beauty, which is its own excuse for being, has resource status and can be conserved. At this form of conservation America is a complete novice compared with older and more crowded countries, such as England. Thus far Americans have exploited and commercialized almost without regard for the ugliness that unbridled materialism can create. They have obliterated much natural beauty unnecessarily, and much more will be spoiled unless they recognize its value. Sparing it might be termed "passive" conservation. Our biggest task, that of restoring lost beauty and enhancing that which remains, might be termed active beautification (28). Both are needed if we shall have the kind of nation and communities we like to envisage. Conservation of beauty may seem fanciful, but in practice it has real economic significance. No one can live on it, but none can live in dignity and contentment without it. Its conservation can be achieved without deviating from good management of other resources and will, indeed, improve the physical ones.

Beauty conservation may well begin with the roadsides since they are constantly on exhibit to our millions of travelers. Our roadsides could be attractive to the eye, or at least inoffensive; strewn with rubbish or cluttered with signboards and claptrap establishments, they lose their eye appeal. The modern "freeways," parkways, and turnpikes along which advertising and vending are prohibited have demonstrated the desirability of roadside sanitation (29). Zoning regulations by local government have proved another approach to the problem (30, 31). Control must extend beyond the public right-of-way unless access be restricted as along the super highways, or construction be eliminated from a zone of specified width paralleling the road. The latter (called set-back) will have to be our accepted solution because we cannot make all our roads into thoroughfares with widely spaced entrances—too much of our traffic is local. Neither can we convert them all into elaborate parkways such as the one suggested in Figure 155.

Gaudy signs and claptrap buildings along the edge of a road are not only unsightly in themselves; often as not they block or corrupt

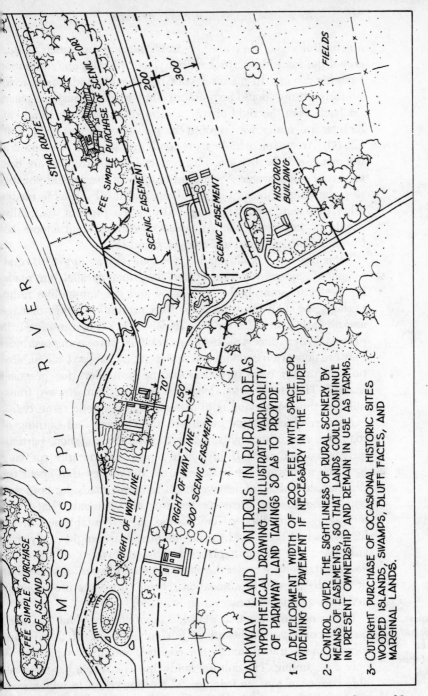

The text within the figure reads:

STAR ROUTE

FEE SIMPLE PURCHASE OF SCENIC FORT

200'
300'

SCENIC EASEMENT

SCENIC EASEMENT

FIELDS

HISTORIC BUILDING

M I S S I S S I P P I   R I V E R

FEE SIMPLE PURCHASE OF ISLAND

70'
150'

RIGHT OF WAY LINE

RIGHT OF WAY LINE

300' SCENIC EASEMENT

PARKWAY LAND CONTROLS IN RURAL AREAS
HYPOTHETICAL DRAWING TO ILLUSTRATE VARIABILITY
OF PARKWAY LAND TAKINGS SO AS TO PROVIDE:

1- A DEVELOPMENT WIDTH OF 200 FEET WITH SPACE FOR
WIDENING OF PAVEMENT IF NECESSARY IN THE FUTURE.

2- CONTROL OVER THE SIGHTLINESS OF RURAL SCENERY BY
MEANS OF EASEMENTS, SO THAT LANDS COULD CONTINUE
IN PRESENT OWNERSHIP AND REMAIN IN USE AS FARMS.

3- OUTRIGHT PURCHASE OF OCCASIONAL HISTORIC SITES
WOODED ISLANDS, SWAMPS, BLUFF FACES, AND
MARGINAL LANDS.

FIGURE 155. *Conservation of scenic routes of travel often involves public ownership and control of sufficient roadside space.* (From Bureau of Public Roads and National Park Service, *Parkway for the Mississippi;* Washington, D.C., 1951.)

a beautiful view. They are also traffic hazards inasmuch as they crowd the roadside, restrict visibility, and distract one's attention from his driving. In the interest of both beauty and safety, road side advertising should be prohibited and roadside business places set back from the right-of-way a safer distance. Both these correctives are under way despite the resistance of vested interest (32, 33). Americans who boycott goods and services advertised at the expense of beauty are conservators just as surely as are conservers of soil or water. A sufficient number of them could possibly stop the vulgar abuse. Let us submit that if all available media, other than outdoor advertising, fail to sell a product, its quality should be improved. The American consumer might choose between the scenes shown in Figures 156 and 157.

Some day we may also find an economical way to get rid of all telephone and power transmission lines that parallel our roads, the better to enjoy both the scenery and the automobile radio. Perhaps we shall bury the lines, thus preventing storm damage and obviating the need for pole replacement. This transition is in process. Where once a maze of parallel lines were strung overhead they are now often contained in underground cables. Communications engineers have turned landscape beautifiers for practical reasons. They have outmoded trunk lines with microwave transmission, thus conserving both material and aesthetic resources.

Another objectionable practice is the clearing and burning of roadsides and other rights-of-way to control vegetation, particularly in wooded areas. If, instead of repeated burning or spraying to check undesirable growth, we used the money thus spent for planting desirable species, we might have our roadsides bordered with demonstration areas for resource management. That trend too, along with billboard eradication, is well established. If all highways had their borders thus improved, we might easily provide adequate stopping places for the enjoyment of travelers. Several states have under development wayside park systems that fit into the general beautification scheme. Roadside protection is definitely a national conservation issue (34).

The cultural landscape has conservable beauty of tone and design

Let us not suppose that roadside improvement alone can adequately conserve the beauty of our environment. Highways are mere ribbons traced across the country, and their sanitation is only a beginning. The cultural landscape as a whole has conservable beauty of tone and design. The countrysides in which men work and live can be beautiful as well as productive. Good land use enhances outward beauty, and generates an atmosphere of peace and stability that only the "inward eye" can see. It has the

FIGURES 156 and 157. *Advertising that spoils the landscape develops sales resistance in the conservator.* (Photo above courtesy Minnesota Highway Department; photo below courtesy National Roadside Council. Both photos from "Roadside Protection," published by the American Automobile Association, 1951.)

FIGURE 158. *Good conservation farming, as exemplified on the Tocopson Creek Watershed in Pennsylvania, enhances the beauty of the rural landscape.* (S.C.S. photo.)

subtle power of conveying a sense of tranquility and well-being. To him who loves the land it reflects harmony between natural attributes and human adaptation, correct matching of physical and cultural qualities. He feels the sensory beauty of green woods, flourishing fields, and lush pastures patterned in accord with the terrain they occupy because he knows that they contribute to human comfort and security. He feels the stark ugliness of ghost towns and abandoned farmsteads because he knows that human failure and suffering attended them. Indeed, the good *cultural* landscape has a deeper beauty than that which meets the untrained eye, a beauty more profound than virgin wilderness could ever boast. It shows human competence, decency, and dignity as clearly as if those qualities were done in oil and framed under glass (Figure 158).

Beauty of cultural landscape is commensurate with the prevailing conservation of land resources. Clear, perennial streams, the alternate curves of stripcropping, the hedgerows, living fences, and habitat islands for wildlife, green fields interspersed with green groves—every evidence of conservational land-use adds charming tone and design. (See how conservation retouched the landscape in Figure 158.) Beauty, the by-product of competent land management, becomes a free bonus for good work and an incentive to do even better. Indeed, the man who works to beautify his place will, almost invariably, also conserve its natural resources.

Cleanliness and tidiness add the finishing touches to our landscape portrait, but we show a sad lack of artistic training. The most picturesque landscape loses its charm when it is cheapened by junk piles or trash heaps and littered with tin cans, bottles, paper cartons, old shoes and other discarded rubbish. The law forbids our printing an adequate indictment of the contemptible people who strew our roadsides with waste (Figure 159) or dump their accumulations of refuse on the property of another. The vile practices are punishable under the law, but we have been lax in its enforcement. Furthermore, the "sneak-thief" who soils the landscape is probably more difficult to apprehend than the one who takes something away with him. Once again, our recourse must be to education, such that stimulates personal pride and elevates human dignity. Everyone can be a conservator of beauty by properly disposing of his own trash, and, with example and suggestion, by dissuading others from scattering theirs about the countryside. Every American has an obligation to the form of conservation that might be called *landscape housekeeping,* and at this moment the "house" could stand a thorough scrubbing. It would be easy to keep if all our citizens were house-broken. Meanwhile, the contemptible persons who soil the environment as shown in Figure 160 should be pursued, punished, and publicly denounced as common criminals.

Splendid scenery, enchanting wilderness, and the varied beauty of cultural landscape may be esteemed the classical offerings in our resource repertoire. Conservation of their recreational and inspirational values might be likened to the fine arts in a college curriculum. How dull the graduate who lacks acquaintance with the arts; how crass the gain from conservation that neglects the finest gifts of nature—intellectual stimulation and spiritual assurance!

Keep the "fine arts" in our conservation curriculum!

A great wealth of these resources is in our possession, all of them vulnerable to erosion and pollution by the humans they benefit. They serve everyone, they can be abused by anyone, and their permanence depends more upon the intellectual idealist than upon the practical realist. They are therefore peculiarly vulnerable to selfish argument supported by dollar statistics. Selfish design and malicious abuse are their greatest threats, and public reservation is only a fair defense against either (35).

If we would have the prized possessions mentioned in this chapter, we must educate our fellow citizens to a fuller appreciation and respect for them. We cannot conserve all of them by public or group ownership, and without public understanding and cooperation we cannot conserve any of them under any form of ownership. Scenic beauty belongs to him who admires it, regardless of title or property line, but if he trespasses in order to admire, he denies himself the privilege. Genuine respect for the rights of others would solve most problems pertinent to the conservation of aesthetic and recreational resources.

Our material progress has so far outstripped our cultural refinement that we stand in greater need of mental and spiritual nourishment than of food for our bodies. We have the wherewithal to conserve the resources that enrich our lives and strengthen our spiritual convictions, and we must meet the challenge! As our nation grows and matures we shall draw increasing benefit from intangibles that renew and define perspective. Those intangibles nurture the high ideals that will aggrandize our national destiny.

FIGURE 159. *Persons who litter our roadsides with trash are unworthy of the privilege of traveling on our highways!* (Photo by Jimmy Ellis, courtesy *Johnson City* [Tennessee] *Press Chronicle*.)

FIGURE 160. *Persons who dump their rubbish along a beautiful woods road are as clearly thieves as if they took the scenic landscape away with them.* (Photo by Reuben Mehling, courtesy East Tennessee State College.)

CHAPTER 14: REFERENCES CITED BY NUMBER

(1) *A Study of the Park and Recreation Problem of the United States,* Department of the Interior, N.P.S.,* Washington, D.C., 1941.

(2) *Areas Administered by the National Park Service,* Washington, D.C., 1949.

(3) Devereux Butcher, *Exploring Our National Parks and Monuments,* National Parks Association and Houghton Mifflin Company, Boston, 1951.

(4) Joseph S. Dixon, *Wildlife Portfolio of the Western National Parks,* N.P.S., 1942.

(5) *State Parks: Areas, Acreages, and Accommodations,* N.P.S., 1950.

(6) *Proceedings of the National Conference on Planning,* American Society of Planning Officials, Minneapolis, Minnesota, 1938.

(7) *National Forest Vacations,* F.S., 1950.

(8) "Our National Forests," *Agriculture Information Bulletin No. 49,* U.S.D.A. (F.S.), 1951.

---

* N.P.S.: National Park Service.

(9) James B. Craig, "Skiing for Everybody," *American Forests,* LV, No. 1, January 1949.

(10) C. Frank Keyser, *The Preservation of Wilderness Areas (An Analysis of Opinion on the Problem),* Legislative Reference Service, Library of Congress, 1949.

(11) Aldo Leopold, "Wilderness As a Land Laboratory," *The Living Wilderness,* VI, No. 6, July 1941—entire issue.

(12) Erwin A. Heers, "Wild Is the Word for Linville," *Nature Magazine,* Vol. 45, No. 4, April 1952.

(13) "Living Museums of Primeval America: A Need and An Opportunity," The Nature Conservancy, Washington, D.C., undated policy statement.

(14) Howard Zahniser, editor, "Nature Sanctuaries in the United States and Canada," *The Living Wilderness,* XV, No. 35, Winter 1950-51.

(15) Arthur H. Carhart, "The Menaced Dinosaur Monument," *National Parks Magazine,* XXVI, No. 108, January-March 1952.

(16) Horace M. Albright and Frank J. Taylor, "How We Saved the Big Trees," *The Saturday Evening Post,* February 7, 1953.

(17) Bernard DeVoto, "Shall We Let Them Ruin Our National Parks?" *The Saturday Evening Post,* July 22, 1950.

(18) Cleveland Van Dresser, "Abuses Under the Mining Laws," *American Forests,* LVIII, Nos. 1-3, January-March 1952.

(19) Jay H. Price, "Threats to Wilderness Areas," *National Parks Magazine,* XIX, No. 81, April-June 1945.

(20) Bernard DeVoto, "Sacred Cows and Public Lands," *Harper's Magazine,* July 1948.

(21) Annette H. Richards, "Public Parks or Public Dumps," *American Forests,* LVIII, No. 5, May 1952.

(22) E. P. Romilly, "How to Cope with Vandalism in the Protection of Park Property through Area and Facility Maintenance," *Planning and Civic Comment,* September 1951.

(23) "Federal Duck Stamps and Their Place in Waterfowl Conservation," *Conservation in Action* No. 3, F.W.S., 1947.

(24) Arthur H. Carhart, "Hunting and Fishing is Bigger Business," *Sports Afield,* June 1951.

(25) "Summary of Answers to Questionnaire About Audubon Magazine," National Audubon Society, New York, 1951, mimeograph.

(26) *The American Magazine's Sixth Annual Travelogue,* The Crowell-Collier Publishing Company, New York, 1950.

(27) *Americans on the Highway: A Report on Vacation Travel in 1950,* American Automobile Association, Washington, D.C., 1951.

(28) Charles N. Elliott, "Landscape," *Conservation of American Resources,* Turner E. Smith and Co., Atlanta, 1951, Unit VIII.

(29) Stanley W. Abbott, "Parkways—A New Philosophy," Harlean James, editor, *American Planning and Civic Annual, 1951,* American Planning and Civic Association, Washington, D.C., 1952, pp. 41-45.

(30) Harlean James, "Highways and Planning," *American Planning and Civic Annual, 1940.*

(31) "Progress in Highway Protection Secured Through County and Town Zoning," *The Roadside Bulletin,* December 1946.

(32) "Can Voluntary Cooperation Check the Roadside Blight?" *The Roadside Bulletin,* February 1950.

(33) "Will We Protect Our Freeways or Let the Billboards Take Them Over?" *National Roadside Council News Letter,* January 1952.

(34) *Roadside Protection,* American Automobile Association, 1951.

(35) Frank A. Tinker, "Vandalism—Nature's No. 1 Enemy," *Nature Magazine,* XLV, No. 6, June-July 1952.

Resources of

Our Bordering Seas

*the wealth of the sea beckons the
conservator to explore a vast resource frontier*

IN ELEVEN CHAPTERS BEFORE THIS WE HAVE EXAMINED THOSE RE-
newable resources which in the main attach to the continental land
mass of the United States—waters, soils, forests, grasslands, wildlife, recreational and scenic properties. We have developed the
treatment in a sequence that parallels the progressive dependence
of resources one upon another, the worth of each in turn commensurate with the composite quality of others. We have trod solid
ground with fixed locations, definitive geographic boundaries, and
specific ownership.

Advisedly, we deferred our discussion of the resources in seas
and bordering oceans because, directly or indirectly, those resources are products of the land whence running water, returning
to its source, carries with it the minerals dispersed in sea water,
and organics that become food for sea creatures. The sea that nurtured elemental life forms until they evolved sufficiently to emerge
from the water and inhabit the land now receives from the land it
populated the substance that sustains those species which remained in their aquatic habitats. (Not for us here to inquire
whether such sea mammals as the whale, the porpoise, and the
sea lion once came onto the land, and were evicted from high
society, or whether they remained behind, and flourished as
competing neighbors departed.) If the seas be enriched by the
land, it is appropriate that marine resources be viewed against a
background of the terrestrial ones, because the abundance and
distribution of the former are conditioned by the latter. The quality of its watershed determines the wealth of sea life beyond a

**The land
returns in kind
the gifts
bestowed by
the sea**

355

river's mouth, and soil erosion and stream pollution spoil marine habitats.

The resources of our bordering seas are so rich and varied that, were they exploited fully, they might yield more wealth than all those on the land. But men have only begun to explore them, let alone exploit them to any extent. The oceans remain a major frontier for modern scientific development. It is not beyond the realm of possibility that scientists will someday economically extract from sea water a long list of scarce minerals, including precious metals and fissionable materials. The present commercial recovery of magnesium and iodine is certainly a mere beginning. One may be confident that clarified and desalted sea water will soon supplement the usable water reserves now available, that ocean tides and currents will be harnessed for power, and that many marine flora and fauna now unknown or neglected will be put to valuable use. But thus far the seas have served mainly as a great highway system and as a source of rain and fish. We cannot presume to alter their role as rain givers. We can improve and protect their usefulness as highways, much as we construct and maintain overland transport facilities, mainly by clearing or preventing any obstruction of terminals by stream or shore sediments. If permitted to become polluted with wastes or overloaded with silt, the very stream by which ships gain the hinterland blocks the threshold. Harbor improvement may be regarded as a form of marine conservation, well enough, but let us limit this discourse to the conservation of material aquatic resources—animal, vegetable, and mineral.

The minerals in sea water remain largely unappraised and neglected—resources the magnitude of which is largely speculative.

Margin note: The oceans roll in wealth— animal, vegetable, and mineral

FIGURE 161. *Irish moss spread out to dry on Peggoty Beach, in Massachusetts. The gathering of marine vegetation is an old industry capable of future expansion.* (F.W.S. photo.)

FIGURE 162. *Kelp (seaweed) on drying racks of Kelp Laboratories, Inc., San Diego, California. From seaweeds come extracts for medicinal and other purposes.* (V. J. Samson, F.W.S., photo.)

Analyses of sea water indicate that most known elements are present, and that several of our most useful minerals may be more abundant in the oceans than on the continents (1, p. 334). Certain industries now recover magnesium, salt, and a few others commercially, and anticipate profitable recovery of many more in the future. Each must wait until improved techniques or scarcity on the land render its exploitation economically feasible.

Mineral and vegetable assets remain largely undeveloped

The utilization of marine vegetation is somewhat more varied, but still almost negligible (2, p. 120). New England Yankees have gathered Irish moss for more than a century (Figure 161). The moss serves as a stabilizer of ice cream, confections, and other foods, as a demulcent in cough remedies, and as a component of dental impression compounds.

During World War I Americans harvested kelp (Figure 162) on the Pacific and Atlantic coasts for the extraction of potash (bromine and iodine were valuable by-products). After the war only a few plants continued to operate, switching to the preparation of fertilizer and cattle feed from dried seaweed. When it was discovered that kelp contains alginic acid which can be used to make algin, the industry flourished once again; algin also serves primarily as stabilizer in ice cream and other dairy products, but its uses are extremely varied. Figures 161 and 162 picture Irish moss and kelp at a certain stage in their harvest.

From certain red seaweeds comes a gum called agar, most prized for making bacteria-growing media in hospitals, and essential in several manufactures. Previously it came from the Orient, but World War II compelled us to search our own coasts for a supply (3). On the California coast were found beds of Gelidium sufficient to meet our bacteriological and medical needs. On the South Atlantic and Gulf coasts Gracilaria was discovered; this yields a substitute for agar in many of its uses, though it is undesirable for bacteriological purposes. By 1945 our extraction of gums or agars from marine algae reached a value of 3 million dollars (4). Under stress of war, Americans learned a little about the value of marine vegetation, but peacetime exploitation is retarded by high processing costs and cheaper supplies from foreign sources.

The conservator feels reassured by the possibility that the sea might spare enough vegetation to maintain a desirable humus content in our soils, were other sources of organic material exhausted. The use of seaweeds for soil maintenance is an established practice in certain maritime cultures as on the Orkneys and the Channel Islands.

Aquatic animals have been food for man since remote antiquity

The fauna of seas and ocean margins have been taken and used by man throughout his history. For most primitive folk fish remains to this day a major item of food, and to peoples culturally advanced it contributes a wholesome, pleasant, and often economical variation of diet. (Had midwesterners eaten more sea foods they might have spared themselves the scourge of goiter, for the prevention of which most table salt is now iodized.)

Animal life is the one aquatic resource that has been exploited extensively, albeit unwisely. Whatever may have been man's first profession, fishing was among the most ancient of his occupations —hunting, fishing, and gathering—for food, shelter, and raiment.

Our colonial fisheries helped us gain our independence

Europeans came west to fish long before they came to settle the land, and soon after they settled fishing became a leading commercial enterprise. In New England the small, stony fields played second fiddle to the rich fishing grounds on the broad continental shelf. Fishing was more attractive than farming; materials for sturdy ships were readily available from the splendid mixed-wood forests; and the demand for fish was strong, especially in Catholic Europe. From fishing (and whaling) came fame and fortune to young America, and historic character to many of her settlements (Gloucester, Wellfleet, New London, and a score of others). The whole business was lucrative but highly competitive, and its successful pursuit required superior shipbuilding and seamanship. Those proficiencies, gained for catching and marketing fish, helped America win her independence and bolstered her economic security thereafter. From that point of view the northeastern fisheries have been invaluable.

Fishing is primarily a quest for food, but men also capture sea animals for many other products, among them ivory, whalebone (baleen), sponges, pearls, furs, vitamins, buttons, oils, leather, tortoise shell, stock feed, glue, paint, perfume, and fertilizer.

We fish for many goods other than food

Baleen from the mouth of the "right" whale (literally the right kind to catch) supplied the corset staves with which the stylish ladies of the Victorian era molded their hourglass figures. Oil from right and sperm whales illuminated the streets so swishing skirts, high-wheeled velocipedes, and horse-drawn carriages might safely mingle. By the middle of the 19th century whales had become the greatest marine resource. America dominated the industry. American whaling fleets numbered 735 boats and employed 40,000 people (2, p. 45). However, the fabulous whaling era was short-lived. The discovery of petroleum at Titusville, Pennsylvania in 1859 took the gilt edge off the industry. The increasing cost of hunting down the monsters that survived in remote ocean areas could not be met with a declining market. Whaling went, faster than it had come, and has never revived as an American industry.

However, a profitable whaling industry survives to this day, dominated by Norway and centered on South Georgia Island in the Antarctic Ocean. Blue and fin whales make up most of the catch, right and sperm whales having been literally chased right out of the oceans. The industry was headed for suicide by sheer extermination of the largest surviving animal when in 1937 the International Conference for the Regulation of Whaling at London drew up protective measures that were signed by all interested nations. The International Agreement has provisions in it that may save a valuable marine resource. It fixes a minimum legal size for each species, prohibits the killing of females accompanied by calves, protects completely all right, gray, and humpback whales, excludes factory ships from calving grounds, and requires the fullest possible use of the whale carcass. Furthermore, the signatory nations enforce the regulations by licensing whaling vessels, supervising factory ship operations, and reporting the weekly catch against seasonal quotas (5). Figure 163 shows the ocean regions on the basis of which regulations have been formulated.

For bone and oil—and profit—we have almost destroyed the whale

Conservation of whales illustrates the requirements of international cooperation in the maintenance of certain fisheries. Scientific equipment and methods have become so effective that unless their employment be restricted the capture of a desirable species may far exceed its reproduction. Petroleum did not jeopardize whaling so much by initial competition as by later powering of modern whaling vessels. Whether international agreement and policing can save the great mammals from extinction remains to be seen.

Skeletons in the cupboard may be a nuisance, but the skeletons called sponges are a convenience in the bathtub or sink. These useful skeletons come from the bottom of the sea. Many people are "spongers," but a colony of Greeks made sponging a legitimate business in west Florida. They began more than three-quarters of a century ago, and the business became centered about Tarpon Springs. In a single year they sponged 2½ million dollars' worth (6, p. 133). The industry prospered, despite many artificial substitutes, until a disease decimated the sponges. Annual production, which reached a peak of 655,000 pounds in 1934, was less than 16,000 pounds in 1951 (30).

The sponge, a simple form of animal life, neither sows nor reaps,

We "sponge" for animal skeletons

FIGURE 163. *World Whaling Regulations. The United States is one of 17 contracting nations comprising the membership of the International Whaling Commission. (F.W.S. map.)*
Legend: A—*Factory ships not allowed to take baleen whales.*
 B—*Proposed sanctuary for baleen and humpback whales.*
 C—*Factory ships allowed to take baleen whales.*
 D—*Factory ships allowed to take baleen whales, but ships operating here cannot be operated in any other waters within one year from termination of that season. Humpback whales may not be taken.*

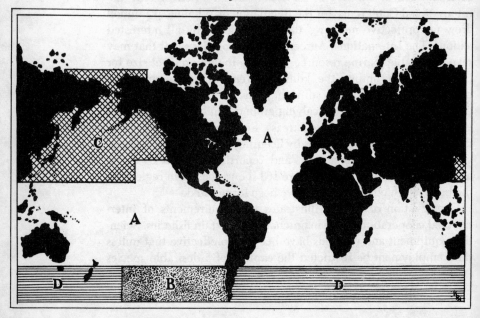

but sits like a puff-ball, attached to the ocean floor. It produces eggs, fertilized and developed within its own body, and released as larvae that drift for a while and then settle down to the slow, monotonous task of growing into big sponges. There is no excitement, no travel, no romance, neither pain nor pleasure in the life of a sponge.

Foam rubber and other substitutes do much of our wiping nowadays, but for special purposes, as in the manufacture of certain hygienic and surgical preparations, natural sponges are still required. They remain valuable, but unless the biologists discover some means of combating sponge diseases, the animal may be lost. Until its biology is better known the resource cannot be conserved. A minimum-size law (five-inch diameter) enforced by the State of Florida was the only significant conservation measure while the industry flourished. British experiments in the Bahamas and Honduras have demonstrated the practicability of artificial propagation from small cuttings, like poatoes (2, p. 119), but if Americans will devote a fair amount of biologic research to the Florida sponging grounds, they may spare themselves the "farming" costs.

From the sea come several luxuries, such as pearls and cameos for the ornament of milady, ambergris (the spew from sick whales) for the base of fine perfumes, and furs for vanity, if not always for comfort. Genuine pearls come from oysters (salt water) and from river mussels (fresh-water). The latter are taken primarily for their shells, from which pearl buttons are made. The hope of finding a pearl adds a touch of glamor to the dull work of "musseling" for the mollusks. During recent decades Hyannis, Massachusetts has developed a flourishing industry in the manufacture of artificial pearls. Still based on a natural resource, the manufactured pearls are made of the scales from certain marine fishes, dissolved by secret formula into a liquid resembling a hand lotion. Only an expert can distinguish artificial pearls from the rarely perfect real gem. They add just as much to a pretty throat, no less to an ugly one; while comparable in quality, they cost somewhat less.

From the sea come pearls, genuine and artificial

By ownership of the Pribilof Islands off Alaska the United States controls the world's largest herd of fur seals (80 per cent of the total). When Alaska was bought from Russia in 1867 the herd numbered almost three million, but the animals were so ruthlessly killed for their fine pelts that by 1910 only about 130,000 remained (7). Seeing the threat to a valuable resource, the government intervened in that year and in 1911 signed, with Great Britain (for Canada), Japan, and Russia, the North Pacific Sealing Convention. The agreement outlawed *pelagic* sealing (killing them in the

Furs worn in the Arctic Sea must be warm and waterproof!

water), which had previously taken a heavy toll of pups by the kill
ing of their mothers.

The international agreement, together with the polygamous
habits of the seals, has completely re-established the herd, bring
ing it back to approximately three million in only 35 years of pro
tection (7). *The fur seal is a splendid example of the recovery a
biotic resource can make if given a fair chance.* Since each old
bull seal keeps a harem of as many as 40 to 60 cows, male offspring
become a social liability, good for nothing except to eat fish. From
frustrated two- and three-year-old bachelors comes our annua'
crop of skins. The bachelors have nothing to look forward to, and
their removal leaves more food for parents and babies. Sometime
when more is known about the fishery resources of the "high seas,'
it may be discovered that the voracious seal eats more fish than he
is worth, but until then any guilt attached to the giving or wearing
of seal should be laid to something other than the killing of the
original owner.

From the sea come most of our health-protective vitamins. Cod-
liver oil was a household remedy long before the vitamin capsule
era which now sustains a major pharmaceutical industry based
largely on fish livers. Once a by-product of cod and halibut fisheries, fish-liver oil—notably that of the despised sharks (8)—has
become a prime object of certain fisheries.

From the sea comes our major supply of protective vitamins

In 1927 the Fishery Research Board of Canada discovered that
the liver of a certain small shark, the dogfish, has as much as ten
times the vitamin-A potency of ordinary cod-liver oil (2, p. 17).
Sharks became popular almost as suddenly as a homely co-ed
when she gets a shiny new convertible. Vast numbers of dogfish,
soupfin, and other sharks were taken only for their livers, the remainder of the carcass thrown back into the sea, until California
passed a law requiring that the entire fish be delivered to port.
Shark steak, smoked shark, fish meal, and leather have become by-
products of the liver fishery. The industry flourishes the length of
our Pacific Coast, and wasteful practices continue—if the cost of
transporting dead sharks a long distance to make meal out of them
raises the price of vitamins, it might be more conservative to pitch
them overboard for their vitamin-making friends to eat! In the interest of good health we should regulate the shark fishery so that
the kill yields a maximum of vitamins without wiping out the
sharks. So vital a resource should not be exploited catch-as-catch-
can. Its money value has attained grand proportions; its health
value defies measurement.

The sharp stench of a fish cannery, of a fish wharf at low tide, or f an ill-kept fish market suggests the value of dead fish and fish wastes as fertilizer. The practice of fertilizing soil with fish ante-dates American history; the Indians, we are told, showed the Pilgrims how to plant a fish under each hill of corn, to ensure higher yield and more cause for Thanksgiving.

From fish comes fertilizer for our soils

Since those early beginnings fertilizer has become an important product and by-product of our expanding fisheries. A major trend in our conservation of fishery resources is the salvage of wastes by legal compulsion. As mentioned before, California demands that a shark taken for his liver must be landed and used, and international agreement places similar requirements upon whaling. The modern whaler would be pleased to take only oil, were he allowed to do so, but in compliance with the law, he gets from an average whale, besides the *oil*, about three tons of *meal* for stock feed and one ton, more or less, of a potent fertilizer (2, p. 45).

The salvage of waste parts of fish in canneries and other fish-processing plants has far to go, but its accomplishment, like the utilization of sawmill wastes, must await such demand for the products and such complementary factory arrangement as will make it profitable. Perhaps legal prohibition of wastes can hasten their economical salvage, but rules too stringent can also injure the industry producing the wastes. Rarely can one justify plant closure to prevent waste, because some waste may be an inevitable part of production. Waste prevention that places undue strain upon a productive enterprise is dubious conservation.

Whether applied as dried scraps ground into meal or as liquid concentrate, the fertilization of soil with fish completes a cycle that portends new horizons in conservation. Wash from the land feeds the diatoms and other plankton (minute sea life); little ones feed on the tiny ones; bigger ones feed on the little ones; man catches the big ones and with them enriches the soil—whence the wash to feed the minute ones! Is man in this case a cog in the natural round, or is he the intellectual member who wittingly completes the cycle and thereby improves his total environment? Perhaps he is both master and servant when he improves the land with waste from the sea.

From fish comes especially nutritious feed for our land animals. Fish meal and fish oil increase our production of meat and eggs, and in a roundabout way enrich the soil as well. So desirable are these by-products that a major fishery has developed to supply them (Figure 180). Menhaden, a herring-like fish that ranges our Atlantic Coast, ranks first among all our fishes in volume of catch, and second only to oysters in value among our Atlantic fisheries.

From fish comes feed for beast and fowl

And it is taken *primarily for "by-products": meals* and *oils*. The meals are fed to swine and poultry. The oils go into special "vitamized" feeding oils for poultry, and have numerous industrial uses as well. The *roe*, saved for food, becomes a by-product of a *by-products* fishery. From the lowly menhaden come one-third of the fish meals and one-fourth of the marine animal oils produced in the United States (9, p. 32). Although the annual catch has mounted to more than one and two-thirds billions of pounds (1953), with a value approaching 31 million dollars (30), nothing has been done to conserve the resource.

Food outranks all other fishing products

Many other marine products, many other fishery by-products, might be mentioned, but let us turn to a consideration of fish taken primarily for food, since they constitute the most valuable and most exploited aquatic resource. No less than *180* different edible species contribute to our annual commercial catch of some five billion pounds. They range in size from the little sardine and anchovy to the giant tuna and swordfish. Large or small, they are excellent food, supplying protein of superior quality, calcium, magnesium, phosphorus, iron, copper, vitamins A and D, and iodine in natural form (10, p. 30). No other meat comes nearer being a complete food in itself than does fish, a fact not adequately appreciated in America. Another century of wholesale land abuse might have *made* fish eaters out of us; conservation will permit us to eat fish by choice, in itself an act of conserving both natural and cultural resources. Wartime meat rationing awakened Americans to the merits of fish, and many retained their taste for fish after the emergency. Even so, we consume only about eleven pounds of fish per capita annually, which is less than a tenth of our consumption of "red" meat and only half our consumption of chicken (11). We could improve our health, save money, and conserve natural resources by eating twice, or three times, as much sea food as we now consume. We should not have to be prodded by high prices or war to do so; the increase would raise our standard of living.

The big three: fin fish, mollusks, and crustaceans

Perhaps none of our great natural resources equals in variety the choice of species offered by our food fisheries, unless it be the forests. However, less than 50 species make up the main catch (12). Most of these are *fin fish*, the kind of creatures that come to mind at the mention of "fish", with fins, bones, and usually scales. The others, often lumped together under the term "shellfish," bear no resemblance to the fin fish. They belong to two major zoological groups, namely *mollusks* and *crustaceans*. (We are omitting frogs, turtles, and other reptiles, because they are relatively unimportant.) The mollusks include oysters, clams, mussels and scallops bivalves), and the abalone with only one shell. The crustaceans include the scorpion-like lobsters and shrimps, and the spider-like crabs. The three classes have little in common except that they all live under water, get caught by fisherman, and become food for humans. Their habits, their modes of capture, and the problems of conserving them differ as greatly as they do in appearance.

Fish and fisheries show considerable regional specialization much as do game and hunting, timber and lumbering, soils and agriculture. Species differ widely from one region to another, and only in general respects to fishing methods and conservation problems of one region resemble those of another. Maine lobsters, Chesapeake "blue points" (oysters), Gulf shrimp, California alba-core (tuna), and Washington salmon are well-known examples of regional fish specialties that support regional fisheries, almost without any similarity. Figures 164 through 168 merely suggest the variety of species and their approximate regional distribution. Fishing gear differs about as much as the fishes: *pots* (box traps) for lobsters, *dredges* for oysters, *trawls* for shrimp, *hooks* for tuna, *traps, seines,* and *nets* for salmon. Several types are shown in Figure 169.

The trawler who puts out from New England and spends weeks in cold and fog to capture cod or haddock on the Great Bank has little in common with the shrimper who makes a daily run from Houma, Louisiana in the warm waters of the Gulf. There is as much difference between the adventure of a tuna cruise and the monotony of oyster dredging as there is between fly-casting for trout and trolling for marlin. Yet, each of the commercial fisheries mentioned holds high national rank and attains pre-eminence in its own locale. Each employs many people and flavors the regional culture.

Until quite recently our highly perishable fish foods were limited in use and distribution by inadequate packaging and transportation facilities. Except in winter, fresh fish was only for those who lived near the water, each species in its season. A quarter-century ago off-season fish was either cured or canned. The herring barrel and anchovy keg vied with great wheels of cheese to dominate the pungent odors in country stores. The infant canning industry supplied a few items, such as salmon and sardines. To farm folk in the Midwest oyster stew was a rare treat. They had never seen a shrimp, much less eaten one.

Then came improved refrigeration, improved canning, and, most recent and revolutionary, quick freezing. Fresh fish—packaged, labeled, and frozen—became available anywhere in the

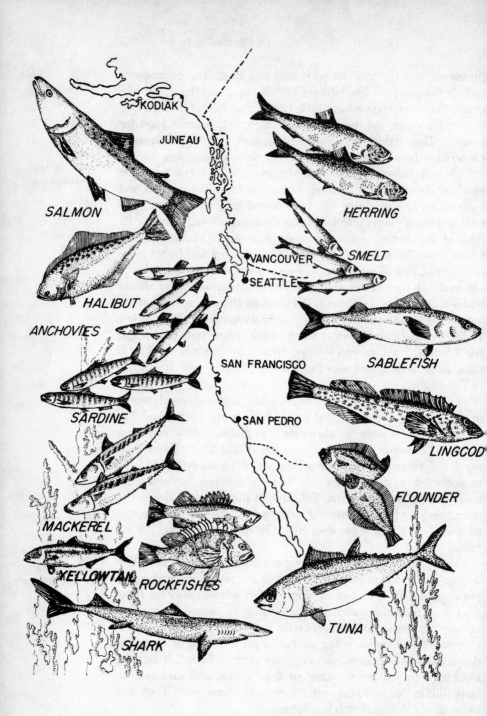

FIGURE 164. *Some important fin fish of our Pacific Coast.*

366

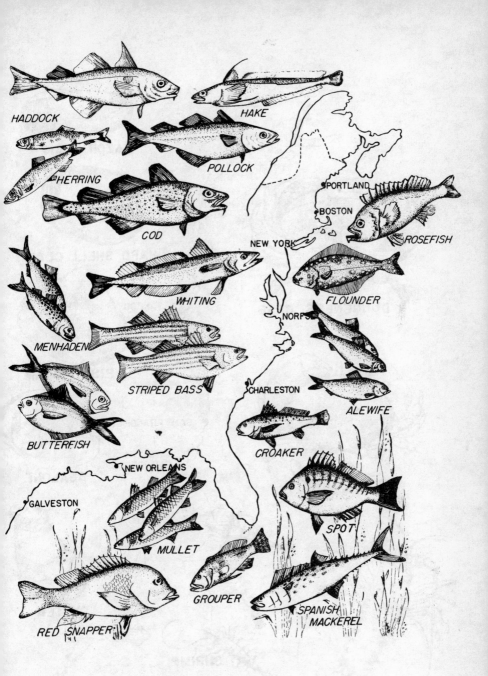

FIGURE 165. *Some important fin fish of our Atlantic Coast.*

367

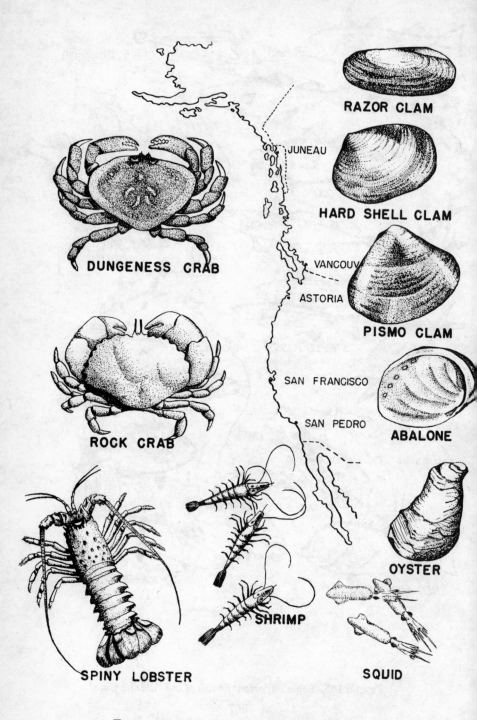

RAZOR CLAM

HARD SHELL CLAM

JUNEAU

VANCOUV

ASTORIA

SAN FRANCISCO

SAN PEDRO

PISMO CLAM

ABALONE

DUNGENESS CRAB

ROCK CRAB

SPINY LOBSTER

SHRIMP

OYSTER

SQUID

FIGURE 166. *Some important West Coast shellfish.*

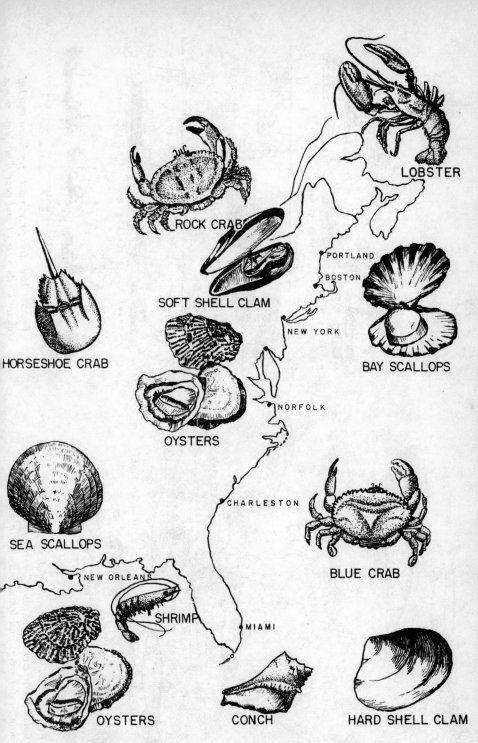

LOBSTER

ROCK CRAB

SOFT SHELL CLAM

HORSESHOE CRAB

• PORTLAND

BOSTON

NEW YORK

BAY SCALLOPS

OYSTERS

NORFOLK

SEA SCALLOPS

CHARLESTON

BLUE CRAB

NEW ORLEANS

SHRIMP

MIAMI

OYSTERS

CONCH

HARD SHELL CLAM

FIGURE 167. *Some important East Coast shellfish. (The horseshoe crab and the conch may contribute relatively more to the artistic balance of the page than to the total catch of fish.)*

369

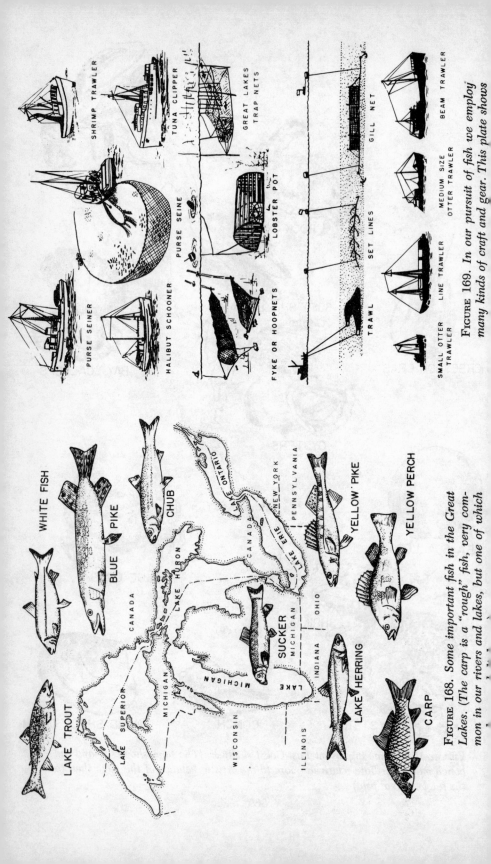

FIGURE 168. Some important fish in the Great Lakes. (The carp is a "rough" fish, very common in our rivers and lakes, but one of which

WHITE FISH

BLUE PIKE

CHUB

LAKE TROUT

CANADA

LAKE SUPERIOR

MICHIGAN

WISCONSIN

ILLINOIS

MICHIGAN

LAKE MICHIGAN

INDIANA

OHIO

LAKE HURON

SUCKER

CANADA

LAKE ONTARIO

NEW YORK

LAKE ERIE

PENNSYLVANIA

YELLOW PIKE

YELLOW PERCH

LAKE HERRING

CARP

SHRIMP TRAWLER

TUNA CLIPPER

GREAT LAKES TRAP NETS

PURSE SEINE

LOBSTER POT

PURSE SEINER

HALIBUT SCHOONER

FYKE OR HOOPNETS

GILL NET

TRAWL

SET LINES

SMALL OTTER TRAWLER

LINE TRAWLER

MEDIUM SIZE OTTER TRAWLER

BEAM TRAWLER

FIGURE 169. In our pursuit of fish we employ many kinds of craft and gear. This plate shows

country, as did also a wide variety safely preserved in cans. The deep freeze replaced the grimy herring barrel. Dakota farmers learned to eat shrimp cocktails, fried oysters, fillet of Pacific halibut, Gulf flounder, New England sole or codfish balls whenever they chose, without fear of food poisoning. Housewives who never saw the ocean tried new sea food recipes, and served their unwary husbands dishes they could not pronounce.

Modern preparation and packaging, transport and storage have all but erased the old deterrents of seasonality, climate, and distance. Similar species from Atlantic and Pacific waters lie side by side in refrigerated display cases, the one most attractively wrapped getting the buyer's nod. But for innovations such as quick freezing and refrigeration in transit, our valuable Gulf Coast fisheries could not have emerged, nor could our fishery resources as a whole have attained the status and potential that commend them to our most careful study and conservation.

While space does not permit us to describe all the freaks of "fishdom," and their idiosyncrasies, it is necessary that we identify a few major groups, or classes, on the basis of habits and habitats by way of introducing our main thesis, for fishing techniques and conservation measures must be adapted to the behavior of the fish. The problem must be defined before its solution can be approached intelligently.

No military commander would engage the enemy without more "intelligence" than we have about our fishes, all the more reason for us to employ the skimpy knowledge we do possess. We know that certain fishes, such as the hardtail, squid, bluefish, and herring, live near the top of the water. We call those *pelagic*. We know that others, such as flounder, halibut, sole, cod, pollock, haddock, hake, and rosefish live on or near the bottom. We call those ground fishes *demersal*. We know that several species, such as the salmon, shad, and smelt live and mature in the sea, but come up the rivers to spawn. Ichthyologists call them *anadromous*. We know that snappers, groupers, and cod live on "banks," that pilchards, porgies, pompanos, and mullets live near shore, and that tuna and swordfish roam the high seas. We know that mackerels, anchovies, and weakfish migrate considerable distances, that crabs and shrimps stay nearer home, and that oysters sit tight in one place.

But we have used our knowledge almost entirely for catching the fish—hardly at all for conserving them. We have applied our information in devising efficient methods of exploitation, and neglected its application toward perpetuating the resource. We

Techniques and problems vary according to habits and habitats

have in some cases maintained our catch of a declining species by improving fishing techniques, thereby obscuring the real problem. The same "intelligence" that makes us expert fishermen must also be directed toward making us better conservators.

Anadromous species fall easy prey to nets and traps when they crowd into the rivers to lay their eggs. If they be denied access to their spawning grounds, or the rivers be so polluted that the young cannot survive, the species will decline, and eventually vanish. Filth has driven shad from certain eastern streams; engineering and pollution have virtually exterminated salmon in certain western ones. Pelagic fishes that migrate in dense schools are also easily caught during their seasonal "runs" when the sea fairly foams with them, but if they be seined out indiscriminately year after year, from one end of their migration to the other, attrition will decimate them. These are the hosts that convey the idea of marine inexhaustibility, but if in a given season a million mackerel eggs produce only three or four fingerlings, mother mackerel's fecundity (500,000 eggs) may be a poor guarantee of profitable fishing (2, pp. 63, 64). Ground fishes, mollusks, and crustaceans are obviously influenced by conditions of the bottom on which they live. Trawling or dredging to harvest them can easily reduce their numbers more by damage to the habitat than by capture. Here, also, as with anadromous species, man's behavior on the land helps or hinders marine resources. Oysters and other shellfish that are either fixed in place or capable of very limited movement succumb when men befoul their "beds" with sewage or bury them in silt.

Mind the unity of land and sea resources

Does conservation hang together? Indeed it does. Forested watersheds, soil held in place, and clear streams with uniform flow·insure the health of marine life in coastal waters. Reverse the picture, and havoc runs the length of the sequence. Cut-over slopes, eroded soils, dirty streams and floods produce dead fish. Kill the little shore fishes, and larger ones farther out die of hunger. The tunas that roam the high seas depend upon farmers in Iowa and Illinois, though less directly than do corn-fed swine. Conservation on the land promotes conservation in the sea. Abuse of the land abuses the sea.

Pollution, erosion, and drainage have ruined fish habitats

Fish killed by stream pollution float down the Potomac right through our capital city, and in many less dignified streams they float even faster, and just as dead. The hardy ones that survive in poisoned water are dangerous to eat, a hazard to human life instead of the food resource they ought to be. Scores of streams in our metropolitan northeast and elsewhere have been so corrupted with sewage, industrial refuse, and mining wastes that they have lost their natural function as homes and spawning grounds for fish.

Any manipulation of water on the land has a direct bearing on fishery resources, near and far. Insofar as such manipulation accelerates run-off it is generally detrimental. Insofar as it impedes run-off, it is generally beneficial unless detention, as for irrigation, causes excessive loss by evaporation and a consequent reduction in the volume delivered to the sea and other water bodies inhabited by fish. Theoretically, if we were to use all the rain that falls and expend our surface waters before any could reach the sea our fishes would be starved by evaporation.

But thus far our fault lies mainly in the other direction. By poor water and soil conservation, including drainage, we run our rain toward the sea so fast that fish have no social security in any phase of the process. Drainage of inland marshes and swamps, canalization for transport or local flood "control," restricts or destroys fish habitats adjacent to the project and damages all those down-stream from the site. Lakes and streams in some seasons shrunken to mere puddles and trickles and at other times full of muddy water are poor homes for respectable fish. When we prevent floods by proper *management of headwaters* and refrain from meddling with *natural water storage* we will increase, simultaneously, both water and fishery resources. In the conservation of renewable resources a little integration of the various phases works infinitely more good than the most fastidious attention to any single phase. Let no one, least of all the conservator, attempt to sever the natural tie that binds them all together.

Salmon, shad, herring, and other anadromous species (also the catadromous eel, which reverses the sequence) have no doubt heaped fishy curses upon the builders of dams across rivers. While creating new homes for fresh-water fishes above them (Figure 170) and reducing the hazards of flood and silting that beset the bottom dwellers of bays and estuaries below, dams across certain streams on the Atlantic Slope have barred shad and herring from their spawning grounds in the headwaters. If one concedes that the barriers serve other purposes more valuable than the fisheries they curtail, he may also challenge the necessity for sacrificing one resource in order to conserve others. River fisheries may in fact be enhanced by impounding the waters. Figure 170 suggests that fresh-water fishes must also be considered in connection with engineering that affects salt-water species.

Engineering works create special fishery problems

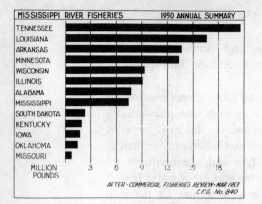

Figure 170. *Mississippi River Fisheries—1950 Annual Summary. Landings of fishery products from the Mississippi and its tributaries during 1950 amounted to 105,795,800 pounds, with an ex-vessel value of $10,104,129.* (Graph and statistics from *Commercial Fisheries Review*, March, 1953.)

In some of our great new dams on the Pacific Slope the engineers built "ladders" whereby salmon might "climb" over the obstruction and gain their upstream spawning areas. (See the ladder pictured in Figure 171.) The ladders have been at least partially successful, but even if they served their purpose completely they would solve only half the problem. When mother salmon has laid her eggs she dies and doubtless goes to fish-heaven, where she encounters no nets or dams, but her innocent young face the stupendous task of clearing the dam before they can go to sea and grow up. How to get the baby salmon past the dam alive and then safely to the ocean is the second half of the problem. Many are killed in flumes and turbines, and many get lost in irrigation ditches. (Grand Coulee and other dams too big for ladders require capture and stripping of the prospective parents below the dam, and artificial planting of the fertilized eggs in suitable streams above.)

Several other kinds of construction have impaired our fishery resources. Causeways across bays that kill oyster beds by blocking the tides, jetties or breakwaters that stop or deflect shore currents, have ruined local enterprises and reduced the total gain from fishing. In future engineering projects on our streams, lakes, and coasts we can very profitably pay more attention to the protection of fish and other aquatic resources than we have in the past. The structures can be only temporary, whereas the biotic resources should be permanent.

We have fished just as we once hunted and trapped, as if our quarry were utterly inexhaustible. And well we might think our fisheries inexhaustible, considering the prodigious populations and amazing fecundity of certain species. A shoal (consolidated schools) of herring may run into the billions, and a female ling can lay 30 million eggs (13). But "Old Devil Sea" harbors a vicious, competitive society, its infant mortality alone often exceeding 99 per cent.

Over-fishing, often the consequence of other handicaps, has reduced many favored commercial species to a fraction of their former importance. California had our first salmon fishery, but it lasted only about a quarter century. The Chinook salmon in the Sacramento River was virtually exterminated, apparently by intensive fishing, between 1864 and 1882 (14). However, during the same period hydraulic mining also damaged the salmon streams. When the fishery had declined to negligible proportions, dams built across the river for water projects barred the salmon from their spawning grounds and possible recovery (14).

Half a century ago, shad ranked third among our commercial fishes, outclassed only by New England cod and Pacific salmon, but by 1945 shad had fallen to thirtieth place among our choice food species (partly because competing species had gained favor). In 1940 the shad fishery produced less than one-fifth the catch taken in 1896 (2, pp. 67, 68).

In the case of salmon and shad, major anadromous food fishes, stream pollution and engineering works have been extremely destructive, but excessive fishing through the years has probably reduced them quite as much as the other handicaps. Ground fishes on the New England Banks, far from the influence of stream pollution and engineering, show downward trends more obviously attributable to over-fishing. Halibut and haddock have been severely reduced; rosefish and certain flounders, more moderately

FIGURE 171. *Fish ladder, Bonneville Dam, Columbia River. The dam was too high for a fish to leap, so the engineers devised a stairway by which salmon can circumnavigate the dam and reach the headwaters for spawning.* (H. B. Carr, F.W.S., photo.)

(2, p. 48). Many favorite fresh-water species once important i
our valuable Great Lakes fisheries have been reduced to insignifi
cance, largely by excessive fishing. Lake Erie cisco, land-locke
sturgeon, blackfin of Lakes Huron and Michigan, and bluefin c
Lake Superior are almost gone. One—the Lake Ontario bloater-
is extinct. Production of whitefish, trout, and perch (Figure 168
has declined in spite of intensified fishing (2, p. 112). Lampre
depredations, mentioned later, have accelerated this decline
Our most desirable mollusks and crustaceans, helpless agains
power trawls and dredges, are suffering gradual declines.

Over-fishing of any species has several negative consequences
(a) reduction in total number of fish in the stock, producing
smaller yields for given amounts of fishing effort, (b) reduction
in average size of fish in the stock, necessitating catching more
fish to sustain the tonnage, and (c) decimation of spawning stock
below the number necessary to maintain the population—all fac
tors leading to progressively smaller annual catches (2, p. 10). I
short, over-fishing does to fisheries what over-cutting does to
lumbering, what over-cropping does to agriculture, and wha
over-grazing does to range cattle raising—it exhausts the resource
upon which the enterprise is based. However, fishermen deal i
transient property without title, and unless they take it when i
is available, they lose it to someone else. Only when regulation
become standardized on a regional basis can fishermen subscribe
to the sustained-yield idea already widely accepted in forestry
agriculture and grazing.

As their catches decline, fishermen seek new fishing grounds
usually more remote than those they have over-exploited. When

**Fishermen seek
new fishing
grounds**

more intensive fishing—more and better gear employed for longer
periods—fails to yield a profitable volume, they extend their
spheres of operation. They go farther and farther from home,
and bring in fish costing more and more. Their maximum distance
is that beyond which the cost of catching and bringing in the
fish comes too near the market price to leave a profit from the
venture.

In bygone days the gallant men of Gloucester took cod and
haddock on Georges Bank, a day's run by schooner with a following wind. Today their grandsons sail diesel-powered trawlers
to far-off Bankereau, 800 miles "east by north" for the same kinds
of fish (15). (See Figure 177.) They began running out of fish
long ago; now they are running out of banks!

The banks fisheries of our northeast, probably because they
are oldest, show best how scarcity extends operations, but the

earch for new fishing grounds grows wider in other regions too. Many fishing runs are now so long that freezing or processing must be done at sea. Cannery ships will quite surely become a major means of harvesting the high seas, of bringing in many species not yet found on our store shelves. Treaties delineating international boundaries in mid-ocean will then be more than mere words—they will indeed have meat in them.

Substitutes are often indications of scarcity, accepted only when the preferred article becomes difficult to procure. Weed trees found a market when better woods grew scarce. "Trash" fish are gaining acceptance because the "fancy" ones are hard to get.

In the Great Lakes catch, suckers, carp, sheepshead, and burbot are replacing more desirable species that have been depleted (2, p. 112), and housewives are learning to accept the substitutes. Better preparation for market (fillets, steaks, fish sticks, and so on) and more attractive packaging are selling many species previously rejected, thereby promoting conservation in two directions, both by sparing depleted stocks so they may recover and by employing stocks that were previously wasted by neglect. Similar circumstances have evolved comparable, two-way conservation in certain marine fisheries.

Housewives accept substitute species

Thus far, restrictions on gear, season, and catch have been the major conservation measures, because too little has been known about the private lives of the fish to aid many of them more constructively. Research by marine and fresh-water biologists is the most urgent need in fishery conservation, but while sufficient basic facts are being accumulated for developing a suitable program, curtailment of capture may be the means whereby enough of the fish will remain to render the program applicable. From plankton, the minute forms, to tuna and other big ones, fishes are food for other fish, and if either those that get eaten or those that eat them become too scarce, the lost balance can be difficult to re-establish. In many cases balance of aquatic life is so delicate and complex that it cannot be regained or maintained without thorough scientific understanding of all relationships involved. For none of our resources is knowledge complete, but for our fisheries it is clearly inadequate. For most species even such fundamental information as that shown in Figure 172 is lacking. Certainly no resource can be well conserved unless its location is known, and for migratory fishes the correlation of location with life cycles and growth stages can be exceedingly complex.

Biologic research is the first step toward fishery conservation

We have noted how salmon and shad are caught en route to

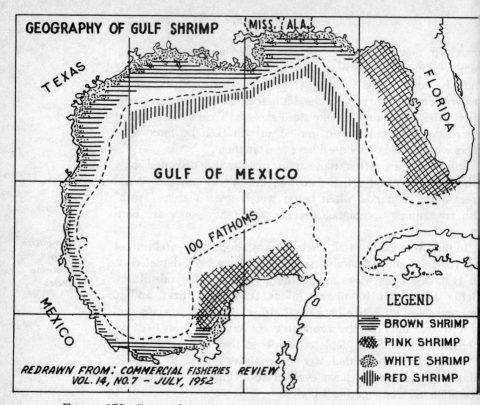

FIGURE 172. *Geography of Gulf Shrimp. Until we know where a resource is located, we can neither exploit nor conserve it. This map shows one valuable type of information collected by the Fish and Wildlife Service.*

their spawning grounds, exactly when they are bent on perpetuating the species. To the commercial fisherman whose family depends on his catch the time to take fish is when they are "running," fat and full of roe, without qualms about the fact that caviar never hatches. Only when his annual catch dwindles can he be convinced that he has been taking each year not only that year's run but those of years to come. Only then does he respect the spawning season and treat more discreetly the parents of his future hauls.

Many species with which we are sufficiently well acquainted are protected during critical periods such as the spawning season in much the same manner as game on the land. However, the protection fails unless it is provided at the right time and in the right place. For species about which our knowledge is too vague for the formulation of protective measures, the first requisite is biologic research to discover their life habits. When we learn where all the important species spawn and where the young grow up, we shall know where and when to spare them, and when

nd where we can fish them most intensively without depleting
he resource. Let the biologist inform, let the law-maker legislate,
et the police enforce, and let the fisherman conform to safe-
;uard his own fortune, whether he likes it or not. Until he co-
operates he is a menace to his own vocation.

The development of fishing gear and fishing techniques compares favorably with our mechanization of farming and lumber-
ng, but unlike farming and logging machinery, the scientific fish-
ng equipment that facilitates fish exploitation has not yet been
equally applied in fish conservation. Good plows and big tractors
id in both soil use and soil defense, but bigger nets and faster
boats simply catch more fish. Thus, our progress in fishing has
been essentially one-sided, and it is imperative that research be
accelerated to take up the slack.

So ruthlessly effective have our gear and craft become that fish
survival is almost more amazing than the phenomenal hauls
brought in. With purse seines as much as 1200 feet long fishermen can encircle and capture a whole school with one setting.
With otter-trawls—bag-like nets with wide mouths—they can
follow and overtake their quarry, be it pelagic or demersal, crab
or shrimp; the nets are towed behind "draggers" and "trawlers"
that can outrun the fish. With dredges several feet wide they can
scrape oysters off their beds and dig clams right out of the mud
in broad swaths across the bottom. These three specialized types,
purse seine, trawl, and *dredge,* take most of our fish, but other
devices are also important, among them haul seines, gill nets,
pound nets, trot lines, traps, weirs, and many more. Even this
partial list puts an edge on the casual expression, "poor fish."
We even find them and catch them with electrical devices such
as graphically illustrated in Figures 173 and 174.

We have mentioned over-fishing of favored species as a major
fishery problem, a problem intensified by every improvement of
equipment and methods. Positive measures to alleviate it have
been mainly in the form of legal restrictions on the use of certain
"implements of mass destruction," and limitation of the catch,
especially of young fish that should be spared for breeding stock.
Minimum size limits and maximum quotas may often be the
answer, and fishermen are beginning to see that such discretions
pay off in the long run. Nets and seines of larger mesh to permit
the escape of immature fish (16, 17, 18) bring to fishing a conservation feature that parallels selective logging for stand improvement and sustained yield of timber. Selection by mesh size
of a sink gill net is shown in Figures 175 and 176. Sparing a fair

*Restriction
of gear and
limitation of
catch became
mandatory*

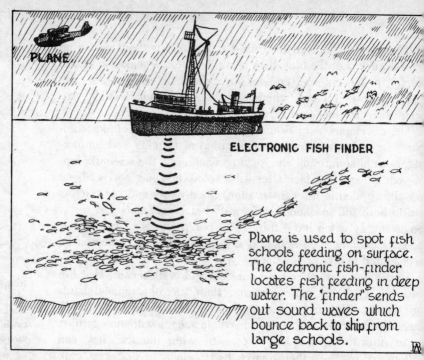

ELECTRONIC FISH FINDER

Plane is used to spot fish schools feeding on surface. The electronic fish-finder locates fish feeding in deep water. The "finder" sends out sound waves which bounce back to ship from large schools.

FIGURES 173 and 174. *Fishing has become increasingly technical and scientific, but the poor fish remain ignorant. If the fish kept pace with technological progress, they might engage electric eels to short-circuit the electrical fishing devices.*

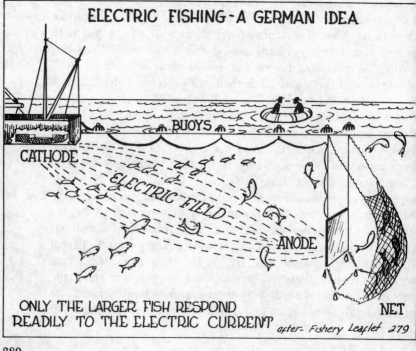

ELECTRIC FISHING - A GERMAN IDEA

BUOYS

CATHODE

ELECTRIC FIELD

ANODE

NET

ONLY THE LARGER FISH RESPOND READILY TO THE ELECTRIC CURRENT *after- Fishery Leaflet 279*

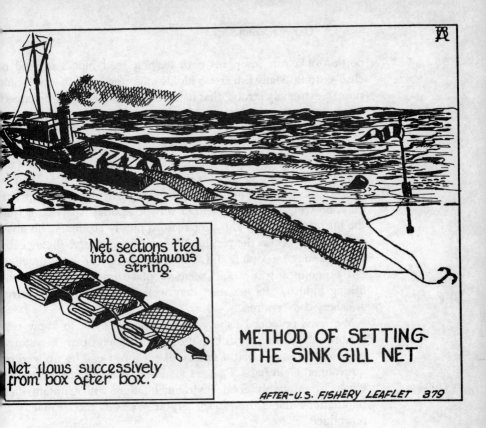

Net sections tied into a continuous string.

Net flows successively from box after box.

METHOD OF SETTING THE SINK GILL NET

AFTER-U.S. FISHERY LEAFLET 379

SELECTIVE GEAR SAVES BREEDING STOCK

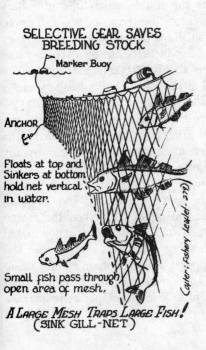

Marker Buoy

Anchor

Floats at top and Sinkers at bottom hold net vertical in water.

(After: Fishery Leaflet - 379)

Small fish pass through open area of mesh.

A LARGE MESH TRAPS LARGE FISH!
(SINK GILL-NET)

FIGURES 175 and 176. *The gill net remains an important type of fishing gear. The large mesh makes the net selective, capturing only the "big ones," and permitting the young, growing stock to escape. This resembles selective cutting of trees. Is this a form of sustained-yield management?*

381

portion of a run compares with leaving seed blocks instead o:
clear-cutting. Many fish are so highly migratory, and their seasona
runs so extremely erratic, that fishermen cannot adopt a sustained
yield program with the same readiness as a timber grower; bu
wisdom compelled by mandate need only prove its merit to gai
acceptance and voluntary application. It has been suggested tha'
economics will save a declining fishery before the species fail:
biologically (19), and there is certainly logic in the idea. When
ever a fisherman can no longer pursue a particular species profitably, he will, of necessity, either turn to another species, or qui'
the business entirely. Thus, for reasons purely economic, he give:
a declining species the respite it needs for recovery. Biologicall
the idea may be sound, and it is certainly operative in practice
but economically it would seem to place undue strain on the
fishing industry. Its negation may well be one of the objectives
of fishery conservation.

We have practiced fishery conservation enough to know tha
it can be highly successful, that depleted species can be restored
to abundance, and that a fishery like a forest can be utilized on
a sustained-yield basis. Fish respond admirably to fair treatment
Given a reasonably good environment, they will maintain their
populations unless the rate of capture exceeds their capacity to
reproduce.

Fishing can be placed on a sustained-yield basis

Concrete examples indicate the future capabilities of fishery
conservation. Good management of the river and the fish saved
the shad fishery of the Hudson. Runs had sunk so low that they
yielded only 40,000 pounds of fish in 1916, but by 1944 they had
made such spectacular recovery that 5,000,000 pounds were taken
(10, p. 17). Study and control of the Pacific halibut fishery under
an International Commission (the United States and Canada) rebuilt and stabilized a resource that was in grave danger of destruction. In places the annual catch had fallen to one third of its
previous volume, despite much more intensive fishing; on many
banks halibut were being removed more rapidly than they could
replace themselves. Under a treaty signed in 1930 the Commission
defined four geographic divisions of the fishery and fixed an
annual quota for each. When the quota was taken the season
was closed. Two areas in which small specimens predominated
were closed entirely. Limitations of catch and season were the
only conservation measures applied, all based upon careful scientific study. The results have convinced even the fishermen that
conservation pays high dividends. A hundred per cent increase

of catch per unit of gear over somewhat more than one decade of time should be convincing (2, pp. 21, 22, 131).

Conservation of Pacific halibut demonstrates the effectiveness of regulation when it is wisely applied to an entire fishery throughout its life range. The best conceived controls cannot accomplish much if they be applied to scattered segments of a fishery, because *a fishery is a biologic unit* and must be treated as such. Until quite recently the lawmakers neglected that fundamental fact, and tried vainly to protect a resource common to several states with unrelated, even conflicting, laws passed and enforced independently by the various states concerned. Fish have no respect for politics or political boundaries—neither should laws for their protection follow political lines. Only recently has acknowledgment of that peculiarity found expression in the interstate fishery commissions which now include all our coastal states in three regional groups: Atlantic, Pacific, and Gulf (20). The Great Lakes fishery is becoming similarly unified by agreement among the bordering states and Canadian provinces.

Protection should be comprehensive and standardized

Species that migrate the length of our Atlantic Coast cannot be conserved by New Jersey or Maryland or South Carolina individually, but only by all the states of the eastern seaboard cooperating in a unified program. It is impossible to restore the Great Lakes fisheries before the bordering states and provinces standardize their regulatory laws and enforce them uniformly. What would it profit Wisconsin to prohibit the taking of Lake Michigan perch if the fish were fair game just beyond the middle of the lake? Could Ontario conserve the whitefish of Lake Erie if they swam across the lake and got caught? Lack of uniformity over the entire range of a species renders a fishery regulation ineffective. Comprehensive regional scope and standardization of regulatory measures are urgently needed. Fisheries, more than any other resource except perhaps migratory waterfowl, depend upon interstate or international agreement and cooperation for their conservation. The need is glaring, the trend well established, and many more species will be written into treaties and coordinated state codes. The United States government is already a party to several international agreements for the conservation of fisheries in which Americans are interested (21). Additional treaties will be necessary as we realize more fully the value of fishery resources and extend the range of our fishing operations. Competitive fishing of international waters foreshadows cooperative conservation by the competing nations. Figure 177 shows

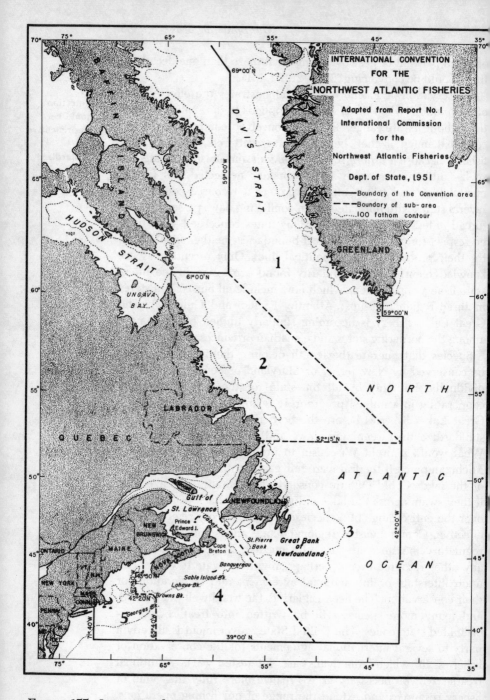

FIGURE 177. *International resources must be internationally conserved. Ten signatories ratified the conventions pertaining to the area shown on the map: Canada, Denmark, Norway, Spain, Italy, Portugal, Iceland, United Kingdom, United States, and France. Regulations are promulgated on the basis of areal units as bounded on the map.*

some historic fishing grounds affected by an international agreement drawn up in 1951.

Favored species of fish need protection against natural enemies other than man, allowing that for fisheries as for other resources conservation is largely a matter of correcting man's own abuses. Since man is only one among many creatures that feed on fish, including fishes themselves, he can increase his share of supply by restraining or destroying his rivals. However, in asserting his superiority he must exercise caution lest he set up a biotic chain reaction that ultimately defeats his purpose. The killing of one rival may multiply another; the killing of all might increase their prey beyond its food supply and cause it to starve. The biotic balance in water is sensitive to disturbance much the same as that on land.

Favored species need protection against natural enemies

The oyster, leading American mollusk, spends its quiet life in constant danger of being eaten by any one of a dozen mortal enemies. Perhaps that is why one oyster can produce as many as 500 million eggs in a single spawning season. Perhaps that is why an oyster can change sex, apparently at will (2, p. 98). One of the worst oyster destroyers, the starfish (Figure 178), has been the object of costly combat with suction dredges and rope "mops." The discovery that it is fatally allergic to lime may offer a solution, unless the lime proves too injurious to valuable species that also frequent oyster beds (22, 23).

Predators of many other kinds infest our fishing grounds, sometimes causing serious depredation before detection, and often continuing their inroads despite our best efforts to eradicate or control them. The lamprey (Figure 179), scourge of the Great Lakes, is one such invader (24, 25). Over-fishing of decent aquatic folk may give many new pirates their opportunity. Wherever man upsets biotic balance he is liable to aggravate problems otherwise naturally subdued.

While popular species are being over-fished, others of known merit and abundance are being neglected or under-utilized (26, pp. 28-41). Neglect here, as the failure to cut a ripe forest tree, entails positive and avoidable waste. Even more overtly wasteful, like slash and slab left from lumbering, is any failure to use completely the fish that are caught.

Neglected species and wasted parts challenge the conservator

The myriads of anchovies along the length of our Pacific Coast went almost untouched while the pilchard population showed definite signs of shrinking due to fishing. The Pacific sardine or pilchard supported the largest fishery in the western hemisphere in 1945 (2, p. 9), and the somewhat smaller anchovy found little

FIGURE 178. *Starfish attacking young oysters. Predator-prey relationships exist in the sea as well as on the land. Starfish predation on oysters costs us millions of dollars annually.* (J. V. Engle, F.W.S., photo.)

use except as live bait for chumming tunas (2, p. 26). The pilchard catch declined as shown in Figure 180. The 1952-53 sardine season was the worst in history, the entire season yielding only "one fair day's catch" (3,320 tons). In its peak year, 1936-37, it amounted to 700,000 tons. In 1952-53, the pilchard fleet turned to anchovies as a substitute (27), thus demonstrating how economic necessity may, in fact, afford opportunity for biologic recovery of a fishery.

At least four Pacific fishes remain under-utilized. Bonito, black sheep of the tuna family, and only slightly inferior to other tunas, makes only a small fraction of its potential contribution to the total catch (2, pp. 41, 42). Sablefish or black cod is a superior food fish neglected by fishermen because housewives have not gained its acquaintance. Pacific cod resembles in quality its east coast counterpart, but few are taken. Lingcod is excellent for food and yields a liver oil exceptionally high in vitamin A. Its catch remains incidental to the halibut fishery (2, p. 23).

The burbot in the Great Lakes, the carp in T.V.A. lakes, the ocean pout of New England, and the squid on both our Atlantic and Pacific coasts are other valuable food resources largely wasted at present. Education and attractive marketing might make them commercially profitable. The ugly burbot gained acceptance during World War II, but fell into disrepute again thereafter. It is too ugly to be relished without camouflage.

Our fisheries present many opportunities for conservation through the salvage of fish parts largely wasted, such as the carcasses of fishes taken for their livers, the oil-rich heads of salmon, the bones, viscera, and other parts thrown away when fish are filleted, and so forth. Salmon canning wastes only a third of the fish, but that waste represents almost total loss. Improved tech-

FIGURE 179. *In 1950 an estimated 70 per cent of our lake trout fishery was lost to the blood-thirsty sea lamprey. Did biotic imbalance due to over-fishing induce the anadromous parasite to stay in the lakes instead of migrating to the sea as was its habit?* (After F.W.S. publications.)

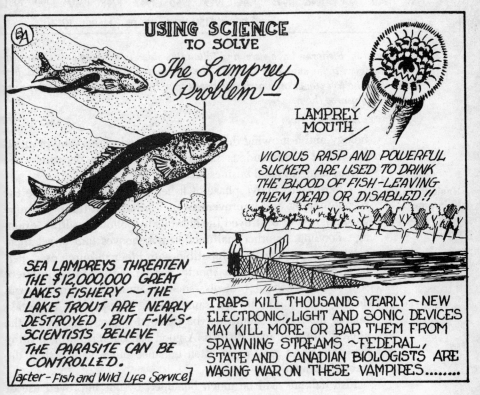

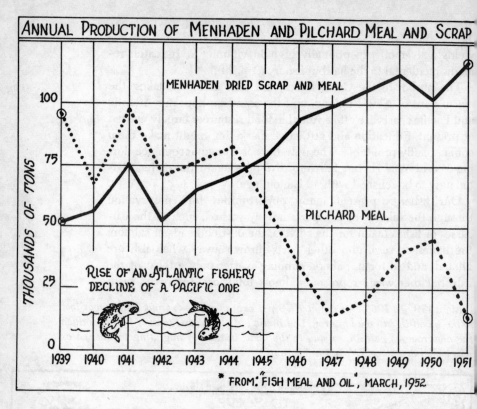

MENHADEN DRIED SCRAP AND MEAL

THOUSANDS OF TONS

100

75

50

25

0

RISE OF AN ATLANTIC FISHERY
DECLINE OF A PACIFIC ONE

PILCHARD MEAL

1939 1940 1941 1942 1943 1944 1945 1946 1947 1948 1949 1950 1951

* FROM: "FISH MEAL AND OIL", MARCH, 1952

FIGURE 180. *Fisheries have risen and fallen like ships in a heavy sea. Conservation can give them smoother sailing. The menhaden fishery has attained first rank, but the fish stocks on which it is based may be in jeopardy unless steps are taken to conserve them.*

nology and a growing demand for low-grade fishery by-products can affect a tremendous saving of fish. Salvage depends upon engineering skill and business acumen.

Habitats must be improved rather than spoiled

A most constructive phase of fishery conservation must be the reconditioning and improvement of fish habitats. Insofar as man has impaired or destroyed the habitats by pollution, silting, drainage, flooding, or other malfunction it behooves him to set them aright by every means compatible with other resource uses. Perhaps fishery conservation should not be permitted to interfere with more essential projects, such as multiple-purpose stream developments, but, by the same token, high-priority undertakings of the future should not be planned without regard for the aquatic life they may disturb. A good fish habitat and a healthy fish population may more often enhance other values than detract from them.

Fish habitats will be much benefited by our improved use of

FLOW CHART of the COMMERCIAL FISHERIES - 1954

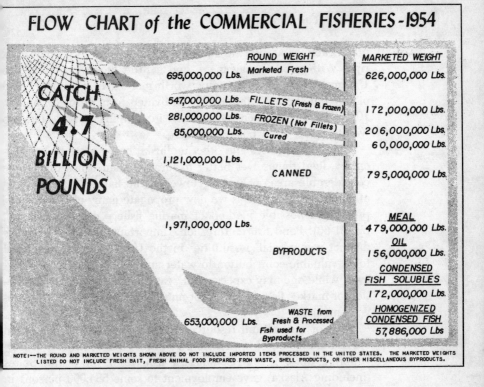

	ROUND WEIGHT	MARKETED WEIGHT
	695,000,000 Lbs. Marketed Fresh	626,000,000 Lbs.
CATCH 4.7 BILLION POUNDS	547,000,000 Lbs. FILLETS (Fresh & Frozen)	172,000,000 Lbs.
	281,000,000 Lbs. FROZEN (Not Fillets)	206,000,000 Lbs.
	85,000,000 Lbs. Cured	60,000,000 Lbs.
	1,121,000,000 Lbs. CANNED	795,000,000 Lbs.
	1,971,000,000 Lbs. BYPRODUCTS	MEAL 479,000,000 Lbs. OIL 156,000,000 Lbs. CONDENSED FISH SOLUBLES 172,000,000 Lbs. HOMOGENIZED CONDENSED FISH 57,886,000 Lbs
	653,000,000 Lbs. WASTE from Fresh & Processed Fish used for Byproducts	

NOTE:—THE ROUND AND MARKETED WEIGHTS SHOWN ABOVE DO NOT INCLUDE IMPORTED ITEMS PROCESSED IN THE UNITED STATES. THE MARKETED WEIGHTS LISTED DO NOT INCLUDE FRESH BAIT, FRESH ANIMAL FOOD PREPARED FROM WASTE, SHELL PRODUCTS, OR OTHER MISCELLANEOUS BYPRODUCTS.

FIGURE 181. *The total catch was somewhat low in 1954, but its end-product distribution was nonetheless interesting. (Commercial Fisheries Review chart.)*

water and land resources generally. Many already spoiled may never be recovered, but many damaged ones can be returned to their natural state without exorbitant expense. Those habitats which remain in good condition can usually be kept so by treating them with common sense. Unfortunately, men who fish for fun are often better conservators than those who fish for a living. Commercial fishermen must learn to fish without tearing the bottom out of the sea.

Artificial propagation of commercial fishes becomes increasingly feasible as our requirements increase and natural sources decline. In certain Gulf and Middle Atlantic localities oysters have been almost "domesticated," their beds cared for much as one tends cultivated fields, and their young stock (spat) transplanted to better feeding grounds much as cattle are driven to good grazing. The oyster farmer gathers seed, sows it on leased sea-bottom land, protects the growing crop against poachers and

Artificial propagation of commercial species becomes increasingly feasible

other enemies as best he can, and harvests the crop when it is ripe. With good management, and a little luck, he gets 100 to 150 bushels per acre annually, worth more than a bumper yield of any but the most intensively cultivated farm crops (2, pp. 99, 102). Those oystermen who persist in scraping public lands do well to gather a few bushels per acre.

Admittedly oysters and other mollusks, being more or less sedentary, lend themselves better to farming than fishes that range considerable areas of water. However, the hatching and rearing of commercial fin fish as we now propagate many of our anglers' prizes is a possible method of marine fishery conservation (26, pp. 51-60). Pond fish culture, long important in the Orient, has distinct commercial possibilities in the United States, incidental to its valuable contribution to water and soil conservation. However, while one may expect an increase in the controlled production of market fish, he need not anticipate any revolutionary developments.

None of our natural resources has been more neglected than our fisheries; none has greater possibilities for profitable conservation (2, pp. 131, 132). Commercial fisheries of the United States (including Alaska) gave employment to some 584,000 persons in 1950—170,000 of them fishermen, the others transporters, shore workers, makers of gear or processing equipment, boat builders, and other allied tradesmen. An estimated 94,000 craft and 4,275 shore establishments were engaged in commercial fishing. The fishing industry represented a capital investment of 890 million dollars. It yielded 4.9 billion pounds of goods, worth more than 1.1 billion dollars retail (30). Figure 181 shows graphically the volume of end products in 1954. During one decade, 1940 to 1950, employment in the industry increased by one third, yet in about the same period our excess of imports over exports (edible fish and inedible fish products) almost tripled.

The life of our valuable fishing industry depends upon systematic conservation

High time it is indeed that we recognize the value of our fishery assets, acknowledge their precarious position due to neglect, and take more positive steps toward their perpetuation. Scientific investigation and systematic conservation will cost large sums of money, but continued neglect would be infinitely more costly. In the national interest, as well as that of coastal regions and fishing centers, we can well afford to invest the necessary funds. The national interest is definitely involved, and greater participation on the national level clearly indicated. Given adequate funds to implement a systematic program and discharge fully its responsibilities, the Fish and Wildlife Service might save our de-

:adent fisheries and place them on a sustained-yield basis. The public must be apprised of its stock in fish, and it must then demand legislation for intelligent management of the bordering seas. As runs increase and profits mount our fishermen should be better able to hear the biologist's recommendations above the noise of the sea, and conform voluntarily. Conservation pays big dividends, be it conservation of soils, forests, grasslands, or fisheries. And dividends make conservators of exploiters. When enough fishermen become conservators our fishery problems can be easily resolved, but unless they have some degree of security during the conversion, many will quit fishing before the dividends appear. We have paid farmers for *not* plowing the soil, but have we ever paid fishermen for *not* catching fish? Might we do so in special cases, to save both fish and fishermen? One of our fishermen delivers, on the average, a third more food than one of our farmers, but while we have given the farmer generous assistance, we have almost ignored the fisherman's problems (2, p. 131). Conservation, of all public activities, should be inclusive, integrated, and equitably subsidized wherever subsidy is necessary.

The wealth of the sea—mineral, vegetable, and animal—presents a major challenge to technology and conservation (28) and a major opportunity for international cooperation (29, pp. 171-204). The nations will be increasingly jealous of their ocean boundaries as marine resources attain greater importance.

CHAPTER 15: REFERENCES CITED BY NUMBER

(1) George T. Renner, Loyal Durand, Jr., C. Langdon White, and Weldon B. Gibson, *World Economic Geography*, Thomas Y. Crowell Company, New York, 1951, Chapters 15 and 16.

(2) *Fishery Resources of the United States*, Senate Document No. 51, 79th Congress, 1st Session, 1945.

(3) Horace H. Selby, "Agar, Agaroids, and the American Agar Industry," *Fishery Leaflet 118*, F.W.S., 1948.

(4) Victor B. Scheffer, "The Commercial Importance of Seaweed Gums in the U.S.," *Fishery Leaflet 156*, F.W.S., Chicago, 1945.

(5) Erik H. Arctander, "Thar She Blows," *Service*, April 1951.

(6) Jennie E. Harris, "Sponge Fishermen of Tarpon ·Springs," *National Geographic Magazine*, XCI, No. 1, January 1947.

(7) Victor B. Scheffer and Karl W. Kenyon, "The Fur Seal Herd Comes of Age," *National Geographic Magazine*, CI, No. 4, April 1952.

(8) Charles Butler, "The Fish Liver Oil Industry," *Fishery Leaflet 233*, F.W.S., 1948.

(9) Rachel L. Carson, "Fish and Shellfish of the South Atlantic and Gulf Coasts," *Conservation Bulletin 37*, Office of the Coordinator of Fisheries, Department of the Interior, 1944.

(10) Rachel L. Carson, "Fish and Shellfish of the Middle Atlantic Coast," *Conservation Bulletin No. 38*, Department of the Interior, 1945.

(11) "United States Per Capita Consumption of Fishery Products," *Fishery Leaflet 352*, F.W.S., 1949.

(12) A. W. Anderson and C. E. Peterson, "Fishery Statistics of the United States—1949," *Statistical Digest 25*, F.W.S., 1952.

(13) "Fish—Greatest Gift of the Sea," *Science Illustrated*, January 1947.

(14) Joel W. Hedgpeth, "The Passing of the Salmon," *The Scientific Monthly*, LIX, No. 5, November 1944, pp. 370-378.

(15) Leonard O. Warner, "New England's Fisheries Viewed as Dying Industry," *Providence Sunday Journal*, 12 January 1947.

(16) John R. Clark, "Experiments on the Escape of Undersized Haddock Through Otter Trawls," *Commercial Fisheries Review*, XIV, No. 9, September 1952.

(17) John R. Clark, "Further Experiments on the Escape of Undersized Haddock Through Otter Trawls," *Commercial Fisheries Review*, XIV, No. 12, December 1952.

(18) Herbert W. Graham, "A Minimum Net-Mesh Size for the New England Haddock Fishery," *Commercial Fisheries Review*, December 1952.

(19) Clarence P. Idyll, "A Concept of Conservation in Marine Fisheries and Its Implications in Fishery Management," *Transactions of the Seventeenth North American Wildlife Conference*, Wildlife Management Institute, Washington, D.C., 1952, p. 367.

(20) Albert M. Day, "Interstate Fishery Cooperation and Conservation," *Commercial Fisheries Review*, XI, No. 10, October 1949. Also available as *Separate No. 238*, F.W.S.

(21) W. M. Chapman, "United States Policy with Regard to High Seas Fisheries," *Separate No. 222*, F.W.S., 1948.

(22) Robert M. Yoder, "The Unsolved Riddle of the Oyster," *The Saturday Evening Post*, 10 November 1951.

(23) Paul S. Galtsoff, "The Oyster and the Oyster Industry in the United States," *Fishery Leaflet 187*, F.W.S., reprinted 1949.

(24) Vernon C. Applegate, "The Sea Lamprey in the Great Lakes," *Fishery Leaflet 384*, F.W.S., 1950.

(25) Lola Tidwell Dees, "Sea Lampreys of the Atlantic Coast and Great Lakes," *Fishery Leaflet 360*, F.W.S., 1950.

(26) *Wildlife and Fish Resources: Proceedings of the United Nations Scientific Conference on the Conservation and Utilization of Resources, 1949*, Vol. VII. United Nations Department of Economic Affairs, New York, 1951, pp. 1-186.

(27) *Commercial Fisheries Review*, XV, No. 2, February 1953.

(28) "The Technology of Ocean Resources," *Report of the President's Materials Policy Commission*, IX: The Promise of Technology, Washington, D. C., 1952.

(29) *Fisheries Yearbook, 1952*, National Fisheries Institute, Inc., Washington, D.C.

(30) Fish and Wildlife Service statistics.

BOTH THE HORSE AND THE HAY ARE FUGITIVE

Conservation of Minerals

being consumed by our use, minerals are conservable only as diligent search, thorough extraction, and efficient employment increase the available supplies and prolong their usefulness

HAVING SURVEYED THE LAND AND SCANNED THE SEAS THAT BORDER it, we are now ready to examine the mineral resources deposited by nature within the earth. We shall not delve deeply into the subject, but without a cursory examination of minerals and their conservation a discussion of natural wealth would lack the broad practical perspective that is paramount to its rational development.

A comprehensive treatment of minerals would fill several volumes much larger than this one, but such treatment does not suit our context. It is more fitting that we examine only those minerals which dominate our mechanized age, and especially those in imminent danger of exhaustion.

Unlike our durable resources, which become permanent and perpetual under conservation, minerals are fixed endowments, expendable once and then gone for our time. In this, the steel age, they hold a commanding position, but that position they cannot retain indefinitely. They are a legacy given like cash, and we are spending it rapidly. Unlike the renewable resources we have discussed, which resemble permanent trust funds, the minerals are ours to spend once only, without any accrued interest to cushion their exhaustion. They are expendable and fugitive. Their rate of accumulation does not approach even remotely the rate at which we are extracting them. There is no evidence that those stores we consume will be significantly replenished during the age of mankind. In fact, the very culture built with those we extract in some cases interferes with the accumulation of new stocks for future use, as when we drain and burn peat bogs that might have become coal had they been left undisturbed.

Minerals are the tools of our mechanical, atomic age, as they have been the tools of civilization ever since prehistoric men threw rocks at each other. Stone, bronze, iron, and steel have, in their turn, dominated the affairs of men and gaged the progress of human culture. From stone age to atomic age minerals have provided implements of war and peace—the spears and plowshares by which tribes and nations have risen or fallen. They remain the decisive factor in war and an essential element of pacific progress. Our national prestige hinges on the comparative abundance of minerals available to us (1, Chaps. 3 and 4).

Tools that forge our mechanical age: destructive and constructive

Certain minerals are as necessary to life and health as are air and water. We cannot live without them. Common salt, for example, is so vital to the human organism that it has been an article of commerce throughout the history of man. It has emerged from its rudimentary role as a component of blood and tissue to a prominent place among industrial raw materials. It is indispensable and invaluable; yet so cheap and abundant that we shall say no more about it. The earth's crust and the seas that lap it contain so much salt that we shall have plenty without conserving it (2).

For the giants of our technological age—the metals for machines and the mineral fuels to drive them—the prospect is quite different. Some of these are neither abundant nor cheap, and we are consuming our reserves at accelerating rates (3, p. 176). They have brought us our high material standards, our superior producing capacity, our leadership in world affairs, and the leisure time to enjoy life and contemplate our bounteous natural wealth. They have been the means of ruthlessly exploiting renewable resources, and are now the most efficient means of conserving them. With machines made of minerals and powered by mineral fuels men till the soil, log the forest, fish the sea, process and distribute the products, and apply conservation measures to ensure a permanent supply of renewable resources. So intimately related are the *renewable organics* and the *non-renewable minerals* in our complex culture that the two groups require some degree of correlation in a treatise on resource conservation. Their relative prominence in the American economy of the immediate future has been predicted as shown in Figure 182.

In variety and versatility, minerals challenge the whole array of renewable resources

The great variety of mineral materials and the versatility with which they serve us every day of our lives are suggestive of their

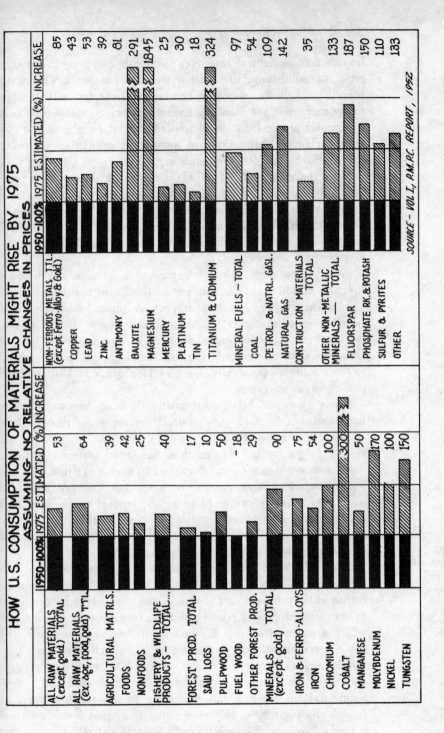

FIGURE 182. *The expanding use of minerals continues the rise toward the climax of our mechanical age.*

importance as natural resources. Minerals compose the earth'
crust, the solid foundation of our world environment. Containec
therein are all the elements known to chemistry and perhap
many more not yet isolated. Every kind of common rock is
compound or combination of minerals—be it simple, as the cal
cium carbonate of limestone, or more complex, as the mixture o
silicon dioxide and other minerals in granite.

Since the main body of soil is disintegrated, decomposed rock
and soil is the main support of life, one might conclude that the
vegetable and animal resources spring from the mineral ones
One might contend that minerals are the primal category. Have
we put the cart before the horse? Are minerals the egg or the
hen among resources?

Perhaps the most valuable contribution of minerals is their
function as soil materials, and not in the forms normally classed
as mineral. Perhaps our most important mineral resources have
been discussed in earlier chapters under soils. Be that as it may,
we are here concerned with minerals of specific kinds, and of
these we shall discuss only the functional groups most essential
to our continued prosperity. Let us take a quick look at the field
and make our selections.

Stone, clay, and other earth materials have almost countless
uses, and, but for their superabundance, we might discuss their
conservation. However, since we may have more stone than we
shall ever quarry for construction, flux, road material, statuary
and monuments, more sand than we can ever make into bifocals,
mirrors, window panes, store fronts and other glass products, and
more clay than we can mold into pots, crocks, bricks, tiles, and
other ceramics, we shall not devote space to them here. They
may be used more and more as other materials grow scarce, but
one cannot foresee any shortage even so.

**Major
functional
groups**

One orthodox classification divides the minerals proper into
three groups—*metals, nonmetals,* and *fuels*—each of which may
be variously subdivided. For our purposes it might be desirable
to consider minerals according to their functional uses: (a) those
which are converted into finished goods, such as aluminum, (b)
those used mainly for processing or manufacturing *other* materials, such as sulfur, (c) those which furnish energy for industry,
commerce, and domestic convenience, such as coal and petroleum, and (d) those which contribute to soil fertility, such as
potash and phosphate. However, since many play a dual or even
a triple role, our discussion would become entirely too lengthy

nd involved. We can conserve space and reduce reading time
oy focussing attention on those that dominate particular groups.
We may thus orient our thinking about a comparatively short
ist instead of attempting an exposition on each one.

SELECTED REPRESENTATIVES OF
FUNCTIONAL GROUPS

Metals:

IRON—king pin of the steel industry; dominant over ferro-alloys

COPPER—strong man of electricity

ALUMINUM—light, structural metal and good conductor of electricity

MAGNESIUM—light metal, partial substitute for aluminum

LEAD, ZINC, TIN—heavy, corrosion-resistant metals for protectors and
containers

MANGANESE, CHROMIUM, NICKLE, TUNGSTEN, COBALT, MOLYBDENUM,
VANADIUM AND COLUMBIUM—ferro-alloys mixed with iron in steel

Fuels:

COAL—leading work horse and synthetic raw material

PETROLEUM—fuel, lubricant, and raw material

NATURAL GAS—fuel, predominantly

Radioactive Materials:

URANIUM, THORIUM—sources of atomic energy

Fertilizers:

PHOSPHATE ROCK—plant food, industrial material and potential fissionable material

POTASH—plant food and industrial material

NITRATE—plant food and explosive

The list omits many useful minerals, among them the precious
metals and stones, but it includes most of those upon which
our industrial prosperity and national security more directly de-

pend. The conservator is more interested in the effective use of wealth than in its classification.

The "big three"
—iron, coal,
and oil

Iron stands unique among the metals, and sets the pace for the others. To date there is no substitute for iron as the bulk component of steel. Other metals are in some degree interchangeable, as for example aluminum for copper in electrical transmission, but iron has no satisfactory stand-in. We may therefore appraise our metal situation in terms of iron, since the others could not be put to work without the steel produced with iron. When we discuss prospects in Chapter 17 we shall make some long-range predictions about replacements for iron, but for the present and the foreseeable future it is our most essential metal (4, p. 561). *Gold reserves are the product, not the means, of industrial prosperity.*

From iron and the ferro-alloys come the machines and tools for making other metals into useful articles, the rotors for generating electricity to be converted and distributed by copper, the cans to be coated with tin and the sheet metal to be galvanized with zinc. Indeed, iron is the prime mover among the metals, if not in the entire mineral field.

Between the metals and the fuels there obtains almost complete interdependence and reciprocity. The fuels would not be available as we know them if metal machines did not extract and distribute them; neither would there be the machines and vehicles for the fuels to drive if the metals were lacking. In the absence of iron and steel, most of our oil and coal would languish in the earth. The little trickles and lumps we might recover would be used to heat and illuminate our homes, in competition with tallow candles and firewood. In the absence of oil and coal we could neither produce nor operate our machines and vehicles. We should revert to hand tools, animal power, and sailing ships. Metals would have little value without the mineral fuels, and the mineral fuels would be largely wasted without the metals to extract and employ them.

Since the metals and fuels are indispensable to each other in functional use, it is logical that the two groups should be conserved jointly rather than independently. Both must be put to optimum use by maintaining their reciprocity as long as possible. Considering our abundance of coal and relative paucity of iron ore in the United States, any expenditure of coal to prolong the life of iron reserves may be good conservation.

If we let iron represent the metals, and allow that natural gas is actually a by-product of petroleum, we can boil the main bulk of mineral resources down to three materials—*iron, coal,* and *oil.* These are the "big three" of industry and the big three in mineral conservation. The big three that work together to keep our mechanical age humming trace their lineage to widely different origins—two organic and the other mineral. Nature provided us with iron ore by separating and accumulating in certain places the iron compounds contained in rock materials of various kinds. Iron is present in rocks and soils almost everywhere, contributing to them the reddish hue of rust. In places, as in our southeastern states, iron hardpan layers have been precipitated in the soil; but our commercial ore deposits are of ancient geologic origin, produced by several different earth processes (4, p. 564). Whatever the exact process by which it developed, iron ore was mineral from the start, and has no organic history.

Coal and petroleum *are* organic products, a fact that strengthens the proposition that biotic resources are those upon which man is actually most dependent. The whole story is too long to relate here, but let us sketch it for both coal and oil, in order to illustrate once again the interminable kinship between minerals and organisms. In the case of mineral fuels, that which we choose to call "mineral" is in fact "organic" in origin. Through long, slow processes living resources have given us our expendable fossil fuels.

Long after Marco Polo returned from a trip and reported that the amazing Chinese were burning rocks, scientists learned that those rocks were the concentrated carbon residues from ancient forests that flourished in fresh-water swamps at least a million years before the advent of man.

Long after petroleum was used by men as a cure for mange on their camels we learned that the oily fluid derives from myriads of salt-water organisms that inhabited the shallow margins of ancient seas and became entombed within layers of sedimentary rock (5).

Somewhere in the dark, distant past both the fresh-water plant remains and the salt-water plankton remains were buried deep under marine sediments, were compressed and concentrated into "seams" of coal and "pools" of oil as we know them today, and lay almost unused until men of the industrial age put them to work. We have made them our servants and become dependent upon them, but they cannot serve us always. When they expire others must take their places, else we should lost the civilization they gained us.

The accompanying diagrams show something about natural

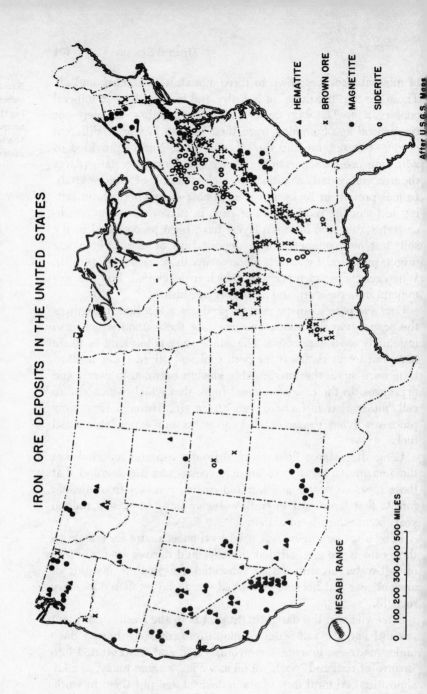

IRON ORE DEPOSITS IN THE UNITED STATES

▲ HEMATITE
✕ BROWN ORE
● MAGNETITE
○ SIDERITE

MESABI RANGE

0 100 200 300 400 500 MILES

FIGURE 183. *We have found iron in many localities and mined it in several, but the bulk of production, to date, has been from the "Iron Range" of Minnesota.*

torage methods, and the maps show where known stores of the
"big three" are located in the United States. We may find other
deposits, but each will contain a fixed quantity, subject to
exhaustion.

Our natural endowment of iron, coal, and oil was greater than
any other nation has ever possessed. We found all three in such
abundance and in such a favorable geographic relationship as no
other nation has ever enjoyed. (Compare Figures 183, 184, and
185.) We dug coal out of the Appalachians long before we attained national independence. In 1859 we struck oil in Pennsylvania, and in 1893 we opened a great new iron mine above the
head of Lake Superior. The oil discovery ran our whaling fleet
on the rocks, and gave us the fuel and lubricant with which
we later became motorized. The coal and iron ore, connected by
water transport, and with magnesium limestone for flux readily
available, became the mainsprings of an iron-and-steel industry
that has brought America unequalled living standards and un--
rivaled power as a nation. All this began as recently as 1893, when
we opened in the Mesabi Range of Minnesota the largest, richest
iron deposit thus far exploited (Figure 183).

We used these minerals lavishly, and spent them faster than
was ever done before. In a few decades we built an industrial
empire based on iron, coal, and oil—but at stupendous cost in
terms of resources. After only four decades of accelerated rise to
greatness, economic depression gave us pause to examine the
inroads made on our stores during a mere paragraph of history.
We were astounded. It was estimated in 1934 that almost half
the rich ores of Mesabi had already been utilized, only 40 years
after we began to use them. The city of Hibbing had lifted its
outskirts and moved aside in order that huge shovels might remove the iron on which she once sat. The fabulous little city
attracted many visitors to see the gigantic open-pit mine—"biggest
man-made hole on earth." It was further estimated that Pennsylvania anthracite coal had been 29 per cent consumed. Many high-
grade seams of bituminous coal were in an advanced stage of
depletion. We had already skimmed the cream off our vast coal
reserves (6, p. 396).

The early oil fields had fared no better than iron and coal. By
1934 there were hundreds of "dead or dying pools"—only three
quarters of a century after the original strike at Titusville. New
discoveries in Texas obscured the incredible speed with which
older ones were being exhausted (6, p. 396). We had put the nation on wheels in twenty years. We had achieved gasoline pro-

We were well
endowed with
iron, coal,
and oil

We spent them
faster than was
ever done
before

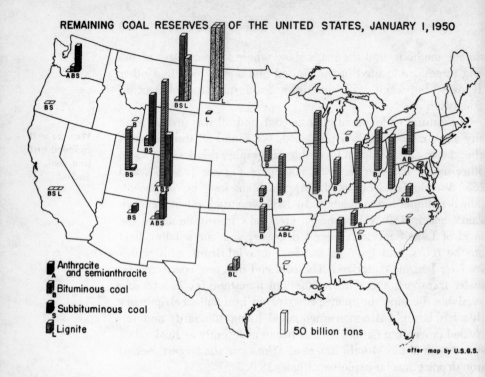

Anthracite and semianthracite

Bituminous coal

Subbituminous coal

Lignite

50 billion tons

after map by U.S.G.S.

FIGURE 184. *The total reserves of coal almost defy calculation, but the better grades are becoming less accessible and more costly to extract.*

pulsion, and every new automobile driver accelerated oil consumption. The whole picture looked dark twenty years ago, in the midst of economic depression!

Among the nations of the world we have become the champion dissipators of expendable natural wealth. From our own domestic reserves we extract annually some 119 million long tons of iron ore (1953) and 460 million metric tons of coal (1952). We produce more than 6¼ million 42-gallon barrels of crude oil daily (1952) (7). How long can the deposits last under such a rate of withdrawal? Let us see how well each of the big three can stand the attrition, mindful that the fuels complement each other whereas iron ore stands alone. (It should be noted that coal production has declined sharply since World War II, while oil, and particularly gas, have attained greater importance as fuels.)

Our coals will last for centuries

We have coal to burn. Estimates place our reserves at 2,500 billion short tons, about half of them recoverable with techniques now employed. We have in the United States about 40 per cent of the world's total coal reserves (8, p. 26), enough to last us almost indefinitely under the highest rate of consumption we can reasonably contemplate. It may well come to pass that coal will be out-moded as a fuel before we exhaust our available reserves, but for a long, long time in the future coal will probably be one of our main sources of energy. From it we will get gas and gasoline after our petroleum and natural gas fields have gone dry. It will also become increasingly important as a raw material for the manufacture of chemicals, textiles, plastics, and many other end products. So vast are our reserves that they can, if intelligently conserved, satisfy these multipurpose requirements for 2500 years (9). Their comparative quality, volume, and general location may be seen in Figure 184.

Why conserve a material so abundant and so widely distrib-uted? Because its usefulness depends on quality and accessibility. Coals are of several kinds, each more or less indicative of the de-gree to which the original peat has been compressed and con-centrated. The three broad classes are, in order of quality (carbon content), anthracite, bituminous, and lignite. Of these, the higher grades of bituminous coal (coking quality), that smelt our iron and make our steel, are so limited in quantity that their extrac-tion is already becoming difficult and expensive. Rising costs of production are often the most convincing evidence that a re-source ought to be conserved. Waste of coal increases the cost of steel, which increases the cost of farm machinery and trans-portation. Every additional cost raises the price of bread and butter. That is one reason why we may concern ourselves with the conservation of coal, although we have the material in great abundance.

We are "quick-rich" in oil stocks, despite repeated warnings of impending destitution. When we took the pulse of our oil re-serves in 1947, we estimated that they would expire in half a century or less (10). Other estimates published from time to time have been even more pessimistic. It is reassuring indeed to know that we are now actually discovering oil faster than we are pro-ducing it (8, p. 2). As shown graphically in Figure 186, proved re-serves are seven times greater now than they were fifty years ago (8, p. 5). "Proved reserves" can be interpreted as the amount of crude oil that our oil men can extract with present methods under prevailing prices. Investigation and technology are constantly increasing the proportion of existing oil that may be recovered economically (3, p. 281).

We are "quick-rich" in oil stocks

Oil statistics are difficult to handle and any estimate in terms of years of supply must be subjective, if not a bold-faced con-jecture. There are too many variables—too many changes that

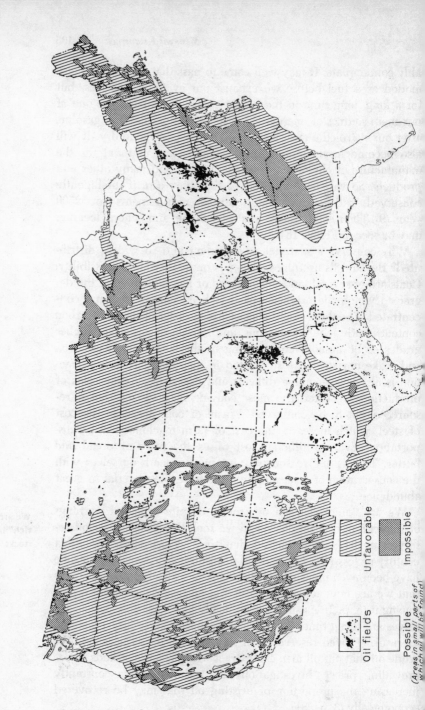

Unfavorable

Impossible

Oil fields

Possible
(Areas in small parts of
which oil will be found)

FIGURE 185. *Oil producing areas and possible oil areas in the United States. Known oil deposits are widely distributed, and many more will be found. This map does not show the important tidewater oil lands off the Gulf Coast and California. (U.S.G.S., map.)*

can alter the picture (11). We are drawing oil out of the earth at the rate of some 2,280 million barrels per year, which is almost 1/12 of our proved reserves. We should thus be running short in about 12 years, unless discovery and development bring in new wells or we drain the old ones more thoroughly. We know that additional reserves will be "proved," and we expect to discover many new reservoirs in the favorable areas in Figure 185. We also hope to increase the recovery of oil-in-place from the average 40% currently profitable to about 75% (8, p. 7). Improved recovery alone could almost double our available reserves, greatly extending our natural petroleum era.

Perhaps we have oil for a hundred years or more, from natural liquid pools, but a century is not a long time, conservation-wise. Since nature is not replenishing those pools, they must eventually run dry. We may be prepared for that eventuality by developing synthetic liquid fuels. We will not be without oil, but we may get it by means not yet in common practice. Meanwhile, we may import increasing quantities as production costs rise at home (12, p. 107).

Iron is the second most abundant commercial metal, being surpassed only by aluminum (3, p. 251). However, iron ores, the natural concentrates of iron that yield our commercial supplies of the metal, are relatively scarce. They are of several kinds, and, like coal, they vary widely in quality. The grade of iron ore is determined by its metallic iron content and the ease with which it may be extracted. Except as those two factors relate to it, the kind of ore—be it hematite, magnetite, limonite, or any other—has very little practical significance. The red ore, hematite, is by far the most important kind exploited in the United States to date. Lake Superior hematite, main strength of the American steel in-

**Our iron is
wearing thin**

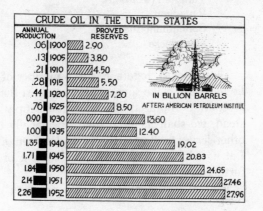

FIGURE 186. *Proved reserves of petroleum have increased steadily despite accelerated production. Who can predict exhaustion while discovery exceeds production?*

CRUDE OIL IN THE UNITED STATES

ANNUAL PRODUCTION		PROVED RESERVES
.06	1900	2.90
.13	1905	3.80
.21	1910	4.50
.28	1915	5.50
.44	1920	7.20
.76	1925	8.50
0.90	1930	13.60
1.00	1935	12.40
1.35	1940	19.02
1.71	1945	20.83
1.84	1950	24.65
2.14	1951	27.46
2.26	1952	27.96

IN BILLION BARRELS
AFTER: AMERICAN PETROLEUM INSTITUTE

dustry, is now wearing somewhat thin and lean by old standards
but the reserve of slightly lower grade ores remains tremendous

As of 1950 our total iron ore reserves economically exploitable
were estimated at 6,400 million long tons—enough to last us only
65 years at prevailing production rates (13, p. 147). From this, a
confirmed pessimist might conclude that our great industrial era
will terminate early in the 21st century. However, the conservator
has a brighter outlook. As we perfect the techniques for concentrating taconite, siliceous, and carbonate iron formations, we multiply the life-span of our iron reserves. Many of the iron deposits
shown in Figure 183 remain unexploited, awaiting the time when
they may be worked profitably. The metallurgical engineer assumes a major responsibility in the conservation of iron, as do
other engineering specialists in the fields of coal and petroleum

**A score of
other metals
have attained
prominence**

We have surveyed the big three quantitatively and separately
because they contribute most to the thermal energy, mechanization, and mobility of our civilization. However, coal, oil, and iron
would not be the aristocrats they are if we lacked the additive
metals (ferro-alloys) which lend unique qualities to steel. Neither
could the aristocracy flourish as it has without the light metals,
such as aluminum, and other non-ferrous metals with a-hundred-
and-one uses. A score of metals other than iron have attained
prominence in our iron-and-steel culture.

Here are the principals:

Ferro-alloys	*Light*	*Non-ferrous*
Chromium	Aluminum	Copper
Nickel	Magnesium	Lead
Molybdenum	Titanium	Zinc
Cobalt	Zirconium	Tin
Tungsten (wolfram)		Antimony
Vanadium		Cadmium
Columbium (niobium)		Bismuth
Manganese		Beryllium

These metals, together with a number of important non-metal-
lic minerals, make such a substantial list that we shall not attempt
a separate appraisal of source and supply for each of them. Instead, we shall mention them specifically only when one or another serves to illustrate a particular form of mineral conservation.
Let us address ourselves to the subject of conservation without
further delay.

Mineral conservation is quite simply a matter of exploration,

xtraction, substitution, maximum use and minimum waste inso-
ar as economic circumstances permit or national security de-
nands. Private interests in open competition cannot apply a con-
ervation measure that deprives them of profit; neither can the
ublic, through mandate, compel the application of such a meas-
re unless the government bears the cost. Excessive conservation
osts imposed on private enterprise can defeat their own pur-
oses by retarding production or suspending operation entirely.
Conservation of minerals must be practical to a degree even
reater than conservation of renewable resources, because miner-
ls are strictly material, with values purely intrinsic. They have
o aesthetic or subjective values in the ordinary sense. Mining
ttracts men and money because it pays; but if restrictions be im-
osed whereby the pay be lost, the men and money must seek
ther employment, leaving the mineral in the ground. Since an
nmined mineral is useless, its abandonment in the earth repre-
ents outright waste—the antithesis of conservation. Preservation
s not the object of mineral conservation. Digging, efficiently, as
ast as it pays is more nearly the correct idea. Protection can
asten the obsolescence of a material by curtailing supply and
timulating substitution, but supply and demand operating with-
ut restraint may be inducement enough to replace scarce ma-
erials. Nothing could be much more embarrassing to future con-
ervators than to discover a century or two hence that materials
ying obsolete and worthless in the ground might once have been
xploited profitably. That which is good, common sense—good
usiness—is usually also good conservation.

Objectives are simple; methods more involved

There are many means of increasing the over-all usefulness of
ur expendable resources, many methods whereby we may
lengthen their service. Some of these conservation methods can
be applied by everyone, since everyone is a user of minerals. Some
methods can be applied only by citizens and corporations who
produce or process mineral materials. Other important means depend upon public policy and practice. There are many striking
parallels between the conservation of expendables and the conservation of permanent resources, and a considerable interdependence as well. We cannot attempt any detailed exposition of procedures, but we shall introduce the general concepts under which
they operate.

More complete recovery of known stores

The greatest physical waste of mineral resources results from
ur inability to recover more than a portion of the stores found
in the earth. Present methods and economics permit only partial
recovery of many. For example, an oil field may be "exhausted"

for all practical purposes when 75 per cent of its original oil content still remains in the ground (14). Such loss now is physical, not financial; but if abandonment now curtails recovery later when improved techniques and higher prices would make it profitable, we have shortened the life of non-renewable wealth. We have, in effect, created future waste by present inefficiency.

A vast quantity of solid minerals, such as coal and ores, lie buried deep in abandoned mines where great walls and pillars were left in place to support the roof and where seams or veins were too thin to be taken out profitably. Both solid and liquid wealth has been wasted in the earth because abundance and quality available elsewhere invoked the law of diminishing returns and forbade more thorough extraction.

Perhaps the most colossal physical waste of a mineral at its source has been that of natural gas released from oil fields (15, p. 55). Until recently most of this ideal fuel was simply blown into the air or "flared" to get rid of it. Flaring is the practice of venting gas through an open upright pipe several feet tall, and

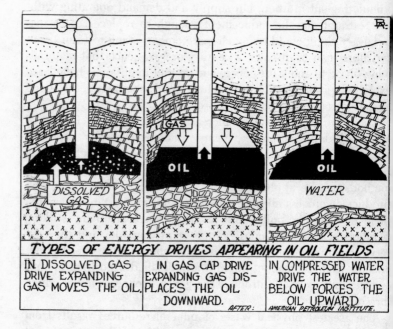

TYPES OF ENERGY DRIVES APPEARING IN OIL FIELDS

IN DISSOLVED GAS DRIVE EXPANDING GAS MOVES THE OIL.	IN GAS CAP DRIVE EXPANDING GAS DISPLACES THE OIL DOWNWARD.	IN COMPRESSED WATER DRIVE THE WATER BELOW FORCES THE OIL UPWARD

AFTER: AMERICAN PETROLEUM INSTITUTE.

FIGURE 187. *Natural pressure helps drive oil from the pools in which it is stored underground.*

ourning it as it comes out at the top. Much has also been burned to make carbon black, a major raw material in the manufacture of rubber tires. Flaring was and is a perfectly logical safety measure. Unless the gas can be used or marketed profitably it is simply a hazard.

Now natural gas has come into its own as the aristocrat among fuels (16). It is piped increasing distances for use in industries and homes. It is estimated that by 1975 about half the homes in the nation will be heated by natural gas (8, p. 20). Thus far consumption has been largely of dry gas, produced independently of oil, but the "wet" varieties (oil-field gas) can greatly increase and prolong the available future supply (3, pp. 270-273).

A double resource tragedy attaches to our wasteful disposal of natural gas at wellheads. The very gas we have burned or blown away might have been used to push more oil out of the reservoir by what is known as "secondary recovery," illustrated in Figures 187 and 188. A pity it is that we took so long to accept a hint demonstrated by nature since the beginning of oil

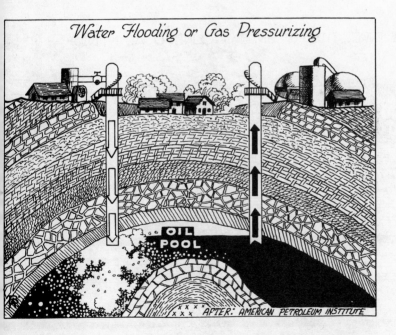

FIGURE 188. *By injecting water or gas to simulate natural "drive," we can get much more oil out of a pool than by ordinary pumping. The procedure is called secondary recovery, since it produces oil that would otherwise be lost.*

production. Here, as in hundreds of other ways, one resource
helps to conserve another. The conservator who despairs can re
gain confidence through nature study.

We are becoming more and more proficient at recovering the
minerals we discover, largely by improving our techniques, but
also by virtue of stronger markets. As prices go up we can afford
to take more pains. Flaring of gas continues at a disgusting rate,
because arrangements for its economical use are not everywhere
possible. Increasing quantities are, however, piped to market
or forced back into the reservoir to pressurize the oil and prolong
economical production (17, p. 108).

More effective than gas in the recovery of petroleum is water
—another oil propellent in the natural arrangement. Water-flood-
ing, or "water drive" has given an extraction rate of 85 per cent
(8, p. 6). We know the techniques for good oil recovery, but their
application depends upon cooperation. To be successful, pres-
surizing or flooding of an oil reservoir must be done on a unit
basis, with all operators participating. Such unity has been difficult to achieve, but we look to the Interstate Oil Compact Com-

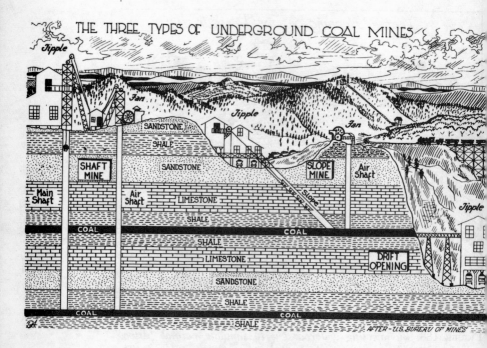

FIGURE 189. *Whatever the type of mine, conservation is achieved when a bed or seam
is worked in such a manner that a minimum of coal is abandoned in the ground.*

mission to accomplish it. Many incidental economies are implicit in such an arrangement.

We are also making progress in the improved recovery of solid minerals, and it is indeed urgent that we do so. Our present recovery of coal from underground mines is generally only about 50 per cent of the total coal present; in some operations as low as 15 per cent (18, p. 5)—see Figures 189 and 190. Back-filling to permit removal of pillars and walls before closure of worked-out coal mines can save 20 to 30 per cent of the original volume (3, p. 203). Better mining machinery and better mine management can work thinner seams at a profit. Strip-mining, the ultimate in complete recovery, can now be accomplished where removal of the overburden was prohibitive a few years ago.

Conservation practices mentioned above are well beyond the experimental stage. Others, even more remarkable and efficient, have been conceived but not yet put to work, among them such ideas as underground horizontal drilling (Figure 191) to drain oil out of sands that vertical wells cannot reach (19). We may be confident that engineering genius alone will for many minerals

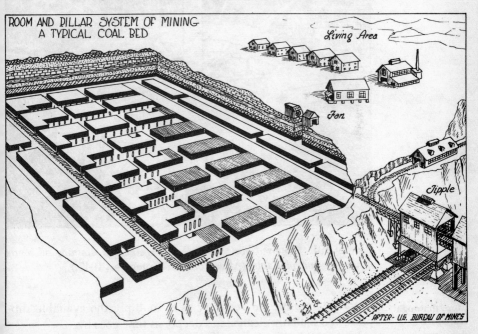

FIGURE 190. *Much coal has been wasted in pillars that support the roofs of abandoned mines. In present workings such waste can be eliminated by back-filling before closing a mine. The Bureau of Mines is conducting experiments to perfect back-filling techniques and demonstrate their practicability.*

Labels within figure:

CRUDE IS PUMPED UP THROUGH MAIN SHAFT

CRUDE OIL SEEPS INTO HOLE AND IS CARRIED OFF THROUGH PIPE

CRUDE FROM ALL HORIZONTAL LINES FLOWS TO WORK CHAMBER

WORK CHAMBER

HOLE DRILLED AS MUCH AS A MILE THROUGH OIL BEARING STRATA

100 FOOT LENGTH OF PIPE

FIGURE 191. *Proposed horizontal oil well system for draining oil sands otherwise unexploitable.* (After *Fortune*, September, 1947.)

More thorough search for new deposits

so vastly improve our recovery as to multiply the available supplies. We shall dig cleaner and deeper as time goes by.

In the field of exploration, the first step toward discovery, there is less cause for pride. Excepting oil, for which intensive search has been conducted by techniques shown in Figure 192, we remain virtually in the horse-and-buggy stage of mineral exploration. (The horse-and-buggy geologist was the hard-rock scientist who could drive across the country and map its geology by the ringing tone of the buggy tires. Shoes on the horse increased his accuracy.) Compared with the technology of recovery, our prospecting remains of the pickaxe variety. Herein lies a major opportunity for the conservation—the increased usefulness—of mineral resources. Such costly procedure as the test drilling illustrated in Figure 193 is often disappointing.

Adequate maps and surveys are basic to scientific mineral exploration. Yet as late as 1950 geological maps were available for only about one tenth of the United States (20, p. 6). There were adequate topographic maps for only about one fourth of the country, and the public domain included 116 million acres of unsurveyed territory. We knew little about sub-surface geology on the land and even less about the submarine geology of the continental shelf. Under the most accelerated programs practicable, it would take about a quarter of a century to complete the mapping of topography, geology, soils, and offshore areas (20, p. 15). The project would probably cost one and a half billion dollars, but it would surely pay big dividends in the planned development and conservation of resources. We spend half that much in one year drilling *dry* "wildcat" wells in search of oil (21), encouraged indeed by special tax provisions permitting deduction of costs.

With good maps to guide us we might employ more effectively all the ingenious methods of detecting minerals—geophysical, geochemical, radiometric, and "commonsensical" (Figure 192). With aerial color photography we can get valuable clues from plant indicators and surface rock exposures (18, p. 27). Photo-geology is the coming method of rapid reconnaissance for minerals; and the "airborne magnetometer" can be carried to help locate mineral bodies while flying an area to photograph it (18, p. 29). Improved aerial photography and the technique called "photogrammetry" have greatly facilitated our mapping program.

Geologists are generally agreed that our undiscovered mineral wealth far exceeds that which we have found. We are assembling the basic map data, albeit too slowly, and perfecting new methods of discovery to ensure that we shall not starve while sitting on a loaf of bread. Possibilities for mineral discovery are tremendous.

We can very materially increase our economic mineral wealth by exploiting ores of lower metallic concentration and rock formations poorer in mineral content. Advancing prices, better techniques, or both, become the direct agents of conservation here

Use of lower concentrations

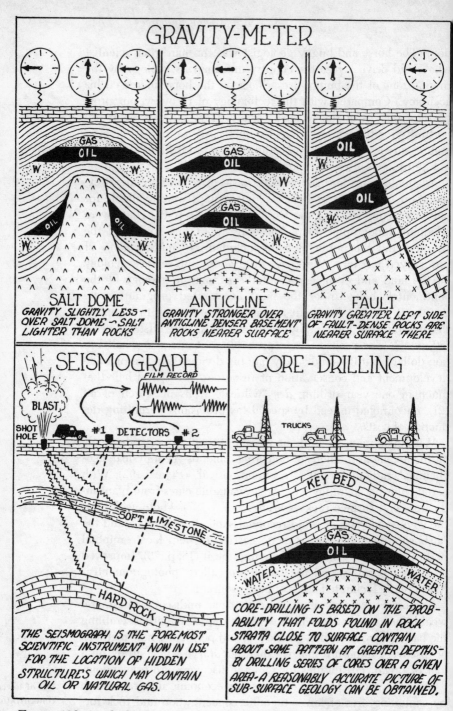

Figure 192. *Methods of search for petroleum. All the indications are helpful, but oilmen still have only one positive proof that oil is present—striking it with the drill. (Adapted from American Petroleum Institute diagrams.)*

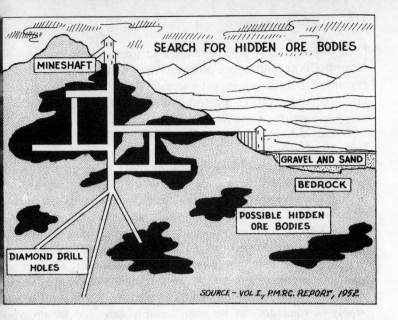

SEARCH FOR HIDDEN ORE BODIES

MINESHAFT

GRAVEL AND SAND

BEDROCK

POSSIBLE HIDDEN
ORE BODIES

DIAMOND DRILL
HOLES

SOURCE - VOL I., P.M.R.C. REPORT, 1952

Figure 193. *Instruments help us locate other minerals besides oil, but only drilling proves the size and quality of a deposit. Geologically, much of our country remains unexplored.*

as with improved recovery. Preferably we would have the low-grade deposits worked because cheaper, more efficient mining or manufacture makes them profitable, but a slight increase in the price of end products can also encourage more careful gleaning of our mineral harvest. Depletion of saw timber has compelled us to accept lumber of declining quality at steadily rising prices. The same rules apply to mineral materials (22, p. 5).

A trend toward the use of lower concentrations is well under way in the metals. Most striking perhaps is the recovery of magnesium from sea water, which contains magnesium on the order of only 13 parts in a thousand (23). Less spectacular examples are numerous. The average grade of copper mined in the United States about 1900 was 5 per cent; in 1950 it was 0.9 per cent (13, p. 35). We *can* recover the metal from ores containing only 0.5 per cent copper.

Fifty-one per cent iron remains the standard in the mining of iron ore, although grades as low as 35 per cent are being mined (13, p. 14). The Lake Superior taconite containing only 25 to 40 per cent iron yields, by beneficiation, concentrates of 65 per cent iron. From magnetite, or magnetic taconite, the iron is easily separated by crushing and magnetic concentration. However the concentrate is so fine and dust-like that it cannot be used in a

417

blast furnace before it is agglomerated (formed into granules or lumps). The agglomeration process (Figure 194) remains relatively expensive, but we can expect our metallurgists and mining engineers to reduce processing costs and bring taconite into prominence as a source of iron (18, p. 42).

When we have exhausted all the bauxite in the world or the less abundant cryolite with which to process it we may still fly airplanes and enjoy the multitude of other aluminum products now in use. When the economic climate of supply and demand persuades us we shall extract the "second most abundant metal" from clays and rocks that are worthless under present price levels (13, p. 138). In the long run our supply of aluminum depends upon sources of electricity with which to process low-grade ores.

Whether by flotation (Figure 195), electrolysis, distillation, roasting, fuming, cracking, leaching (Figure 196), washing, or any other process of separation or refinement, the present and future supply of minerals can be immeasurably extended by progressively greater use of low-content material. The whole earth's crust and all the seas are ours to explore and refine before anyone can truthfully say that a single element has been completely exhausted. If it be true that man can neither create nor destroy matter, but may only transform it, we shall never lack a material except as its presence eludes us.

Reduction of waste in processing, conversion, and fabrication

Minerals wasted in processing and fabrication afford an opportunity for immediate and direct conservation. Many losses in the mineral industries can be reduced by improved techniques and more careful handling. Recovery and conversion of milling wastes has the same role in steel mills and machine shops as in sawmills and woodworking plants, with the added advantage that metal scraps may be reworked without the stigma that attaches to sawdust and shavings. Many losses incidental to the distribution and marketing of minerals warrant attention. Liquids and gases are particularly difficult to contain and transport without considerable loss. Fortunately, they are the very ones shipped by pipeline, which reduces leakage, spillage, and evaporation to a minimum.

Milling and shipping losses are minor compared with losses incidental to the treatment and smelting of ore, the coking of coal, and other conversions. We have made good progress along these lines, as a few examples will show, but there are many possibilities for further improvement.

By catalytic cracking we now produce gasoline of 77-octane number from the same grade of crude oil that yielded only 66-octane by thermal cracking, thus, in effect, raising the quality of

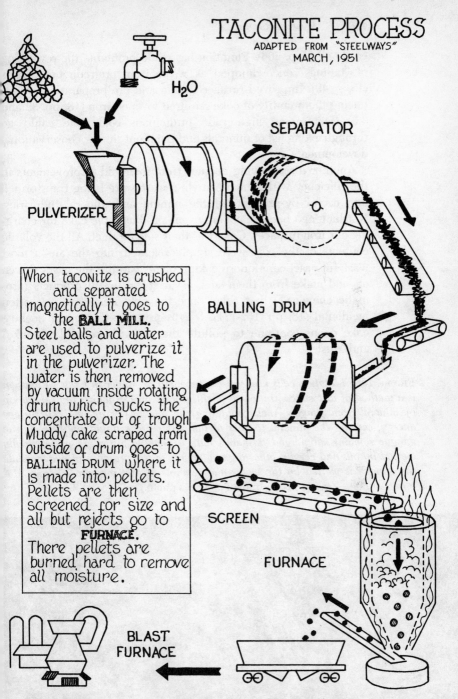

TACONITE PROCESS
ADAPTED FROM "STEELWAYS"
MARCH, 1951

H₂O

SEPARATOR

PULVERIZER

BALLING DRUM

When taconite is crushed and separated magnetically it goes to the **BALL MILL.** Steel balls and water are used to pulverize it in the pulverizer. The water is then removed by vacuum inside rotating drum which sucks the concentrate out of trough. Muddy cake scraped from outside of drum goes to BALLING DRUM where it is made into pellets. Pellets are then screened for size and all but rejects go to **FURNACE.** There pellets are burned hard to remove all moisture.

SCREEN

FURNACE

BLAST FURNACE

FIGURE 194. *Vast quantities of taconite (low-grade iron ore) await concentration. As a supplier of our great inland steel industry, taconite may have a much longer history than hematite. Upon completion of the St. Lawrence Seaway, imported ores may compete increasingly with domestic ones.*

crude oil (3, p. 206). Flotation has made profitable the reworking of "tailings" once dumped as waste from ore-reduction plants (15, p. 49). Improved furnace design and ore preparation are reducing the quantity of coke required to smelt iron (18, pp. 32 and 33), thus saving high-grade bituminous coal. One could go through a long list of minerals and point out similar conservational developments.

Another direct saving accrues from manifold improvements in the efficiency with which erstwhile wastes are being transformed into useful by-products of the mining and mineral industries. Not long ago beehive coking ovens produced the coke for charging our iron furnaces. Coke was their sole product. All the volatile contents of the coal were simply released into the air—a most wasteful practice. Modern coking plants capture the gases driven off and make from them such a variety of useful products (aromatic chemicals) that coke, once the only item saved, is often incidental (18, pp. 162-171). It is regrettable that many beehive coke ovens continue to pollute the air with *valuable* "smoke" and "dust."

FIGURE 195. *Flotation cells used for the recovery of copper in Utah. "Flotation is a method of wet concentration of finely ground ores in which the separation of mineral from gangue [rock containing the mineral] is effected by surface energy, causing the mineral to float at the surface of a liquid pulp, while the gangue remains submerged. Minerals with a metallic luster are preferentially wetted by oils and certain other organic agents in the presence of water, while the gangue is wetted by the water and remains in that medium." (From Materials Survey—Zinc, p. II-25; Bureau of Mines photo.)*

FIGURE 196. *Recovery of copper at Ray, Arizona, by leaching old waste dumps left from conventional mining operations. Water sprinkled on top of a waste dump percolates through the material, picking up copper in solution as it goes. The solution water caught at the bottom of the dump is passed over old tin cans that have been burned and crushed for the purpose. The copper is precipitated on the cans. One waste material conserves another.* (Kennecott Copper Corporation photo.)

"Co-product" magic has been wrought in many other ways. The sulphur fumes that once poisoned the countryside around copper smelters are now converted into sulfuric acid, and the basic slag spewed by blast furnaces has become an effective soil amendment. Reassuring indeed is the profitable recovery of erstwhile wastes that would otherwise pollute air and water, such as dust from coal workings and fly ash from thermal power plants. Fly ash has attained commercial importance as a complement to cement in concrete, lending notably superior strength and quality to the concrete (24). A major use of fly ash has been in the concrete for large dams (25). This kind of waste salvage will, when universally applied, greatly reduce our problems of landscape sanitation. Smoke and dust abatement does double duty as a conservation measure, and at least some part of its cost can be defrayed with the wastes that are recovered.

The return of stack gases to the fire for more complete combustion illustrates an important conservation device, the "principle of recycling"—in plain words, salvage and re-use, which lengthen the useful life of minerals. Although minerals are non-renewable

Application of recycling: salvage and re-use

in character, many of them have an advantage over renewable resources in their capacity for wear. In general, an organic material serves only once and is consumed, but certain metals have such endurance that they can serve over and over again when properly salvaged and put back to work. Everyone can be a conserver of metal by selling his scrap, and there are many rich junk peddlers as living proof that such conservation really pays. In business circles they are known as "secondary metal dealers" —a solid, respectable segment of heavy industry.

Under the stress of World War II we reclaimed anything metallic, from abandoned streetcar tracks and worn-out machinery to horseshoes and tin cans. Reclaimed metal helped give us the machines that crushed Hitler's armored legions and the ships that sank Tojo's scrap-iron fleet. We became scrap-conscious as never before. But we have too readily reverted to the reckless, wasteful discard of material that is typically American. We are wont to throw our worn-out tools and utensils into a gully or dump them on another's land. When a farmer's implement breaks down beyond repair he pulls it aside and leaves it in some odd corner to rot and rust away. But for that enterprising scavenger, the junk collector, many such articles would crumble to dust instead of being returned to the smelters as they should. Hats off to the "scrap scrounger," conservator *par excellence.*

For some metals, notably iron, copper, and lead, reclaimed scrap constitutes a major source of supply. We could not maintain our great steel industry without the scrap cycle shown in Figure 197. The metal charge that goes into a steel furnace is approximately a 50-50 mixture of scrap iron (or scrap steel) and pig iron, and 60 per cent of the scrap comes from junk (18, p. 7). During recent years scrap has contributed more than 50 per cent of our copper supply and as much as 80 per cent of our lead (12, p. 136). Moral: the battered copper kettle may one day sing in a big electric generator and the dead storage battery may be reborn to another useful lifetime.

Salvage adds more or less to many other metal reserves, and could be substantially increased by making it more systematic. With the tremendous variety of alloys and mixtures now in use, it is often difficult to determine where a particular piece of scrap belongs. If necessary identification costs too much the piece is of course worthless. Experts have proposed that a standardized code system be adopted under which parts and articles might be identified at the factory by stamping on them a symbol representing the metallic formulation they contain. This would be an

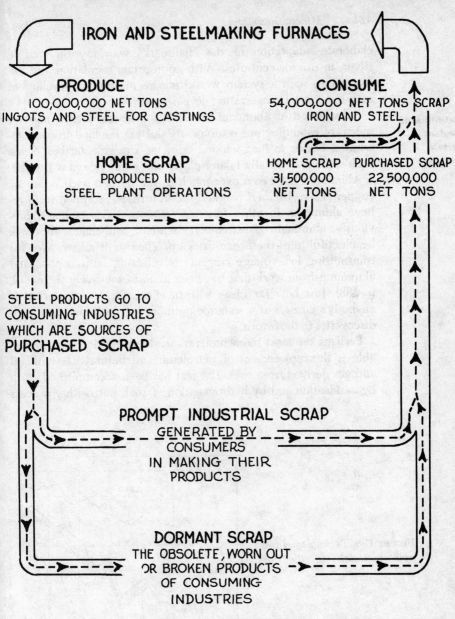

IRON AND STEELMAKING FURNACES

PRODUCE
100,000,000 NET TONS
INGOTS AND STEEL FOR CASTINGS

CONSUME
54,000,000 NET TONS SCRAP
IRON AND STEEL

HOME SCRAP
PRODUCED IN
STEEL PLANT OPERATIONS

HOME SCRAP
31,500,000
NET TONS

PURCHASED SCRAP
22,500,000
NET TONS

STEEL PRODUCTS GO TO
CONSUMING INDUSTRIES
WHICH ARE SOURCES OF
PURCHASED SCRAP

PROMPT INDUSTRIAL SCRAP
GENERATED BY
CONSUMERS
IN MAKING THEIR
PRODUCTS

DORMANT SCRAP
THE OBSOLETE, WORN OUT
OR BROKEN PRODUCTS →
OF CONSUMING
INDUSTRIES

AFTER : AMERICAN IRON AND STEEL INSTITUTE

FIGURE 197. *Scrap cycle in steelmaking. Some of the principal scrap resources are shown here (assuming steel output of 100 million net tons with scrap ratios based upon four-year average, 1947-1950).*

elaborate adaptation of the "hallmark" warranty on sterling silver, in use for centuries. With appropriate regulation and enforcement, such a system would ensure maximum recycling of metals, a logical conservation development.

Substitution of abundant minerals for scarce ones

Substitution of abundant minerals for scarce ones is another means of extending our reserves. By shifting the load from short-winded horses to long-winded ones we can ride farther. Some such shifts are actually taking place, and many others will come.

Aluminum has taken over much of the burden once borne by copper (12, p. 10), and magnesium, in turn, has stepped in to relieve aluminum in other functions (Figure 198). As noted previously, aluminum is extremely abundant, and magnesium will be plentiful until the ocean dries up. The use of microwaves for transmitting low-voltage currents is releasing both copper and aluminum from work that has been almost exclusively theirs (12, p. 138). Just how far ideas will, in effect, displace materials is anybody's guess, but a resource optimist will look for many such discoveries in the future.

Perhaps the most momentous mineral substitution now forseeable is the replacement of petroleum and natural gas with oil and gas derived from coal. The feat has been accomplished, both by gasification and by hydrogenation of coal, but neither process

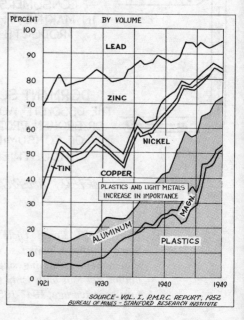

FIGURE 198. *Technology brings new materials to the fore.*

can compete commercially with natural gas or oil at prices now prevailing (26). In due time, the coal with which we are so abundantly blessed will not only stand alone as a mineral fuel, but will also fall heir to a host of materials functions now performed by gas, petroleum, and other minerals. Its chemical derivatives will be a major source of rubber, textiles, plastics, and other synthetic products. Coal also has possibilities as a raw material for the manufacture of fertilizer (18, p. 184-186). Thus, the probable future scope of mineral substitution defies prediction.

Useful employment of idle substances, an objective in several fields of conservation, holds special promise among mineral resources. We are using only a few of our known minerals, and the enlistment of new ones is a continuing challenge to the conservator. Every addition enlarges the aggregate wealth and prolongs the combined usefulness of the whole lot. Half a century ago aluminum was almost unknown; now it ranks second only to steel. Its consumption has multiplied ninefold during the last quarter-century (13, p. 66). So quickly can a mineral rise from obscurity to prominence! Only the fissionable materials have made a more revolutionary impact on the mineral industry.

Employment of substances now idle

One after another, new metals make their commercial debut. Recent introductions include boron, barium, calcium, ductile titanium, beryllium, and ductile zirconium, to mention a few interesting ones.

Zirconium and titanium belong to the family of light metals (aluminum and magnesium), and wait only for perfection of techniques to elevate them to the rank of their fellows. Titanium is especially resistant to marine corrosion, has almost the strength of steel although it weighs only 42% as much. It is, however, not resistant to high temperatures (13, p. 76). Zirconium, on the other hand, has such tolerance of high temperatures that it may become important as an alloy for rockets and jets. It is exceptionally noncorrosive, and particularly promising as a construction material for nuclear reactors (13, p. 78).

Beryllium has been used primarily to harden and strengthen copper, giving it more resistance to wear and fatigue, and improving its capacity to conduct electrical current under high temperatures. Its most promising new use is as a moderator and neutron reflector in the atomic energy industry (13, p. 59).

Boron is scarcely known except as borax or boric acid, and the metal as such has no use at present. Experiments indicate good possibilities for boron as a coating material and, within certain limitations, as a structural material. It may become important

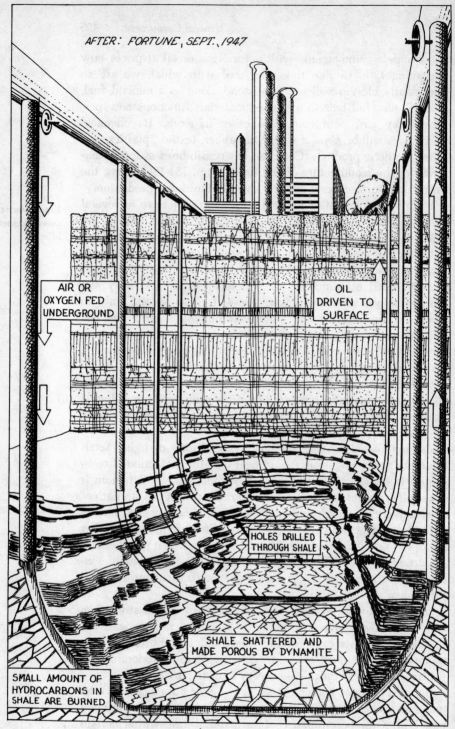

AIR OR
OXYGEN FED
UNDERGROUND

OIL
DRIVEN TO
SURFACE

HOLES DRILLED
THROUGH SHALE

SHALE SHATTERED AND
MADE POROUS BY DYNAMITE.

SMALL AMOUNT OF
HYDROCARBONS IN
SHALE ARE BURNED

FIGURE 199. *The theory for retorting oil underground and thereby driving out oil—horizontal strategy.*

in propellents and be elevated from its position as janitor to real prestige among the metals. It is relatively scarce, but locally concentrated at Death Valley.

Barium and calcium interest the conservator because, although extremely abundant, they are very little used as metals. Barium is in fact the most common "getter" for vacuum tubes, in addition to other uses in electronics. Calcium serves several purposes in metallurgical processes, but in its own right remains unimportant. Both barium and calcium are too reactive to water and atmospheric moisture to serve any structural purposes without protective coating. These two metals, and the most abundant of all, *silicon,* may some day become ranking mineral materials. Their commercial destiny is a major challenge to metallurgy and conservation.

Research and investigation point clearly to our future exploitation of materials now idle to supplement or supplant our present sources of mineral fuel. We may anticipate commercial development of oil shale, lignite, and sub-bituminous coal to produce "synthetic liquid fuels." During the past decade the Bureau of Mines, assisted by private interests, has made gratifying progress in this direction (26, 27). Low-grade coals compose the largest mineral resource we possess, and will almost immeasurably enlarge our fuel reserves when we can economically gasify, liquify, or by other process convert them into useable concentrations. Our oil-shale formations are also tremendously extensive and rich. A single geologic formation in Utah and Wyoming (the Green River) covers more than 14,000 square miles. One test revealed a section 90 feet thick, averaging 25 gallons of shale oil per ton of shale (27, p. 1). Whether we quarry the shale and extract the oil above ground, crush the shale and extract the oil in underground mines, or by more ingenious contrivance draw off the oil without handling the rock containing it (Figure 199), the exploitation will add hundreds of billions of barrels to our liquid fuel reserves (12, p. 109). Refined, or treated, shale oil yields products nicely comparable with the counterparts obtained from petroleum, including gasoline suitable for automobiles. (Pessimists take note: We may soon be touring our scenic country with *rock* in the gas tank.) How many idle substances can be put to work? Who can tell? Many await our pleasure!

Importation from foreign sources is often an excellent means of conserving domestic mineral supplies. In the interest of the nation as a whole we should welcome, and even encourage, the procurement of mineral materials from other lands (28). Every

Imports conserve domestic supplies

delivery conserves the supply at home; and it is indeed a grave mistake to raise any artificial barrier against it, as was done with tariffs on oil and copper under the pretext of stimulating domestic enterprise. Had the stimulation worked, which it did not, it should simply have stimulated us to exhaust our reserves at an earlier date. From the standpoint of conservation—and *national security* —it is utterly preposterous that we collect import duty on several critical minerals for the supply of which we are largely dependent upon foreign sources (12, p. 78). In a practical, calculating world one might see more logic in the restriction of mineral exports. If in the interest of security or self-sufficiency we wish to accelerate the discovery and production of minerals, let us do so by bounties at home rather than by excluding materials economically available from overseas.

Foreign trade in minerals has a flavor quite different from trade in reproducible materials such as cotton, lumber, meat, or grain. The organics are replaceable; the minerals are not. The world contains fixed quantities of the minerals, and the advantage goes to him into whose hands they fall. Wherever they come from, they benefit most that nation that consumes them. Collection from abroad and stockpiling at home may be a most fortuitous conservation practice, especially as national security is one of our major objectives in conserving natural resources. Wise conservators should formulate the foreign policy that embraces the minerals classified in Figure 200.

At the hazard of appearing stuffy and old-fashioned, one must submit that discretion and thrift in the end-use of minerals might greatly magnify their services, that more efficient and selective employment might greatly prolong their terms of service. But with these *conservative* means of conservation we have made little progress; just enough to indicate their potential.

Discretion and thrift in mineral consumption

At the turn of the century we burned 7 pounds of coal to generate one kilowatt-hour of electric energy. By 1925 we had reduced the average coal requirement to 2 pounds, and by 1952 to 1.1 (7). Our most efficient thermal generating plants are now approaching a ratio of a half-pound of coal to one kilowatt-hour of electrical energy (Figure 201). By the year 2000 the average ratio ought to be considerably better than one to one.

Selectivity of use may have advantages comparable with those accruing from efficient conversion. If we were to burn natural gas exclusively for the heating which best exploits its superior qualities and let inferior fuels do the less exacting work, we might double the life of our gas reserves (12, p. 112). If we would use

```
┌─────────────────────────────────────────────────────────────────┐
│ DOMESTIC SUPPLY POSITION OF SELECTED MINERAL MATERIALS            │
├─────────────────────────────────────────────────────────────────┤
│    KNOWN ECONOMIC RESERVES ADEQUATE FOR WELL OVER 25 YEARS        │
│                                                                   │
│   MAGNESIUM        POTASH              GYPSUM                      │
│   MOLYBDENUM       LIME                BORAX                       │
│   COAL             SALT                BARITE                      │
│   PHOSPHATE        SAND       CLAY     FELDSPAR                    │
├─────────────────────────────────────────────────────────────────┤
│            KNOWN ECONOMIC RESERVES INADEQUATE                     │
│                                                                   │
│ Discoveries geologically likely - though not necessarily adequate.│
│   COPPER           VANADIUM            PETROLEUM                   │
│   LEAD             TUNGSTEN            NATURAL GAS                 │
│   ZINC             ANTIMONY            SULFUR                      │
│   URANIUM                                                         │
│                                                                   │
│ Beneficiation progress expected.                                  │
│   IRON             BERYLLIUM           FLUORINE                    │
│   ALUMINUM         THORIUM             GRAPHITE                    │
│   TITANIUM         OIL FROM SHALE                                 │
│ Synthesis progress expected.                                      │
│   OIL FROM COAL                 GAS FROM COAL                     │
├─────────────────────────────────────────────────────────────────┤
│   LITTLE OR NO KNOWN ECONOMIC RESERVES, SIGNIFICANT DISCOVERIES   │
│                        NOT LIKELY                                 │
│ Beneficiation progress expected.                                  │
│   MANGANESE                                                       │
│                                                                   │
│ Synthesis progress expected.                                      │
│   INDUSTRIAL DIAMONDS           QUARTZ CRYSTALS                   │
│   SHEET MICA                    ASBESTOS                          │
│                                                                   │
│ Significant beneficiation progress or synthesis not expected.     │
│   CHROMIUM         TIN                 PLATINUM                    │
│   NICKEL           COBALT              MERCURY                     │
│                                                                   │
│              FROM: VOL 1. P.M.P.C. REPORT, 1952                   │
└─────────────────────────────────────────────────────────────────┘
```

FIGURE 200. *Should we import more and export less?*

Figure 201. *The steam-electric plant at Salem Harbor, Massachusetts, holds a high efficiency rating, averaging about 0.70 pound of coal per kilowatt-hour. The national average in 1919 was 3.2 pounds of coal per KWH; in 1952 it was 1.1 pounds per KWH, evincing an economy gain of 65.6 per cent in 33 years. (A BTU-KWH ratio might be a better criterion, since various grades of coal differ greatly in energy content.)* (Photo courtesy the New England Electric System.)

aluminum wherever it can replace sheet iron, we could save not only the iron but also its protective coating of zinc or tin. If all our minerals were put to their optimum selective use, they would serve us better for a longer period of time. They would be conserved by judicious consumption.

Thrift is a virtue that wealth and ease have almost divorced from American culture. Our sacrifice of substance to needless speed, vain display, and sheer negligence has reached prodigious proportions, and there is little evidence that we may retard or reverse the trend. Our wasteful habits as consumers of goods are particularly revolting when they dissipate irreplaceable mineral wealth. Would our economy suffer if we discarded our wasteful habits?

The American craze for flashy, high-speed automobiles illustrates the sorry extravagance with which we waste the end-product of minerals. We insist on shiny metal trimmings. We burn leaded gasoline for more "zip" and higher speed. We drive automobiles when walking would be quicker, and infinitely more beneficial, and we drive them aimlessly, without destination. We give them hard use and little care, and we trade them in, "slightly used," when a new model takes our fancy. We treat many other consumer goods in the same manner. Must the conservator condone the needless abuse of goods as a necessary accelerator of business and industrial activity?

Since almost every commercial mineral is represented in an automobile and since wear, tear, and fuel consumption are directly related to speed, it follows that a slight moderation of performance standards would be a desirable conservation measure. A little less speed on our highways would also show an incidental saving of metal that goes into coffins for crash victims. Certainly speeding and killing on the highways cannot be justified in the interest of economics!

Every American can conserve mineral resources by taking *decent* care of "things" he uses: by mending a bucket when it springs a leak, by oiling a bearing when it runs hot, by painting or housing a machine to protect it against rust or corrosion, by turning off the lights in any empty room as well as when courting his best girl, and in countless other ways. Such individual acts of conservation yield invaluable collateral in the forms of personal satisfaction, dignity, character, and self-respect. Revival of thrift might well be a conservator's crowning achievement.

Two groups of minerals—energy materials and fertilizer materials—command the special respect of conservators, the latter because soil fertility determines the reproductive capacity of organic resources, the former because energy or power is the agent of conversion whereby other resources, especially the metals, assume usable forms. Energy and soil fertility are the supporting foundation of industry and enterprise, of wealth and prestige. They are the alpha and omega among natural resources. All of our material wealth derives from them; all of it would be lost if they were consumed. It is therefore most reassuring to know that both can be maintained far into the future, from sources already discovered, by processes that our present, limited knowledge makes available to us.

The "energy mix"—that is, the proportionate share of the total contributed by various sources—will change gradually with time and circumstances, and conversion losses will increase as secondary forms such as electricity and gasoline gain greater prominence. Natural gas and petroleum will probably continue their present upward trend relative to coal for the remainder of the century (29). See in Figure 202 a prediction of the energy mix for 1975.

Hydroelectric power, which was quadrupled during the quarter century 1925-1950, remains in the subordinate position shown by

(margin note) Mark the supremacy of energy and fertilizer sources

Figure 203, and can never carry more than a fraction of our total power load (8, p. 33). The atomic energy industry remains a heavy net consumer of power (8, p. 39), and will probably not become a net producer for a long time to come. Thus it appears that the mineral fuels will dominate the energy picture for an indefinite period. Coal will probably regain and retain top rank (30).

As mineral fuels are to energy so are the mineral fertilizers to soil maintenance. The availability of phosphorus, potash, and nitrogen with which to replenish the supply of these essential plant foods in crop-producing soils transcends all other aspects of mineral conservation. We shall probably need food from the soil long after we have consumed or discarded all the metals and fuels mentioned in this chapter. What is more, we shall probably not hunger. Many generations of pessimists will die of ulcers before their optimistic contemporaries must begin to tighten their belts.

Of our three most *precious* minerals only one, phosphorus, gives us any cause for concern. Our nitrate supplies were precarious until we learned the secret of the legumes and began "fixing" nitrogen from the immeasurable volume contained in the atmosphere. Now we can have all the nitrogen we want as long as we have the air to take it from and enough energy to perform the task: 0.75 kilowatt-hour per pound of ammonia (18, p. 3). Domestic deposits of potash salts (mineral) may last the United States about 100 years; those of the world can supply all the nations for about 1000 years (13, p. 157). When we exhaust these supplies we can take potash from the sea. Phosphate rock, our source of phosphorus, though less abundant is sufficient to last us several hundreds of years (3, pp. 283-284). Although the supply presents no immediate problem, it would be comforting to know that we

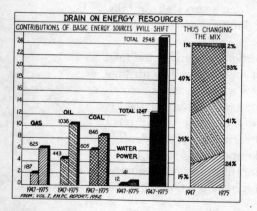

FIGURE 202. *Oil took first place in 1953, surpassing coal as a source of energy for the nation.*

might extract phosphorus from the sea or the atmosphere when the phosphate mines have been worked out. Perhaps the phosphorescence in the wake of a ship will show us the way. Perhaps we shall spread on the land quantities of native rock containing phosphorus when the rich phosphates have been exhausted (31).

From the foregoing one may conclude that our mineral resources, as now mined, smelted, and converted, will sustain our mechanical culture for a long, long time, and that by the application of intelligent profitable conservation we can multiply their usefulness. One may predict that many transitions in use will accompany the inevitable decline of reserves and the constant advance of technology. But he *cannot* subscribe to any confounded idea that the ultimate exhaustion of one, two, or several of the commercial minerals now worked can stop, or greatly impede, the progress of civilization, and of our own nation in particular. Expired minerals will send no ghosts to haunt us. Other materials will take the places once filled by the departed ones.

Be not afraid of ghosts!

Finally, a responsibility to conserve associated resources attaches to the exploitation and utilization of minerals. Several times we have alluded to the interplay between permanent and expendable wealth. In many cases they are complementary, as when water carries ore and coal cargoes, and in other cases inimical, as when underground water interferes with anthracite mining (32). In many instances we have extracted or processed minerals to the extreme detriment of the land and its life. We have mutilated the soil mantle to get at minerals lying under it; we have killed the vegetative cover with poisonous fumes; and we have soiled our waters and choked our stream channels with mining wastes. In short, we have often sacrificed permanent wealth in our quest for momentary gain. Sometimes our devastation has been greater than our gain, an error we will avoid in the future if we apply in practice the concept of unity that should pervade all conservation.

Guard well the permanent wealth while extracting and consuming the temporal!

We have seen how poisonous fumes and smokes may be profitably captured and put to use. Many other mineral wastes can be similarly salvaged, minimizing their injury to the landscape. Even strip-mining, that most thorough extracting method that tears the land apart, can be offset by reclamation practices. At the very worst, strip-mined lands can be converted into highly productive wildlife and recreation areas as shown in Figure 204. By planting or sowing they can become forest or pasture rather quickly; and by leveling and soil-building they can be made suitable for most any kind of land use (33, 34).

The raw spoil banks of strip-mining, like giant furrows across

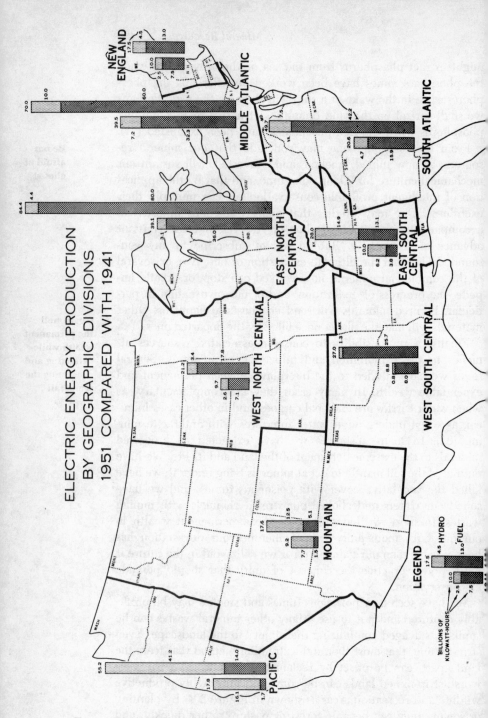

FIGURE 203. *Some regions doubled, some tripled, their production of electricity in a single decade. Fossil fuels accounted for most of the increase.* (Map courtesy the Federal Power Commission.)

FIGURE 204. *Land mutilated by strip-mining heals slowly unless the giant furrows are smoothed out and reclothed with vegetation. This stripped coal area was reclaimed by reforestation. Rough as it is, it makes excellent wildlife habitat, and will produce good tree crops.* (Bureau of Mines photo.)

the landscape, have symbolized the destruction of permanent wealth to recover a material of only temporary value. Their gradual erasure from the American scene is a good sign of conservation progress.

The eternal land, its soils and its waters, must not be unduly disturbed or damaged to procure any substance of relatively minor benefit in the long run. The wise choice between surface and subterranean resources at any given time and place is a responsibility of the voting citizen. He must decide how long we shall condone the abusive treatment of public lands before we amend our mining laws. He must determine the regulations under which minerals will be produced. As umpire of the all-American resource game, he should learn the ground rules and keep his eye on the ball. As fans, we can insist that the plays be called accurately, but we must first know the plays ourselves. We, the people, as both fans and umpire, must abide by decisions that we ourselves pronounce. Let us resolve to make them good! Let us guard well the permanent values while extracting and consuming temporal wealth!

435

CHAPTER 16: REFERENCES CITED BY NUMBER

(1) T. S. Lovering, *Minerals in World Affairs*, Prentice-Hall, Inc., New York, 1943.

(2) Robert Froman, "14,000 Uses and 2¢ per Pound," *Collier's*, September 6, 1952.

(3) Bureau of Mines and Geological Survey, "Mineral Position of the United States," *Hearings before a Subcommittee on Investigation of the Factors Affecting Minerals, Fuels, Forestry, and Reclamation Projects*, Senate Committee on Public Lands, 80th Congress, 1st Session, 1947, Appendix.

(4) Alan M. Bateman, *Economic Mineral Deposits*, second edition, John Wiley and Sons, Inc., New York, 1950.

(5) Eugene Stebinger, "Petroleum in the Ground," Wallace E. Pratt and Dorothy Good, editors, *World Geography of Petroleum*, American Geographical Society Special Publication No. 31, Princeton University Press, 1950, Part I.

(6) "Report of the Planning Committee for Mineral Policy," *National Resources Board Report*, Washington, D.C., 1934, Part IV.

(7) Bureau of Mines statistics.

(8) *Report of the President's Materials Policy Commission; III: The Outlook for Energy Sources*, Washington, D.C., 1952.

(9) "Coal; I: The Industrial Darkness," *Fortune*, XXXV, No. 3, March 1947.

(10) E. Willard Miller, "Some Aspects of the United States Mineral Self-Sufficiency," *Economic Geography*, XXII, No. 2, April 1947.

(11) Neilsen B. O'Rear, Acting Chief, Office of Minerals Reports, Bureau of Mines; personal communication dated September 15, 1952.

(12) *Report of the President's Materials Policy Commission; I: Foundations For Growth and Security*, 1952, Chaps. 3-7.

(13) *Report of the President's Materials Policy Commission; II: The Outlook for Key Commodities*, 1952.

(14) Adolph Knopf, "Strategic Mineral Supplies," *Scientific Monthly*, LXII, No. 1, January 1946.

(15) Herbert H. Helble and Oscar H. Reinholt, *Waste of Wealth*, C. C. Nelson Publishing Company, Appleton, Wisconsin, 1941.

(16) "Natural Gas," *The Lamp*, December 1945.

(17) *Petroleum: The Story of an American Industry*, American Petroleum Institute, New York, 1949.

(18) *Report of the President's Materials Policy Commission; IV: The Promise of Technology*, 1952, Chaps. 1-8.

(19) "Horizontal Drilling," *Fortune*, XXXVI, No. 3, September 1947.

(20) *A Program to Strengthen the Scientific Foundation in Natural Resources*, House Document No. 706, 81st Congress, 2nd Session, 1950.

(21) E. L. DeGolyer, "How Men Find Oil," *Fortune*, XL, No. 2, August 1949.

(22) Theodore Jesse Hoover, *The Economics of Mining (Non-Ferrous Metals)*, third edition, Stanford University Press, Stanford, California, 1948.

(23) Edward E. Keso and Huber Self, "The Magnesium Industry," *Economic Geography*, XXV, No. 4, October 1949.

(24) "Use of Chicago Fly Ash in Modern Concrete Mixes," undated folder, Chicago Fly Ash Company, Chicago, Illinois.

(25) R. D. Maxson, Vice-President, Commonwealth Edison Company, personal communication dated January 20, 1954.

(26) "Oil from Coal," *Synthetic Liquid Fuels: Annual Report of the Secretary of the Interior for 1951*, Washington, D.C., 1952, Part I.

(27) "Oil from Oil Shale," *Synthetic Liquid Fuels: Annual Report of the Secretary of the Interior for 1951*, Part II.

(28) Nels A. Bengtson, "Petroleum in Relation to Current Problems; I: Should American Petroleum Imports be Restricted?" *Journal of Geography*, XLIX, No. 9, December 1950.

(29) William H. Walsh, "Life Blood of Our Lively Century—Oil," *Service*, April 1950.

(30) "Coal; III: The Fuel Revolution," *Fortune*, XXXV, No. 4, April 1947.

(31) W. D. Keller, "Native Rocks and Minerals as Fertilizers," *Scientific Monthly*, LXVI, No. 2, February 1948.

(32) Robert E. Nolan, Jr., "The Problem of Excess Water in the Northern Field of the Anthracite Region," unpublished research paper submitted to Bureau of Mines, 1951.

(33) Leslie A. Holmes, "Reclaiming Stripped Lands in Illinois," *Scientific Monthly*, LIX, No. 6, December 1944.

(34) W. C. Bramble, "Strip Mining: Waste or Conservation," *American Forests*, LV, No. 6, June 1949.

Prospect

and Responsibility

*by advancing our knowledge of resources
and employing them accordingly we can
progress and prosper through ages to come*

THE FUTURE OF OUR PEOPLE AND OUR NATION DEPENDS UPON THE
intelligent use of natural resources. Unless it be spiritual conviction or moral fiber, nothing we can muster holds greater promise
of continuing prosperity than systematic, unified conservation.
We have attained economic leadership by exploiting natural
wealth. We can maintain that enviable position indefinitely if we
husband carefully the wealth that remains. We should certainly
lose, not only our material standing but also our democratic freedoms, if we continued the waste and abuse that attended our
rise to greatness. One cannot overdraw his accounts continuously
without finally exhausting them. Up to the present, withdrawals in
the form of soil and water—the real capital assets—have been
monstrous, and from the shrinking reserves we are still squander-
ing more than we can afford. Worst of all, many of the losses are,
for practical purposes, complete and final. Land divested of its
soil, and water reservoirs caved-in or filled with debris, have lost
most of their usefulness for the immediate future, if not for all
time.

 Sick soil can be cured and filthy water can be purified, but if
malignancy and contamination be permitted to spread faster than
treatment or prevention, the main resource "body," the land, must
grow progressively weaker and less amenable to conservation.
Land morbidity leads directly to economic bankruptcy and social decay.

 Conservation literature contains many stern warnings that we

*Conservation—
the key to
future
prosperity*

439

are riding toward starvation full tilt, with Malthus spurring our horses (1, 2). (Malthus propounded the theory that population increase is ultimately checked by the limitation of food supply.) Unless we mend our ways we shall starve; pessimism and procrastination can only hasten our hunger. But if we heed the ominous warnings and take positive action to conserve our resources, we may project the curve of *population increase* and the curve of *food supply* somewhat after the manner of parallel lines that meet only in infinity.

We have given freely of American abundance that other nations might live, but the "stars in our crown" will shine with a false glitter if in their winning we waste the substance entrusted to us. Ours the wherewithal to grow and prosper as a nation for an indefinite time to come if we but use our resources wisely. If we *must* subscribe to the Malthusian theory that man will multiply until he eats himself right off the earth, let us determine that we shall be the last to go. No other nation has natural wealth equal to ours, and if we apply conservation better than any potential adversary, who then shall prevail against us? Indeed, conservation holds the key to our future far beyond the shifting currents of international politics. Not only is conservation the guarantee of strength with which to defend our freedom against any threat; it is also the assurance of prosperity after the threat has been dissipated. *Conserved resources are coveted resources;* but the same wealth that provokes hostile design also provides the means with which to repel hostile attack. Strength keeps us free; conservation can keep us strong.

Among our demographers (population experts) are those who oppose vigorously the defeatist attitude toward world hunger. They predict that conservation and technology can provide a century hence a more adequate diet for 5 billion people than is now available to a world population of 2½ billion (3, 4). If by such means the redundant peoples of the Orient are better fed and attain a higher level of living, their potential in world affairs will become more nearly commensurate with their numbers. Therein lies a real challenge to American conservation! We need not fear hunger, at least not for centuries to come; but we must respect the competition of superior numbers. If living standards equalize, then *international competition* for *world resources* will also become more nearly equal. Other nations will require a larger share of world products.

Meanwhile, our American population is expected to increase rapidly (Figure 205), and might attain the 228 million mark about the year 1975 (5). We may also assume that our level of living and per capita requirements will rise substantially during the years intervening. Thus our natural resources will be taxed more and more heavily as years go by, and it is imperative right now that we take full advantage of techniques and procedures for magnifying their usefulness.

We have displayed much less intelligence in conservation than in technology and exploitation. We have advanced scientific theory, economic order, and social behavior, and neglected their resource base. We have recognized resource problems when they became spectacular, dangerous, or tragic—too late for preventive action. We have applied first aid to the recurrent eruption of boils and failed to treat the blood infection causing them. First aid is no cure for a chronic malady. We have taken futile emergency measures when disaster struck, and failed to follow through to avert its recurrence.

Emergency first aid cures no malady

Each devastating flood, each disastrous forest fire, each dust storm, each water shortage, and each passing of a wildlife species has moved us to feverish activity at the moment, but our results have been only temporary or superficial because we tackled consequences and not causes. When the waters have gathered it is too late to stem the flood. It is too late to save the forest when it goes up in smoke, too late to hold the soil when it is blowing away, too late to store water when it has reached the sea, and too late to save a species of animal when it has lost the capacity for competitive survival. Conservation must be preventive, and it must attack the causes of calamity, not the calamity itself. It must discern those causes in time to avert their consequences. It must be deliberate, continuous, and systematic, not dictated by emergencies and forgotten between times. Thus far we have administered

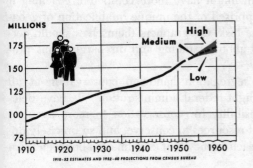

FIGURE 205. *Growth of United States population (1910-52, and projected 1952-60). We shall have to live together more intelligently as the nation becomes more densely populated.* (U.S.D.A., B.A.E. graph.)

much resource first aid without diagnosing the ailments to pre-scribe permanent cures.

Neither can we conserve by attacking isolated problems or by attempting to conserve any particular resource independently. Since all natural resources together constitute the indivisible en-vironmental composite set forth in Chapter 2, it is impossible to conserve one without regard for the others. This fundamental concept of conservation we have often failed to respect, and have never fully applied. Instead, we have engaged in specialized con-servation of one resource or another, apparently oblivious to others related thereto. We have made fragmentary and desultory attacks upon an integrated problem, often aggravating one phase while trying, vainly, to resolve another. Conservation cannot be accomplished in detached segments. Chapter headings in this book suggest the common error of isolating resources, but the book was so organized for the sake of simplicity. Because the di-vision is artificial and the sequence in some places arbitrary, there have been numerous reminders that the entire subject mat-ter is in reality intimately related.

Fragmentary and desultory attacks cannot solve the integrated problem

Specialists are prone to compartmentalize resources, and it is inevitable that they should, because one technician cannot pos-sibly master all the skills involved in the total conservation pro-gram. Hydrologists work with water, geologists with minerals, pedologists with soils, foresters with trees, zoologists with wild-life, ichthyologists with fish, agrostologists with grass, recreation-ists with recreation, engineers with structures, and teachers with education—ad infinitum. We need the services of all these and other experts, but we need even more the comprehensive coordi-nation of their work. The over-all direction of conservation has evolved very slowly and remains seriously deficient. Technical .conservationists might be likened to players on a football team, and any football coach will agree that the best lineup of players will lose the ball unless they combine their talents in teamwork. The conservation team might have more competent coaching if administrators were apprised of the unique qualification of geog-raphers to perform the task. Geographers themselves should cer-tainly be less reticent about assuming and discharging this pro-fessional responsibility.

Bureaucratic duplication wastes time, energy, and resources

Specialization and segregation handicap conservation at all levels, including top-flight federal administration. We have dele-gated national responsibility for conservation to more agencies than there are kinds of resources to conserve, and so precisely de-fined the authority of each agency that coordination between them is difficult even when they themselves might wish to cooperate. The Department of Agriculture conserves soils and forests, also presuming responsibility for soil moisture and any grass that grows among the trees. After the water has passed through the soil it comes under the jurisdiction of the Department of the Interior, for immediate surveillance of the Geological Survey. Where the water is scarce it is further diverted to the Bureau of Reclamation, still answerable to the Department of the Interior. If the hapless water becomes confused or obstreperous the Army's Corps of Engineers may see fit to take "disciplinary action" against it without so much as notifying the water's "Commanding Officer," the Secretary of the Interior. Perhaps some of our water problems are traceable to "dementia hydraulica."

Let us cite a few more examples of bureaucratic confusion and duplication on the national level. "Interior" is also charged with wildlife, fisheries, minerals, and federal land including national parks and the public range. "Agriculture's" soils and forests produce "Interior" wildlife, and "Defense" waters produce "Interior" fish. We have "Interior" forests on the grasslands, and "Agriculture" grasslands in the forests; "Agriculture" soils cover "Interior" minerals, including "Interior" fertilizers to enrich the "Agriculture" soils. In addition to regularly established bureaus, services, and divisions, a maze of appointed commissions, committees, and boards deal with various resources. Administrative confusion, competition, and duplication retard the progress of conservation (6).

Regional or group interests often hinder conservation by violating the general program to gain local advantage or special privileges. These handicaps are inherent in geographical differences and human weaknesses, and cannot be attributed to sectional malice or selfish ambition. Rather they are a matter of narrow perspective and short vision, neither of which fosters a comprehensive national scheme. Regionalism offers a logical framework for planning and conservation (7) and might well have been the basis for organizing the subject matter of this book, but regional schemes are not always in the national interest. Whereas the conservator would encourage private or group interests, and expressly defend them as the most practical means of achieving conservation, he cannot endorse drummed-up projects or programs sponsored by any locality or pressure group when such undertakings victimize the very people they ostensibly profit, and waste public funds that could be put to good use elsewhere. He should evaluate from the national point of view every regional de-

Regional developments may hinder the national program

velopment that is federally financed. Sectional illusions of grandeur have caused extravagant waste of public funds, and may actually handicap areas in which the monies were invested, as when a short-lived reclamation project becomes defunct and requires relocation of the families it attracted.

Public
ignorance
and apathy are
the worst
obstacles

Worst obstacle to conservation is the general ignorance of resource problems, and public apathy toward the solution of problems that have been acknowledged. In a democracy such as ours the private citizen decides what the conservationists, planners, and administrators shall do, but at this time John Q. Public, U.S.A. is not sufficiently informed to act wisely and not sufficiently aroused to acquire the necessary information. This book is one among many written to apprise John Q. of his personal stock in conservation and thereby stir him out of his lethargy. His incompetence and detachment constitute the most perverse barrier to good resource management. In the final analysis, it is his fault that we waste scientific knowledge and technical skill incidental to poor organization and confused administration. The voter has himself to blame when conservation policies and practices fail in America. He is the American conservator, and until he backs them up more wisely and resolutely our conservationists cannot attain the goals for which they strive on his behalf.

We must preach conservation to our fellows as a missionary preaches religion to heathens, and we need many more inspired missionaries to get a sufficient number of converts. Public education should be our most fruitful medium, and every thinking layman can help the school teachers. Only when a much greater number of our people recognize its full significance will conservation become a reality (Figure 206).

New frontiers
of technology
broaden
conservation
concepts

New frontiers of our technological age constantly broaden conservation concepts. Discovery, invention, and adaptation alter the prospect and shift the points of focus. Conservation cannot be a static proposition; it must keep pace with scientific, industrial, and commercial progress. Every change in the relative utility or availability of a resource has its impact upon others, and conservators must take account of the revised status. Conservation must be dynamic and flexible if it shall serve its purpose. The pessimistic dogma that has crept into the literature incurs a certain skepticism in view of modifications and substitutions that disprove it. It is well to warn people that certain resources upon which they now depend will one day be consumed, but in the same breath one should express some degree of confidence that means will be found to meet the eventuality (Figure 207). If one contemplates cultural stagnation whenever an "essential" material becomes exhausted, he lacks the confidence in scientific genius that it so well deserves. Let the conservator, rather than bemoaning future shortage, encourage timely research to circumvent or alleviate its consequences. This challenge could be elaborated through several volumes the size of this one, but let us be content with a few cursory suggestions.

Solar energy transformed into power drives the wheels of our technological age, and, as seen in Chapter 16, we derive most of our present needs from fossil fuels, through indirect and inefficient application. We have done very little to harness sun power in other forms. We have converted only about a fifth of the energy in water precipitated on the land. If all of it were developed, it would exceed our present consumption of electric power from all sources (8). We have discovered the revolutionary possibilities of atomic power, but unless we can extract fissionable material from other than rare and fugitive minerals we cannot rely on atomic energy to satisfy our future power needs. We have almost ignored the energy manifest in the ebb and flow of ocean tides, the endless sweep of winds over the earth, and the light rays that produce sunburn. We should have ample power without any of our present sources; we need only redesign our engines. We know the scientific principles involved.

Modern technology, dependent upon energy released by com-

FIGURE 206. *Group attacking the beast.*

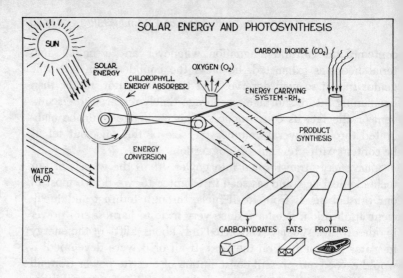

FIGURE 207. *We will arrange for more direct procurement of sun products.* (Redrawn from *The Physical and Economic Foundations of Natural Resources,* I: *Photosynthesis—Basic Features of the Problem;* U.S. House of Representatives, 1952.)

Conservation of air

bustion, and increasingly proficient at chemical reduction and combination, makes of the very air we breathe a conservable resource. Atmospheric pollution around industrial centers has reached dangerous proportions (9, p. 451). We are contaminating our air much as we have contaminated our waters. We have coined a new word, "smog," to identify the dirty pall that blankets many of our cities when there is no wind to clear it away. Smog or drifting smoke has long been recognized as a nuisance and inconvenience that soils and corrodes what it touches. It has caused housewives no end of grief and their husbands exorbitant expenses in the form of cleaning bills. Whether it pours out of a smudge pot in California or a chimney pot in London, smoke is disagreeable stuff with which to live. (The notorious London "fogs" are not natural phenomena; they are the combined filth from a million coal-burning fireplaces slightly diluted with condensed water vapor. They represent a colossal waste of coal, Britain's great energy resource.)

Local concentrations of smoke, dust, gasses, or fumes in the atmosphere are not only unpleasant; they have become destructive of life, both plant and animal. Notable examples include the desert around Copper Hill, Tennessee made by fumes from the smelters, and the disaster at Donora, Pennsylvania in 1948, when several people were killed by toxic smog (10).

Polluted air is a menace to health as a contributing cause of diseases in the respiratory tract (11), and a direct hazard to life as an obstruction to visibility in air and surface travel. Air, the most abundant substance on earth, as water, the second most abundant, approaches resource status because men contaminate it with waste from other resources. Conservation in other fields will go far toward solving the problem (12). Another development of recent years, namely cloud seeding to produce rain, further substantiates the suggestion that air approaches resource status. "Free as the air" may soon be an outmoded maxim, and the conservation alarmists may ask us to refrain from deep breathing. Artificial rain-making is intended to increase our water resources and equalize their distribution (13), but since it involves air as the carrier of moisture, the air becomes a direct medium for resource conservation.

Without entangling ourselves in technical argument, and assuming that rain can be precipitated artificially when the air is not quite ready to release it naturally (14), we may envisage a conservation frontier fraught with fascinating possibilities and vexing problems. If men can precipitate atmospheric moisture where they want it, when they wish, they can solve most of the problems noted in Chapter 11, the water deficiencies in Chapter 6, the fire problem in Chapter 10, and many others that now beset us. If they can turn it on, can they also turn it off at will, thus preventing floods and water erosion? *There* is a frontier *beyond* a frontier!

Unless tailor-made rain can be made to coincide with property lines, we shall have no end of damage suits. It Farmer Brown engages a rain-maker to fill out his corn and the ensuing deluge falls on Farmer Smith's cotton and ruins it, who will adjudge Brown liable for Smith's loss? If moisture from the Gulf headed toward Nebraska is "stimulated" over Oklahoma and falls on Kansas, shall Kansas be required to pay Nebraska for the water precipitated by Oklahoma? These theoretical cases are not mere jokes; they presage a new body of conservation law (15). Consider whether an installation such as shown in Figure 208 should be licensed.

Less problematical than artificial rain is the likelihood that we shall soon devise an economical process whereby sea water can be desalted for domestic and industrial use. Of course we know how to remove the salt and other minerals by distillation; men learned

Artificial rain

All the seas to drink

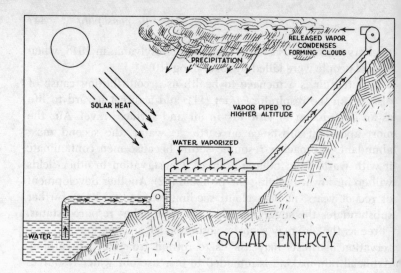

FIGURE 208. *Meteoric water can be precipitated artificially when na-ture is undecided about releasing it. Will a process such as this come to compete with sea-water distillation? Will the air compete with the sea as a source of water supply?*

that simple process long ago. But we have yet to perfect a method, or build a machine, that will yield a large volume of desalted water at a price we can afford to pay; while the cost of distilled sea water remains well over $1.00 for 1000 gallons (16) it has little demand. The possibility holds such promise that Congress author-ized for research the expenditure of two million dollars over a five-year period (17). Desalted sea water will be most immediately at hand in the very areas most harassed by a precarious water supply—the metropolitan centers on our northeastern and south-western coasts. Los Angeles will probably operate the first eco-nomical desalting plant because New York might possibly draw fresh water from the Great Lakes more economically than she could process salt water from the Atlantic. Mineral by-products will probably defray part of the operating costs. A few years hence we can expect to pump water from the sea to the hinterland instead of draining the hinterland to keep the coast supplied (Figure 209). Pipelines and pumping stations may deliver sea water far inland when wells and storage reservoirs fail. Might one hazard a prediction that water piped from the sea will vivify cer-tain hydroelectric installations and irrigation developments after the impoundments which now serve them have become ineffectual? When all the seas are ours to drink or put to other uses, many water problems will take on a brighter complexion. Distance from the sea will become an important factor in water supply. In remote areas, the reclamation of used water will gain favor as a means of replenishing underground storage.

Innovations in soil conditioning show considerable promise for improvement of the soil-water partnership basic to all durable resources. Chapter 8 stressed the importance of humus as a sponge to absorb and store soil moisture. Humus has the effect of loosening and opening the soil so that rain can soak in easily and occupy the storage space between solid particles. Compact or tight soil repels water, causing it to run off, and may discourage plant growth by becoming alternately too wet and too dry. Some soils are naturally too dense to be useful, and many more have got that way through depletion and erosion. Depleted soils have lost their humus, and subsoils exposed by erosion are usually much more compact than the topsoils that once covered them. For one reason or another, many of our soils lack the porosity they must have in order to produce crops and resist erosion. The problem responds very slowly to accepted conservation practices, but our chemists reacted to it and decided to have a go. Soil "drugs" remain in the experimental stage, and this is not an unqualified endorsement of

Soil conditioning

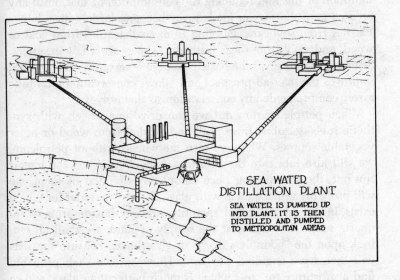

SEA WATER
DISTILLATION PLANT

SEA WATER IS PUMPED UP
INTO PLANT. IT IS THEN
DISTILLED AND PUMPED
TO METROPOLITAN AREAS

FIGURE 209. *Economical desalting and distribution of sea water may be anticipated in the near future. Pipeline construction may boom as never before.*

them; however, they merit comment because of their probable future value.

Flocculation or granulation was nothing new to chemistry, but its application to soil conditioning was revolutionary. If one could economically granulate, or aggregate, plastic clay soils and hard-pan layers with chemical applications, he might solve many stubborn soil problems. The granulation has been accomplished (18), and initial field tests have given good results. Practical application by land users may become an important soil conserving measure. However, farmers might well be cautious when they modify anything of such far-reaching influence as soil structure or soil texture. They should make certain that end results will be more desirable than detrimental. Chemical soil conditioners may be compared with chemical weed killers and insecticides, which, though immediately expedient, may have dangerous consequences. Used with discretion, both should prove extremely valuable.

Synthetics and substitutes broaden the resource base

Most revolutionary of all technological innovations is the development of synthetics and substitutes as industrial raw materials. One discovery after another changes the status and prospect of various resources, and requires the conservator to revise his estimates. New processes and new uses constantly shift the burden of dependence from one resource to another, increasing the consumption of this and reducing the consumption of that, until any prediction of shortage or inadequacy becomes largely speculative. Plastics from soybeans, gasoline from coal, textiles from coal or wood, and wool from rocks instead of sheep are a few examples. Scientific genius gives the basic resources a versatility that greatly improves the over-all prospect and allows conservation a latitude rarely comprehended by conservationists themselves.

When petroleum runs out we can drive our wheels with synthetic fuels—gasoline from coal, and alcohol from wood or other vegetable sources. When we turn the wheels without petroleum, we will also lubricate the bearings without it. When the metals run out, the seas having been completely divested of them, we will probably replace them with glass, the raw material for which exists in almost unlimited quantity—silicon dioxide from plain quartz sand. If we exhaust the supply of sand, we shall all embark upon the "boundless deep" in glass boats, because the seas will then have engulfed the land. However, we shall probably find a substitute for steel which is much better than glass, and so obviate the need for undermining ourselves in quest of silicon dioxide. Besides, who can say with certainty that men will use wheels in the remote nonmetal age? Let this perverted humor suffice to ridicule the finality that some people attach to the impending exhaustion of certain expendable materials essential to industry in its 20th century stage. The prospect is bright and unlimited if we but view it optimistically.

As we exhaust our minerals we shall become increasingly dependent upon soils, plants, and water as the bases of cultural progress. The renewable resources will prevail after the expendables have corroded and evaporated away (19). It is therefore much more important to perpetuate those capable of renewal than to stretch the fugitive ones. Their relative future value may be approximated in the proportionate space devoted to them in this book. A long view indeed, but a conservator must not be short-sighted. He must see the prophetic significance of such scenes as that shown in Figure 210.

The renewable resources will prevail

Steel towns will be ghost towns when their supply of ore has gone, unless they anticipate their dilemma and take steps to meet it. All of those now flourishing may not boom and glow in the year 2000 as they do today. Unless they make transition while still smelting iron, they will be hard-hit when the furnace fires go out. No enterprise, no community, no culture based upon extractive exploitation can endure after the resource upon which it depends has been expended. It must either find a renewable resource to support itself or die a natural death. The alert conservator would commence the transition before the crises arrive. Crises did we say? There will be no crises; supply and demand, through price, will make the transition. The ascendency of renewable resources over the expendables is implicit in a new term, "chemurgy," coined to identify the fabrication of "home-made" materials into "store-bought" articles, the conversion of products from the soil into products from the factory (20). Previously mentioned were plastics from soybeans, a good example; one might enumerate a long list of other useful articles made by applying technology to a vegetable material. Many plastics are wholly or partly of mineral substances at present, but they may contain fewer mineral ingredients as time goes by. The rapid growth of the plastics industry during recent years indicates almost unlimited future possibilities (21). It may thrive indefinitely if we reorient our mineral conservation. Instead of fretting about shrinking ore bodies and oil pools, let us pay more attention to the mineral plant nutrients and trace elements essential to high soil fertility. Without them to produce healthy plants we should really be in a quandary, and without any known substitute to make it a dilemma. In the dark and distant future, phosphate, nitrate, and potash may be the big three; not coal, iron, and oil. Our needed supplies may be won from the sea, by methods more scientific than that shown in Figure 211.

From the limited perspective we now command it appears likely that civilization will one day depend entirely upon the renewable, regenerative resources. The change will not come soon, and it will not come suddenly; but come it must, in due time. It will probably begin before the year 2000, accompanied by intensified search for expendables. Could it be that the shift has, indeed, commenced even now?

Planned allocation of space becomes increasingly urgent

As our expendables decline, as our population grows, and our needs increase, the planned allocation of surface space becomes increasingly urgent, the better to sustain and employ our durable wealth from land and water. Our future prosperity will be commensurate with our vision in developing surface land use, reorganizing economic structure, and rearranging industrial facilities to suit the new order. Attributes of land and water will reorient our geographic culture pattern as mineral deposits relax their magnetic grip. People and industry will gravitate ever more

FIGURE 210. *Renewable resources will become increasingly prominent as the fugitive ones are exhausted.*

FARMING THE SEA

FIGURE 211. *The sea may ultimately furnish any material of which the land has been divested.*

toward areas with a good combination of soil and water resources. Cultural stability and social security will improve in the degree to which conservation attends the process.

The propitious allotment of space for various purposes will become more and more important in conservation, and early planning is our best assurance that it will be wisely brought about. Factors of surface space and pattern deserve more attention than conservators have given them. They will assert themselves with increasing force as our land fills up and the nation matures. While total population may neither crowd our space nor strain the reproductive capacity of our durable resources for some time to come (Figure 212), the spotted distribution of our people and

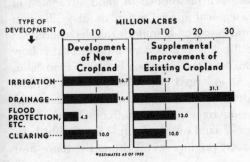

FIGURE 212. *Expansion will be increasingly competitive as population and food requirements rise and other land uses claim more and more space.*

TYPE OF DEVELOPMENT

MILLION ACRES

	Development of New Cropland	Supplemental Improvement of Existing Cropland
IRRIGATION	16.7	8.7
DRAINAGE	16.4	31.1
FLOOD PROTECTION, ETC.	4.3	13.0
CLEARING	10.0	10.0

*ESTIMATES AS OF 1950

the continual change of regional population densities have already created many problems for the conservator (22). The recurrent rerouting of highways and the constant extension of road nets lay increased claim to space in competition with other land uses. The question whether any given area shall be devoted to basic production, to facilities, or to conveniences must be faced by the planner-conservators. That question resolved, they must be further concerned with the relegation to crops, pasture, forest, water storage, or other use, according to land capability and human needs, of the space earmarked for productive management. Planning experts are well aware of these responsibilities, and their demonstrated competence to discharge them gives us added confidence in the future. Optimum employment of space is a prime objective of planning, be it national, regional, or local in scope. With this facet perhaps more than with any other, planning is indispensable to conservation, and geography indispensable to planning.

Planning calls to mind the opportunity for better regional coordination and technical integration in our conservation work.

Regional coordination and technical integration must be achieved

Natural resources differ from one region to another almost as much as milady's temperament, and techniques should be adapted accordingly. Much as the people might wish it, no region can conserve resources with which it is not endowed. Attempts to do so are bound to fail, doing more ill than good. When men try to make fields out of rough timber land or land too dry for any use more intensive than open range, they handicap themselves by flaunting the natural order. They penalize other parts of the nation that must pay for the experiment. The nation fares best when each of its component parts contributes what it can most efficiently and reliably produce. This dynamic phase of regional economic geography should never be neglected by the conservator.

Regional division of labor pertains to conservation as well as to any other activity, and can be applied to good advantage in resource management. Regional specialization or diversification will coincide with natural resource boundaries under conditions of open and free competition. That is as it should be. That is how a farm conservation plan lays out divisions between crop land, pasture and woodland. An enlarged farm plan could be devised for the nation. It is an ideal toward which planning and conservation project us. Planners envisage regions that complement each other much as do classes of land on one farm. They would have regions best suited to forest produce wood primarily, those best suited to grazing, meat and wool, and so on. Resource conservation becomes operative on a grand scale when regional planning puts human occupance in harmony with natural attributes, when cultural emphasis is placed where it belongs. Let us quit the folly of trying to build a regional economy that the region cannot sustain. Permanence with flexibility constitutes a major tenet of conservation.

In areas well endowed with natural wealth, diversification of resource use is desirable, reducing the problem of outside coordination while at the same time multiplying technical problems within. A general, or combination, land economy lends security to a region much as crop diversification does to an individual farm, but either case complicates resource management. A specialized area may need only one kind of technician, whereas a diversified one must have several. This is where our administrative organization appears defective; it is not consistent with the need for technical integration. Fortunately, the defects are much less serious in practice than they appear on paper. Capable administrators almost ignore departmental lines in their employment of technical experts from various fields. The Soil Conservation Service, for example, employs specialists in virtually every branch of conservation, from hydrology to wildlife management. The specialists are by training biased and prejudiced to a degree —a forester thinks in terms of trees, an agronomist in terms of field crops, a pedologist in terms of soil, and so on. Application of their combined knowledge in proper proportion to solve a given problem is a delicate function of administration. Whereas the specialist concerns himself only with his own narrow field of science, the administrator must view conservation in broad perspective. Whether any specialist, by virtue of seniority or appointment, is qualified to prescribe and supervise the work of specialists in fields other than his own is a debatable question. It is probably better to select administrators who understand conservation generally and know what each discipline can contribute to a total program. Leading conservators, both practical and academic, have recently recognized the unique value of "generalists," and elevated to professional level the university graduate, trained for a general *conservation* career. Much of the optimism expressed in this book springs from the confidence that young men who study conservation in all its aspects and practical ramifications will elevate it to genuine professional status. They may have more to do with our future than all the scientific specialists put together. Every professional conservator should be

The technical work of experts needs coordination by a "general manager"

thoroughly grounded in geography, lest he be handicapped by narrow perspective.

A unified program must replace divergent approaches

A unified program incorporating all aspects of conservation and every kind of resource must replace divergent approaches and isolated projects. Our environment is a mosaic of many parts, each of which influences every other. One resource cannot be exalted and another debased when all are so related that they rise or fall together. Experience has taught us the utter futility of guarding one resource and ignoring others upon which the chosen one depends. It has been a costly lesson, and one we cannot afford to forget. Conservators must constantly remind themselves that the unity in nature is their best guide to good resource management, and that regional variety is a source of national strength.

Unity in conservation must be achieved without infringing upon democratic freedoms, because such a price would be too high to pay for any kind of material wealth. Resources would lose their worth were they to be conserved at the expense of individual dignity and free enterprise. American democracy was bought and paid for with natural resources; it can best be preserved by ensuring their permanence. That is a tenet on which the conservator should base his propositions.

There are several ways by which unification in conservation can proceed and several trends that indicate progress. Administrative reorganization is one way, geographic consolidation another, and group association of private interests, a third. All three have possibilities. At first blush one might assume that private operators in a competitive economy are too busy trying to beat the other fellow to take time out and talk with him. The facts are quite different. Competition continues, it is true, but cooperation has become remarkably important in industrial circles. "Dirty competitors" are also "worthy associates" in the common interest of the business they represent.

Some sort of association, institute, or other group organization serves virtually all the major resource users or producers—lumbermen, stockmen, coal miners, oil producers, farmers, sportsmen, fishermen, and many more. Their purpose is not monopoly, but common security, which demands a unified approach to conservation. This voluntary, practical unification has many good implications for our future prospect.

Geographic consolidation relates to the regional coordination discussed a few paragraphs ago, with certain elaborations and refinements. Along with argument for regional treatment one must remember that several resources are often intermingled or interspersed in one unit of space, as, for example, soils, water, plants, and wildlife on a farm (23). One must remember that regional organization on paper can be a pretense, as when river basins are "developed" with attention only to water (24). The fanfare and noise do no good unless accompanied by intelligent action that encompasses all the resources. One should be mindful also that drainage units or watersheds, for all their inherent advantages, constitute only one kind of natural division, and that other geographic factors such as climate, topography, soil or vegetation may also be logical bases for regional resource management. The strongest unifying factor, the most valuable resource, be it water or something else, might be the best criterion for regional definition and resource management.

Assuming that natural geographic boundaries have an important bearing on conservation, how may we better employ them? Shall we erase the arbitrary lines that separate our counties and states and redraw them to coincide with natural boundaries, or shall we continue the involved process of combining numerous political segments into one superimposed conservation unit? T.V.A. incorporates parts of seven states, but it took a big stick from Congress to unite them. Shall we proclaim that resource unity transcends politics, or shall we retain our extravagant political compartments (25)? From a purely economic standpoint the subdivision of states into horse-and-buggy counties is preposterous. Whenever economy dictates consolidation or dissolution of delinquent counties it affords an opportunity to reconcile political and geographic boundaries—a fertile field for the planner-conservator. A dozen "natural" counties would probably be enough for any state, including Texas, which now contains 254. The reduction would improve government, reduce graft and other costs, and facilitate conservation. Concurrent with internal unification, planners might go a step further and eliminate useless boundaries between the states. The savings from politico-geographic reorganization might pay for a unified conservation program, but the prospect for a more logical political arrangement is dubious at best. Wishful thinking may be the beginning, so let us wish.

Natural versus political boundaries

Reorganization of state and federal governments for closer coordination of conservation activities shows positive trends that augur well for the future. During recent years several mergers and transfers of administrative agencies have strengthened conservation at both state and federal levels. Several states have established under one name or another permanent departments

Governmental organization will be improved

for the conservation of natural resources. Missouri and Ohio are good examples (26). These states, and a few others, are far ahead of the federal government in organized resource management.

Organization at the federal level has experienced some renovating, despite difficulties; cabinet members and department and bureau heads often resist changes that might deflate their little empires. This is not a slur on any of the officials, most of whom are simply demonstrating the courage of their convictions when they guard their own establishments; it is merely by way of indicating that structural alterations can rarely be expected from within. One recent exception was the merger of the Biological Survey and the Bureau of Fisheries to form the Fish and Wildlife Service, all within the Department of the Interior. Changes at cabinet level, even more rare, were made to evolve the present Bureau of Land Management. Many more changes can be anticipated as public opinion grows strong enough to assert itself. Eventually we may have a Secretary of Conservation in Washington with his fingers on every major resource (27, 28, 29). It will not be easy to determine whether soils belong under "Agriculture" or "Resources," whether "Interior" shall be dissolved or renamed, but Americans may have to decide those issues at some future date. The prospect for a wise reorganization depends upon public enlightenment.

In the last analysis, the American citizen will determine how well we conserve our natural wealth, because every citizen in a democracy is a policy maker. The conservator can do nothing **The citizen** more constructive than to inform the people and arouse citizen **must be sold** interest. Resource management cannot be successful and com- **the idea of** prehensive before public consciousness decrees that it shall be so. **conservation** Man, whose creature existence depends upon his use of resources, must be made to see clearly that all his worldly goods, his health, his comforts, and his happiness can be secured indefinitely for him and his children by wise conservation. Above all, he must grasp the idea that complete use of a resource for maximum benefit to mankind is, in fact, conservation. When a sufficient majority of our people have learned that fundamental concept, group action will vouchsafe for us and posterity the perpetual replenishment of natural stores that sustain life and society. Until then education and information will remain the conservator's best tools (30).

Conservation is not difficult to sell if the approach is right.

Sales resistance breaks down when the merchandise is honestly shown. A clever saleslady sells gowns to co-eds by exclaiming with forced enthusiasm, "it really *does* something for you." The conservator can say truthfully to everyone that conservation does much for him, directly or indirectly, sooner or later (31, 32). Good soil in the country means good business in town. Good grass on the plains means good steaks in the city, today and tomorrow. Conservation is our assurance of good business and good steaks day after tomorrow, next year, and in the year 2000.

Adequately informed, the individual turns conservator for his own good, and often as not identifies himself with one group or other actively interested in some phase of conservation. Almost every resource now has its group of defenders—practical, idealistic, or otherwise—and the groups are beginning to reconcile their views and pull together (33). (The appendix contains a partial listing of organizations.) The manifest unity in nature and the universal interdependence of resources will inevitably assert a unifying influence on conservation activities. Education stimulates interest; interest motivates to action; and action by individuals and groups achieves the desired results. Education must come first, and the others follow. Our manifold media for disseminating information—press, radio, television, schools, churches, movies, and so on—lay the foundation for conservation by informing our self-governing public.

Information first, then action

The public is becoming informed and concerned. What is more, the public is becoming articulate and active in conservation matters. People in all walks of life are beginning to see the real importance of natural resources and the urgency of conserving them. That fact strengthens our hope for the future, because genuine progress under democracy must come by democratic procedures.

Emergent citizen interest paves the way to future prosperity

The emergence of a considered public opinion is admirably illustrated in a policy statement adopted by the Natural Resources Council of America at its fifth annual meeting, convened October 1, 1951 in Franklin, North Carolina. The Council is a central service agency for 39 member organizations, many of whom endorsed the policy statement. (No statement was issued on the non-renewable resources.) The *policy for renewable resources,* reproduced in full herewith, constitutes a Magna Charta for conservation to which every American citizen might well subscribe:

POLICY FOR RENEWABLE NATURAL RESOURCES

PREAMBLE

We, the members of the Natural Resources Council of America, in order to provide the means for a high standard of living in a healthful environment, present the following fundamental policy for the use of our basic resources of soil, water, plants, and animals, so as to maintain them through the years and prevent their waste and depletion.

To attain these objectives, we recommend the following policy:

INVENTORIES OF RENEWABLE RESOURCES

1. Adequate and continuing inventories of the renewable natural resources of the nation are needed to determine their condition, productivity, and potential use in relation to human needs and should be supported as a guide to the proper utilization and treatment of these resources.

SCIENTIFIC CONSERVATION PLAN

2. The orderly development and application of a comprehensive scientific conservation plan for every farm, ranch, small watershed, and other operating unit of the nation's land and water are imperative, and can best be achieved through the efforts of locally controlled groups.

Natural resource developments, including flood control, irrigation, and dam construction, are practically and ecologically most adequate when undertaken in relation to, or in conjunction with, upstream watershed programs.

POLICY OF USE

3. A sound policy includes the conservation, development, and proper utilization of renewable natural resources for: (a) sustained and improved agricultural production without waste, (b) protection and sustained-yield management of forest lands, (c) prevention of erosion, protection of streams from excessive siltation, and flood control to safeguard land from destructive overflow, (d) protection of community and industrial water supplies, (e) maintenance of underground water sources, (f) development and stabilization of irrigation and drainage as needed for sound land use, (g) maintenance of maximum fish and wildlife resources, (h) preservation, and proper utilization of areas best suited for needed recreational, esthetic, cultural, and ecological purposes, and (i) protection and revegetation, where necessary, of grasslands suited to range utilization.

RESPONSIBILITY OF LAND OWNERSHIP

4. Good management, public interest, and human welfare require that all

landowners, public or private, care for soil and water under their control in a manner that will ensure that future generations may derive from them full enjoyment and benefit. Landowners have no moral right to abuse their lands.

PRESERVATION OF SPECIAL AREAS

5. A sufficient number of examples of every type of natural area should be preserved and kept perpetually as inviolate natural and wilderness areas for their scientific, educational, and esthetic values. These should include examples of vegetation types and areas providing habitat for rare plants and animals. Public lands dedicated to special recreational and conservation purposes—parks, monuments, wilderness and primitive areas, wildlife refuges, and similar lands—should not be used for any purpose alien to the primary purposes of the area.

EFFICIENT RESOURCE ADMINISTRATION

6. All public service should be conducted efficiently to avoid unnecessary burden on the tax-paying public. Any overlapping functions of the several governmental agencies concerned with the administration of natural resources should be eliminated and all operations should be coordinated.

PUBLIC PARTICIPATION IN CONSERVATION

7. Local, county, and state responsibility in regional and basin-wide programs, involving the use and development of soil, water, and the living resources, must include full participation in the planning, financing, management, and other phases of such programs.

NATIONAL NEED VS POLITICAL EXPEDIENCY

8. Power developments, flood control projects, irrigation and drainage activities, and similar developments, planned and constructed largely at Federal expense, which materially change or influence existing natural resources and their protection or use, should be required to result in "national" benefit. Justification, economic and social, of projects should be realistic, should be considerate of all values, and should not rest on hopeful expectancy. Methods should be developed for equitable distribution of the project cost among the beneficiaries.

BOARD OF REVIEW

9. An independent Board of Review, composed of five members who have no affiliation with any federal agency but have outstanding interest in public affairs, should be created to review the need, cost, and desirability of all federal land and water projects and basin-wide programs. This Board should have authority to determine whether or not all projects conform to basic policies. In this way it will be possible to secure planning and consideration at every

level of all phases of resource use and management, including not only hydro-electric power, flood and sediment control, navigation, irrigation, and drainage, but soil conservation, forestry, water supply, pollution abatement, recreation, fish and wildlife, parks, wilderness, and all other aspects of the entire program required for the long-range use and care of these resources.

Members of this Board should be appointed by the President to serve staggered terms and should be confirmed by the Senate. The Board should have an adequate budget and sufficient personnel to permit the prompt investigation and impartial evaluation of all development proposals. Congress should in its policy statement declare that it will not approve any proposed federal development programs nor appropriate money for such works until the findings and recommendations of this Board of Review are available.

POLICY LEGISLATION

10. To make this policy effective, Congress should pass legislation enacting it into basic law.

JUSTIFICATION

There is a growing understanding that soil, water, and living resources, and man are intimately related. At the same time, there is a greater realization that natural resources constitute the basic strength and wealth of a nation. In the emergency now facing this country—an emergency which may last for many years—the manner in which these resources are managed will be vital to the defense of America, its institutions and liberties.

Natural resources can be exploited needlessly under an unnecessarily narrow concept, as is being done, or they can be managed wisely and utilized for unprecedented strength under a broader policy, as herein advocated. Natural resources need not and should not be sacrificed because of the national emergency. That is a habit that must be discarded. Surely this nation has learned that precious resources can be used to give continuing material productivity without sacrificing moral strength and regeneration of spirit.

While it is imperative to have a basic policy for developing and managing natural resources, it is equally important that the policy be realistic as to present needs and mindful that the long-time goal is a peaceful, prosperous future.

Natural watersheds and river basins are becoming more and more widely accepted as the most desirable and practical units for planning resource developments. Watershed and basin development proposals have most frequently emphasized power, irrigation, and flood control opportunities. These are not, however, the only possible uses of water; indeed, they may not be the primary or the most fruitful ones. Land, water, forest, and wildlife management; the protection of watersheds; preservation of wilderness; development of recreational opportunities in parks, forests, and national monuments; and the protection and development of fishing in both inland and coastal waters certainly warrant equal attention. Experience shows, and science has proved, that natural resources are interdependent, either thriving together or wasting together according to the manner in which they are treated. Natural resource management must be considered not only in its separate categories, but as an entity.

Watershed development must be comprehensive; it must consider not only flood control and power and irrigation, which are conflicting and cannot be adequately handled in the same reservoirs, but "all" natural resources in proper balance and in rightful priority in relation to needs.

From time to time, the needs of the nation and the needs of the people change. Furthermore, the needs of the people in one part of the country usually are quite different from those in other sections of this vast land. Power may be more important during the next two decades in the Pacific Northwest than in the Southeast. Recreational opportunities in nearby natural surroundings may be more urgently needed during the next ten years in some areas, for newly concentrated masses of people, than in others. This does not mean that sufficient power and recreation are not needed in all places, but it does illustrate the importance of time, degree, and priority.

As the nation proceeds with the development and management of its natural resources, either on a watershed basis or otherwise, the work should be undertaken on a broad and comprehensive basis. There is need for national policy, national planning, and national goals. Within this framework, there is a compelling need for overall planning within individual watersheds, which considers relative degrees of importance, or priorities, among the several objectives that are sought.

Planning for the development and use of natural resources can be handed down from on high as is being done now in much of the water development, or it can grow gradually from the ideas and needs of the local citizens and groups most concerned. The latter, which is in the American tradition, promises the greatest returns over the longest period of time.

The aim of this policy is to achieve unified scientific management and perpetuation of land, water, and the living resources in the widest public interest, not only during the prolonged years of emergency ahead but into the future days of peace that will follow.

Concerted implementation of such a policy can be a reality tomorrow if we instruct our youth intelligently today. On nothing else does our future so much depend; in no area of instruction can the rewards be greater. No subject lends itself better to informal presentation and practical approach, and none better to active student participation (Figure 213). None has so many potential instructors, because in the teaching of applied conservation good common sense often means more than formal training and fancy words. It can be taught well under many different cir-

Education of our youth secures the future

FIGURE 213. *The author and conservation students planting slash pine seedlings in the spring of 1955. The conservation teacher who demonstrates and supervises the planting of forest seedlings should remember that the impact of the experience on young minds is the main objective. Tree survival and growth are quite incidental, except as the young planters retain an interest in their project. A few inexpensive seedlings can generate a genuine community interest.* (Photo by Harold J. Price, courtesy East Tennessee State College.)

cumstances, in many different ways, and by many different kinds of people.

Everyone who uses a resource wisely, be he farmer, manufacturer, sportsman, fisherman, or tourist, gives object lessons in conservation. The technicians and administrators who work in conservation endeavor to teach the public how to use resources without wasting or abusing them. Professional and business people who know where their bread is buttered also spread the word. Thus, much conservation teaching is done by persons who are not regarded as teachers in the ordinary sense. They dispense practical knowledge, without classrooms or recitations.

From kindergarten to university, we need good teacher-conservators!

For our school teachers, privileged to instruct young people, the challenge and opportunity are especially great; and it is appropriate that we devote some space to the *teacher-conservators* who instill in young minds the sense of values and responsibility on which we pin our highest hopes for the future.

The work can begin in the first grade, allied with such basic personality traits as thrift, respect for property, and the Golden Rule. Conservation has a place in religious instruction, and should certainly be an important part of citizenship training. The fundamental concepts of conservation and the general idea of resource consciousness can be incorporated with several areas of elementary learning, such as nature study, health, art appreciation, and others. The good elementary teacher sows the seeds of conservation upon which we have based our optimistic forecast. The seeds strike root without benefit of big words like "resources" and "conservation" (34).

Throughout the grades and high school, opportunities for teaching conservation become progressively more varied and definite, notably in the areas of natural and social sciences, and especially in geography. It is vitally important that sound conservation concepts be developed at this level of instruction, lest our future conservators be only those fortunate enough to attend college. Whether conservation should be taught in elementary and secondary schools as a separate subject or integrated with others is a matter for school administrators and supervisors to determine. The objectives can probably be gained about as well under one system as the other if administrative policy is favorable and the teachers themselves sufficiently indoctrinated. This book should assist with the suitable indoctrination of elementary and high school teachers, and should contribute something to the understandings of those who determine what shall be taught—superintendents, board members, and parents.

A survey of natural resources and their conservation should certainly be offered in every liberal arts college in the United States (35). No general education curriculum can be considered adequate without it; and a teacher training program that omits it is positively defective. It is gratifying to note that many of our teacher training institutions offer at least one separate course in conservation of natural resources, and that many such institutions conduct special short courses to keep in-service teachers up to date. The conservation conference that mingles several academic specialists with their counterparts in practical work can be a most profitable experience for everyone concerned. A project such as the tree plantation pictured in Figure 214 can be an object lesson to students and a generator of community interest as well.

So broad is the scope of conservation that no subject matter

FIGURE 214. *The author's conservation classes have planted a young forest on college property. The students* learn *by* doing, *although they plant only 1,000 seedlings each spring. This planting was six years old when the photo was taken.* (Photo by Reuben Mehling, courtesy East Tennessee State College.)

Many disciplines contribute to conservation education

area or discipline can claim it entirely as its own. It combines many fields of learning, and treats many kinds of material. On the one hand, it borrows from basic earth sciences such as geology, pedology, meteorology, ecology, and oceanography; on the other hand, it employs applied sciences such as agriculture, forestry, and engineering, under conditions dictated by economics, sociology, history, and politics. It combines natural, physical, and social sciences in the interest of material culture.

Since conservation depends upon a unified program, it appears that successful conservation teaching should have a unified, comprehensive approach (36). It should not give undue attention to

466

one resource at the expense of another, nor should it emphasize natural factors to the neglect of the cultural. Since a central theme of geography is the interpretation of man's relationship to his total earth environment, correlation of the material with the cultural, it follows that trained geographers are admirably qualified to teach resource conservation (37, 38). Other sciences such as biology, agronomy, chemistry, and economics make distinct and essential contributions to conservation, but none of them has the inclusive viewpoint of geography (39). Other educators may conduct a balanced conservation course by engaging an appropriate variety of scientists and practical conservationists, but continuity and perspective may be difficult to maintain unless they have the assistance of a geographer. Geography bridges the gap between the physical and social sciences; and that bridge is indeed the essence of conservation.

Conservation education is a task so big and so vital that there is no time to quarrel about its academic province; rather, let every instructor cooperate whenever possible in any program designed to convey to young men and women the basic concepts of resource conservation. Let the teaching be practical rather than theoretical. Let the ideas inculcated be applicable and profitable rather than academic and idealistic. Let it be emphasized that conservation must pay its own way, and can pay its way when intelligently applied (40). Such teaching is the foundation of perpetual wealth and continuing prosperity. School teachers hold the keys to America's future. Their labors will ultimately secure the concerted public action by which conservation can be fully assured. Public action is the means—action individually and collectively—but action will not come before a consciousness is aroused. Arousing that consciousness is a major challenge to our educational system.

Be a conservator-patriot!

Our prospect will be what our actions make it. If we persist in waste, abuse, pollution, and dissipation of natural wealth, we shall indeed starve (41). If we apply our technical knowledge with a fraction of the intelligence it took to get it, we may be twice as numerous in the year 2000 as now, and better off besides (42). When eroded land, burned forests, silted reservoirs, dirty waters, dispossessed wildlife, unused minerals, soiled landscapes, and abandoned spaces become acknowledged as the forms of sabotage they are, we may envisage the bright future that conservation can secure for our democracy. Let us resolve to conserve our natural wealth with the same determination that has preserved our constitutional liberties. Wise planning and diligent conservation vouchsafe for the future the great national heritage it is our good fortune to possess. Let every true American be a conservator-patriot.

CHAPTER 17: REFERENCES CITED BY NUMBER

(1) Thomas Robert Malthus, *An Essay on Population,* 1798.

(2) William Vogt, *Road to Survival,* William Sloan Associates, New York, 1948.

(3) Gilbert F. White, "Toward An Appraisal of World Resources—New Views of Conservation Problems," *Geographical Review,* XXXIX, No. 4, 1949.

(4) Colin Clark, "World Resources and World Population," *Proceedings of the U. N. Scientific Conference on the Conservation and Utilization of Resources, Lake Success, August 17–September 6, 1949;* I: Plenary Meetings, United Nations, New York, 1951.

(5) "37 Million Babies—Key to Business Future" *U.S. News & World Report,* an independent weekly news magazine published in Washington. Copyright 1955, United States News Publishing Corporation. July 29, 1955, pp. 30-32.

(6) A. B. Roberts, "Duplication and Overlapping," *Task Force Report on Water Resources Projects;* Appendix K: *Certain Aspects of Power, Irrigation, and Flood Control Projects,* Commission on Organization of the Executive Branch of the Government, Washington, D.C., 1949, Chapter 5.

(7) *Regional Planning,* National Resources Committee report series (e.g., Part III: *New England,* Washington, D.C., 1936).

(8) *Thirty-first Annual Report of the Federal Power Commission, 1951,* pp. 14 and 73.

(9) Louis C. McCabe, chairman, *Proceedings of the United States Technical Conference on Air Pollution;* Part V: *Health Panel on Air Pollution,* McGraw-Hill Book Company, Inc., New York, 1952.

(10) Robert D. Fletcher, "The Donora Smog Disaster—A Problem in Atmospheric Pollution," *Weatherwise,* II, No. 3, June 1949.

(11) C. A. Mills and Porter M. Mills, "Health Costs of Urban Air Pollution," *Occupational Medicine,* V, No. 6, 1948.

(12) *Smoke Control,* a report of the Joint State Government Commission to the General Assembly of the Commonwealth of Pennsylvania, Session of 1951, Harrisburg, Pennsylvania.

(13) Waldemar Kaempffert, "Rain Made By Cloud-Seeding Might Possibly Relieve New York City's Water Scarcity," *New York Times,* Sunday, January 29, 1950, Section 4.

(14) "Rain Making Debated," *Science News Letter,* LVII, No. 4, January 28, 1950.

(15) "Would Curb Rain-Makers," *Science Digest,* XXV, No. 5, May 1949.

(16) W. W. Aultman, "Desalting Sea Water for Domestic Use," *Journal, American Water Works Association,* XLII, No. 8, August 1950, pp. 786-794.

(17) "President Names Chief of Salt Water Research," United Press News Release, July 14, 1952.

(18) "Krilium Helps Soil Trap Raindrops," *The Land News,* Series XXX, No. 2, 1952.

(19) Conrad Hammar, "Society and Conservation," *Journal of Farm Economics,* XXIV, No. 1, February 1942, p. 109.

(20) Wheeler McMillen, *New Riches from the Soil,* D. Van Nostrand Company, New York, 1946.

(21) "Plastics: A 1950 Guide," *Fortune,* XLI, No. 5, May 1950.

(22) National Resources Committee, *The Problems of a Changing Population,* Washington, 1948, Chapters 2 and 3.

(23) Ira N. Gabrielson, "Twilight for Wildlife," *American Forests,* LV, No. 3, March 1949.

(24) Bernard Frank and Anthony Netboy, "Mirage of River Basin Development," *American Forests,* LVI, No. 3, March 1950.

(25) Houston Thompson, "The Law of Conservation," *The Land,* VIII, No. 2, Summer 1949.

(26) Arthur H. Carhart, editor, *Conservation, Please,* The Garden Club of America, 1950, p. 40.

(27) *Minority Task Force Report on Natural Resources,* prepared for the Commission on Organization of the Executive Branch of the Government, Washington, D.C., 1949.

(28) Leslie A. Miller, "The Case for a Department of Natural Resources," *American Forests,* LV, No. 11, November 1949.

(29) G. H. Collingwood, "Conservation and the Hoover Report," *American Forests,* LV, No. 4, April 1949.

(30) Erle Kauffman, "Conservation's Great Need" (editorial), *American Forests,* LIV, No. 10, October 1948.

(31) F. A. Wirt, "What Conservation Means to Business," *American Forests,* LV, No. 11, November 1949.

(32) *Policy Declaration on Natural Resources,* Chamber of Commerce of the United States, Washington, D.C., 1951.

(33) Henry Clepper, "The Conservation Association," *American Forests*, LIX, No. 1, January 1953.

(34) "Youth Can Help Conserve These Resources: Soil, Water, Woodland, Wildlife, Grass," *Agricultural Information Bulletin No. 52*, U.S.D.A., 1951.

(35) Delbert Willis, "A Geographer and the Soil," *Soil Conservation*, XVIII, No. 2, September 1952.

(36) George F. Grant, "Education in the Use of Natural Resources," *44th Yearbook*, National Society for the Study of Education, Washington, D.C., 1945, Chapter 9, pp. 188-208.

(37) William W. Reitz, "Teaching Resource Conservation Through Geography," *Journal of Geography*, XLVI, No. 6, September 1947.

(38) Wesley Calef, "Special Geographic Contributions to Conservation Education," *Journal of Geography*, LI, No. 3, March 1952.

(39) L. H. Halverson, "Whither Conservation Education?" *Journal of Geography*, XLVI, No. 5, May 1947.

(40) John H. Southern, "Noise Is Not Enough," *The Land*, VIII, No. 4, Winter 1949-50.

(41) J. A. Hall, "Democracy Can Starve Itself," *The Land*, VIII, No. 4.

(42) "300 Million Americans," *Fortune*, XLI, No. 5, May 1950.

(26) Henry Clepper, "The Conservation Association," *Audubon*, Vol. 64, No. 1, January 1962.

(27) "Tennessee Hen Coming: The . . . Resources and Water Woodland Wildlife Cross, Agricultural . . . Institutionally . . . Vol. 23 TRANS, 1951.

(28) Robert Willis, "A. C. atmosphere and the End," *Soil Conservation*, Vol. 3, September 1953.

(29) George Perkins . . . Education in the Use of Natural Resources . . . for . . . Nation's Society for the Study of Education, Washington, D.C., 1952, Chapter 9, pp. 183–204.

(30) William W. Bauer, "Teaching Resource Conservation Through Geography," *School of Geography*, Vol. XVII, No. 5, September 1947.

(31) Wesley . . . Calef, "Space Geography Contribution to Conservation Education," *Journal of Geography*, Vol. 46, No. 5, March 1947.

(32) R. H. Brown, ". . . Nation Conservation Education," *Journal of Geography*, Vol. XLVI, No. 5, May 1947.

(33) Henry H. Smithson, "Biology for Modern Youth," *The Land*, Vol. X, No. 1, Winter 1951–52.

(34) T. J. Hill, *Conservation Culture*, ... Vol. 21, No. VIII, ... 1941.

(35) . . . Million American Resources . . . Vol. 22, No. 5, May 1951.

Teaching Aids

Teaching Aids

THE CONSERVATION TEACHER BORROWS FROM SEVERAL FIELDS OF KNOWLEDGE, each with its own literature and philosophy. Eight major resource classes have been discussed in this book. Each of those classes should be treated in any survey course in resource conservation. None should be neglected, but relative emphasis might be judiciously gaged to area interests and problems. All resource classes, or fields, should be reduced to the common denominator—conservation, with its central theme of "better use for better living." To incline students toward critical evaluation and deliberate acceptance of conservation as a personal responsibility, to lead them to discover its origin in natural unity and observe its culmination in cultural progress should be the teacher's main objectives. These cannot be achieved unless the teacher maintains a sufficiently broad perspective, reinforced with current information on developments and trends. The following suggestions and compilations are intended to help the teacher acquire or strengthen the professional competencies and practical techniques pertinent to the immense subject area of resource conservation.

This appendix contains items of interest to teachers at all levels of instruction from the lower grades to college. It is hoped that instructors in teacher-training institutions may find it particularly valuable. The listings provided here should be helpful in presenting conservation "methods and materials" to prospective or in-service teachers. Choice and employment of the aids to suit a given situation and a particular level of instruction must devolve upon the individual teacher. Although several listings appear lengthy, indicating the scope and variety of subject areas, none of the lists is exhaustive.

SECTION A

The author would not presume to tell the established teacher how to teach a course or manage a class, but on the basis of long experience, he feels privileged to offer a few suggestions that may help the inexperienced teacher conduct a course or a unit of work in resource conservation. Here are his admonitions to anyone who contemplates conservation teaching:

1. Stress resource relationships rather than treating components as detached segments.

2. Take care that the emphasis on material things does not obscure the higher spiritual and intellectual values.

3. Be mindful that, although nature study contributes to basic understandings, the objectives of conservation are social. Do not confuse the means with the ends.

4. Remember that a teacher's primary responsibility is the conservation of people and minds, and not the direct conservation of natural resources. Beware the error of pursuing a conservation project for its own sake and neglecting its educational implications.

5. Be more concerned with concepts and attitudes than with facts and figures. Wisdom begins with knowledge.

6. Do not attempt to engage student interest with a pessimistic, negative approach. A student's "so what?" may be difficult to answer adequately. The positive, optimistic approach will stimulate more interest and better participation.

7. All outdoors is a conservation study hall and laboratory. A well-planned day in the field can be more instructive than a week in the classroom.

8. In a survey course, such as this book might serve, make the work sufficiently stimulating to attract good students and sufficiently easy to attract poor ones. The dullard may be a greater menace to resources than a more intelligent person. Do not restrict enrollment in a conservation class by imposing prerequisites.

9. In conducting a unit of study on an elementary or high school level, take special care that students understand the limitation of scope. Otherwise they may exaggerate their qualifications as conservators. A little knowledge can be dangerous in conservation as well as in other spheres.

10. Develop some kind of constructive project involving student participation, thus combining practice with theory. Let the students choose, plan, and carry out the activity. The skillful teacher will maneuver the students into a good choice without making the decision for them.

11. Place emphasis on the practical values of conservation rather than on sentiment and idealism. Do not confuse poetry with profits. On the other hand, do not be materialistic to the exclusion of intangible, aesthetic considerations.

12. Focus on present problems, not on those that may arise in the future. Young people are not easily persuaded to worry about posterity, perhaps because they do not wish to deprive their elders of a popular

pastime. Begin with vicinal problems and proceed to state, regional, and national ones.

13. Encourage individual students to submit for class discussion any resource problem of immediate concern to themselves or their families. If a need is clearly indicated, the teacher may seek the advice of an appropriate technician or official, and possibly bring him before the class.

14. Encourage every student to become an active member of an organization concerned with conservation. Of course, the teacher should belong to at least one such group. (See sections E and F.)

15. Explore both sides of current conservation issues. Avoid snap judgment on any controversy. Debate by opposing groups of students may be a good medium of presentation.

16. Seek the advice of experienced conservationists and conservators. Establish a working arrangement with those who can best contribute to a planned program of instruction. The visiting expert adds both substance and prestige to a course.

17. Make readily available to the students a collection of conservation literature appropriate to their educational level. (Several selections may be made from references listed in this book. See also sections D, F, H, and I in this appendix.)

18. Practice what you preach!

SECTION B

In this list subject areas are grouped by numbers. One each of those grouped under one number might be considered a minimum for a college or high school course in resource conservation. Motion pictures available are so numerous and excellent that a teacher may well conduct a once-weekly film showing open to the public as well as to students and parents. Such programs have proved highly successful. The teacher should be careful not to violate any loan agreement that prohibits an admission charge. All films should be handled carefully, shown by a competent operator, and returned promptly, by insured mail or express. Those marked "free loan" are usually available for return shipping charges only.

It is assumed that the conservation teacher will select films to present a balance from three points of view, namely national, regional, and community interests. Unfortunately, no film now available treats the conservation of commercial fisheries nor the general subject of mineral conservation. In other resource areas there is often a considerable choice. New films are being produced so rapidly that each edition of the *Educational Film Guide* should be checked for additions. All films are 16 mm., sound and color, unless otherwise indicated.

1a. *Yours Is the Land,* 1950, 20 minutes; Encyclopedia Britannica Films, Inc., 1150 Wilmette Ave., Wilmette, Ill.; produced in affiliation with the Conservation Foundation. (Waste of resources, necessary conservation.)

1b. *To Conserve our Heritage,* 1954, free loan, 37 minutes; Minneapolis-Moline Company, Minneapolis, Minn. (Need to conserve natural resources.)

2a. *Pipeline to the Clouds,* 1951, free loan, 25 minutes; General Electric Company, Schenectady 5, N.Y.; produced with assistance of the American Water Works Association and the U.S. Public Health Service. (Importance of water, water problems, some means of solving problems.)

2b. *Clean Waters,* 1946, 21 minutes, free loan; General Electric Company; produced by Raphael G. Wolff Studios, with cooperation of U.S. Public Health Service. (Importance of natural waters, danger of pollution, proper sewage treatment.)

2c. *Valley of Still Waters,* 1952, free loan, 22 minutes; University of Nebraska, Division of Motion Pictures U.S.D.A. (Watershed conservation—Salt-Wahoo as illustration.)

2d. *Man's Problem* (Living Water Series), 1953, 19 minutes; Encyclopedia Britannica Films; produced by Conservation Foundation and N.Y. Zoological Society. (Conservation of water.)

3a. *Soil and Water Conservation,* 1948, 10 minutes, black and white; S.C.S. (Conservation farming practices.)

3b. *The Good Earth for a Better Life,* 1952, 44 minutes, free loan; Minneapolis-Moline Company. (Soil maintenance, with special attention to trace elements and farm implements.)

4a. *The Living Forest Series: Forest Grows, Forest Produces, Forest Conservation,* 33 minutes, Encyclopedia Britannica Films, produced in affiliation with Conservation Foundation and N.Y. Zoological Society. (Why our forest resources have shrunk, necessity of wise forest management.)

4b. *Green Harvest,* 1948, 29 minutes, free loan; Weyerhaeuser Forest Products, First National Bank Bldg., St. Paul 1, Minn. (Commercial forestry, logging, and conservation.)

5a. *Richer Range Rewards,* 1946, 33 minutes, free loan; U.S. Forest Service. (Practical measures for range conservation and better range economy.)

5b. *Strips and Curves,* 1947, 22 minutes, free loan; J. I. Case Company, Education Division, Racine, Wis. (Erosion control on the Great Plains.)

5c. *Under Western Skies,* 1946, 28 minutes, free loan; George W. Colburn Laboratory, Agency for International Harvester Film Library, 164 N. Wacker Drive, Chicago 6, Ill. (Dry and irrigation farming in the West.)

6a. *Conservation in Action,* 1950, 11 minutes, free loan; U.S. Fish and Wildlife Service. (Emphasis on wildlife conservation; maligns the coyote and cougar.)

6b. *Wildlife and the Human Touch,* 1952, 18 minutes, free loan; U.S. Forest Service. (Work of Forest Service in wildlife conservation, with a good touch of aesthetics.)

7. *A Community Problem,* 1950, 13 minutes, free loan; Caterpillar Tractor Company, Advertising Department, Peoria 8, Ill. (Waste disposal by sanitary landfill.)

8. *Living Earth Series: Arteries of Life, Birth of the Soil, Seeds of Destruction, This Vital Earth,* 1948, 10 minutes each; Encyclopedia Britannica Films; produced in affiliation with Conservation Foundation and N.Y. Zoological Society. (A more elaborate treatment of same subject as in number 1a above.)

9. *Understanding Our Earth—Soil,* 1953, 10 minutes, black and white; Coronet Films, Coronet Bldg., Chicago 1, Ill. (Elementary introduction to soils.)

10. *Marsh Waters—Waste or Wealth,* 1953, 15 minutes; University of Minnesota, Audio-Visual Education Service, Westbrook Hall, Minneapolis 14, Minn. (Value of marsh in its natural state.)

11. *Air, Water, and Industry,* 1952, 22 minutes, free loan; sponsored and produced by the Dow Chemical Company, Advertising Department, Midland, Mich. (Industrial pollution, its control.)

12. *Story of Menhaden,* 1951, 21 minutes, free loan; U.S. Fish and Wildlife Service; sponsored by members of Menhaden Industry. (Uses of fish in industry; catching, processing.)

13. *A Story of Copper,* 1951, 33 minutes; Bureau of Mines in cooperation with the Phelps Dodge Corporation.

14. *Evolution of the Oil Industry,* 1952, 29 minutes, free loan; U.S. Bureau of Mines. (Short story of the American petroleum industry.)

15. *Powering America's Progress—Modern Story of Bituminous Coal,* 1952, 25 minutes, free loan; U.S. Bureau of Mines; sponsored by the Bituminous Coal Institute. (Importance of coal in American industry.)

SECTION C

"A Glossary of Special Terms Used in the Soils Yearbook," *Soils and Men: Yearbook of Agriculture, 1938,* Washington, D. C., pp. 1162-1180.

A Glossary of the Mining and Mineral Industry, U.S. Bureau of Mines, Bulletin 95, Washington, D.C., 1920, reprinted 1947.

Carpenter, J. Richard, *An Ecological Glossary,* University of Oklahoma Press, Norman, Okla., 1938.

Dayton, W. A., *Glossary of Botanical Terms Commonly Used in Range Research,* U.S.D.A. Misc. Publ. No. 110, issued June, 1931; revised June, 1950.

Five-page glossary of fishery terms at the back of "Fishery Science" by G. A. Rounsefell and W. H. Everhart, John Wiley & Sons, New York, 1953.

Forest Terminology, Society of American Foresters, Washington, D.C., 1950.

Range Conservation Glossary, Soil Conservation Service, (18 pages, mimeographed), June, 1944.

Rice, Clara Mabel, *Dictionary of Geological Terms*, Edwards Bros. Inc., Ann Arbor, Mich., 1949.

Soil and Water Conservation Glossary, Soil Conservation Society of America, Des Moines, Iowa, 1952.

"Some Words Woodsmen Use," *Trees: Yearbook of Agriculture, 1949*, Washington, D.C., pp. 911-916.

Thiessen, Alfred H., compiler, *Weather Glossary*, U.S. Weather Bureau, 1946, reprinted 1949.

SECTION D

The following agencies (public and semi-public) should be contacted by the conservation teacher as appropriate. Several of them can furnish materials specially prepared for the teacher. Some are in position to sponsor certain activities, to participate in the school program, or to help the teacher in other ways.

(1) Federal Agencies with a primary interest in resource use and conservation: (Periodicals listed under certain agencies are available from the Superintendent of Documents, Washington, D.C., for a nominal subscription fee.) The first seven agencies listed have area representatives from whom a teacher may get personal advice and assistance. Several of these agencies have special educational displays, posters, and attractive reading material available to teachers for the asking. A copy of their annual reports will help keep teacher and students up-to-date.

National Park Service, Dept. of Interior.

Office of Defense Mobilization, Executive Office of the President, Washington 25, D.C.

Tennessee Valley Authority, Knoxville, Tenn.

U.S. Bureau of Land Management, Dept. of Interior, Washington 25, D.C. Pub: *Our Public Lands*.

U.S. Bureau of Mines, Dept. of Interior.

U.S. Bureau of Reclamation, Dept. of Interior. Pub: *The Reclamation Era*.

U.S. Fish and Wildlife Service, Dept. of Interior. Pub: *Wildlife Review* and *Commercial Fisheries Review*.

U.S. Forest Service, U.S.D.A.

U.S. Soil Conservation Service, U.S.D.A., Washington 25, D.C. Pub.: *Soil Conservation*.

(2) Federal agencies whose activities and publications are of special interest to the conservator, although conservation is not their special responsibility:

Bureau of Agricultural Economics, U.S.D.A.

Bureau of the Census.

Federal Power Commission.

Industrial Reference Service, Dept. of Commerce, Bur. of Foreign and Domestic Commerce.

Interstate Commerce Commission, Dept. of Commerce.

Legislative Reference Service, Library of Congress.

National Production Authority, Dept. of Commerce.

Production and Marketing Administration, U.S.D.A.

Public Health Service.

Public Roads Administration.

U.S. Corps of Engineers (Army), Dept. of the Army.

U.S. Geological Survey, Dept. of Interior.

U.S. Office of Education.

U.S. Weather Bureau. Pub.: *Monthly Weather Review* and *Daily Weather Map.*

(3) State agencies of special interest to the teacher-conservator are variously organized and named in different states. The conservation teacher should refer to a directory of state offices or officials in order to establish desirable contacts. It makes little difference whether a particular agency is designated a department, board, commission, bureau, or something else; key words such as the following are a better guide:

Agriculture	Fisheries	Geology	Planning
Conservation	Forestry	Health	Resources
Education	Game and Fish	Mines	State Parks

The teacher should be acquainted with several state office designations, at least. An inquiry directed to any one of them will either be answered by that office or be routed to another office better qualified to make reply. Ignorance of state government is not a valid excuse for ignorance of state resources and conservation activities. Most states publish a good conservation magazine or bulletin that the conservation teacher should read.

(4) Local contacts: Local persons and groups may help a teacher carry out desirable school activities or projects. At the local level, civic and semi-official agencies can be especially helpful. Local contacts can be invaluable to the conservation teacher. One or several of the following officials and organizations may give practical assistance:

Banks and Loan Associations
Business, professional, and civic or commercial clubs
Chamber of Commerce
College or University Departments offering work in conservation

Community Clubs
County Agent
Fire Warden
Game Warden
Industrialists
Merchants

SECTION E

Organizations from whom the teacher may obtain periodic or timely reports dealing with particular resource and conservation developments:

American Automobile Association, Pennsylvania Ave. at 17th St., Washington 6, D.C.

American Camping Association, 343 South Dearborn St., Chicago 4, Ill.

American Congress on Surveying and Mapping, c/o Tennessee Valley Authority, GSA Bldg., Washington 25, D.C.

American Fisheries Society, 822 Investment Bldg., Washington, D.C.

American Forest Products Industries, Inc., 1319 Eighteenth St., N.W., Washington 6, D.C.

American Meteorological Society, 3 Joy Street, Boston 8, Mass. (Pubs.: *Bulletin,* Abstracts, Monographs.)

American National Livestock Association, Cooper Bldg., Denver 2, Colo.

American Nature Study Society, Secretary, c/o State Teachers College, Fitchburg, Mass.

American Petroleum Institute, 50 West 50th St., New York 20, N.Y.

American Planning and Civic Association, 901 Union Trust Bldg., 15th and H Streets, N.W., Washington 5, D.C.

American Shore and Beach Preservation Association, 1060 Broad St., Newark, N.J. (Pub.: *Shore and Beach,* semiannual.)

American Society of Civil Engineers, 33 West 39th Street, New York 18, N.Y.

American Society of Planning Officials, 1313 East 60th St., Chicago 37, Ill.

Anthracite Institute, 543 Transportation Bldg., 17th & H Streets, N.W., Washington, D.C.

Battelle Memorial Institute, 505 King Ave., Columbus 1, Ohio.

Better Fishing, Inc., 509 South Wabash Ave., Chicago 5, Ill.

Bituminous Coal Research, Inc. (affiliate of Nat. Coal Assn.), Southern Bldg., Washington, D.C.

Boy Scouts of America, 321 South Green St., Chicago 7, Ill.

Camp Fire Girls, 16 East 48th St., New York 17, N.Y.

Chamber of Commerce of the United States, 1615 H St., Washington, D.C.

Charles Lathrop Pack Forestry Foundation, 1214 16th St., N.W., Washington 6, D.C.

Citizens for Conservation, Inc., 1710 16th St. N.W., Washington 9, D.C.

Conservation Education Association, P.O. Box 1510, Annapolis, Md.

Conservation Foundation, 30 East 40th Street, New York 16, N.Y.

Defenders of Fur Bearers, 1214 Sixteenth St. N.W., Washington 6, D.C.

Federation of Western Outdoor Clubs, President, 315 Montgomery St., San Francisco 4, Calif.

Forest Conservation Society of America, 2144 P Street, N.W., Washington 7, D.C.

Future Farmers of America, Dept. of Health, Education and Welfare, Washington 25, D.C.

Future Home Makers of America, American Home Economics Assn., 1600 20th St., N.W., Washington 9, D.C.

Game Conservation Society, Inc., 1819 Broadway, New York 23, N.Y.

Garden Club of America, 15 East 58th St., New York 22, N.Y.

General Federation of Women's Clubs, 1734 N Street, N.W., Washington, D.C.

Grassland Research Foundation, Inc., U.S.P.H.S., 441 Federal Office Bldg., San Francisco, Calif.

International Harvester Co., 180 North Michigan Ave., Chicago 1, Ill.

Keep America Beautiful, Inc., 99 Park Ave., New York 16, N.Y.

National Conference on State Parks, 901 Union Trust Bldg., Washington 5, D.C.

National Council of State Garden Clubs, 30 Rockefeller Plaza, New York, N.Y.

National Education Association, 1201 Sixteenth St., N.W., Washington 6, D.C.

National Fisheries Institute, Inc., 1614 Twentieth St. N.W., Washington 9, D.C.

National Lumber Manufacturers Association, 1319 18th St. N.W., Washington 6, D.C.

National Rifle Association of America, 1600 Rhode Island Ave., N.W., Washington 6, D.C.

National Society for the Study of Education, 5835 Kimbark Ave., Chicago 37, Ill.

National Waterfowl Council (National Flyway Council) Arkansas Game & Fish Dept., State Capitol Grounds, Little Rock, Ark.

Natural Resources Council of America, 822 Investment Bldg., Washington 5, D.C.

Nature Conservancy (An Association for the Conservation of Natural Areas), 4200 22nd St., N.E., Washington 18, D.C.

New York Zoological Society, 30 East 40th Street, New York 16, N.Y.

North American Wildlife Foundation, 709 Wire Bldg., Washington 5, D.C.

Oceanographic Society of the Pacific, Scripps Institution of Oceanography, La Jolla, Calif.

Outdoor Education Association, 369 Lexington Ave., New York 17, N.Y.

Pacific Northwest Bird and Mammal Society, University of Washington, Seattle, Wash.

Regional Planning Association of America, 26 W. 45th St., New York, N.Y.

Resources for the Future, Inc., 706 Cafritz Bldg., 1625 Eye St., N.W., Washington 6, D.C.

Save-the-Redwoods League, 250 Administration Bldg., University of California, Berkeley 4, Calif.

Sierra Club, 1050 Mills Tower, San Francisco 4, California.

Southern Pine Association, 520 Canal Bldg., New Orleans, La.

Southern Pulpwood Conservation Association, 1224 Peachtree St., N.E., Atlanta 5, Ga.

Sport Fishing Institute, Bond Building, Washington 5, D.C.

West Coast Lumbermen's Association, 1410 S.W. Morrison St., Portland 5, Ore.

Wild Flower Preservation Society, 3740 Oliver St., Washington 15, D.C.

Wildlife Management Institute, 709 Wire Bldg., Washington 5, D.C.

Woods Hole Oceanographic Institute, Woods Hole, Mass.

Many leading manufacturers and several other industrial organizations have excellent teaching aids available free of charge. They may be contacted through their magazine advertisements.

SECTION F

Periodicals of special interest to the teacher-conservator (obviously the organizations that publish the periodicals are concerned with resources and conservation, and may provide special assistance):

American Biology Teacher, National Association of Biology Teachers, 110 E. Hines St., Midland, Mich.

American Economic Review, American Economics Association, Northwestern University, Evanston, Ill.

American Forests, The American Forestry Association, 919 17th St. N. W., Washington 6, D.C.

American Geophysical Union, Transactions, 1530 P St., N.W., Washington 5, D.C. *Transactions* published by the National Research Council of The National Academy of Sciences, Washington, D.C.

American Institute of Planners, Journal, Massachusetts Institute of Technology, 77 Massachusetts Ave., Cambridge 39, Mass.

Annals, American Academy of Political and Social Science, 3457 Walnut St., Philadelphia 4, Pa.

Annals and *Professional Geographer,* The Association of American Geographers, AAG, Map Division, The Library of Congress, Washington 25, D.C.

Audubon Magazine, The National Audubon Society, 1130 Fifth Avenue, New York 28, N.Y.

Auk, American Ornithological Union, Lancaster, Pa.

Better Roads Magazine, 173 West Madison St., Chicago 2, Ill.

Chemical Week, McGraw-Hill Book Company, Inc., 330 W. 42nd St., New York 36, N.Y.

Civil Engineering, American Society of Civil Engineers, 33 W. 39th St., New York 18, N.Y.

Conservation News and *Conservation Report,* National Wildlife Federation, 232 Carroll Street, N.W., Washington 12, D.C.

Ecological Monographs, Ecological Society of America, Duke University Press, Durham, N.C.

Ecology, Ecological Society of America, Prince and Lemon Streets, Lancaster, Pa.

Economic Geography, Clark University, Graduate School of Geography, Worcester, Mass.

Economic Geology, Economic Geology Publishing Co., Natural Resources Bldg., University of Illinois, Urbana, Ill.

Engineering and Mining Journal, McGraw-Hill Book Company, Inc., 330 W. 42nd St., New York 36, N.Y.

Geographical Review and *Focus,* American Geographical Society, Broadway at 156th St., New York 32, N.Y.

Geological News Letter, American Geological Institute, 2101 Constitution Ave., Washington 25, D.C.

Geological Society of America, Bulletin, Mt. Royal and Guilford Avenues, Baltimore 2, Md.

Journal of Agricultural and Food Chemistry, American Chemical Society, 1155 16th St., N.W., Washington 6, D.C.

Journal of the American Water Works Association, 521 Fifth Ave., New York 17, N.Y.

Journal of Farm Economics, American Farm Economic Association, Menasha, Wis.

Journal of Forestry, Society of American Foresters, Mills Bldg., Washington 6, D.C.

Journal of Geography, published by A. J. Nystrom & Co. for the National Council of Geography Teachers, 3333 Elston Ave., Chicago 18, Ill.

Journal of Geology, University of Chicago Press, 5750 Ellis Ave., Chicago, Ill.

Journal of Range Management, American Society of Range Management, Box 7745, Albina Station, Portland 12, Ore.

Journal of Soil and Water Conservation, Soil Conservation Society of America, 1016 Paramount Bldg., Des Moines, Iowa.

Journal of Wildlife Management, The Wildlife Society, c/o Fish and Wildlife Service, Washington 25, D.C.

Land Economics, University of Wisconsin, Madison 6, Wis.

Mining Engineering, American Institute of Mining and Metallurgical Engineers, 29 West 39th St., New York 18, N.Y.

Modern Metals, Modern Metals Publishing Co., 435 N. Michigan Ave., Chicago, Ill.

National 4-H News, National Committee of Boys and Girls Club Work, Inc., 59 E. Van Buren St., Chicago, Ill.

National Geographic Magazine, National Geographic Society, Washington 6, D.C.

National Parks Magazine, National Parks Association, 1840 Mintwood Place, N.W., Washington 9, D.C.

Natural History, American Museum of Natural History, Central Park West at 79th St., New York 24, N.Y.

Nature Magazine, American Nature Association, 1214 16th St., N.W., Washington 6, D.C.

Outdoor America, Izaak Walton League of America, Inc., 31 North State St., Chicago 2, Ill.

Pacific Fisherman, Miller Freeman Publications, 71 Columbia St., Seattle, Wash.

Parks and Recreation Magazine, American Institute of Park Executives, Inc., American Association of Zoological Parks and Aquariums, published by Finch and McCullough, 84 S. LaSalle St., Aurora, Ill.

Proceedings, National Watershed Congress, 1320 18th St., N.W., Washington, D.C.

Proceedings, Soil Science Society of America, 2702 Monroe St., Madison 5, Wis.

Recreation, National Recreation Association, 315 Fourth Ave., New York 10, N.Y.

Science Digest, Science Digest, Inc., 200 E. Ontario St., Chicago 11, Ill.

"Science in Review," Sunday *New York Times,* 229 West 43rd St., New York, N.Y.

Science News Letter, Science Service, Inc., 1719 N St., N.W., Washington 6, D.C.

Scientific American, Scientific American, Inc., 2 West 45th St., New York 36, N.Y.

Steel Facts and *Steelways,* American Iron and Steel Institute, 350 Fifth Ave., New York 1, N.Y.

The Farm Quarterly, The Automobile Digest Publishing Co., 22 East 12th Street, Cincinnati 10, O.

The Fisherman, official publication of the Federation of Freshwater Fisheries, The Marine Publishing Company, 406 Howard St., Grand Haven, Mich.

The Forest Farmer, The Forest Farmers Association Cooperative, P.O. Box 7284, Station C, Atlanta, Ga.

The Johnson National Driller's Journal, 2304 Long Avenue, St. Paul 4, Minn.

The Land, Friends of the Land, Route 3, Zanesville, O.

The Living Wilderness, The Wilderness Society, 2144 P Street, N.W., Washington 7, D.C.

The Roadside Bulletin, National Roadside Council, 119 East 19th St., New York 3, N.Y.

The Scientific Monthly, American Association for the Advancement of Science, 1515 Massachusetts Ave., N.W., Washington 5, D.C.

Watershed, American Watershed Council, Inc., 202 Transportation Bldg., Washington 6, D.C.

Weatherwise (The Magazine About Weather), Amateur Weathermen of America, Franklin Institute, Philadelphia 3, Pa.

What's New in Crops and Soils and *Agronomy Journal,* The American Society of Agronomy, 2702 Monroe St., Madison 5, Wis.

Excellent articles on conservation appear in farm journals and other magazines, both popular and erudite.

SECTION G

Practical aids for planning and conducting conservation education:

1. *Geography in the High School,* Geographic Education Series, National Council of Geography Teachers. (Especially Part Six: "Teaching Conservation in the High School.") McKnight & McKnight, Bloomington, Ill., 1949.

2. Beard, Ward P., *Teaching Conservation, A Guide in Natural Resources Education,* American Forestry Association, Washington, D.C., 1948.

3. *Conservation—A Handbook for Teachers,* Cornell Rural School Leaflet, Teachers' Number, Vol. 45, No. 1, Sept. 1951.

4. Rhyne, Conway L. and Lory, Ellsworth E., *Conservation of Natural Resources* (Text Units in the Social Studies), Charles E. Merrill Co. Inc., Columbus 15, Ohio, 1948.

5. Thomas, R. Lee, Bailey, James L., and Caldwell, John, *Taking Conservation to the Schools,* Bulletin No. 9, Tennessee Department of Conservation, Nashville, Tenn.

6. Renner, George T., *Conservation of National Resources—An Educational Approach to the Problem,* John Wiley & Sons, Inc., N.Y., 1942.

7. *How to Preserve an Area for Its Natural Value,* Information Bulletin No. 4, Revised June, 1954, The Nature Conservancy, Washington, D.C. (8 page mimeograph, practical).

8. *Conservation Education Series* (Demonstrations of teacher-student projects in teaching conservation fundamentals), Series of 5 Bulletins, National Wildlife Federation, Washington, D.C.

9. *A Curriculum Unit on the Conservation of Natural Resources,* Bulletin of the California State Department of Education, Vol. XXI, No. 1, January, 1952, Sacramento. (Teaching guide and graded bibliography.)

10. Thurston, Lee M., *Community School Camping,* Michigan Department of Public Instruction, Lansing, Mich., 1951.

11. *Conservation in Camping,* American Camping Association, 343 South Dearborn St., Chicago 4, Ill.

12. "Conducted Trips," *Training Bulletin for Field Employees* (in Service Training Series), Natural History Division, National Park Service, Washington, D.C., 1954. (47 pages of practical suggestions for conducting a successful group trip.)

13. Hafstad, M. R. and Hafstad, G. E., *Use Without Waste,* Webster Publishing Co., St. Louis, Mo., 1944. (Teaching units.)

14. Visher, Halene Hatcher, "Conservation Education Thru the Social Studies," *Journal of Geography,* Vol. LI, No. 3, March, 1952.

15. Ordway, Samuel H. Jr., *A Conservation Handbook,* The Conservation Foundation, 30 East 40th St., New York 16, N.Y., 1949.

16. Kauffman, Erle, editor, *The Conservation Yearbook* (annual), The Conservation Yearbook, 26 Enterprise Bldg., 1740 K St., N.W., Washington 6, D.C.

17. "Talks," *Training Bulletin for Field Employees* (in Service Training Series), Natural History Division, National Park Service, Washington, 1953. (29 pages of helpful ideas for telling something to a group.)

18. Lathrop, H. O., "An Experiment in Conservation Education," *Journal of Geography,* Vol. XLVI, No. 3, March, 1947.

19. Warren, Gertrude L., *Building a Better America Through the 4-H Clubs,* Extension Service, U.S.D.A., AIB 58, July, 1951.

20. *American Conservation in Picture and in Story,* American Forestry Association, Washington, D.C., 1941.

21. *Goode's School Atlas,* Rand McNally & Co., New York, N.Y.

22. Shoemaker, Carl D., *Directory of Organizations and Officials Concerned with the Protection of Wildlife and Other Natural Resources,* National Wildlife Federation, Washington 12, D.C., 1 July 1953.

23. Herbert, Paul A., "Teaching Conservation," *Maryland Conservationist,* Vol. XXX, No. 1, Spring, 1953. (Beneficial to man, conservation should be a part of a sound education program, integrated with all school activities.)

24. *County Soil Survey Reports,* for the local area, if available. U.S.D.A.

25. Caldwell, John C., Bailey, James L. and Watkins, R. W., *Our Land and Our Living,* L. W. Singer Co., Syracuse, N.Y., 1941.

26. *Wet Laboratories,* Cornell Rural School Leaflet, New York State College of Agriculture, Cornell University, Ithaca, N.Y., Vol. 45, No. 2, Fall, 1951.

27. *Youth Can Help Conserve These Resources: Soil, Water, Woodland, Wildlife, Grass,* Agric. Information Bul. No. 52, U.S.D.A. Soil Conservation Service, Washington, D.C., 1951.

28. *Conservation Education for American Youth,* (outline for teachers), 50 pages, National Wildlife Federation, Washington, D.C.

29. *My Land and Your Land Series* (Elementary and intermediate reading), National Wildlife Federation, Washington, D.C.

30. *Approaches to Conservation,* (Series of leaflets on various phases of conservation; high school and adult level), National Wildlife Federation, Washington, D.C.

31. Riedman, Sarah R., *Water for People,* Henry Schuman, New York, N.Y., 1952. (Intermediate reading.)

32. Bronson, Wilfrid S., *Freedom and Plenty—Ours to Save,* Harcourt, Brace, and Company, New York, N.Y., 1953. (Intermediate reading.)

33. *Learning by Living (Education for Wise Use of Resources),* A Report on the Resource-Use Education Project sponsored jointly by the Southern States Work Conference on Educational Problems and the Committee on Southern Regional Studies and Education, American Council on Education, 1950. Available from Distributor of Publications for the Southern States Work Conference, State Dept. of Education, Tallahassee, Fla.

34. *Suggestions for Integrating Forestry in the Modern Curriculum,* U.S. Forest Service.

35. *Starting a Community Forest* (An outline of suggested procedure), U.S. Forest Service.

36. *The Instructor Series of Illustrated Units* (For all grade levels), F. A. Owen Publishing Company, Dansville, N.Y.

37. *Visual Aids to Modern Farming,* J. I. Case Co., Inc., 601 State Street, Racine, Wis.

38. *K-28, Materials to Help Teach Forest Conservation,* U.S. Forest Service.

39. Steele, W. Crosby, *Conserving Our Resources,* Oxford Book Company, 222 Fourth Ave., New York 3, N.Y.

40. *The Teaching of Conservation, 1949,* Handbook for elementary teachers, grades 1 to 8, Iowa Department of Public Instruction, Des Moines, Iowa.

41. Foster, Albert D., *Approved Practices in Soil Conservation,* The Interstate Printers and Publishers, Danville, Ill., 1954.

42. *The Forest Adventures of Mark Edwards* (A conservation reader for grades 4, 5, and 6), American Forest Products Industries, Inc., Washington, D.C., Oct., 1954.

43. *Johnny Grass Seed—A Conservation Action Project for All,* Izaak Walton League of America, Inc. (Undated bulletin explaining how the grass-sowing project works.)

44. Wight, Edgar L., and A. Golden Kilburn, *Classroom Activities Related to Natural Resources,* Department of Interior, Bureau of Indian Affairs, and Utah State Agricultural College, Brigham City, Utah, 1955.

SECTION H

Bibliographies useful to the conservation teacher:

Air Pollution, a Bibliography, Superintendent of Documents, Washington, D.C., 1954. Catalog No. I 28.3: 537, 448 pages.

Bibliography on Conservation Books, Booklets, and Teaching Aids, National Wildlife Federation.

Books, Booklets, Bulletins on Soil and Water Conservation, U.S. Soil Conservation Service Agriculture Information Bulletin, No. 63. (Graded lists, elementary to college.)

Burroughs, R. D., *Bulletins, Books, and Visual Aids,* Education Division, Michigan Department of Conservation, Lansing, Mich., 1951.

———, *Helps for Teachers* (Conservation Compendium), A Bibliography Relating to the Wise Use of Natural Resources (graded bibliographies), Education Division, Michigan Dept. of Conservation, Lansing, Mich., May, 1952.

Catalog of Free Teaching Aids, Gordon S. Salsbury, P.O. Box 943, Riverside, Calif., 1954.

Cole, Elizabeth, *Guide to Conservation Study,* Education Division, Michigan Department of Conservation, Lansing, Mich., 1949.

"Conservation" (a selected list of official United States Government Publications), Descriptive folder and price list, Code number 0-269699, Superintendent of Documents, U.S. Government Printing Office, Washington 25, D.C., 1953.

Conservation of Natural Resources, (bibliographies, teaching units, etc.) 10-page mimeo. World Book Encyclopedia Reference Library, Field Enterprises, Educational Division, Merchandise Mart Plaza, Chicago 54, Ill.

Educational Film Guide, Annual, H. W. Wilson Co., 950 University Ave., New York 52, N.Y.

Fairchild, Wilma Belden, "Renewable Resources: A World Dilemma; Recent Publications on Conservation" *Geographical Review,* Vol. 39, pp. 89-98, 1949.

Hatcher, Halene, *Helps for Teachers of Geography and Conservation,* Circular No. 310, Division of Secondary Education, Federal Security Agency, Office of Education, Washington 25, D.C., Aug., 1949.

International Index of Films on the Conservation of Resources, prepared for the United Nations Scientific Conference on the Conservation and Utilization of Resources, Aug.-Sept., 1949.

Jorgensen, Arthur W., *Current and Selected References on Conservation* (For teachers and pupils), Publication No. 616-54, Wisconsin Conservation Department, Madison 1, Wis., 1954.

Recommended Reading List on the Conservation of Human and Natural Resources, School of Librarianship, University of Denver, Denver, Colo.

Reid, Seerley, and Carpenter, Anita, *A Directory of 2660 16mm Film Libraries*, Office of Education Bulletin, 1953, No. 7, 172 pages, Superintendent of Documents.

Selected Bibliography on Geography Education for Curriculum Committees, Professional Paper No. 12, National Council of Geography Teachers, Chicago, March, 1951.

Some References on Forests and Related Natural Resources, U.S. Forest Service, September 1, 1952 (mimeo).

Sources of Information Concerning the Commercial Fisheries, Fishery Leaflet 362, Revised Jan., 1952, U.S. Fish and Wildlife Service. Original by Elliott, R. Paul, revision by Keefe, Ruth V.

Visual Materials on Soil and Water Conservation, Soil Conservation Service, 1951.

SECTION I

Professional readings for the conservation teacher, in addition to those cited or listed for Chapter 17:

Becker, Henry F., "Some Implications of Resource-Use Education for Geographers," *Journal of Geography*, Vol. LI, No. 3, March, 1952.

Bennett, Hugh H., *Our American Land—The Story of Its Abuse and Its Conservation*, U.S.D.A. Misc. Pub. 596, Washington, D.C., 1950.

Boatman, Julien L., "Teachers and Conservation" in *Trees: The Yearbook of Agriculture, 1949*, pp. 658-661.

Calef, Wesley, "Special Geographic Contributions to Conservation Education," *Journal of Geography*, Vol. LI, No. 3, March, 1952.

Carskadon, Thomas R., and Modley, Rudolf, *U.S.A.: Measure of a Nation*, Macmillan, New York, N.Y., 1949.

Diettrich, Sigismond DeR., "Geography and Resource-Use Education," *Journal of Geography*, Vol. LIII, No. 3, March 1954, pp. 131-138.

Funderburk, R. S., *History of Conservation Education in the United States* (Contribution to Education, No. 392), Peabody Press, Nashville, Tenn., 1948.

Gant, George F., "Education in the Use of Natural Resources," Chapter IX in 44th Yearbook, National Society for the Study of Education, Washington, D.C., 1945, pp. 188-208.

Hall, O. F., McCabe, Robert A., Lagler, Karl F., Marshall, William H., and Weaver, Richard L., *Training the Conservation Worker* (7-page leaflet), reprinted from *Bulletin*, American Institute of Biological Science, Jan., 1954. (National Association of Biology Teachers.)

Halverson, L. H., "Whither Conservation Education?" *Journal of Geography*, Vol. XLVI, No. 5, May, 1947.

Kazeck, Melvin E., "Conservation Aims," *Journal of Geography*, Vol. LIV, No. 1, Jan., 1955, pp. 32-34.

Kitchens, J. H. Jr., "Educating the Educators," *American Forests*, Vol. 55, No. 1, Jan., 1949.

Olsen, Edward G., *School and Community Programs*, Prentice-Hall, Inc., New York, N.Y., 1949.

Reitz, William W., "Teaching Resource Conservation Thru Geography," *Journal of Geography*, Vol. XLVI, No. 6, Sept., 1947.

Rotter, George E., "Conservation Education in Our Schools," *Soil Conservation*, XVIII, No. 1, August, 1952.

Sharpe, George, "A Mountain Camp Where Boys and Girls Learn About Conservation," *Soil Conservation*, XVII, No. 11, June, 1952.

Southern, John H., "Noise Is Not Enough," *The Land*, Vol. VIII, No. 4, Winter, 1949-50.

Stout, Dorman G., *Teacher and Community*, World Book Co., Yonkers-on-Hudson, N.Y., 1941.

Whitaker, J. R., *The Life and Death of the Land*, Peabody Press, Nashville, Tenn., 1946.

Conservation Education in American Schools, American Association of School Administrators, Washington, D.C., 1951.

Conservation, Please!, The Garden Club of America, New York, N.Y., 1950.

Geography in the High School, Part 6; National Council of Geography Teachers, McKnight and McKnight, Bloomington, Ill., 1949.

Large Was Our Bounty, Natural Resources and the Schools, Yearbook, Association for Supervision and Curriculum Development, Washington, D.C., 1948.

Present Needs for Research on the Use and Care of Natural Resources (Bulletin 288 of the National Academy of Sciences), National Research Council, Washington, D.C., 1954.

"Report to the People of Wisconsin on Progress in Conservation Education," *Wisconsin Conservation Bulletin*, Vol. 17, No. 2, Feb., 1952.

SECTION J

Suggested class activities and group projects: (Obviously, the choice and manner of employment will vary with locale, educational level, curriculum, and school situation.)

1. Activities:

   a. Field trips:

      (1) To study the soil profile,

      (2) To make a soil test.

      (3) To observe soil erosion or its consequences.

      (4) To observe water pollution.

      (5) To compare wildlife habitats.

      (6) To compare conditions in a healthy forest or grassland area with those resulting from burning or over-grazing.

      (7) To observe good and bad forestry practices, range management, or farming.

      (8) To trace the local water supply from source to outlet.

   b. Camping:

   The group camp is an elaboration of the field trip technique, with the advantages of more concentrated study, experience in group living, and better opportunity to learn good outdoor manners by actual practice. The nature camp conducted in an area removed from cultural developments affords special opportunity for children to acquire such fundamental concepts as natural unity, natural balance, and natural cycles.

   Whether or not camping is incorporated with school work, children might be encouraged to participate in such youth camps as conducted by the Boy Scouts and the 4-H Clubs.

   c. Visits and conducted tours (any one of the following has good educational possibilities):

      (1) Visit to a well-managed farm or ranch.

      (2) Tour of a logging operation and pulp or saw mill.

      (3) Tour of an integrated wood-using plant.

      (4) Visit to a mine or oil field.

      (5) Visit to a fish wharf, fish market, or fish cannery. (If possible, include a fishing cruise.)

      (6) National park tour conducted by a park naturalist.

      (7) Visit to a nature area, wildlife refuge, or wilderness.

      (8) Visit to a "hydro" development for power, irrigation, flood prevention, and so forth.

      (9) Visit to a sanitary landfill.

      (10) Tour of a sewage treatment plant.

      (11) Visit to a fish hatchery or game farm.

      (12) Visit to a public park for a cook-out. (A unique opportunity for teaching fire discipline and landscape sanitation by the direct, informal method.)

(13) Visit to a U.S.D.A. Experiment Station or other experimental establishment involving natural resources.

(14) Visit to a forest tree nursery.

(15) Visit to a metal concentration plant or ore smelter.

(16) Visit to any of the public or private agencies named in this appendix.

(17) Visit to a wood-preserving plant.

(18) Visit to a smelter, flotation plant, or other mineral concentrating establishment.

d. Student investigations and reports:

Student contributions to a conservation course, either as individuals or in committee, may run the whole gamut of resource problems from local water supply or land economy to state law and national policy.

The class should have a voice in the selection of problems for special study, and, as far as possible, each student should be allowed a choice of research topics. Findings should be delivered orally for class discussion, the better to benefit both the investigator and his classmates. The possible choice of topics is almost unlimited. The number assigned should be gauged carefully against available class time to avoid the frustration caused by omitting a report after it has been readied for presentation.

e. Collection of literature and teaching materials:

The instructor of in-service and prospective teachers may elect to assemble for each a file of free and inexpensive conservation literature for school use. The author knows from experience that a very considerable collection can be acquired during a twelve-week course. (A wooden apple box serves well as a file.) Also on the basis of experience, the author would caution against the waste of useful materials occasioned by delivering them to students who fail to use them.

Many of the agencies and organizations named in this appendix are sources of material, but perhaps only a few selected ones should be contacted during any term or semester course. Any type or item of information desired should be requested by one letter in sufficient copies for the entire class, thereby saving secretarial time and shipping expense. Never should the instructor permit several students to address individual inquiries to the same source.

f. Course or program planning for teachers:

In a teacher-training institution that offers only one course in conservation, that course should include some work in materials and methods. Actual preparation for conservation teaching may be facilitated by dividing the class into groups according to the grade level at which the class members teach or intend to teach, and requiring each group to prepare a definite plan or guide for future use. Such group planning can be a most profitable experience. When combined with the collection activity (Section *e* above), and including evaluation and graduation of the collected materials, it is particularly valuable. (A teacher-training institution, especially if it operates on a term basis, should offer two terms of work in conservation—a preliminary *survey* course which introduces the entire conservation field and a *professional* course dealing with materials and methods in conservation education.)

g. Essay contests and publicity campaigns:

Conservation students should be encouraged to enter essay contests sponsored by various organizations and business firms, with teacher emphasis, of course, on educational values rather than on prize money.

College students might be encouraged and coached to write timely articles for the local press or to speak on conservation topics before local business clubs, church groups, etc. Findings under Section *d* above might well merit some off-campus dissemination.

2. Projects:

a. School ground or campus improvement:

Object lessons in landscape housekeeping may be learned without leaving the school ground or campus. Students can be taught to deposit waste paper, candy wrappers, paper cups, empty bottles, etc., in proper receptacles. They can be taught to *conserve* the grass by keeping to the walks (even on corners). They can conserve, and by example, teach their schoolmates to conserve, the beauty of their school environment.

This technique for teaching conservation may be used at any grade level. The author has a standing rule, announced in the first meeting of each conservation class, that any member observed littering the campus with trash or cutting across grassed areas automatically fails the course. He allows points toward a final course grade to class members who persuade other students to refrain from spoiling the campus. (Male athletes often accumulate a considerable conservation score.)

Beautification of the school ground by planting trees and shrubs or sowing grass can be an excellent learning experience for children. Bare spots and any eroding areas should be considered invitations for a conservation class to apply suitable soil-conserving measures.

Many a barren, dissected school ground has been made whole and beautiful by young children supervised by a competent teacher.

(Discretion must be exercised in any school ground or campus project. Prevention of normal playground wear must not be contemplated, certainly. The teacher must have administrative sanction before any alteration of grounds is commenced. If permission is granted reluctantly, the project itself, if well done, may be the means of getting enthusiastic administrative endorsement of subsequent proposals. By being conspicuous, beautification has certain advantages as the initial endeavor of a conservation teacher.)

b. Roadside sanitation:

Particularly in rural areas, the conservation teacher can achieve excellent training of students in landscape sanitation by assigning the class (or each of several classes) the task of cleaning, and keeping clean, a certain length of roadsides extending from the school.

The act of collecting and burying all the assorted trash found along a stretch of road or highway succeeds better than discussion to convince children that public slovenliness is wasteful of resources. Roadside planting or seeding for erosion control and beautification may be incorporated with sanitation where opportunity affords and official authorization is forthcoming.

The teacher whose class undertakes any kind of roadside improvement should take special precautions against traffic hazards. Arrangements should be made with the Police Department or the Highway Patrol to establish a speed zone where the children are working. The passing motorist, stopped by a police officer and ordered to proceed slowly, may observe what is taking place and be embarrassed by his observation. He may depart the scene a better landscape housekeeper than he was on arrival, taught by child conservators.

c. Forestation or reforestation:

The planting of forest seedlings as a school project can be specially recommended both for humid regions (tree plantations) and for dry regions (windbreaks and shelter belts). It is suitable for any age group, from intermediate grades to college. It yields a high educational return for time expended. A class of thirty students can plant an acre of forest in one hour and enjoy themselves while doing the work; they will observe *their* trees with interest year after year and be reminded of conservation concepts symbolized by those trees. Even to many college students, the simple process of planting a small seedling is strangely mysterious until it is demonstrated by the instructor. Its mastery becomes both educational and satisfying to the student.

The author's spring classes in conservation plant an acre of forest (1,000 seedlings) each year. Both men and women participate in setting the trees, one young man and one co-ed constituting a team. The young man opens holes with a mattock, and kicks life into the seedling after it has been placed in the hole by his partner. The young ladies carry the seedlings in buckets half filled with water.

The conservation teacher desirous of instituting tree-planting as a class or school project should make certain arrangements in advance of the spring planting season. Free seedlings can usually be obtained from public or industrial nurseries. Requests may be made through the County Agent or other official, specifying number and species desired. If the request is honored, the seedlings will be delivered when season and weather are deemed suitable. Land to be planted must be selected, and approval of the owner secured. Protection against fire and domestic animals should be considered in land selection. The teacher would be well-advised to consult the local representative of the U.S. Forest Service or Soil Conservation Service for assistance with project planning.

d. Range seeding or reseeding:

In range regions grass sowing can be a good alternative or complement to tree planting. ("Johnny Grass Seed" serves cooperatively or independently in a "Keep Green" program.) The teacher who contemplates a range-seeding project should contact a representative of the Bureau of Land Management or the Soil Conservation Service for help with choice of site, seed, time of sowing, etc.

e. Preservation of a nature area:

A preservation project involves continuous follow-up demanding sponsorship by a reliable organization. The teacher may organize a sponsoring club, if necessary. Maintenance is infinitely more critical than initial establishment.

Item 7 in Section G will be helpful. Specific instructions may also be obtained from organizations (Sections E, F) and agencies (Section D, 1), identified with nature areas, sanctuaries, refuges, or wilderness.

f. Establishment of a school or community forest:

This is an ambitious undertaking, requiring careful planning and adequate organizational sponsorship. It can be correlated with the nature project suggested in *e* above. The teacher should obtain the advisement of a U.S. Forest Service representative or the State Forester. The support of local civic organizations should be solicited.

g. Wildlife habitat improvement:

Planting of living fences is only one among many possible projects in this category. Sponsorship by a sportsmen's club might be most helpful. Of course, no planting should be done on private property without the owner's permission. One successful demonstration should be the first objective. The demonstration should, preferably, be observable from a well-traveled highway. Opportunities for wildlife habitat improvement are present almost everywhere, ranging in scope from the protection of a bird's nest to the establishment of a nature sanctuary as suggested in *e* above.

h. Scrap metal salvage drive:

The collection of discarded metal objects can be both instructive and profitable. Definite arrangements for purchase of the objects by a reliable dealer should be made before the drive is launched. Planned use of proceeds for some good purpose might be publicized before collection is commenced. Care should be taken to organize carefully and operate the project systematically. The students should be afforded the opportunity to observe how the salvaged materials are sorted and prepared for shipment. Time and distance permitting, the drive might be climaxed with a visit to a steel plant to see the importance of scrap in steel production.

i. Community improvement:

The conservation teacher may find an excellent opportunity for class, club, or school participation in a community project or program launched by another group or agency. Cooperative effort identifies the genuine conservator.

j. Miscellaneous:

Other possibilities for applied conservation by a group of students are legion, including:

(1) Fire prevention
(2) School garden
(3) House to house inspection and repair of leaky water faucets
(4) Building and erection of bird houses
(5) Building a compost pile with leaves

The well trained and inspired conservation teacher will have no difficulty discovering good conservation projects. Selection of one or two best suited to locale and students poses the greater problem.

Selected Bibliography

Selected Bibliography

CHAPTER 1: THE IDEA AND THE BOOK

Atwood, Wallace W., "The Conservation Movement in America," Chapter I, in *Our National Resources and their Conservation*, edited by A. E. Parkins and J. R. Whitaker, John Wiley and Sons, Inc., New York, 1936.

Beatty, Robert O., "The Conservation Movement," Reprinted from: *The Annals* of the American Academy of Political and Social Science, May, 1952.

Boerker, Richard H. D., *Behold Our Green Mansions*, Chapter I: "What is Conservation?" University of North Carolina Press, Chapel Hill, N.C., 1945.

Bromfield, Louis, *Out of the Earth*, Harper and Brothers, New York, 1950.

Brown, Ralph H., *Historical Geography of the United States*, Harcourt, Brace, and Company, New York, 1948.

Bunce, Arthur C., "Society and Conservation," *Land Policy Review*, Vol. IV, No. 6, June, 1941, pp. 13-22.

Burch, Guy Irving, "Conservation and Population," *American Forests*, Vol. 55, No. 11, p. 13, November, 1949.

Dana, S. T., editor, *History of Activities in the Field of Natural Resources*, University of Michigan Press, Ann Arbor, Michigan, 1953.

Fairchild, Wilma Belden, "The American Scene," in *Readings in the Geography of North America* (A Selection of Articles from the Geographical Review), American Geographical Society, New York, 1952.

Fonda, Morris E., "A New Concept of Conservation," *Journal of Soil and Water Conservation*, Vol. 7, No. 4, pp. 171-173, September, 1952.

Gustafson, A. F., Guise, C. H., Hamilton, W. J., Jr., and Ries, H., *Conservation in the United States*, Comstock Publishing Company, Ithaca, New York, 3rd edition, 1949.

Jones, C. F. and Darkenwald, G. G., *Economic Geography*, The Macmillan Company, New York, Revised 1954.

Lowdermilk, W. C., *Conquest of the Land Through Seven Thousand Years,* U.S.D.A., Washington, D.C., 1944.

Miller, Paul A., "A Social Phase to the Conservation Task," *Journal of Soil and Water Conservation,* Vol. 7, No. 5, pp. 237-242, November, 1952.

Osborn, Fairfield, *Our Plundered Planet,* Little, Brown and Co., New York, 1948.

Parkins, A. E. and Whitaker, J. R., *Our Natural Resources and Their Conservation,* John Wiley and Sons, Inc., New York, 1936.

Partain, Lloyd E., "Exploitation of Resources," *Transactions,* Seventeenth North American Wildlife Conference, Miami, Florida, 1952, Wildlife Management Institute, pp. 71-81.

Paullin, C. O. and Wright, John K., *Atlas of Historical Geography of the United States,* American Geographical Society, New York, 1932.

Peffer, E. Louise, *The Closing of the Public Domain, Disposal and Reservation Policies, 1900-1950,* Stanford University Press, Stanford, California, 1951.

Renner, George T., *The Conservation of National Resources,* John Wiley and Sons, Inc., New York, 1942.

Renner, G. T. and Hartley, W. H., *Conservation and Citizenship,* D. C. Heath and Company, Boston, 1940.

Semple, Ellen Churchill and Jones, Clarence Fielden, *American History and Its Geographic Conditions,* Houghton Mifflin Co., New York, (Revised Edition), 1933.

Smith, Guy-Harold, editor, *Conservation of Natural Resources,* John Wiley and Sons, Inc., New York, 1950.

Sprout, Harold, and Sprout, Margaret, *Foundations of National Power,* Princeton University Press, 1945. (Especially Chapter 16: "The United States.")

Van Hise, Charles Richard, *The Conservation of Natural Resources in the United States,* The Macmillian Company, New York, 1910.

Van Hise, Charles Richard, and Havemeyer, Louis, *Conservation of Our Natural Resources,* The Macmillan Company, New York, 1930.

Van Valkenburg, Samuel, and Stotz, Carl L., *Elements of Political Geography,* Second Edition, 1954, Prentice-Hall, Inc., New York. (Chapters 11 and 12)

Whitaker, J. Russell, and Ackerman, Edward A., *American Resources, Their Management and Conservation,* Harcourt, Brace, and Company, New York, 1951.

A Program to Strengthen the Scientific Foundation in National Resources, House Document No. 706, 81st Congress, Second Session, Public Lands Committee, House of Representatives, U.S. Congress, November, 1950.

"Scientists Look at Resources," (1st Report from Gatlinburg Conference III), *Bulletin of the Bureau of School Service,* Vol. XX, No. 4, University of Kentucky, June, 1948.

"The Conservation Tangle," (A symposium of Opinions with Editorial Comment), *The Land,* Vol. XII, No. 1, Spring, 1953.

CHAPTER 2: NATURAL ENVIRONMENT AND RESOURCES

Atwood, Wallace, W., *The Physiographic Provinces of North America*, Ginn and Company, Boston, 1940.

Bowie, William, *Shaping the Earth*, Publication 3153, Smithsonian Institution, Washington, D.C., 1931.

Carter, Vernon Gill, *Man On the Landscape*, National Wildlife Federation, Washington, D.C., 1949.

De Martonne, Emmanuel, "The Interdependence of Resources," Vol. I, Plenary Meetings U.N. Scientific Conference on the Conservation and Utilization of Resources, Lake Success, N.Y., 1949, pp. 55-58.

Dice, Lee R., *Natural Communities*, University of Michigan Press, Ann Arbor, Michigan, 1952.

Dreibelbis, F. R., "Some Relationships of Precipitation and Soil Loss on Small Agricultural Watersheds," *Journal of Soil and Water Conservation*, Vol. 7, No. 3, July, 1952, pp. 113-116 and 127.

Ekblaw, W. Elmer, "The Attributes of Place," *The Journal of Geography*, Vol. XXXVI, No. 6, September, 1937.

——, "The Role of Soils in Geographic Interpretation," *Annals* of the Association of American Geographers, Vol. XXVII, September, 1937, pp. 149-154.

Fawcett, C. B., "The Numbers and Distribution of Mankind," *Scientific Monthly*, Vol. LXIV, No. 5, May, 1947.

James, Preston E., *A Geography of Man*, Ginn and Company, Boston, 1951, (Especially appendices B, C, and D).

Landsberg, Helmut, "Climate As A Natural Resource," *Scientific Monthly*, Vol. LXII, No. 4, October, 1946.

Lobeck, A. K., *Geomorphology*, McGraw-Hill Book Company, Inc., New York, 1939.

Lowdermilk, W. C., *Man-Made Deserts*, U.S. Department of Agriculture, Soil Conservation Service, (an article from *Pacific Affairs*, Vol. VIII, No. 4, December, 1935).

Osborn, Ben, "Range Soil Conditions Influence Water Intake," *Journal of Soil and Water Conservation*, Vol. 7, No. 3, pp. 128-132, July, 1952.

Sears, Paul B., "Darwin and the Living Landscape," *The Land*, Vol. IX, No. 3, Autumn, 1950.

Semple, Ellen Churchill, *Influences of Geographic Environment*, Henry Holt and Company, Inc., New York, 1930.

Shantz, H. L., "Plants as Soil Indicators," in U.S. Department of Agriculture *Soils and Men: Yearbook of Agriculture, 1938*, pp. 835-860.

Storer, John H., *The Web of Life*, Devin-Adair Company, New York, 1953.

Thornthwaite, C. W., "An Approach Toward a Rational Classification of Climate," *Geographical Review*, Vol. 38, No. 1, January, 1948.

Visher, Stephen S., *Climatic Atlas of the United States,* Harvard Universit
    Press, Cambridge, 1954.

——, "Torrential Rains as a Serious Handicap in the South," *Geographical Re
    view,* Vol. XXXI, No. 4, October, 1941.

Woolf, D. O., *The Identification of Rock Types,* U.S. Department of Commerce
    Bureau of Public Roads, Washington, D.C., 1950.

Yarnell, David L., *Rainfall Intensity-Frequency Data,* U.S.D.A. Miscellaneou
    Publication No. 204, 1935.

*Conservation of Renewable Natural Resources, (Some Fundamental Aspect
    of the Problem),* University of Pennsylvania Press, Philadelphia, 1941.

"A Symposium On Cycles In Animal Populations" (eleven contributors), *Th
    Journal of Wildlife Management,* Vol. 18, No. 1, January, 1954, pp.1-112

CHAPTER 3: WATER ON THE LAND

Bennett, Hugh Hammond, "Warning: The Water Problem is National,"
    The Saturday Evening Post, 13 May, 1950.

Borchert, John R., "The Surface Water Supply of American Municipalities,"
    Annals of the Association of American Geographers, Vol. XLIV, No. I
    March, 1954, pp. 15-32.

Brown, Carl B., "Damages Resulting From Uncontrolled Runoff and Si
    Movement," Delivered to 5 December, 1947 meeting of Soil Conserva
    tion Society of America, U.S.D.A. Soil Conservation Service, 5 pag
    mimeo.

——, Chapter 22, "Effects of Soil Conservation," in Parker D. Trask, ed
    Applied Sedimentation, published by John Wiley and Sons, Inc., Nev
    York, 1950.

Langbein, Walter, *Topographic Characteristics of Drainage Basins,* Wate
    Supply Paper 968-C, U.S.G.S., Washington, D.C., 1947.

Langbein, Walter B. and others, *Annual Runoff in the United States,* U.S.G.S
    Circular 52, June, 1949.

Mahlie, W. S., "Good Water and Human Longevity," *Scientific Monthly,* Vo
    LX, No. 6, June, 1945.

McGuinness, C. L., *The Water Situation in the United States with Specia
    Reference to Ground Water,* U.S.G.S. Circular 114, Washington, D.C.
    June, 1951.

Meinzer, Oscar Edward, *The Occurrence of Ground Water in the United States
    Water Supply Paper No. 489, U.S.G.S., 1943.

——, *Outline of Ground-Water Hydrology,* Water Supply Paper No. 494
    U.S.G.S., Washington, D.C., 1923.

Meinzer, O. E., Burdick, Charles B., and Morris, Samuel B., "Ground Water–
    A Vital National Resource," *Journal, American Water Works Association
    Vol. 34, No. 11, November, 1942.

Munns, E. N., "Our Growing Water Problem," *American Forests,* Vol. 54, Nos. 8 and 9, August and September, 1948.

Ullman, Edward L., "Rivers as Regional Bonds: The Columbia-Snake Example," *Geographical Review,* Vol. XLI, No. 2, April 1951.

White, Gilbert, "Water Limits to Human Activity in the United States," Proceedings of the Inter-American Conference on Conservation of Renewable National Resources, Denver, 1948, U.S. Department of State Publication 3382, Washington, D.C.

Wolman, Abel, "Characteristics and Problems of Industrial Water Supply," *Journal, American Water Works Association,* Vol. 44, No. 4, pp. 279-286, April, 1952.

A History of Navigation on the Tennessee River System, Message from the President, U.S. Government Printing Office, 75th Congress, 1st Session, House Document No. 254, Washington, D.C., 1937.

A Summary of the Water Situation in the United States with Special Reference to Surface Water, prepared for the President's Water Resources Policy Commission, U.S.G.S., September, 1950.

Climate and Man: Yearbook of Agriculture, 1941, Washington, D.C.

"Water in the United States," *Focus,* Vol. I, No. 4, 15 January, 1951.

The Physical and Economic Foundation of Natural Resources, Vol. II, *The Physical Basis of Water Supply and its Principal Uses,* Vol. III, *Groundwater Regions of the United States—Their Storage Facilities,* Interior and Insular Affairs Committee, House of Representatives, U.S. Congress, 1952.

CHAPTER 4: OUR SOILS—BASIC WEALTH

Auten, John T. and Plair, T. B., "Forests and Soils," in: *Trees: Yearbook of Agriculture, 1949,* pp. 114-119.

Beeson, Kenneth C., "Better Soils, Better Food," in: *Science in Farming: Yearbook of Agriculture 1943-1947,* pp. 485-489.

Ekblaw, W. Elmer, "Soil Science and Geography," Soil Science Society of America, *Proceedings,* Vol. I, 1937.

Ferguson, John W., "You Can Learn About Soil—With a Scorecard," *The Ohio Conservation Bulletin,* Vol. 16, No. 12, December, 1952.

Forman, Jonathan, and Fink, Ollie E., editors, *Soil, Food, and Health,* Friends of the Land, Columbus, Ohio, 1948.

Gull, P. W., and Hoffer, G. H., "There's a Hidden Crop in Your Soil," *What's New in Crops and Soils,* Vol. 5, No. 4, pp. 16-18, January, 1953.

Kellogg, Charles E., *Development and Significance of the Great Soil Groups of the United States,* U.S.D.A. Miscellaneous Publication 229, 1936.

———, *The Soils that Support Us,* The Macmillan Company, New York, 1941.

———, "Soil Survey in Relation to Soil Conservation," in: Vol. VI, *Land Resources,* Proceedings of the United Nations Scientific Conference on the Conservation and Utilization of Resources, 1949, pp. 114-119.

———, "Soil and the People," *Annals,* Association of American Geographers, Vol. 27, No. 3, September, 1937, pp. 142-148.

Kendall, Henry M., Glendinning, Robert M., and MacFadden, Clifford H., *Introduction to Geography,* Harcourt, Brace, and Company, New York, 1951, Chapter 15.

Lyon, T. Lyttleton, Buckman, Harry O., and Brady, Nyle C., *The Nature and Properties of Soils,* The Macmillan Company, New York, Fifth Edition, 1952.

Marbut, Curtis F., "Soils of the United States," Part III, *Atlas of American Agriculture,* Washington, D.C., 1935.

Mickey, Karl B., *Man and the Soil,* International Harvester Company, Chicago, 1945.

Norman, A. G., "Organic Matter in Soils," in: *Science in Farming, Yearbook of Agriculture, 1943-1947,* pp. 499-510.

Paulson, E. N., and Swarner, L. R., "Elements in the Soil," *The Reclamation Era,* Vol. 38, No. 2, p. 28, February, 1952.

Soils and Men, Yearbook of Agriculture, 1938, Parts III, IV, and V, Washington, D.C.

Stiles, Walter, *Trace Elements in Plants and Animals,* The Macmillan Company, New York, 1946.

Thorp, James, "How Soils Develop Under Grass," in: *Grass: Yearbook of Agriculture, 1948,* Washington, D.C.

CHAPTER 5: LAND MANAGEMENT

Auten, John T., "Forests for Old Fields," *Science in Farming: Yearbook of Agriculture, 1943-1947,* pp. 473-480.

Baker, O. E., *A Graphic Summary of Physical Features and Land Utilization in the United States,* U.S. Department of Agriculture Miscellaneous Publication No. 260, 1937.

Barnes, Carleton P., and others, *Maladjustments in Land Use in the United States,* Part VI—Supplementary Report of the Land Planning Committee of the National Resources Board, Washington, D.C., 1935.

Benedict, Murray R., *Farm Policies of the United States 1790-1950: A Study of Their Origins and Development,* 20th Century Fund, 330 West 42nd St., New York 36, N.Y., 1953.

Bennett, Hugh H., "Adjustment of Agriculture to Its Environment," *Annals,* Association of American Geographers, Vol. XXXIII, No. 4, December, 1943.

Brodell, A. P., and Ewing, J. A., *Use of Tractor Power, Animal Power, and Hand Methods in Crop Production*, U.S. Department of Agriculture, Washington, D.C., 1948.

Efferson, J. Norman, *Principles of Farm Management*, McGraw-Hill Book Company, Inc., New York, 1953.

Ely, Richard J., and Wehrwein, George S., *Land Economics*, The Macmillan Company, New York, 1940.

Fredine, C. Gordon, "Wildlife's Place in a Wet-Land-Use Program," *Transactions*, Seventeenth North American Wildlife Conference, 1952, Wildlife Management Institute, pp. 106-115.

Graham, Edward, *Natural Principles of Land Use*, Oxford University Press, New York, 1944.

Gray, L. C., "Our Major Land Use Problems and Suggested Lines of Action," *Farmers in a Changing World: Yearbook of Agriculture, 1940*, pp. 398-415, Washington, D.C., 1941.

Heady, Earl O., *Economics of Agricultural Production and Resource Use*, especially Chapter 26, "Fundamentals of Conservation and Land Use," Prentice-Hall, Inc., New York, 1952.

Hillman, Arthur, *Community Organization and Planning*, The Macmillan Company, New York, 1949.

Hudson, H. E., Jr., Brown, Carl B., Shaw, Harry B., and Longwell, J. S., "Effect of Land Use on Reservoir Siltation," *Journal, American Waterworks Association*, Vol. 41, No. 10, October, 1949.

Joerg, W. L. G., "Geography and National Land Planning," *Geographical Review*, Vol. XXV, No. 2, pp. 177-208, April, 1935.

Johnson, V. W., and Barlowe, R., *Land Problems and Policies*, McGraw-Hill Book Company, Inc., New York, 1954.

Lord, Russell, *Behold Our Land*, Houghton Mifflin Company, Chicago, 1938.

McMurry, K. C., "Geographic Contributions to Land-Use Planning," *Annals*, Association of American Geographers, Vol. XXVI, No. 1, March, 1936, pp. 91-98.

Partain, Lloyd E., "Land—Key to Industrial Progress," *Journal of Soil and Water Conservation*, Vol. 8, No. 1, pp. 9-13, 36, January, 1953.

Parson, Ruben L., "Land Planning," *Southern Conservationist*, Vol. I, No. 7, October, 1937, Jackson, Mississippi.

Raper, Arthur F., *Rural Trends*, U.S. Department of Agriculture, Extension Service and Bureau of Agricultural Economics, Washington, D.C., 1952.

——, and Raper, Martha J., *Guide to Agriculture U.S.A.*, U.S. Department of Agriculture, Agriculture Information Bulletin No. 30, Washington, D.C., 1951.

Reuss, L. A., Wooten, H. H., and Marschner, F. J., *Inventory of Major Land Uses in the United States*, U.S. Department of Agriculture, Miscellaneous Publication 663, Washington, D.C., 1948.

Robbins, Roy M., *Our Landed Heritage: The Public Domain, 1776-1936,* Princeton University Press, Princeton, N.J., 1942.

Sawyer, Robert W., "The Whole Story," *American Forests,* Vol. 59, No. 3, March 1953, pp. 10-12, 39.

Selby, H. E., "How Many Acres Do We Require?" *Land Policy Review,* Vol. III, No. 6, September, 1940.

Steele, J. G., *The Measure of Our Land,* Soil Conservation Service, Washington, D.C., 1951.

Terrell, R. Paul, "The Wood Pulp Industry of the Southeast," Paper presented at 48th Annual Meeting, Association of American Geographers, Washington, D.C., August 6-7, 1952.

Timmons, John F., and Murray, William G., editors, *Land Problems and Policies,* especially Chapters 4, 5, 13, 14, and 15, Iowa State College Press, Ames, Iowa, 1950.

Wickstrom, John H., "Conservation—Everyone's Way of Life," *Journal of Soil and Water Conservation,* Vol. 7, No. 4, pp. 192-194, September, 1952.

Land Utilization—A Graphic Summary, Vol. V, Part 4, Cooperative Report, Bureau of the Census and Bureau of Agricultural Economics, Washington, D.C., 1952.

Farm Tenancy, National Resources Committee, Washington, D.C., February, 1937.

Generalized Types of Farming in the United States, Bureau of Agricultural Economics, U.S.D.A. Agriculture Information Bulletin No. 3, February, 1950.

Graphic Summary of Land Utilization in the United States, Cooperative Report, Bureau of the Census and Bureau of Agricultural Economics, Washington, D.C., 1947.

Land Classification in the United States, Report of the Land Committee, National Resources Planning Board, Washington, D.C., 1941.

Report of the Land Planning Committee, Part II, Report of the National Resources Board, Washington, D.C., 1934.

Report on Economic Conditions of the South, National Emergency Council, Washington, D.C., 1938.

Rural Zoning—A Monograph, New England Regional Planning Commission, Boston, Publication No. 49, April, 1937.

CHAPTER 6: WATER CONSERVATION

Barrows, H. K., *Floods, Their Hydrology and Control,* McGraw-Hill Book Company, Inc., New York, 1948.

Bennison, E. W., editor, "Ground Water Resources and Their Conservation," *The Johnson National Driller's Journal,* Volumes 22, 23, and 24, 1950-1-2, Edward E. Johnson, Inc., St. Paul, Minnesota.

Bolinger, Dwight L., "There's Gold in the Sewers," reprinted from *The Progressive*, "The Land," Vol. VIII, No. 4, Winter 1949-50.

Brown, Carl B., "How Effective are Soil Conservation Measures in Sedimentation Control?," Delivered before Federal Inter-Agency Sedimentation Conference, Denver, Colorado, May 6-8, 1947.

———, "Planning the Watershed," *Journal of Soil and Water Conservation*, Vol. 7, No. 1, January, 1952, pp. 16-21.

Colman, E. A., *Vegetation and Watershed Management*, The Ronald Press, New York, 1953.

Conkling, Harold, "Utilization of Ground-Water Storage in Stream System Development," Paper No. 2272, Reprinted from *Transactions*, American Society of Civil Engineers, Vol. III, 1946, pp. 275-354.

Coyle, David Cushman, *Land of Hope, The Way of Life in the Tennessee Valley*, Row, Peterson and Company, Evanston, Illinois, 1941.

Frank, Bernard, and Netboy, Anthony, *Water, Land, and People*, Alfred A. Knopf, New York, 1950.

Grahame, Arthur, "Battle for the Brandywine," *Outdoor Life*, October, 1951.

Hardenbergh, W. A., *Sewerage and Sewage Treatment*, International Textbook Company, Scranton, Pennsylvania, Third Edition, 1950.

Heard, W. L., "Putting the Watershed Plan to Work," *Journal of Soil and Water Conservation*, Vol. 7, No. 1, January, 1952, pp. 22-27.

Huffman, Roy E., *Irrigation Development and Public Water Policy*, The Ronald Press, New York, 1953.

Lee, David B., "The States and Water Pollution Control," *Transactions*, Seventeenth North American Wildlife Conference, 1952, Wildlife Management Institute, pp. 34-43.

Leopold, Luna B., and Maddock, Thomas, Jr., *The Flood Control Controversy—Big Dams, Little Dams, and Land Management*, The Ronald Press, New York, 1954.

Leuchtenburg, William Edward, *Flood Control Politics—The Connecticut River Valley Problem, 1927-1950*, Harvard University Press, Cambridge, Mass., 1953.

McMeans, George B., "Steel Plant Water Conservation," Paper presented at San Francisco regional meeting, 1951, American Iron and Steel Institute.

Mitchelson, A. T., "Conservation of Water Through Recharge of the Underground Supply," *Civil Engineering*, Vol. 9, No. 3, March, 1939.

Munns, E. N., "A Comprehensive Water Policy," *American Planning and Civic Annual*, 1951, pp. 1-7, edited by Harlean James, American Planning and Civic Association, Washington, D.C., 1952.

Richards, Annette H., "The New Look in Valleys," *Survey*, August, 1950.

Roper, Roswell M., Ground Water Replenishment By Surface Water Diffusion, *Journal, American Water Works Association*, Vol. 31, No. 2, February, 1939.

Ryan, W. J., *Water Treatment and Purification*, McGraw-Hill Book Company, Inc., New York, 1946, Second Edition.

Taylor, Samuel M., *The Gardeners Are Coming*, Vantage Press, New York, 1954.

National Power Survey, Interim Report, Power Series No. 1, Federal Power Commission, Washington, D.C., 1935.

Report of the Water Planning Committee, Part III, Report of the National Resources Board, Washington, D.C., 1934.

Report of the President's Water Resources Policy Commission, 1950, Vol. I—A Water Policy for the American People (General Report), Vol. II—Ten Rivers in America's Future, Vol. III—Water Resources Law.

Subsurface Facilities of Water Management and Patterns of Supply—Type Area Studies (Vol. IV in series on *The Physical and Economic Foundation of Natural Resources*), Interior and Insular Affairs Committee, House of Representatives, U.S. Congress, 1953.

"Supplying Industry With Water," Chapter 10, in Vol. I—Foundations for Growth and Security, Report of President's Materials Policy Commission, Washington, D.C., June, 1952.

Task Force Report on Water Resources Projects (Appendix K), prepared for the Commission on Organization of the Executive Branch of the Government, January, 1949.

"The Missouri Valley," *Fortune*, Vol. XL, No. 2, August, 1949, p. 59.

"Water Pollution Control," Excerpts from *A Water Policy for the American People*, Federal Security Agency, Public Health Service, 1951.

Water Pollution in the United States, House Document No. 155, 76th Congress, 1st Session, Washington, D.C., 1939.

Water Supply and the Texas Economy, U.S. Senate Document No. 57, 83rd Congress, 1st Session, 1953, Prepared by the Bureau of Reclamation, Area Planning Office, Austin, Texas.

CHAPTER 7: SOIL DEPRECIATION

Baur, Arnold J., and Adams, Henry R., "Some Aids in Evaluating Sheet Erosion in the Northeastern States," *Journal of Soil and Water Conservation*, Vol. 8, No. 2, March, 1953, pp. 79-81, 89.

Bennett, Hugh H., "Stream Pollution by Erosion Silt," (Reprinted from hearings before the Committee on Rivers and Harbors, House of Representatives, 79th Congress, 1st Session, On Bills for the Control of Water Pollution, Nov. 3, 14, 15, and 20, 1945) Soil Conservation Service, Washington, D.C.

———, Bell, Forest G., and Robinson, Bert D., "Raindrops and Erosion," U.S.D.A. Circular No. 895, 1951.

Berson, Kenneth C., *Cobalt: Occurrence in Soils and Forages in Relation to a Nutritional Disorder in Ruminants*, U.S.D.A. Agriculture Information Bulletin No. 7, Washington, D.C., March, 1950.

Caldwell, Erskine, and Bourke-White, Margaret, *You Have Seen Their Faces,* Modern Age Books, Inc., New York, 1937.

Chase, Stuart, *Rich Land, Poor Land,* Whittlesey House, New York, 1936.

Craven, Avery, "Soil Exhaustion as a Factor in the Agricultural History of Virginia and Maryland, 1606-1860," *University of Illinois Studies in the Social Sciences,* Vol. XIII, No. 1, 1926.

Gottchalk, L. C., "Effects of Soil Erosion on Navigation in Upper Chesapeake Bay," *Geographical Review,* Vol. 35, No. 2, April, 1945.

Jacks, G. V., and Whyte, R. O., *Vanishing Lands: A World Survey of Soil Erosion,* Doubleday, Doran and Company, Inc., New York, 1939.

Middleton, H. E., *Properties of Soils Which Influence Erosion,* U.S.D.A. Technical Bulletin 178, Washington, D.C., 1930.

Purvis, E. R., "Molybdenum Deficiency Observed in Alfalfa, Citrus, and Lettuce," *What's New in Crops and Soils,* Vol. 5, No. 6, March, 1953.

Rockie, W. A., "Man's Effects on the Palouse," *Geographical Review,* Vol. XXIX, No. 1, January, 1939, pp. 34-45.

Sears, Paul B., *Deserts on the March,* University of Oklahoma Press, Norman, Oklahoma, 1935, revised 1947.

Sharpe, C. F. Stewart, *What Is Soil Erosion?,* U.S.D.A. Miscellaneous Publication No. 286, Washington, D.C., 1938.

Stallings, J. H., "Raindrops Puddle Surface Soil," *Journal of Soil and Water Conservation,* Vol. 7, No. 2, April, 1952, pp. 70-74, 88.

Farm Tenancy, Report of the President's Committee, Prepared under the auspices of the National Resources Committee, Washington, D.C., 1937.

"Symposium on Land Erosion," *Transactions,* American Geophysical Union, Vol. 35, No. 2, April, 1954, pp. 243-281.

Soils and Men: Yearbook of Agriculture, 1938, pp. 60-197, Washington, D.C.

CHAPTER 8: SOIL CONSERVATION

Bear, Firman E., et al., *Diagnostic Techniques for Soils and Crops,* American Potash Institute, Washington, D.C., 1948.

Becker, R. J., and Sauer, E. L., "It Pays to Invest Money in Soil Conservation and Related Farm Improvements," *Journal of Soil and Water Conservation,* Vol. 8, No. 3, May, 1953.

Bennett, Henry G., "Land and Independence—America's Experience," in: *Land Reform—A World Challenge,* Department of State Publication 4445, February, 1952, pp. 67-81.

Bennett, Hugh H., *Elements of Soil Conservation,* McGraw-Hill Book Company, Inc., New York, 1955.
———, *Soil Conservation,* McGraw-Hill Book Company, Inc., New York, 1939.

Cooper, M. R., Roth, W. J., Maddox, J. G., Schickele, R., and Turner, H. A., "The Causes: Defects in Farming Systems and Farm Tenancy," *Soils and Men: Yearbook of Agriculture, 1938*, pp. 137-157.

Cox, Joseph F., and Jackson, Lyman E., *Crop Management and Soil Conservation*, John Wiley and Sons, New York, 1948.

Dale, Tom, "Conservation Farming for the Hard Lands of the Southern Great Plains," U.S.D.A., S.C.S., Washington, D.C., 1941.

Duley, F. L., and Mathews, O. R., "Ways to Till the Soil," in: *Science in Farming: Yearbook of Agriculture 1943-1947*, pp. 518-526.

Edminster, Frank C., "Streambank Plantings for Erosion Control in the Northeast," U.S.D.A. Leaflet 258, Washington, D.C., 1949.

Faulkner, Edward H., *Plowman's Folly*, University of Oklahoma Press, Norman, Oklahoma, 1943.

Feustel, Irvin C., "The Nature and Use of Organic Amendments," in: *Soils and Men: Yearbook of Agriculture, 1938*, pp. 462-468.

Hoover, Max M., Hein, M. A., Dayton, William A., and Erlanson, C. O., "The Main Grasses for Farm and Home," in: *Grass: Yearbook of Agriculture, 1948*.

Hopkins, Donald P., *Chemicals, Humus, and the Soil*, Faber and Faber, Ltd., London, 1945.

Jacobson, Paul, and Weiss, Walter, *Farming Terraced Land*, U.S.D.A., S.C.S. Leaflet No. 335, Washington, D.C., 1953.

Klages, Karl H. W., *Ecological Crop Geography*, Chapters V, VI, XI-XVI, XXI, and Part IV, The Macmillan Company, New York, 1949.

Lord, Russell, *To Hold This Soil*, Soil Conservation Service, U.S.D.A. Miscellaneous Publication No. 321, Washington, D.C., 1938.

—— and Lord, Kate, *Forever the Land*, Harper and Brothers, New York, 1950.

McKee, Roland, "The Legumes of Many Uses," in: *Grass: Yearbook of Agriculture, 1948*, pp. 701-726.

Musser, R. H., *Use the Land and Save the Soil*, U.S.D.A. Soil Conservation Service, Program Aid 71, Washington, D.C., 1949.

Richards, L. A., editor, and other members of United States Salinity Laboratory Staff, *Diagnosis and Improvement of Saline and Alkali Soils*, Agriculture Handbook No. 60, U.S.D.A., February, 1954.

Rockie, William A., "Soil Conservation," Chapter 4 in *Conservation of Natural Resources*, edited by Smith, Guy-Harold, John Wiley and Sons, Inc., New York, 1950.

Rule, Glenn K., et al., *Toward Soil Security on the Northern Great Plains*, U.S.D.A. Farmers' Bulletin No. 1864, 1941.

Tower, Harold E. and Gardner, Harry H., *Strip Cropping for Conservation and Production*, U.S.D.A. Farmers' Bulletin, No. 1981, October, 1953.

Van Dersal, William R., and Graham, Edward H., *The Land Renewed, the Story of Soil Conservation*, Oxford University Press, New York, 1946.

Wickenden, Lawrence, *Gardening With Nature,* Devin-Adair Company, New York, 1954.

A *Manual on Soil and Water Conservation,* U.S.D.A., Soil Conservation Service, Agriculture Handbook No. 61, Washington, D.C., 1954.

Physical Land Surveys, Numbered county studies titled "Physical Land Conditions," (For Use in Conservation Farm Planning), S.C.S. in cooperation with Agricultural Experiment Stations, Washington, D.C.

Proceedings of the U.N. Scientific Conference on the Conservation and Utilization of Resources, 17 Aug.—6 Sept. 1949, Lake Success, N.Y., Vol. VI, Land Resources, U.N., Department of Economic Affairs, 1951, pp. 1-173.

Technical Skill for Soil and Water Conservation, U.S.D.A., S.C.S., Washington, D.C., 23 December, 1949.

CHAPTER 9: *FOREST EXPLOITATION*

Bates, Carlos G., *The Windbreak as a Farm Asset,* U.S.D.A. Farmers' Bulletin No. 1405, revised September, 1944.

Boerker, Richard H. D., *Behold Our Green Mansions,* University of North Carolina Press, Chapel Hill, N.C., 1945.

Brown, Nelson Courtlandt, *Forest Products,* John Wiley and Sons, Inc., New York, 1950.

Bruere, Martha Bensley, *What Forests Give,* U.S.D.A. Forest Service, 1938.

Dayton, William A., "Forest Types of the United States," in: *Trees: Yearbook of Agriculture, 1949,* pp. 109-114.

Dutton, Walt L., "Forest Grazing in the United States," *Journal of Forestry,* Vol. 51, No. 4, April, 1953, pp. 248-251.

Hall, J. Alfred, and Mosley, T. J., *Products of American Forests,* U.S.D.A., Forest Service, revised August, 1946.

Hoover, M. D., and Croft, A. R., "The Relations of Forest to Our Water Supply," *Journal of Forestry,* Vol. 49, No. 4, April, 1951, pp. 245-249.

James, Lee M., and Yoho, James G., "Income From Timber Products in the United States," *Journal of Forestry,* Vol. 51, No. 2, February, 1953, pp. 83-87.

Kendall, Harry T., "A Discussion of the Forest Products and Lumber Industries," delivered before the Atlantic States Shippers Advisory Board, Newark, New Jersey, Weyerhauser Sales Company, St. Paul, Minnesota (undated).

Mattoon, W. R., *Forest Trees and Forest Regions of the United States,* U.S.D.A. Miscellaneous Publication 217, Washington, D.C., 1936.

Merrick, Gordon D., *Wood Used in Manufacture—1948,* Forest Resource Report No. 2, U.S.D.A. Forest Service, May, 1951.

Panshin, A. J., Harrar, E. S., Baker, W. J., and Proctor, P. B., *Forest Products,* McGraw-Hill Book Company, Inc., New York, 1950.

Sparhawk, W. N., "The History of Forestry in America," in: *Trees: Yearbook of Agriculture, 1949*, U.S.D.A., Washington, D.C.

Steer, Henry B., *Lumber Production in the United States 1799-1946*, U.S.D.A. Forest Service, Miscellaneous Publication No. 669, October, 1948.

Stoeckler, Joseph H. and Williams, Ross A., "Windbreaks and Shelterbelts," in: *Trees: Yearbook of Agriculture, 1949*, Washington, D.C., pp. 191-199.

Wilde, S. A., *Forest Soils and Forest Growth*, especially Chapters I, V, and XII, Chronica Botanica Company, Waltham, Mass., 1946.

Williams, Ross, "Trees that Beat the Blizzard," *American Forests*, Vol. 55, No. 8, August, 1949.

Zon, Raphael, *Forests*, in section on "Natural Vegetation," *Atlas of American Agriculture*, U.S.D.A., Washington, D.C., 1924.

Glesinger, Egon, *The Coming Age of Wood*, Simon and Schuster, Inc., New York, 1949.

Crops in Peace and War: Yearbook of Agriculture, 1950-1951, U.S.D.A., Washington, D.C., pp. 793-826.

Forest Cover Types of North America, 1954 edition, Society of American Foresters, Washington, D.C.

Forest Cover Types of the Eastern United States, Committee on Eastern Forest Types, Society of American Foresters, Washington, D.C., 1942.

Forest Cover Types of Western North America, Committee on Western Forest Types, Society of American Foresters, Washington, D.C., 1945.

Industrial Uses of Selected Timber Species, Industrial Series No. 69, U.S. Department of Commerce, Washington, D.C., 1947.

Living and Forest Lands, U.S.D.A. Miscellaneous Publication No. 388, Forest Service, Washington, D.C., 1940.

Lumber and Timber Basic Products, Census of Manufacturers—1947, Bureau of the Census, Washington, D.C., 1949.

Our Forests: What They Are and What They Mean to Us, U.S.D.A. Miscellaneous Publication No. 162, Washington, D.C., revised October, 1950.

"Protective Functions of the Forests," Volume V, *Forest Resources*, Proceedings, U.N. Scientific Conference on Conservation and Utilization of Resources, 1949, pp. 133-174.

Science in Farming: Yearbook of Agriculture, 1943-1947, U.S.D.A. Washington, D.C., pp. 455-484, 843-846.

Some Plain Facts About the Forests, Forest Service, U.S.D.A. Miscellaneous Publication 543, Washington, D.C., revised 1949.

"The New Age of Wood," *Fortune*, Vol. XXVI, No. 4, October, 1942, p. 117.

Water and Our Forests, Miscellaneous Publication No. 600, U.S.D.A. Forest Service, Washington, D.C., 1946.

"World Shortage of Pulp," *Fortune*, Vol. XXXVI, No. 4, October, 1947.

CHAPTER 10: PERMANENT FORESTS

Arnst, Albert, "No More Pulp Waste," *American Forests*, Vol. 55, No. 1, January, 1949.

Bond, W. E., *Cutting For Profit in Southern Pine Woodlands*, U.S.D.A. Farmers' Bulletin No. 2027, 1951.

Callahan, James D., "Crossett—Monument to Planned Forestry," *American Forests*, Vol. 54, No. 4, April, 1948.

Carhart, Arthur H., *Timber in Your Life*, J. B. Lippincott Co., New York, 1955.

Cassady, John T., and Shepherd, W. O., "Grazing on Forested Lands," in: *Grass: Yearbook of Agriculture, 1948*, Washington, D.C.

Chapman, Herman H., *Forest Management*, The Hildreth Press, Publishers, Bristol, Conn., 1950.

Cowan, Major C. S., "The Place of Second-Growth in Washington's Future Forest Economy," presented before 53rd Annual Convention of Washington State Assessors Association at Longview, Washington, 18 September, 1950.

Dana, Samuel T., "The Growth of Forestry in the Past Half Century," *Journal of Forestry*, Vol. 49, No. 2, February, 1951.

Davis, Clint, "Only You Can Prevent Forest Fires," *American Forests*, Vol. 57, No. 4, April, 1951.

Davis, R. E., "Protecting the Farm Forest from Fire," *The Forest Farmer*, Vol. XII, No. 4, January, 1953.

Everard, W. P., *Modern Turpentining Practices*, U.S.D.A. Farmers' Bulletin No. 1984, 1947.

Eyre, F. H., and LeBarron, Russell K., *Management of Jack Pine Stands in the Lake States*, U.S.D.A. Technical Bulletin No. 863, February, 1944.

——, and Zehngraff, Paul, *Red Pine Management in Minnesota*, U.S.D.A. Circular No. 778, 1948.

Fitzgerald, O. A., "Cash from Slash," *American Forests*, Vol. 58, No. 8, August, 1952.

Fritz, Emanuel, "Winning the Battle of Timber," *Fortune*, Vol. XLII, No. 2, August, 1950, p. 63.

Gross, L. S., *Timber Management Plans on the National Forests*, U.S.D.A. Forest Service, Washington, D.C., 1950.

Greeley, W. B., "A Rational Approach to Forest Practices on Private Lands," *American Forests*, Vol. 56, No. 5, May, 1950.

Hall, A. G., "The Silent Saboteurs," *American Forests*, Vol. 59, No. 2, February, 1953.

Hawley, Ralph C., *The Practice of Silviculture*, John Wiley and Sons, Inc., New York, 5th edition, 1950.

———, and Stickel, P. W., *Forest Protection*, John Wiley and Sons, Inc., New York, 2nd edition, 1949.

Harper, V. L., "Wood For the Future," *The Land*, Vol. XI, No. 3, January, 1953, pp. 270-275.

Holbrook, Stewart H., *Burning an Empire*, The Macmillan Company, New York, 1943.

Hunt, John Clark, "There Is Gold in Wood Waste," *Our Public Lands*, Vol. 1, No. 3, October, 1951.

Jemison, George M., and Hepting, George H., Timber Stand Improvement in the Southern Appalachian Region, U.S.D.A. Forest Service, Miscellaneous Publication No. 693, 1949.

Kerr, Edward F., "Hard-Boiled Forest Law Enforcement," *The Forest Farmer*, Vol. XII, No. 4, January, 1953.

Koroleff, A., and Fitzwater, J. A., *Managing Small Woodlands*, American Forestry Association, Washington, D.C., 1947.

LeBarron, Russell K., *Silvicultural Management of Black Spruce in Minnesota*, Circular No. 791, U.S.D.A. Forest Service, Washington, D.C., 1948.

May, Curtis, and Baker, Whiteford L., "Insects and Spread of Forest-Tree Diseases," in: *Insects: Yearbook of Agriculture, 1952*, U.S.D.A., Washington, D.C., pp. 677-682.

McCulley, Robert D., Bond, W. E., and others, "Symposium on Southern Silviculture," *Journal of Forestry*, Vol. 51, No. 2, February, 1953, pp. 88-97.

Mellinger, Ross H., *They Are Your Woods*, Conservation Commission of West Virginia, Charleston, West Virginia, 1952.

Muntz, H. H., *How to Grow Longleaf Pine*, U.S.D.A. Farmers' Bulletin No. 2061, January, 1954.

Nelson, Alfred L., "Trees Pay Off on Farms," *The Conservation Volunteer*, Vol. XVI, No. 91, January-February, 1953, pp. 34-36, Minnesota Department of Conservation, St. Paul, Minnesota.

Pearson, G. A., *Management of Ponderosa Pine in the Southwest*, U.S.D.A. Agriculture Monograph No. 6, Forest Service, Washington, D.C., 1950.

Reynolds, R. R., *Fifteen Years of Management on the Crossett Farm Forestry Forties*, Southern Forest Experiment Station, Occasional Paper 130, July, 1953.

Shepherd, Weldon O., Southwell, Byron L., and Stevenson, J. W., *Grazing Longleaf-Slash Pine Forests*, U.S.D.A. Circular No. 928, November, 1953.

Swingler, W. S., "Forestry as a part of the Farm Enterprise," *Journal of Soil and Water Conservation*, Vol. 8, No. 1, January, 1953.

Westveld, R. H., *Applied Silviculture in the United States*, Edwards Bros., Inc., Ann Arbor, Michigan, 1935.

———, and Peck, R. H., *Forestry in Farm Management*, Second Edition, revised by R. H. Westveld, John Wiley and Sons, Inc., New York, 1951.

Elements of Forest Fire Control, Food and Agriculture Organization of the United Nations, Rome, 1953 (FAO Forestry and Forest Products Studies).

Forestry Handbook for the Upper Mississippi Region (Fifth Edition), U.S.D.A. Soil Conservation Service, Washington, D.C., 1950.

"Forests for the Future," prepared by The Conservation Foundation, Part II of *American Forests,* Supplement, Washington, D.C., December, 1952.

General Recommendations Regarding Methods for Wood Waste Utilization, U.S.D.A. Forest Service, Forest Products Laboratory, Madison, Wisconsin, revised August, 1950.

Grazing and Forest Economy, Food and Agriculture Organization of the United Nations, 1953.

Highlights in the History of Forest Conservation, U.S. Forest Service, U.S.D.A. Agriculture Information Bulletin No. 83, August, 1952.

Managing the Small Forest, U.S.D.A. Farmers' Bulletin No. 1989, revised January, 1948.

Special Tax Edition, *The Forest Farmer,* Vol. XI, No. 9, June, 1952.

The Forest Farmer Manual, Forest Farmers Association Cooperative, Valdosta, Georgia, Second Edition, 1951.

The Progress of Forestry 1945 to 1950, The American Forestry Association, Washington, D.C., 1951.

Trees: Yearbook of Agriculture, 1949, pp. 120-126, 458-461, 485-498, and 508-527. U.S.D.A. Washington, D.C.

Volume V, "Forest Resources," *Proceedings* of the United Nations Scientific Conference on the Conservation and Utilization of Resources, 1949, United Nations, Department of Economic Affairs, New York, 1951.

CHAPTER 11: OUR DRY GRASSLANDS

Albertson, F. W., "Ecology of Mixed Prairie in West Central Kansas," Reprinted from: *Ecological Monographs* 7:481-547, October, 1937.

——, and Weaver, J. E., "Effects of Drought, Dust, and Intensity of Grazing on Cover and Yield of Short-Grass Pastures," Reprinted from: *Ecological Monographs,* 14:1-129, January, 1944.

——, "History of the Native Vegetation of Western Kansas During Seven Years of Continuous Drought," Reprinted from: *Ecological Monographs,* 12:23-51, January, 1942.

Archer, Sellers G., and Bunch, Clarence E., *The American Grass Book: A Manual of Pasture and Range Practices,* Oklahoma University Press, Norman, Oklahoma, 1953.

Benson, Lyman, and Darrow, Robert A., *The Trees and Shrubs of the Southwestern Deserts,* University of Arizona Press, Tucson, Arizona, and University of New Mexico Press, Albuquerque, N.M., 1954.

Bowman, Isaiah, "Our Expanding and Contracting Desert," *Geographical Review,* Vol. 25, No. 1, 1935, pp. 43-61.

Campbell, R. S., Ellison, Lincoln, and Renner, F. G., "Management that Restores the Range," in: *Grass: Yearbook of Agriculture, 1948*, pp. 221-226.

Chilcott, E. C., "Dry-land Farming in the Great Plains Area," *Yearbook of Agriculture, 1907*, pp. 451-468. U.S.D.A., Washington, D.C.

Choun, H. F., "Duststorms in the Southwestern Plains," *Monthly Weather Review*, Vol. 64, No. 6, June, 1936.

Clawson, Marion, *The Federal Range Code for Grazing Districts*, Bureau of Land Management, Washington, D.C., February, 1952.

——, *The Western Range Livestock Industry*, McGraw-Hill Book Company, Inc., New York, 1950.

Climate and Man: Yearbook of Agriculture, 1941, U.S.D.A., Washington, D.C.

Dale, Tom, *For Insurance Against Drought—Soil and Water Conservation*, Farmers' Bulletin No. 2002, U.S.D.A., Washington, D.C., March, 1950.

DeVoto, Bernard, "Our Great West—Boom or Bust?" *Collier's*, Vol. 132, No. 15, 25 December, 1953, p. 46.

Duck, Lester G. "What About Dust Storms?" *Oklahoma Game and Fish News*, May, 1954, pp. 3-5.

Edwards, Everett E., "The Settlement of Grasslands," in: *Grass: Yearbook of Agriculture, 1948*, U.S.D.A., Washington, D.C.

Frandsen, W. R., "Management of Reseeded Ranges," *Journal of Range Management*, Vol. 3, No. 2, pp. 125-129, 1950.

George, Ernest J., *Thirty-One-Year Results in Growing Shelterbelts on the Northern Great Plains*, U.S.D.A. Circular No. 924, August, 1953.

Hibbard, Benjamin Horace, *A History of the Public Land Policies*, especially Chapters XVII, XVIII, XIX, and XX, Peter Smith, New York, 1939.

Hitchcock, A. S., *Manual of the Grasses of the United States*, Second Edition, revised by Chase, Agnes, U.S.D.A. Miscellaneous Publication No. 200, 1951.

Holscher, Clark E., and Woolfolk, E. J., *Forage Utilization by Cattle on Northern Great Plains Ranges*, U.S.D.A. Circular No. 918, June, 1953.

Humphrey, R. R., "The Desert Grassland, Past and Present," *Journal of Range Management*, Vol. 6, No. 3, May, 1953, pp. 159-164.

Hutchings, Selar S., and Stewart, George, *Increasing Forage Yields and Sheep Production on Inter-Mountain Winter Ranges*, U.S.D.A. Circular No. 925, September, 1953.

Lackey, Earl E., "Annual-Variability Rainfall Maps of the Great Plains," *Geographical Review*, Vol. 27, No. 4, October, 1937, pp. 665-670.

Loomer, C. W., and Johnson, V. Webster, *Group Tenure in Administration of Public Lands*, U.S.D.A. Circular No. 829, Washington, D.C., December, 1949.

Lloyd, Bob, "The Dust Blows Again," *American Forests*, Vol. 60, No. 8, August, 1954, pp. 8-12, 51.

McCorkle, J. S., *Grass—The Rancher's Crop*, Leaflet No. 346, U.S.D.A. Soil Conservation Service, January, 1954.

———, and Dale, Tom, *Conservation Practices for the Range Lands of the Southern Great Plains*, U.S.D.A. Soil Conservation Service, Washington, D.C., 1941.

Malin, James Claude, *The Grassland of North America, Prolegomena to its History*, Lawrence, Kansas, 1947.

Meigs, Peveril, "Outlook for the Arid Realm of the United States," *Focus*, Vol. IV, No. 4, December, 1953.

Osterli, Victor P., and Love, R. Merton, "From Brush to Grass to Cattle!" *What's New in Crops and Soils*, Vol. 5, No. 6, March, 1953.

Packer, Paul E., "Effects of Trampling Disturbances on Watershed Condition, Runoff, and Erosion," *Journal of Forestry*, Vol. 51, No. 1, January, 1953, pp. 28-31.

Parker, Kenneth W., "New Trends in Standards of Range Use," *Journal of Forestry*, Vol. 50, No. 11, November, 1952, pp. 856-859.

———, "Application of Ecology in the Determination of Range Condition and Trend," *Journal of Range Management*, Vol. 7, No. 1, January, 1954, pp. 14-22.

Pierson, Royale K., "Dormant Roots," *Our Public Lands*, Vol. 1, No. 2, July, 1951, p. 5.

Renne, R. R., "Conservation of the Western Range," *Journal of Range Management*, Vol. 2, No. 3, pp. 133-141, 1949.

Riegel, Andrew, "Life History and Habits of Blue Grama," *Transactions*, Kansas Academy of Science, Vol. 44, 1941, pp. 76-85.

Rogler, G. A., "A Twenty-Five Year Comparison of Continuous and Rotation Grazing in the Northern Plains," *Journal of Range Management*, Vol. 4, No. 1, pp. 35-41, 1951.

Saunderson, Mont H., *Western Land and Water Use*, University of Oklahoma Press, Norman, Oklahoma, 1950.

Semple, A. T., *Improving the World's Grasslands*, Agricultural Studies, No. 16, Food and Agriculture Organization of the United Nations, 1951.

Shantz, H. L., *Natural Vegetation as an Indicator of the Capabilities of Land for Crop Production in the Great Plains*, Bureau of Plant Industry Bulletin 20, U.S.D.A., 1911.

Tannehill, Ivan Ray, *Drought, Its Causes and Effects*, Princeton University Press, Princeton, New Jersey, 1947.

Weaver, J. E., *North American Prairie*, Johnson Publishing Co., Lincoln, Nebr., 1954.

———, and Albertson, F. W., "Nature and Degree of Recovery of Grassland from the Great Drought of 1933 to 1940," Reprinted from *Ecological Monographs* 14: October, 1944, pp. 393-479.

Webb, John J., Jr., "The Life History of Buffalo Grass," *Transactions*, Kansas Academy of Science, Vol. 44, 1941, pp. 58-75.

Webb, Walter Prescott, *The Great Plains,* Ginn and Company, Boston, 1931.

Weintraub, Frances C., *Grasses Introduced into the United States,* U.S.D.A. Forest Service, Agriculture Handbook No. 58, 1953.

The Future of the Great Plains, U.S. Great Plains Committee, Washington, D.C., 1936.

Northern Great Plains, National Resources Planning Board, Washington, D.C., May, 1940.

Proceedings of the United Nations Scientific Conference on the Conservation and Utilization of Resources, 17 August-6 September, 1949, Lake Success, N.Y., Vol. VI, *Land Resources,* pp. 499-560.

The Taylor Grazing Act of June 28, 1934, with Amendments to October 1, 1949, Bureau of Land Management, Washington, D.C.

CHAPTERS 12 AND 13: WILDLIFE

Allen, Durward L., *Our Wildlife Legacy,* Funk and Wagnalls Company, New York, 1954.

Baker, John H., "Saving Man's Wildlife Heritage," *National Geographic Magazine,* Vol. CVI, No. 5, Nov., 1954, pp. 581-620.

Black, John D., *Biological Conservation: With Particular Emphasis on Wildlife,* The Blakiston Company, Inc., New York, 1954.

Bovey, Martin, *The Saga of the Waterfowl,* The Wildlife Management Institute, Washington, D.C., 1949.

Bennitt, Rudolph, "Wildlife Conservation and Geography," *Journal of Geography,* Vol. XXXIX, No. 6, September, 1940.

Carhart, Arthur H., "It's A Little Dog's Life," *Nature Magazine,* Vol. 46, No. 4, April, 1953, pp. 189-191, 220.

Carson, Rachel L., *Under the Sea-Wind,* Oxford University Press, New York, 1941.

Cook, Dave, "Concerning Predators," reprinted from: *Audubon Magazine,* Vol. XLVIII, No. 3, May-June, 1946.

Dana, Samuel T., "Wildlife in Today's Economy," *Outdoor America,* Vol. 17, No. 1, January-February, 1952.

Darling, J. N., Sheldon, H. P., and Gabrielson, Ira N., *Game Management on the Farm,* U.S.D.A. Farmers' Bulletin, 1759, Washington, D.C., 1936.

Grange, Wallace Byron, *The Way to Game Abundance,* Charles Scribner's Sons, New York, 1949.

Hornaday, William T., *Wild Life Conservation,* Yale University Press, New Haven, Connecticut, 1914.

Kimsey, Alden, "5 Years of Habitat Improvement," *Oklahoma Game and Fish News,* Vol. IX, No. 5, May, 1953, pp. 3-5.

Lack, David, *The Natural Regulation of Animal Numbers,* Oxford University Press, New York, 1954.

Leopold, Aldo, *Game Management,* Charles Scribner's Sons, New York, 1933.

Martin, A. C., and Uhler, F. M., Research Report 30, *Food of Game Ducks in the United States and Canada,* Fish and Wildlife Service, Washington, D.C., 1951.

Martin, A. C., Zim, Herbert S. and Nelson, Arnold L., *American Wildlife and Plants—A Guide to Wildlife Food Habits,* McGraw-Hill Book Company, Inc., New York, 1951.

Odum, Eugene P., *Fundamentals of Ecology,* W. B. Saunders Company, Philadelphia, 1953.

Palmer, E. Laurence, *Cover,* Cornell Rural School Leaflet, New York State College of Agriculture, Cornell University, Ithaca, N.Y., Vol. 38, No. 4, Spring, 1945.

Palmer, L. J., and Shaw, S. B., "A Home for Wildlife," in Forest Service, *Western Range;* Senate Document No. 199, 74th Congress, Washington, D.C., 1936, pp. 341-361.

Peterson, Elmer, "Marsh Drainage and Waterfowl," *Transactions,* Seventeenth North American Wildlife Conference, 1952, Wildlife Management Institute, pp. 123-131.

Rostlund, Erhard, *Freshwater Fish and Fishing in Native North America,* University of California Publications in Geography, Volume 9, University of California Press, Berkeley and Los Angeles, 1952.

Salter, Robert M., "Wildlife as a Managed Crop," *Soil Conservation,* Vol. XVIII, No. 11, June, 1953.

Sheldon, H. P. and Lincoln, Frederick C., *Sportsman's Guide to Wild Ducks* (Illustrated in full natural colors), Wildlife Management Institute, Washington, D.C., 1946.

Swift, Ernest, "Modification of Forest Practice in the Lake States for Wildlife Habitat Betterment," *Journal of Forestry,* Vol. 51, No. 6, June, 1953.

Thomas, E. A., "There's No Profit in Burning Broomsedge," *West Virginia Conservation,* Vol. XVI, No. 12, February, 1953, pp. 10-11.

Trippensee, Reuben Edwin, *Wildlife Management* (Volumes I, II), McGraw-Hill Book Company, Inc., New York, 1948, 1953.

Uhler, Francis M., and Llewellyn, Leonard M. "Fur Productivity of Submarginal Farmland," *Journal of Wildlife Management,* Vol. 16, No. 1, January, 1952, pp. 79-86.

Walker, Lewis W., "Photoflashing Western Owls," *National Geographic Magazine,* Vol. LXXXVII, No. 4, April, 1945.

Wilson, Kenneth A., "Raccoon Predation on Muskrats Near Currituck, North Carolina," *Journal of Wildlife Management,* Vol. 17, No. 2, April, 1953, pp. 113-119.

Big-Game Inventory of the United States, 1948, Wildlife Leaflet 321, Fish and Wildlife Service, Washington, D.C., March, 1952.

"Biology and Land Use," *Soil Conservation*, Vol. VII, No. 50, April, 1942, whole issue.

Game and Fur Conservation, Volume VII, *Wildlife and Fish Resources, Proceedings* of the U.N. Scientific Conference on the Conservation and Utilization of Resources, 1949, United Nations, Department of Economic Affairs, New York, 1951, pp. 187-256.

"Symposium on Farm Fish Ponds and Management," *Journal of Wildlife Management*, Vol. 16, No. 3, July, 1952, pp. 233.

Wildlife Issue, *Soil Conservation*, Vol. IV, No. 9, March, 1939.

CHAPTER 14: RECREATION AND INSPIRATION

Bard, Albert S., "Controlling Billboards Along New York's Thruway," *The American City*, Vol. 67, No. 5, May, 1952.

Bauer, Erwin A., "Farmers Control the Gates to Good Fishing," (reprinted from the *Fisherman*), *Ohio Conservation Bulletin*, Vol. 17, No. 2, February, 1953, pp. 12-13.

Brown, J. Lee, "The Role of Parks in the City Plan," *Parks and Recreation*, Vol. 36, No. 3, March, 1953, p. 6.

Bunce, Frank H., "Outdoor Manners," *Parks and Recreation*, Vol. 36, No. 4, April, 1953, pp. 11-13.

Cooper, C. E., "Tourism," *Journal of Geography*, Vol. XLVI, No. 3, March, 1947.

Doell, Charles E., "Origin and Development of Parks," *Parks and Recreation*, Vol. 35, No. 10 and No. 11, October and November, 1952.

Drury, Newton B., "Recreational-Natural-Aesthetic Values," *Transactions*, Seventeenth North American Wildlife Conference, Miami, Florida, March, 1952, Wildlife Management Institute, Washington, D.C., pp. 62-71.

——, "Preserving Nature—Our National Policy," *The Living Wilderness*, Vol. 17, No. 40, Spring, 1952.

——, "The Dilemma of Our Parks," *American Forests*, Vol. 55, No. 6, June, 1949.

Duthie, George A., "The Community Forest," *American Forests*, Vol. 59, No. 5, May, 1953, p. 14.

Harms, Ernest, "Nature Study—Aid to Mental Health," *Nature Magazine*, Vol. 46, No. 4, April, 1953, pp. 201-204.

Levin, David R., *Public Control of Highway Access and Roadside Development*, Public Roads Administration, Federal Works Agency, Washington, D.C., January, 1947.

MacKaye, Benton, "Wilderness as a Folk School," *The Living Wilderness*, Vol. 17, No. 43, Winter, 1952-53, pp. 1-6.

Mann, Roberts, "Picnic Grounds in a Metropolitan Reservation," *Parks and Recreation*, Vol. 36, No. 3, March, 1953, pp. 7-13.

Richey, Charles A., "National Parks, An Essential Land Use," *American Planning and Civic Annual,* 1951, edited by Harlean James, American Planning and Civic Association, Washington, D.C., 1952, pp. 7-16.

Ross, W. A., and Scranton, L. L., "Landscaping the Farmstead," Vocational Educational Bulletin No. 189, Agriculture Series No. 51, Office of Education, Washington, D.C., (undated).

Stamp, L. Dudley, "Replanning London," *Geographical Review,* Vol. XXXV, No. 4, October, 1945.

Tilden, Freeman, *The National Parks: What They Mean to You and Me,* Alfred A. Knopf, Inc., New York, 1951 (Pocket Edition, 1954).

Wagar, J. V. K., "An Analysis of the Wilderness and Natural Area Concept," *Journal of Forestry,* Vol. 51, No. 3, March, 1953.

Wright, A. W., "Pequot-sepos, a Unique Community Program," *Nature Magazine,* Vol. 46, No. 5, May, 1953, pp. 265-267, 276.

Weaver, Leo, and Keagy, Donald M., *The Sanitary Landfill Method of Refuse Disposal in Northern States,* Federal Security Agency, Public Health Service, Public Health Service Publication No. 226, Washington, D.C., 1952.

Wirth, Conrad L., "Threats to Our National Parks," *Audubon Magazine,* Vol. 56, No. 4, July-August, 1954, pp. 174-178.

Zierer, Clifford M., "Tourism and Recreation in the West," *Geographical Review,* Vol. XLII, No. 3, July, 1952.

Annual Reports of the Director, National Park Service, Department of the Interior, Washington, D.C.

Conservation in Action Series, (Descriptive Pamphlets on National Wildlife Refuges), Fish and Wildlife Service, Washington, D.C.

Industrial Dispersion Handbook for Communities, Domestic Commerce Series No. 31, U.S. Department of Commerce, Office of Industry and Commerce, Area Development Division, Washington, D.C., 1952.

Map: *Recreational Areas of the United States,* National Park Service, Washington, D.C., 1948.

National Conference on State Parks, Appendix, Yearbook, Park and Recreation Progress, Washington, D.C., 1943.

National Monument Series of illustrated folders presenting each monument individually, National Park Service, Washington, D.C.

National Park Series of illustrated pamphlets describing each park individually, National Park Service, Washington, D.C.

Parkway for the Mississippi—A Report to the Congress by the Bureau of Public Roads, Department of Commerce and the National Park Service, Department of the Interior, Washington, D.C., 1951.

"Recreational Land Requirements," in: Part II, *Report of the Land Planning Committee,* National Resources Board Report, Washington, D.C., 1934, pp. 144-147.

"Recreational Use of Land in the United States," *Report on Land Planning,* Part XI, National Park Service, Washington, D.C., 1938.

The Scenic Resources of the Tennessee Valley, T.V.A., Department of Regional Planning Studies, Knoxville, Tennessee, 1938.

The Little Thicket Nature Sanctuary, (undated folder), Outdoor Nature Club, Houston, Texas.

25th Anniversary Yearbook, Parks and Recreation Progress, National Conference on State Parks, Washington, D.C., 1946.

CHAPTER 15: OCEANIC RESOURCES

Anderson, W. W., Lindner, M. J., and King, J. E., *The Shrimp Fishery of the Southern United States*, Fishery Leaflet 368, U.S. Fish and Wildlife Service, Washington, D.C., March, 1950.

Brann, W. Paul, *Fresh-Water Mussel Shells*, Fishery Leaflet 246, U.S. Fish and Wildlife Service, Chicago, June, 1947.

Butler, Charles, *Fish Reduction Processes*, Fishery Leaflet 126, U.S. Fish and Wildlife Service, Washington, D.C., revised April, 1949.

Caboniss, William I., "Louisiana School-Lunch Program Uses More Fish," *Commercial Fisheries Review*, Vol. 15, No. 2, February, 1953.

Carson, Rachel L., *The Sea Around Us*, Oxford University Press, New York, 1951.

Chapman, Walter A., Jr., "A Serious Situation Confronting the Oyster Industry," *Commercial Fisheries Review*, Vol. 10, No. 6, June, 1948.

Clark, Frances N., "Review of the California Sardine Fishery," *California Game and Fish*, Vol. 38, No. 3, July, 1952, pp. 367-379.

Clark, John R., and Schuck, Howard A., "Georges Bank Haddock Fishery—1951," Part I—Analysis of 1951 Fishery, Part II—Accuracy of 1951 Prediction, *Commercial Fisheries Review*, Vol. 14, No. 8, August, 1952.

Colton, F. Barrows, "Our Global Ocean—Last and Vast Frontier," *National Geographic Magazine*, Vol. LXXXVII, No. 1, January, 1945, pp. 105-128.

Connolly, James Brendan, *The Book of the Gloucester Fishermen*, The John Day Company, New York, 1927.

Cushing, D. H., Devold, Finn, Marr, John C., and Kristjohnsson, H., *Some Modern Methods of Fish Detection*, FAO Fisheries Bulletin 5, Nos. 3-4, pp. 95-119 (May-August, 1952).

Darling, J. S., "Management of the Oyster Resources," *Commercial Fisheries Review*, Vol. 10, No. 9, Fish and Wildlife Service Separate No. 214, Washington, D.C., September, 1948.

Davidson, Bill, "Now—Bread from the Sea," *Collier's* Vol. 133, No. 8, 16 April, 1954, pp. 62-66.

Day, Albert M., "The Fish and Wildlife Service—Ten Years of Progress," *Commercial Fisheries Review*, Vol. 12, No. 3, March, 1950.

Fiedler, R. H., "Fisheries of North America, With Special Reference to the United States," *Geographical Review*, Vol. XXX, No. 2, April, 1940, pp. 201-214.

Fitch, John E., "The Decline of the Pacific Mackerel Fishery," *California Fish and Game*, Vol. 38, No. 3, March, 1953.

Hile, Ralph, "Changes In the Lake Trout Fishery In the Three Upper Lakes," *The Fisherman*, Vol. 20, No. 6, Early Fall issue, 1952.

Houston, Robert B., Jr., *German Commercial Electrical Fishing Device*, Fishery Leaflet 348, U.S. Fish and Wildlife Service, Washington, D.C., December, 1949.

Lindgren, B. E., and Seifert, R. P., "Use of Fish in New England Schools Increased by Demonstrations," *Commercial Fisheries Review*, Vol. 15, No. 2, February, 1953, pp. 18-22.

Loosanoff, V. L., *Commercial Clams of the Atlantic Coast of the United States*, Fishery Leaflet 13, Fish and Wildlife Service, Washington, D.C., revised December, 1946.

——, *Commercial Clams of the Pacific Coast of the United States*, Fishery Leaflet 223, Fish and Wildlife Service, Washington, D.C., April, 1947.

Merriman, Daniel, *Food Shortages and the Sea*, Publication 4039, Smithsonian Institution, Washington, D.C., 1951, reprinted from *The Yale Review*, Vol. 39, No. 3, Spring, 1950.

Nelson, J. Richards, Flower, H. Butler, and Hopkins, A. E., "Mechanization of Oyster Cultivation," *Commercial Fisheries Review*, Vol. 10, No. 9, Fish and Wildlife Separate No. 216, Washington, D.C., September, 1948.

Premetz, Ernest D., and Snow, George W., "Status of New England Sea-Scallop Fishery," *Commercial Fisheries Review*, Vol. 15, No. 5, May, 1953.

Scattergood, Leslie W., and Taylor, Clyde C., *The Mussel Resources of the North Atlantic Region*, Fishery Leaflet 364, U.S. Fish and Wildlife Service, Washington, D.C., January, 1950.

Springer, Stewart, and Bullis, Harvey R., *Exploratory Shrimp Fishing in the Gulf of Mexico, 1950-51*, Fishery Leaflet 406, Fish and Wildlife Service, Washington, D.C., September, 1952.

Sweet, Gordon, "Oyster Conservation in Connecticut: Past and Present," *Geographical Review*, Vol. XXXI, No. 4, October, 1941, pp. 591-608.

Tiller, Richard E., Glude, John B., and Stringer, Louis D., "Hard-Clam Fishery of the Atlantic Coast," *Commercial Fisheries Review*, Vol. 14, No. 10, October, 1952, pp. 1-25.

Tressler, Donald K., *The Wealth of the Sea*, The Century Company, New York and London, 1927.

Wharton, James, *The Chesapeake Bay Crab Industry*, Fishery Leaflet 358, U.S. Fish and Wildlife Service, Washington, D.C., November, 1949.

"New Aids to Fishing," *Commercial Fisheries Abstracts*, Vol. 5, No. 7, July, 1952, p. 15.

The Pacific Sardine Fishery, Fishery Leaflet No. 129, Fish and Wildlife Service, Washington, D.C., revised May, 1947.

CHAPTER 16: MINERAL CONSERVATION

Andrews, W. B., Neely, J. A., and Edwards, F. E., *Anhydrous Ammonia as a Source of Nitrogen,* Bulletin 482, Mississippi State College Agricultural Experiment Station, State College, Mississippi, April, 1951.

Austin, William W., Jr., "The Behavior of Zirconium and Titanium in Steels With Particular Emphasis on the Conservation of Manganese," Paper presented at Birmingham Regional Meeting, 1951, American Iron and Steel Institute.

Babcock, Donald E., "Sulphur Control and Manganese Conservation in Open Hearth Furnaces," General Meeting of American Iron and Steel Institute, New York, May, 1949.

Bateman, Alan M., *The Formation of Mineral Deposits,* John Wiley and Sons, Inc., New York, 1951.

Beall, John V., "Cobalt," reprint from *Mining Engineering,* Vol. 3, No. 1, January, 1951.

Clarke, F. W., and Washington, H. S., *The Composition of the Earth's Crust,* U.S.G.S. Prof. Paper, 127, Washington, D.C., 1924.

Collier, James E., "Aluminum Resources of the United States," *Economic Geography,* Vol. 24, No. 1, January, 1948.

Cope, Willard C., "Ammonia—Part I: U. S. Production Facilities. Part II: Cost of Production and End-Use Pattern," *Chemical Industries,* Issues of June and July, 1949, Maclean-Hunter Publishing Corporation, New York 18, N.Y.

Dahle, F. B., "Role of Technology in the Future of Metallic Production Wastes," Part D of "Waste Suppression," No. 2 of *Group V—Across the Board Studies,* Battelle Memorial Institute, Columbus, Ohio, 1951.

DeMille, John B., *Strategic Minerals, A Summary of Uses, World Output, Stockpiles, Procurement,* McGraw-Hill Book Company, Inc., New York, 1947.

Fanning, Leonard M., editor, *Our Oil Resources,* McGraw-Hill Book Company, Inc., New York, second edition, 1950.

Fieldner, A. C., "National Reserves of Energy Sources," *Railway Age,* Vol. 122, January, 1947.

Grant, Bruce F., Bossler, Robert B., and Rough, Robert L., "Effect of Flowing on Oil Production From a Secondary-Recovery Air-Injection Project in Pennsylvania," Reprinted from *Producers Monthly,* December, 1952.

Goodrich, W. H., "Waste Dump Leaching at the Chino Mines Division, Kennecott Copper Corporation, Santa Rita, N.M.," *The Mines Magazine,* March, 1952, pp. 65-67.

Hatcher, Harlan, *A Century of Iron and Men,* The Bobbs-Merrill Company, Inc., Indianapolis, 1950.

Harding, G. E., "American Coal Production and Use," *Economic Geography,* Vol. 22, No. 1, January, 1946.

Henning, C. C., and Braund, R. W., "Present and Prospective Sources of Supply of Steelmaking Raw Materials," General Meeting of American Iron and Steel Institute, New York, May, 1950.

Holman, Eugene, "Our Inexhaustible Resources," *Atlantic Monthly,* Vol. 189, No. 6, June, 1952, condensed in *Reader's Digest,* July, 1952.

Horner, C. Kenneth, *Phosphate Rock and Superphosphate (Synopsis of Information),* Industrial Reference Service, Vol. 5, Part 2, Number 12, February, 1947, Office of International Trade, U.S. Department of Commerce, Washington, D.C.

——, and Concannon, C. C., *Potash Fertilizer Materials (A Synopsis of Information),* Industrial Reference Service, Vol. 3—Part 2, No. 23, June, 1945, Bureau of Foreign and Domestic Commerce, U.S. Department of Commerce, Washington, D.C.

Hunt, Morton M., "Taconite: Iron Ore Bonanza," *Steelways,* Vol. 7, No. 2, March, 1951.

Kura, John G., "Nonferrous Scrap," Part C of "Waste Suppression," No. 2 of *Group V—Across the Board Studies,* Battelle Memorial Institute, Columbus, Ohio, 1951.

Lessing, Lawrence P., "The New Metals Age," *Fortune,* Vol. XLVII, No. 1, January, 1953, p. 109.

Moulton, Benjamin, "The Copper Resources of the United States," *The Scientific Monthly,* Vol. LXV, No. 2, August, 1947 pp. 143-147.

Payne, James E., "The Story of Scarce Metals," *Steelways,* Vol. 7, No. 4, July, 1951.

Pray, H. A., and Fink, F. W., "Role of Technology in the Future of Corrosion Control," No. 3 of *Group V—Across the Board Studies,* Battelle Memorial Institute, Columbus, Ohio, 21 September, 1951.

Renken, Howard C., "Role of Technology in the Future of Smelting and Refining Wastes," Part F of "Waste Suppression," No. 2 of *Group V—Across the Board Studies,* Battelle Memorial Institute, Columbus, Ohio, 1951.

Richardson, A. C., "Role of Technology in Increasing Mineral Supplies by Suppression of Waste in Beneficiation," Part E of "Waste Suppression," No. 2 of *Group V—Across the Board Studies,* Battelle Memorial Institute, Columbus, Ohio, 1951.

Ryerson, G. E., and Huddleston, Ken, "The Farm Equipment Industry in Soil Conservation," *Journal of Soil and Water Conservation,* Vol. 8, No. 1, January, 1953.

Sherman, Allan, and MacMurphy, Allen B., *Facts About Coal,* Bureau of Mines, Washington, D.C., 1950.

Stong, Phil, "Minnesota's Iron Giant," *Holiday,* Vol. 8, No. 1, July, 1950, pp. 90-97, 112-116.

Thompson, H. L., Guillaumeron, Pierre, and Updegraff, Norman C., "Ammonia Synthesis at 1000 Atmospheres," Reprinted from: *Chemical Engineering Progress,* September, 1952.

Tyler, Paul M., *From the Ground Up,* McGraw-Hill Book Company, Inc., New York, 1948.

Van Dresser, Cleveland, "Abuses Under the Mining Laws," *American Forests,* Vol. 58, Nos. 1, 2, and 3, 1952.

Voskuil, Walter H., "Fundamentals of Mineral Conservation," *Journal of Geography,* Vol. LIV, No. 1, Jan., 1955, pp. 34-40.

"Alloy Steelmaking Gains Faster Than Alloy Use," *Steel Facts,* No. 115, August, 1952.

Energy Resources and National Policy, National Resources Committee, Washington, D.C., 1939.

Industrial Uses of Selected Minerals—Guide List of Industrial Uses of Mineral Resources, Industrial Series No. 72, Office of Domestic Commerce, U.S. Department of Commerce, Washington, D.C., 1947.

"Manganese Need Spurs Search for Slag Source," *Steel Facts,* No. 115, August, 1952.

Materials Survey Series, compiled for the Materials Office, National Security Resources Board by the U.S. Department of Interior, Bureau of Mines, with cooperation of the Geological Survey. (Continuing under Office of Defense Mobilization.)

"New Tin Plating Process Stretches Supply of Tin," *Steel Facts,* No. 112, February, 1952.

"Pennsylvania Petroleum: A Sketch in Oil," *The Business Review,* Federal Reserve Bank of Philadelphia, October, 1950.

Production of Electric Energy—Capacity of Generating Plants—1951, Federal Power Commission, Washington, D.C.

"Rapid Growth in Water Projects Takes Large Tonnages of Steel," *Steel Facts,* No. 116, October, 1952.

Resources for Defense, Report of the Secretary of the Interior, Washington, D.C., 1952.

"Second Harvest," *The Lamp,* Vol. 32, No. 4, November, 1950.

Secondary Recovery of Oil in the United States (Second Edition), American Petroleum Institute, New York, 1950.

"Synthetics: The Great Oil Reserve," *Fortune,* Vol. XXXVII, No. 5, May, 1948.

Thirty-first Annual Report of the Federal Power Commission—1951, Washington, D.C., 1952.

"Titanium: The New Metal," *Fortune,* Vol. XXXIX, No. 5, p. 121, May, 1949.

Volume II, *Mineral Resources, Proceedings* of the United Nations Scientific Conference on the Conservation and Utilization of Resources, 1949, United Nations, Department of Economic Affairs, New York, 1951.

Volume III, *Fuel and Energy Resources, Proceedings* of the United Nations Scientific Conference on the Conservation and Utilization of Resources, 1949, United Nations, Department of Economic Affairs, New York, 1951.

CHAPTER 17: PROSPECT AND RESPONSIBILITY

Adams, Earl J., "School Forests–'Conservation Educators,'" *The Conservation Volunteer,* Official Bulletin, Minnesota Department of Conservation, St. Paul, November-December, 1952.

Adams, James P., "The Bounties of Nature," *American Forests,* Vol. 56, No. 11, November, 1950.

Ayres, Eugene, and Scarlott, Charles, *Energy Sources, The Wealth of the World,* The McGraw-Hill Book Co., Inc., New York, 1952.

Baker, O. E., "The Population Prospect in Relation to the World's Agricultural Resources," *Journal of Geography,* Vol. XLVI, No. 6, September, 1947.

Bennett, Hugh H., *Progress in Soil Conservation,* U.S.D.A. Soil Conservation Service, Washington, D.C., October, 1951.

Boudreau, Frank G., "The World's Food Supply," in *Soil, Food, and Health,* edited by Forman, Jonathan, and Fink, O. E., Friends of the Land, Zanesville, Ohio, 1948, pp. 253-264.

Bromfield, Louis, *Pleasant Valley,* Harper and Brothers, New York, 1945.

———, "We Don't Have to Starve," *Atlantic Monthly,* Vol. CLXXXIV, No. 1, July, 1949, pp. 57-61.

Browne, W. A., The Geographer as Coordinator," *Journal of Geography,* Vol. LIV, No. 2, February, 1955, pp. 89-96.

Burch, Guy Irving, "Conservation and Population," *American Forests,* Vol. 55, No. 11, November, 1949.

Burdette, J. W., "Junior High School Goes to Camp," *Soil Conservation,* Vol. XVIII, No. 8, March, 1953.

de Castro, Josué, *Geography of Hunger,* Victor Gollancz, Ltd., London, 1952.

Chapman, Oscar L., "Geography and Natural Resources in the Development of the American Way of Life," Address before the Knapp Fund Committee, University of Wisconsin, Madison, Wisconsin, 20 November, 1952.

Cochran, Rod, "DDT, Menace or Miracle," *The Ohio Conservation Bulletin,* Vol. 17, No. 4, April, 1953, pp. 20-21.

Collingwood, G. H., "The Tradition of Conservation," *American Forests,* Vol. 59, No. 10, October, 1953, pp. 10-12, 30.

Craig, James B., "Target–A New Era of Reason in Conservation," *American Forests,* Vol. 60, No. 8, August, 1954, pp. 13, 48-51.

Cross, Clark I., "Land Management Education as a Function of College Geography," *Journal of Geography,* Vol. LII, No. 9, December, 1953, pp. 395-400.

Darwin, Charles Galton, *The Next Million Years,* Rupert Hart-Davis, London, 1952.

Dean, Gordon, "Atomic Miracles We Will See," *Look,* 25 August, 1953.

Dewhurst, Frederic J., and associates, *America's Needs and Resources,* The Twentieth Century Fund, New York, 1947.

Ekblaw, W. Elmer, "Why Should We Plan?" from National Conference on Planning, Boston, Massachusetts, 1939, American Society of Planning Officials.

Ellis, Cecil B., *Fresh Water from the Ocean for Cities, Industries, and Irrigation,* The Ronald Press, New York, 1954.

Forman, Jonathan, "Population Pressures Versus the Food Supply," in *Soil, Food, and Health,* edited by Forman, Jonathan and Fink, O. E., Friends of the Land, Zanesville, Ohio, 1948, pp. 231-252.

Hall, J. A., "Industrial Food—No Panacea," *The Land,* Vol. VIII, No. 3, Autumn, 1949.

Hall, William B., "Conservation Comes of Age in Michigan," *Journal of Soil and Water Conservation,* Vol. 8, No. 2, March, 1953, pp. 70-73.

Hammarlund, Charles N., Jr., "Conservation Programs for Youth," *Parks and Recreation,* Vol. 35, No. 12, December, 1952, pp. 5-6.

Hudson, G. Donald, "Geography and Regional Planning," in *Geography in the High School,* pp. 33-43, McKnight and McKnight, Bloomington, Illinois, 1949.

James, Preston E., "Toward A Further Understanding of the Regional Concept," *Annals,* Association of American Geographers, Vol. XLII, No. 3, September, 1952, pp. 195-222.

Marbut, C. F., "The Rise, Decline, and Revival of Malthusianism in Relation to Geography and Character of Soils," *Annals,* Association of American Geographers, Vol. XV, No. 1, March, 1925, pp. 1-29.

Mills, Clarence A., "Implications of Air Pollution in Chronic Respiratory and Cardiac Disorders," *Bulletin,* American Meteorological Society, Vol. 33, No. 8, October, 1952, pp. 322-325.

Munger, Hamnett P., "Waste Going into the Atmosphere," Part B of "Waste Suppression," No. 2 of *Group V—Across the Board Studies,* Battelle Memorial Institute, Columbus, Ohio, 1951.

Nelson, A. Z., "Must We Sacrifice Our Forest for Dams?" *American Forests,* Vol. 58, No. 6, June, 1952.

Ordway, Samuel H., Jr., *Resources and the American Dream,* The Ronald Press, New York, 1953.

Orville, Howard T., "Weather Made to Order?" *Colliers,* Vol. 133, No. 11, 28 May, 1954.

Parson, Ruben L., "The Responsibility of Geographers in Land Planning," *Education,* Vol. 60, No. 4, December, 1939.

Pearson, R. W., and Jamison, V. C., "Improving Land Conditions for Conservation and Production with Chemical Soil Conditioners," *Journal of Soil and Water Conservation*, Vol. 8, No. 3, May, 1953.

Peattie, Roderick, "Are You a Malthusian?" *Journal of Geography*, Vol. XLIX, No. 9, December, 1950.

Renner, F. G., "The Future of Our Range Resources," *Journal of Range Management*, Vol. 7, No. 2, March, 1954, pp. 55-56.

Riley, Charles V., "Striplands Can Produce Wildlife," *Ohio Conservation Bulletin*, Vol. 17, No. 6, June, 1953.

Salter, Robert M., "America's Capacity to Produce Food," *Soil Conservation*, Vol. XVII, No. 12, July, 1952.

———, "Survey of Our Soil Resources," *Soil Conservation*, Vol. XVII, No. 9, April, 1953, pp. 195-200.

Schulz, William F., Jr., *Conservation Law and Administration: A Case Study of Law and Resource Use in Pennsylvania*, The Ronald Press, New York, 1953.

Stamp, L. Dudley, *Land For Tomorrow, The Underdeveloped World*, Indiana University Press, Bloomington, Indiana, 1952.

Sugarman, Ruth, "Conservation Education Can Begin In the Early Years," *Journal of Geography*, Vol. LII, No. 1, January, 1953, pp. 14-15.

Swanson, C. L. W., "A New Concept—Using Chemicals for Soil Structure Improvement," *Journal of Soil and Water Conservation*," Vol. 7, No. 2, April, 1952.

———, "Soil Conditioners," *Scientific American*, Vol. 189, No. 2, August, 1953, pp. 36-38.

Thompson, Laura, "The Basic Conservation Problem," *Scientific Monthly*, Vol. 68, No. 2, Feb., 1949, p. 129.

Van Royen, William, *The Agricultural Resources of the World; Atlas of the World's Resources*, Vol. I, Prentice-Hall, Inc., New York, 1954.

———, and Bowles, Oliver, *The Mineral Resources of the World; Atlas of the World's Resources*, Vol. II, Prentice-Hall, Inc., New York, 1952.

Whelpton, P. K., *Forecasts of the Population of the United States, 1945-1975*, Bureau of the Census, Washington, D.C., 1947.

Whitaker, J. Russell, "Conservation and the College Professor," Professional Paper No. 13, National Council of Geography Teachers, March 1952, Reprinted from: *Peabody Journal of Education*, Vol. 27, pp. 329-338, May, 1950.

Zimmerman, Erich W., *World Resources and Industries*, Revised Edition, Harper and Brothers, New York, 1951.

A Policy for Renewable Natural Resources, Adopted at the 5th Annual Meeting of the Council, Franklin, North Carolina, 1 October, 1951, Natural Resources Council of America, Washington, D.C., 1952.

A Program to Strengthen the Scientific Foundation in Natural Resources, 81st Congress, 2nd Session, House Document No. 706, Washington, D.C., 1950.

"Conservation Education in American Schools," *29th Yearbook,* American Association of School Administrators, National Education Association, Washington, D.C., 1951.

"Conservation: Its Advances, Conflicts, Flaws, and Failures," a Series of Appraisals, *The Land,* Vol. X, No. 4, Winter 1951-52.

"Crisis Spots in Conservation," Izaak Walton League of America, Inc., Chicago, 1949.

"Free Trade is Inevitable," *Fortune,* Vol. 47, No. 3, March, 1953, p. 96.

"Man-made Obstacles to Planning," Vol. 47, No. 3, from National Conference on Planning, Boston, Massachusetts, 1939.

"On Atmospheric Pollution," *Meteorological Monographs,* Vol. 1, No. 4, November, 1951.

Organization and Policy in the Field of Natural Resources, prepared for the Commission on Organization of the Executive Branch of the Government, Washington, D.C., 1949.

"Our Renewable Resources Can Be Sustained—A Symposium," Chamber of Commerce of the United States, Washington, D.C., 1949.

Photosynthesis—Basic Features of the Process (Vol. I, in series on the *Physical and Economic Foundation of Natural Resources*), Interior and Insular Affairs Committee, House of Representatives, United States Congress, 1952.

Resources for Defense, Report, Secretary of the Interior, Washington, D.C., 1952.

"Solar Power in the Pyrenees," *Life,* Vol. 14, No. 6, 23 March, 1953, (International Edition).

"The Load On the Land, A Symposium," *The Land,* Vol. XI, No. 2, Review of the Summer, 1952, pp. 199-220.

The Promise of Technology, Report of the President's Materials Policy Commission, Vol IV, Washington, D.C., June, 1952.

T V A: Two Decades of Progress, Tennessee Valley Authority, Knoxville, Tennessee, 1953.

"Tennessee Valley Authority," *Fortune,* Vol. VIII, No. 4, October, 1933.

Unified Valley Development—T V A Reports, Government Printing Office, Washington, D.C., 1946.

Weather Control and Augmented Potable Water Supply, Joint Hearings before several Committees, U.S. Senate, 82nd Congress, 1st Session, 1951.

Years of Progress: 1945-1952, U.S. Department of the Interior, Oscar L. Chapman, Secretary, 1953.

You and Forest Fires, U.S.D.A. Forest Service Program Aid 64, Washington, D.C., 1948.

Index

C

e